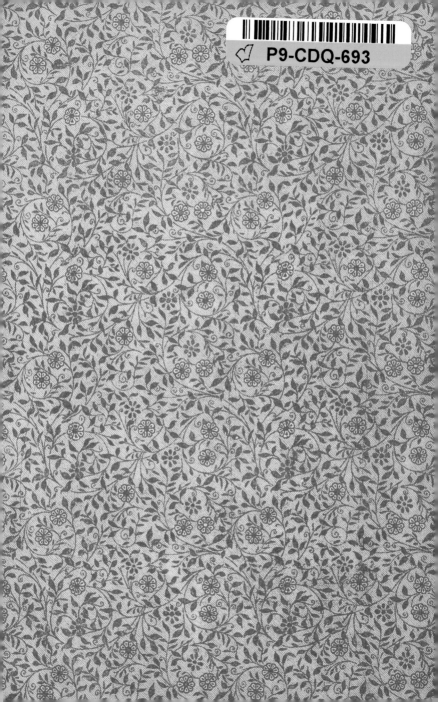

SKETCH OF EL MEDINAH BY A NATIVE ARTIST

THE STUYVESANT EDITION

# THE WORKS

OF

# WASHINGTON IRVING

IN SEVEN VOLUMES

## VOL. III.

CHRONICLE OF THE CONQUEST OF GRANADA

MAHOMET AND HIS SUCCESSORS

NEW YORK

G. P. PUTNAM'S SONS

27 AND 29 WEST 23D STREET

# CHRONICLE

## OF THE

# CONQUEST OF GRANADA

### FROM THE MSS. OF

## FRAY ANTONIO AGAPIDA

### BY

## WASHINGTON IRVING

---

*AUTHOR'S REVISED EDITION*

# CONTENTS.

## CHAPTER I.

PAGE

7

## CHAPTER VII.

## CHAPTER VIII.

## CHAPTER IX.

## CHAPTER X.

## CHAPTER XI.

## CHAPTER XII.

## CHAPTER XIII.

## CHAPTER XIV.

## CHAPTER XV.

## CHAPTER XVI.

## CHAPTER XXVI.

## CHAPTER XXVII.

## CHAPTER XXVIII.

## CHAPTER XXIX.

## CHAPTER XXX.

## CHAPTER XXXI.

## CHAPTER XXXII.

## CHAPTER XXXIII.

## CHAPTER XXXIV.

# CHAPTER XXXV.

# CHAPTER XXXVI.

# CHAPTER XXXVII.

# CHAPTER XXXVIII.

# CHAPTER XXXIX.

# CHAPTER XL.

# CHAPTER XLI.

# CHAPTER XLII.

# CHAPTER XLIII.

## CHAPTER XLIV.

## CHAPTER XLV.

## CHAPTER XLVI.

## CHAPTER XLVII.

## CHAPTER XLVIII.

## CHAPTER XLIX.

## CHAPTER L.

## CHAPTER LI.

## CHAPTER LII.

## CHAPTER LIII.

## CHAPTER LIV.

## CHAPTER LV.

## CHAPTER LVI.

## CHAPTER LVII.

## CHAPTER LVIII.

## CHAPTER LIX.

## CHAPTER LX.

## CHAPTER LXI.

## CHAPTER LXII.

## CHAPTER LXIII.

## CHAPTER LXIV.

## CHAPTER LXV.

## CHAPTER LXVI.

## CHAPTER LXVII.

## CHAPTER LXVIII.

## CHAPTER LXIX.

# CHAPTER LXX.

# CHAPTER LXXI.

# CHAPTER LXXII.

# CHAPTER LXXIII.

# CHAPTER LXXIV.

# CHAPTER LXXV.

# CHAPTER LXXVI.

# CHAPTER LXXVII.

# CHAPTER LXXVIII.

# CHAPTER LXXIX.

# CHAPTER LXXX.

# CHAPTER LXXXI.

# CHAPTER LXXXII.

# CHAPTER LXXXIII.

# CHAPTER LXXXIV.

# CHAPTER LXXXV.

# CHAPTER LXXXVI.

# CHAPTER LXXXVII.

# CHAPTER LXXXVIII.

## CHAPTER LXXXIX.

## CHAPTER XC.

## CHAPTER XCI.

## CHAPTER XCII.

## CHAPTER XCIII.

## CHAPTER XCIV.

## CHAPTER XCV.

## CHAPTER XCVI.

## CHAPTER XCVII.

2

# 18  *CONTENTS.*

# A CHRONICLE

OF THE

# CONQUEST OF GRANADA.

---

## CHAPTER I.

OF THE KINGDOM OF GRANADA, AND THE TRIBUTE WHICH IT PAID TO THE
CASTILIAN CROWN.

THE history of those bloody and disastrous wars,
which have caused the downfall of mighty empires (observes Fray Antonio Agapida), has
ever been considered a study highly delectable, and full
of precious edification. What then must be the history
of a pious crusade, waged by the most Catholic of sovereigns, to rescue from the power of the infidels one of
the most beautiful but benighted regions of the globe?
Listen then, while, from the solitude of my cell, I relate
the events of the conquest of Granada, where Christian knight and turbaned infidel disputed, inch by inch,
the fair land of Andalusia, until the crescent, that symbol of heathenish abomination, was cast down, and the

21

blessed cross, the tree of our redemption, erected in its stead.

Nearly eight hundred years were past and gone, since the Arabian invaders had sealed the perdition of Spain, by the defeat of Don Roderick, the last of her Gothic kings. Since that disastrous event, one portion after another of the peninsula had been gradually recovered by the Christian princes, until the single, but powerful and warlike territory of Granada, alone remained under the domination of the Moors.

This renowned kingdom, situated in the southern part of Spain, and washed on one side by the Mediterranean sea, was traversed in every direction by sierras or chains of lofty and rugged mountains, naked, rocky, and precipitous, rendering it almost impregnable, but locking up within their sterile embraces deep, rich, and verdant valleys of prodigal fertility.

In the centre of the kingdom lay its capital, the beautiful city of Granada, sheltered, as it were, in the lap of the Sierra Nevada, or Snowy Mountains. Its houses, seventy thousand in number, covered two lofty hills with their declivities, and a deep valley between them, through which flowed the Darro. The streets were narrow, as is usual in Moorish and Arab cities, but there were occasionally small squares and open places. The houses had gardens and interior courts, set out with orange, citron, and pomegranate trees, and refreshed by fountains, so that as the edifices ranged above each other

up the sides of the hills, they presented a delightful
appearance of mingled grove and city. One of the hills
was surmounted by the Alcazaba, a strong fortress, commanding all that part of the city; the other by the Alhambra, a royal palace and warrior castle, capable of
containing within its alcazar and towers a garrison of
forty thousand men; but possessing also its harem, the
voluptuous abode of the Moorish monarchs, laid out
with courts and gardens, fountains and baths, and stately
halls, decorated in the most costly style of oriental
luxury. According to Moorish tradition, the king who
built this mighty and magnificent pile, was skilled in the
occult sciences, and furnished himself with the necessary funds by means of alchemy.* Such was its lavish
splendor that even at the present day, the stranger,
wandering through its silent courts and deserted halls,
gazes with astonishment at gilded ceilings and fretted
domes, the brilliancy and beauty of which have survived
the vicissitudes of war and the silent dilapidation of
ages.

The city was surrounded by high walls, three leagues
in circuit, furnished with twelve gates, and a thousand
and thirty towers. Its elevation above the sea, and the
neighborhood of the Sierra Nevada crowned with perpetual snows, tempered the fervid rays of summer; so
that, while other cities were panting with the sultry and

---

* Zurita, lib. 20, c. 42.

stifling heat of the dog-days, the most salubrious breezes played through the marble halls of Granada.

The glory of the city, however, was its vega or plain, which spread out to a circumference of thirty-seven leagues, surrounded by lofty mountains, and was proudly compared to the famous plain of Damascus. It was a vast garden of delight, refreshed by numerous fountains, and by the silver windings of the Xenil. The labor and ingenuity of the Moors had diverted the waters of this river into thousands of rills and streams, and diffused them over the whole surface of the plain. Indeed, they had wrought up this happy region to a degree of wonderful prosperity, and took a pride in decorating it, as if it had been a favorite mistress. The hills were clothed with orchards and vineyards, the valleys embroidered with gardens, and the wide plains covered with waving grain. Here were seen in profusion the orange, the citron, the fig, and pomegranate, with great plantations of mulberry trees, from which was produced the finest silk. The vine clambered from tree to tree; the grapes hung in rich clusters about the peasant's cottage, and the groves were rejoiced by the perpetual song of the nightingale. In a word, so beautiful was the earth, so pure the air, and so serene the sky of this delicious region, that the Moors imagined the paradise of their prophet to be situated in that part of the heaven which overhung the kingdom of Granada.

Within this favored realm, so prodigally endowed and

strongly fortified by nature, the Moslem wealth, valor, and intelligence, which had once shed such a lustre over Spain, had gradually retired, and here they made their final stand. Granada had risen to splendor on the ruin of other Moslem kingdoms; but in so doing had become the sole object of Christian hostility, and had to maintain its very existence by the sword. The Moorish capital accordingly presented a singular scene of Asiatic luxury and refinement, mingled with the glitter and the din of arms. Letters were still cultivated, philosophy and poetry had their schools and disciples, and the language spoken was said to be the most elegant Arabic. A passion for dress and ornament pervaded all ranks. That of the princesses and ladies of high rank, says Al Kattib, one of their own writers, was carried to a height of luxury and magnificence that bordered on delirium. They wore girdles and bracelets and anklets of gold and silver, wrought with exquisite art and delicacy, and studded with jacinths, chrysolites, emeralds, and other precious stones. They were fond of braiding and decorating their beautiful long tresses, or confining them in knots sparkling with jewels. They were finely formed, excessively fair, graceful in their manners, and fascinating in their conversation; when they smiled, says Al Kattib, they displayed teeth of dazzling whiteness, and their breath was as the perfume of flowers.

The Moorish cavaliers, when not in armor, delighted in dressing themselves in Persian style, in garments of

wool, of silk, or cotton, of the finest texture, beautifully
wrought with stripes of various colors. In winter they
wore, as an outer garment, the African cloak or Tunisian
albornoz; but in the heat of summer, they arrayed themselves in linen of spotless whiteness. The same luxury
prevailed in their military equipments. Their armor
was inlaid and chased with gold and silver. The sheaths
of their scimetars were richly labored and enameled, the
blades were of Damascus, bearing texts from the Koran,
or martial and amorous mottoes; the belts were of golden
filigree, studded with gems; their poniards of Fez, were
wrought in the arabesque fashion; their lances bore gay
bandaroles; their horses were sumptuously caparisoned
with housings of green and crimson velvet, wrought with
silk and enameled with gold and silver. All this warlike
luxury of the youthful chivalry was encouraged by the
Moorish kings, who ordained that no tax should be imposed on the gold and silver employed in these embel-
lishments; and the same exception was extended to the
bracelets and other ornaments worn by the fair dames of
Granada.

Of the chivalrous gallantry which prevailed between
the sexes in this romantic period of Moorish history, we
have traces in the thousand ballads which have come
down to our day, and which have given a tone and color-
ing to Spanish amatory literature, and to everything in
Spain connected with the tender passion.

War was the normal state of Granada and its inhabitants; the common people were subject at any moment to be summoned to the field, and all the upper class was a brilliant chivalry. The Christian princes, so successful in regaining the rest of the peninsula, found their triumphs checked at the mountain boundaries of this kingdom. Every peak had its atalaya or watch-tower, ready to make its fire by night or to send up its column of smoke by day, a signal of invasion, at which the whole country was on the alert. To penetrate the defiles of this perilous country, to surprise a frontier fortress or to make a foray into the vega and a hasty ravage within sight of the very capital, were among the most favorite and daring exploits of the Castilian chivalry. But they never pretended to hold the region thus ravaged; it was sack, burn, plunder, and away! and these desolating inroads were retaliated in kind by the Moorish cavaliers, whose greatest delight was a *tala*, or predatory incursion into the Christian territories beyond the mountains.

A partisan warfare of this kind had long existed between Granada and its most formidable antagonist, the kingdoms of Castile and Leon. It was one which called out the keen yet generous rivalry of Christian and Moslem cavaliers, and gave rise to individual acts of chivalrous gallantry and daring prowess ; but it was one which was gradually exhausting the resources and sapping the strength of Granada. One of the latest of its kings, therefore, Aben Ismael by name, disheartened by a foray which had laid waste the vega, and conscious that the

balance of warfare was against his kingdom, made a
truce in 1457 with Henry IV., King of Castile and Leon,
stipulating to pay him an annual tribute of twelve thousand doblas or pistoles of gold, and to liberate annually
six hundred Christian captives, or in default of captives
to give an equal number of Moors as hostages; all to be
delivered at the city of Cordova.*

The truce, however, was of a partial nature, with singular reservations.  It did not include the Moorish frontier towards Jaen, which was to remain open for the warlike enterprises of either nation; neither did it prohibit
sudden attacks upon towns and castles, provided they
were mere forays, conducted furtively, without sound of
trumpet or display of banners, or pitching of camps, or
regular investment, and that they did not last above
three days.†

Aben Ismael was faithful in observing the conditions
of the truce, but they were regarded with impatience by
his eldest son, Muley Abul Hassan, a prince of a fiery
and belligerent spirit, and fond of casing himself in armor and mounting his war-horse.  He had been present
at Cordova at one of the payments of tribute, and had
witnessed the scoffs and taunts of the Christians, and his
blood boiled whenever he recalled the humiliating scene.
When he came to the throne in 1465, on the death of his

* Garibay, *Compend.* lib. 17, c. 3.

† Zurita, *Anales de Aragon*, lib. 20, c. 42.   Mariana, *Hist. de España*,
lib. 25, c. 1.   Bleda, *Coron. de Moros*, lib. 5, c. 3.

father, he ceased the payment of the tribute altogether, and it was sufficient to put him into a tempest of rage only to mention it.

"He was a fierce and warlike infidel," says the pious Fray Antonio Agapida; "his bitterness against the holy Christian faith had been signalized in battle during the lifetime of his father, and the same diabolical spirit of hostility was apparent in his ceasing to pay this most righteous tribute."

# CHAPTER II.

OF THE EMBASSY OF DON JUAN DE VERA TO DEMAND ARREARS OF TRIBUTE
FROM THE MOORISH MONARCH.

THE flagrant want of faith of Muley Abul Hassan in fulfilling treaty stipulations, passed unresented during the residue of the reign of Henry the Impotent, and the truce was tacitly continued without the enforcement of tribute, during the first three years of the reign of his successors, Ferdinand and Isabella, of glorious and happy memory, who were too much engrossed by civil commotions in their own dominions and by a war of succession waged with them by the king of Portugal, to risk an additional conflict with the Moorish sovereign. When, however, at the expiration of the term of truce, Muley Abul Hassan sought a renewal of it, the pride and piety of the Castilian sovereigns were awakened to the flagrant defalcation of the infidel king, and they felt themselves called upon, by their religious obligations as champions of the faith, to make a formal demand for the payment of arrearages.

In the year of grace 1478, therefore, Don Juan de

Vera, a zealous and devout knight, full of ardor for the faith and loyalty to the crown, was sent as ambassador for the purpose. He was armed at all points, gallantly mounted, and followed by a moderate but well-appointed retinue; in this way he crossed the Moorish frontier, and passed slowly through the country, looking round him with the eyes of a practiced warrior, and carefully noting its military points and capabilities. He saw that the Moor was well prepared for possible hostilities. Every town was strongly fortified. The vega was studded with towers of refuge for the peasantry, every pass of the mountain had its castle of defense, every lofty height its watch-tower. As the Christian cavaliers passed under the walls of the fortresses, lances and scimetars flashed from their battlements, and the Moorish sentinels darted from their dark eyes glances of hatred and defiance. It was evident that a war with this kingdom must be a war of posts, full of doughty peril and valiant enterprise; where every step must be gained by toil and bloodshed, and maintained with the utmost difficulty. The warrior spirit of the cavaliers kindled at the thoughts, and they were impatient for hostilities; "not," says Antonio Agapida, "from any thirst for rapine and revenge, but from that pure and holy indignation which every Spanish knight entertained at beholding this beautiful dominion of his ancestors defiled by the footsteps of infidel usurpers. It was impossible," he adds, "to contemplate this delicious country, and not long to see it

restored to the dominion of the true faith, and the sway
of the Christian monarchs."

Arrived at the gates of Granada, Don Juan de Vera
and his companions saw the same vigilant preparations
on the part of the Moorish king. His walls and towers
were of vast strength, in complete repair, and mounted
with lombards and other heavy ordnance. His magazines were well stored with munitions of war; he had a
mighty host of foot-soldiers, together with squadrons of
cavalry, ready to scour the country, and carry on either
defensive or predatory warfare. The Christian warriors
noted these things without dismay; their hearts rather
glowed with emulation, at the thoughts of encountering
so worthy a foe. As they slowly pranced through the
streets of Granada, they looked round with eagerness on
its stately palaces and sumptuous mosques; on its alcay-
ceria or bazar, crowded with silks and cloth of silver and
gold, with jewels and precious stones, and other rich
merchandise, the luxuries of every clime; and they
longed for the time when all this wealth should be the
spoil of the soldiers of the faith, and when each tramp of
their steeds might be fetlock deep in the blood and carnage of the infidels.

The Moorish inhabitants looked jealously at this small
but proud array of Spanish chivalry, as it paraded, with
that stateliness possessed only by Spanish cavaliers,
through the renowned gate of Elvira. They were struck
with the stern and lofty demeanor of Don Juan de Vera,

and his sinewy frame, which showed him formed for hardy deeds of arms; and they supposed he had come in search of distinction, by defying the Moorish knights in open tourney, or in the famous tilt with reeds, for which they were so renowned; for it was still the custom of the knights of either nation to mingle in these courteous and chivalrous contests during the intervals of war. When they learned, however, that he was come to demand the tribute so abhorrent to the ears of the fiery monarch, they observed that it well required a warrior of his apparent nerve to execute such an embassy.

Muley Abul Hassan received the cavalier in state, seated on a magnificent divan, and surrounded by the officers of his court, in the hall of ambassadors, one of the most sumptuous apartments of the Alhambra. When De Vera had delivered his message, a haughty and bitter smile curled the lip of the fierce monarch. "Tell your sovereigns," said he, "that the kings of Granada, who used to pay tribute in money to the Castilian crown, are dead. Our mint at present coins nothing but blades of scimetars and heads of lances."*

The defiance couched in this proud reply was heard with secret satisfaction by Don Juan de Vera, for he was a bold soldier and a devout hater of the infidels; and he saw iron war in the words of the Moorish monarch. Being master, however, of all points of etiquette, he re-

* Garibay, lib. 40, c. 29. Conde, *Hist. Arab.*, pt. 4, c. 34.

3

tained an inflexible demeanor, and retired from the apartment with stately and ceremonious gravity. His treatment was suited to his rank and dignity; a magnificent apartment in the Alhambra was assigned to him; and before his departure a scimetar was sent to him by the king; the blade of the finest Damascus steel, the hilt of agate, enriched with precious stones, and the guard of gold. De Vera drew it, and smiled grimly as he noticed the admirable temper of the blade. "His majesty has given me a trenchant weapon," said he: "I trust a time will come when I may show him that I know how to use his royal present." The reply was considered a compliment, of course; the bystanders little knew the bitter hostility that lay couched beneath.

On his return to Cordova, Don Juan de Vera delivered the reply of the Moor, but at the same time reported the state of his territories. These had been strengthened and augmented during the weak reign of Henry IV. and the recent troubles of Castile. Many cities and strong places contiguous to Granada, but heretofore conquered by the Christians, had renewed their allegiance to Muley Abul Hassan, so that his kingdom now contained fourteen cities, ninety-seven fortified places, besides numerous unwalled towns and villages defended by formidable castles, while Granada towered in the centre as the citadel.

The wary Ferdinand, as he listened to the military report of Don Juan de Vera, saw that the present was no time for hostilities with a warrior kingdom, so bristled over with means of defense. The internal discords of Castile still continued, as did the war with Portugal; under these circumstances he forebore to insist upon the payment of tribute, and tacitly permitted the truce to continue; but the defiance contained in the reply of Muley Abul Hassan remained rankling in his bosom as a future ground of war; and De Vera's description of Granada as the centre of a system of strongholds and rock-built castles, suggested to him his plan of conquest; by taking town after town, and fortress after fortress, and gradually plucking away all the supports before he attempted the capital. He expressed his resolution in a memorable pun, or play upon the name of Granada, which signifies a pomegranate. "I will pick out the seeds of this pomegranate one by one," said the cool and crafty Ferdinand.

NOTE.—In the first edition of this work the author recounted a characteristic adventure of the stout Juan de Vera, as happening on the occasion of this embassy; a further consultation of historical authorities has induced him to transfer it to a second embassy of De Vera's; which the reader will find related in a subsequent chapter.

# CHAPTER III.

DOMESTIC FEUDS IN THE ALHAMBRA.—RIVAL SULTANAS.—PREDICTIONS CON-
CERNING BOABDIL THE HEIR TO THE THRONE.—HOW FERDINAND MEDI-
TATES WAR AGAINST GRANADA, AND HOW HE IS ANTICIPATED.

THOUGH Muley Abul Hassan was at peace in his external relations, a civil war raged in his harem, which it is proper to notice, as it had a fatal effect upon the fortunes of the kingdom. Though cruel by nature, he was uxorious, and somewhat prone to be managed by his wives. Early in life he had married his kinswoman, Ayxa (or Ayesha), daughter of his great uncle the Sultan Mohammed VII., surnamed El Hayzari, or the left-handed. She was a woman of almost masculine spirit and energy, and of such immaculate and inaccessible virtue, that she was generally called La Horra, or the Chaste. By her he had a son, Abu Abdallah; or, as he is commonly named by historians, Boabdil. The court astrologers, according to custom, cast the horoscope of the infant, but were seized with fear and trembling as they regarded it. "Allah Achbar! God is great!" exclaimed they, "He alone controls the fate of empires. It is written in the book of fate that this child

will one day sit upon the throne, but that the downfall of
the kingdom will be accomplished during his reign."
From that time the prince had been regarded with aver-
sion by his father; and the prediction which hung over
him, and the persecutions to which he became subjected,
procured him the surname of El Zogoybi, or The Unfortunate. He grew up, however, under the protection
of his valiant-hearted mother, who, by the energy of her
character, long maintained an undisputed sway in the
harem, until, as her youth passed away and her beauty
declined, a formidable rival arose.

In one of the forays of the Moorish chivalry into the
Christian territories, they had surprised a frontier fortress, commanded by Sancho Ximenes de Solis, a noble
and valiant cavalier, who fell in bravely defending it.
Among the captives was his daughter Isabella, then almost in her infancy; who was brought to Granada, delicately raised, and educated in the Moslem faith.* Her
Moorish captors gave her the name of Fatima, but as she
grew up her surpassing beauty gained her the surname
of Zoraya, or the Morning Star, by which she has become
known in history. Her charms at length attracted the
notice of Muley Abul Hassan, and she soon became a
member of his harem. Some have spoken of her as a
Christian slave, whom he had made his concubine; but
others, with more truth, represent her as one of his

* *Cronica del Gran. Cardinal,* cap. 71.

wives, and ultimately his favorite Sultana; and indeed it was often the case that female captives of rank and beauty, when converted to the faith of Islam, became united to the proudest and loftiest of their captors.

Zoraya soon acquired complete ascendency over the mind of Muley Abul Hassan. She was as ambitious as she was beautiful, and, having become the mother of two sons, looked forward to the possibility of one of them sitting on the throne of Granada. These ambitious views were encouraged, if not suggested, by a faction which gathered round her, inspired by kindred sympathies. The king's vizier, Abul Cacem Vanegas, who had great influence over him, was, like Zoraya, of Christian descent, being of the noble house of Luque. His father, one of the Vanegas of Cordova, had been captured in infancy and brought up as a Moslem.* From him sprang the vizier, Abul Cacem Vanegas, and his brother Reduan Vanegas, likewise high in rank in the court of Muley Abul Hassan; and they had about them numerous and powerful connections, all basking in court favor. Though Moslems in faith, they were all drawn to Zoraya by the tie of foreign and Christian descent, and sought to elevate her and her children to the disparagement of Ayxa la Horra and her son Boabdil. The latter, on the other hand, were supported by the noble and once potent family of the Abencerrages, and by Aben Comixer,

* *Cura de los Palacios, Hist. de los Reyes Catol.* cap. 56.

alcayde of the Alhambra; and between these two factions, headed by rival sultanas, the harem of Muley Abul Hassan became the scene of inveterate jealousies and intrigues which, in time, as will be shown, led to popular commotions and civil wars.*

While these female feuds were threatening Muley Abul Hassan with trouble and disaster at home, his evil genius prompted him to an enterprise which involved him in tenfold danger from abroad. The reader has already been apprised of a singular clause in the truce existing between the Christians and the Moors, permitting hasty dashes into each other's territories, and assaults of towns and fortresses, provided they were carried on as mere forays, and without the parade of regular warfare. A long time had elapsed, however, without any incursion of the kind on the part of the Moors, and the Christian towns on the frontiers had, in consequence, fallen into a state of the most negligent security. In an unlucky moment, Muley Abul Hassan was tempted to one of these forays by learning that the fortress of Zahara, on the frontier between Ronda and Medina Sidonia, was but feebly garrisoned and scantily supplied, and that its alcayde was careless of his charge. This important post was built on the crest of a rocky mountain, with a

* It is to be noted that several historians have erroneously represented Zoraya as the mother of Boabdil, instead of Ayxa la Horra; and the Abencerrages as the opponents of Boabdil, instead of his strenuous adherents. The statement in the text is according to the most reliable authorities.

strong castle perched above it, upon a cliff, so high that
it was said to be above the flight of birds or drift of
clouds. The streets and many of the houses were mere
excavations, wrought out of the living rock. The town
had but one gate, opening to the west, and defended by
towers and bulwarks. The only ascent to this cragged
fortress was by roads cut in the rock, so rugged in many
places as to resemble broken stairs. In a word, the impregnable security of Zahara had become so proverbial
throughout Spain, that a woman of forbidding and inaccessible virtue was called a Zahareña. But the strongest
fortress and sternest virtue have weak points, and require unremitting vigilance to guard them: let warrior
and dame take warning from the fate of Zahara.

CONQUEST OF GRANADA.

# CHAPTER IV.

EXPEDITION OF MULEY ABUL HASSAN AGAINST THE FORTRESS OF ZAHARA.

IN the year of our Lord one thousand four hundred and eighty-one, and but a night or two after the festival of the most blessed Nativity, the inhabitants of Zahara were sunk in profound sleep; the very sentinel had deserted his post, and sought shelter from a tempest which had raged for three nights in succession; for it appeared but little probable that an enemy would be abroad during such an uproar of the elements. But evil spirits work best during a storm. In the midst of the night, an uproar rose within the walls of Zahara, more awful than the raging of the storm. A fearful alarm cry—"The Moor! the Moor!" resounded through the streets, mingled with the clash of arms, the shriek of anguish, and the shout of victory. Muley Abul Hassan, at the head of a powerful force, had hurried from Granada, and passed unobserved through the mountains in the obscurity of the tempest. While the storm pelted the sentinel from his post, and howled round tower and battlement, the Moors had planted their scaling-ladders, and mounted securely into both town

41

and castle. The garrison was unsuspicious of danger, until battle and massacre burst forth within its very walls. It seemed to the affrighted inhabitants, as if the fiends of the air had come upon the wings of the wind, and possessed themselves of tower and turret. The war-cry resounded on every side, shout answering shout above, below, on the battlements of the castle, in the streets of the town—the foe was in all parts, wrapped in obscurity, but acting in concert by the aid of precon-certed signals. Starting from sleep, the soldiers were intercepted and cut down as they rushed from their quarters; or if they escaped, they knew not where to assemble, or where to strike. Wherever lights appeared, the flashing scimetar was at its deadly work, and all who attempted resistance fell beneath its edge.

In a little while the struggle was at an end. Those who were not slain took refuge in the secret places of their houses, or gave themselves up as captives. The clash of arms ceased; and the storm continued its howl-ing, mingled with the occasional shout of the Moorish soldiery, roaming in search of plunder. While the in-habitants were trembling for their fate, a trumpet re-sounded through the streets, summoning them all to assemble, unarmed, in the public square. Here they were surrounded by soldiery, and strictly guarded, until daybreak. When the day dawned, it was piteous to be-hold this once prosperous community, who had laid down to rest in peaceful security, now crowded together without distinction of age, or rank, or sex, and almost without raiment, during the severity of a wintry storm. The fierce Muley Abul Hassan turned a deaf ear to all their prayers and remonstrances, and ordered them to be conducted captives to Granada. Leaving a strong garrison in both town and castle, with orders to put them in a complete state of defense, he returned, flushed with victory, to his capital, entering it at the head of his troops, laden with spoil, and bearing in triumph the banners and pennons taken at Zahara.

While preparations were making for jousts and other festivities, in honor of this victory over the Christians, the captives of Zahara arrived—a wretched train of men, women, and children, worn out with fatigue and haggard with despair, and driven like cattle into the city gates, by a detachment of Moorish soldiery.

Deep was the grief and indignation of the people of Granada at this cruel scene. Old men, who had experienced the calamities of warfare, anticipated coming troubles. Mothers clasped their infants to their breasts, as they beheld the hapless females of Zahara, with their children expiring in their arms. On every side, the accents of pity for the sufferers were mingled with execrations of the barbarity of the king. The preparations for festivity were neglected; and the viands, which were to have feasted the conquerors, were distributed among the captives.

The nobles and alfaquis, however, repaired to the Al-

hambra to congratulate the king; for, whatever storms
may rage in the lower regions of society, rarely do any
clouds, but clouds of incense, rise to the awful eminence
of the throne. In this instance, however, a voice rose
from the midst of the obsequious crowd, and burst like
thunder upon the ears of Abul Hassan. "Woe! woe!
woe! to Granada!" exclaimed the voice; "its hour of
desolation approaches. The ruins of Zahara will fall
upon our heads; my spirit tells me that the end of our
empire is at hand!" All shrank back aghast, and left the
denouncer of woe standing alone in the centre of the hall.
He was an ancient and hoary man, in the rude attire of a
dervise. Age had withered his form without quenching
the fire of his spirit, which glared in baleful lustre from
his eyes. He was (say the Arabian historians) one of
those holy men termed santons, who pass their lives
in hermitages, in fasting, meditation, and prayer, until
they attain to the purity of saints and the foresight of
prophets. "He was," says the indignant Fray Antonio
Agapida, "a son of Belial, one of those fanatic infidels
possessed by the devil, who are sometimes permitted to
predict the truth to their followers; but with the proviso,
that their predictions shall be of no avail."

The voice of the santon resounded through the lofty
hall of the Alhambra, and struck silence and awe into
the crowd of courtly sycophants. Muley Abul Hassan
alone was unmoved; he eyed the hoary anchorite with
scorn as he stood dauntless before him, and treated his

predictions as the ravings of a maniac. The santon rushed from the royal presence, and, descending into the city, hurried through its streets and squares with frantic gesticulations. His voice was heard, in every part, in awful denunciation. "The peace is broken! exterminating war is commenced. Woe! woe! woe to Granada! its fall is at hand! desolation will dwell in its palaces; its strong men will fall beneath the sword, its children and maidens be led into captivity. Zahara is but a type of Granada!"

Terror seized upon the populace, for they considered these ravings as the inspirations of prophecy. Some hid themselves in their dwellings, as in a time of general mourning; while some gathered together in knots in the streets and squares, alarming each other with dismal forebodings, and cursing the rashness and cruelty of the king.

The Moorish monarch heeded not their murmurs. Knowing that his exploit must draw upon him the vengeance of the Christians, he now threw off all reserve, and made attempts to surprise Castellan and Elvira, though without success. He sent alfaquis, also, to the Barbary powers, informing them that the sword was drawn, and inviting the African princes to aid him with men and supplies in maintaining the kingdom of Granada, and the religion of Mahomet, against the violence of unbelievers.

While discontent exhaled itself in murmurs among the

common people, however, it fomented in dangerous conspiracies among the nobles, and Muley Abul Hassan was
startled by information of a design to depose him and
place his son Boabdil upon the throne. His first measure was to confine the prince and his mother in the
tower of Comares; then, calling to mind the prediction
of the astrologers, that the youth would one day sit on
the throne of Granada, he impiously set the stars at
defiance. "The sword of the executioner," said he,
"shall prove the fallacy of those lying horoscopes, and
shall silence the ambition of Boabdil."

The Sultana Ayxa, apprised of the imminent danger
of her son, concerted a plan for his escape. At the dead
of the night she gained access to his prison, and tying
together the shawls and scarfs of herself and her female
attendants, lowered him down from a balcony of the Alhambra to the steep, rocky hill-side which sweeps down
to the Darro. Here some of her devoted adherents were
waiting to receive him, who, mounting him on a swift
horse, spirited him away to the city of Guadix, in the Al-
puxaras.

CONQUEST OF GRANADA.

wrote, the many valiant cavaliers who rallied round
the flower of Ferdinand and Isabella, one of the most
eminent in rank and renowned in arms was Don Rodrigo Ponce de Leon, Marquis of Cadiz. As he was
the distinguished champion of this holy war, and commanded in most of its enterprises, and battles, it is
meet that some particular record should be given of
him. He was born in 1443, of the illustrious lineage of
that should

# CHAPTER V.

EXPEDITION OF THE MARQUES OF CADIZ AGAINST ALHAMA.

REAT was the indignation of King Ferdinand
when he heard of the storming of Zahara;
though the outrage of the Moor happened most
opportunely. The war between Castile and Portugal
had come to a close; the factions of the Spanish nobles
were for the most part quelled. The Castilian monarchs
had now, therefore, turned their thoughts to the cherished object of their ambition, the conquest of Granada.
The pious heart of Isabella yearned to behold the entire
peninsula redeemed from the domination of the infidel;
while Ferdinand, in whom religious zeal was mingled
with temporal policy, looked with a craving eye to the
rich territory of the Moor, studded with wealthy towns
and cities. Muley Abul Hassan had rashly or unwarily
thrown the brand that was to produce the wide conflagration. Ferdinand was not the one to quench the
flames. He immediately issued orders to all the adelan-
tados and alcaydes of the frontiers, to maintain the utmost vigilance at their posts, and to prepare to carry fire
and sword into the territories of the Moors.

47

Among the many valiant cavaliers who rallied round
the throne of Ferdinand and Isabella, one of the most
eminent in rank and renowned in arms was Don Roderigo Ponce de Leon, Marques of Cadiz. As he was
the distinguished champion of this holy war, and commanded in most of its enterprises and battles, it is
meet that some particular account should be given of
him. He was born in 1443, of the valiant lineage of the
Ponces, and from his earliest youth had rendered himself
illustrious in the field. He was of the middle stature,
with a muscular and powerful frame, capable of great exertion and fatigue. His hair and beard were red and
curled, his countenance was open and magnanimous, of a
ruddy complexion, and slightly marked with the small-
pox. He was temperate, chaste, valiant, vigilant; a just
and generous master to his vassals; frank and noble in
his deportment towards his equals; loving and faithful
to his friends; fierce and terrible, yet magnanimous, to
his enemies. He was considered the mirror of chivalry
of his times, and compared by contemporary historians
to the immortal Cid.

The marques of Cadiz had vast possessions in the most
fertile parts of Andalusia, including many towns and
castles, and could lead forth an army into the field from
his own vassals and dependents. On receiving the
orders of the king, he burned to signalize himself by
some sudden incursion into the kingdom of Granada,
that should give a brilliant commencement to the war,

and should console the sovereigns for the insult they had received in the capture of Zahara. As his estates lay near to the Moorish frontiers, and were subject to sudden inroads, he had always in his pay numbers of adalides, or scouts and guides, many of them converted Moors. These he sent out in all directions, to watch the movements of the enemy, and to procure all kinds of information important to the security of the frontier. One of these spies came to him one day in his town of Marchena, and informed him that the Moorish town of Alhama was slightly garrisoned and negligently guarded, and might be taken by surprise. This was a large, wealthy, and populous place, within a few leagues of Granada. It was situated on a rocky height, nearly surrounded by a river, and defended by a fortress to which there was no access but by a steep and cragged ascent. The strength of its situation, and its being embosomed in the centre of the kingdom, had produced the careless security which now invited attack.

To ascertain fully the state of the fortress, the marques dispatched secretly a veteran soldier, who was highly in his confidence. His name was Ortega de Prado, a man of great activity, shrewdness, and valor, and captain of escaladors (soldiers employed to scale the walls of fortresses in time of attack). Ortega approached Alhama one moonless night, and paced along its walls with noiseless step, laying his ear occasionally to the ground or to the wall. Every time, he distinguished he measured

4

tread of a sentinel, and now and then the challenge of the night-watch going its rounds. Finding the town thus guarded he clambered to the castle:—there all was silent. As he ranged its lofty battlements, between him and the sky he saw no sentinel on duty. He noticed certain places where the wall might be ascended by scaling-ladders; and having marked the hour of relieving guard, and made all necessary observations, he retired without being discovered.

Ortega returned to Marchena, and assured the marques of Cadiz of the practicability of scaling the castle of Alhama, and taking it by surprise. The marques had a secret conference with Don Pedro Enriquez, Adelantado of Andalusia; Don Diego de Merlo, commander of Seville; Sancho de Avila, Alcayde of Carmona, and others, who all agreed to aid him with their forces. On an appointed day, the several commanders assembled at Marchena with their troops and retainers. None but the leaders knew the object or destination of the enterprise; but it was enough to rouse the Andalusian spirit, to know that a foray was intended into the country of their old enemies, the Moors. Secrecy and celerity were necessary for success. They set out promptly, with three thousand genetes, or light cavalry, and four thousand infantry. They chose a route but little travelled, by the way of Antiquera, passing with great labor through rugged and solitary defiles of the Sierra or chain of mountains of Arrecife, and left all their baggage on the banks of the river Yeguas, to be brought after them. This march was principally in the night; all day they remained quiet; no noise was suffered in their camp, and no fires were made, lest the smoke should betray them. On the third day they resumed their march as the evening darkened, and forcing themselves forward at as quick a pace as the rugged and dangerous mountain roads would permit, they descended towards midnight into a small deep valley, only half a league from Alhama. Here they made a halt, fatigued by this forced march, during a long dark evening towards the end of February.

The marques of Cadiz now explained to the troops the object of the expedition. He told them it was for the glory of the most holy faith, and to avenge the wrongs of their countrymen at Zahara; and that the town of Alhama, full of wealthy spoil, was the place to be attacked. The troops were roused to new ardor by these words, and desired to be led forthwith to the assault. They arrived close to Alhama about two hours before daybreak. Here the army remained in ambush, while three hundred men were dispatched to scale the walls and get possession of the castle. They were picked men, many of them alcaydes and officers, men who preferred death to dishonor. This gallant band was guided by the escalador Ortega de Prado, at the head of thirty men with scaling-ladders. They clambered the ascent to the castle in silence, and arrived under the dark shadow of its towers without being discovered. Not a light was to be seen, not a sound to be heard ; the whole place was wrapped in profound repose.

Fixing their ladders, they ascended cautiously and with noiseless steps. Ortega was the first that mounted upon the battlements, followed by one Martin Galindo, a youthful esquire, full of spirit and eager for distinction. Moving stealthily along the parapet to the portal of the citadel, they came upon the sentinel by surprise. Ortega seized him by the throat, brandished a dagger before his eyes, and ordered him to point the way to the guard-room. The infidel obeyed, and was instantly dispatched, to prevent his giving an alarm. The guard-room was a scene rather of massacre than combat. Some of the soldiery were killed while sleeping, others were cut down almost without resistance, bewildered by so unexpected an assault : all were dispatched, for the scaling party was too small to make prisoners or to spare. The alarm spread throughout the castle, but by this time the three hundred picked men had mounted the battlements. The garrison, startled from sleep, found the enemy already masters of the towers. Some of the Moors were cut down at once, others fought desperately from room to room, and the whole castle resounded with the clash of arms, the cries of the combatants, and the groans of the wounded. The army in ambush, finding by the uproar that the castle was surprised, now rushed from their concealment, and approached the walls with loud shouts, and sound of kettle-drums and trumpets, to increase the confusion and dismay of the garrison. A violent conflict took place in the court of the castle, where several of the scaling party sought to throw open the gates to admit their countrymen. Here fell two valiant alcaydes, Nicholas de Roja and Sancho de Avila; but they fell honorably, upon a heap of slain. At length Ortega de Prado succeeded in throwing open a postern, through which the marques of Cadiz, the adelantado of Andalusia, and Don Diego de Merlo, entered with a host of followers, and the citadel remained in full possession of the Christians.

As the Spanish cavaliers were ranging from room to room, the marques of Cadiz, entering an apartment of superior richness to the rest, beheld, by the light of a silver lamp, a beautiful Moorish female, the wife of the alcayde of the castle, whose husband was absent, attending a wedding feast at Velez Malaga. She would have fled at the sight of a Christian warrior in her apartment, but, entangled in the covering of the bed, she fell at the feet of the marques, imploring mercy. That Christian cavalier, who had a soul full of honor and courtesy towards the sex, raised her from the floor, and endeavored to allay her fears; but they were increased at the sight of her female attendants, pursued into the room by the Spanish soldiery. The marques reproached his soldiers with unmanly conduct, and reminded them that they made war upon men, not on defenseless women. Having soothed the terrors of the females by the promise of honorable protection, he appointed a trusty guard to watch over the security of their apartment.

The castle was now taken; but the town below it was in arms. It was broad day, and the people, recovered from their panic, were enabled to see and estimate the force of the enemy. The inhabitants were chiefly merchants and tradespeople; but the Moors all possessed a knowledge of the use of weapons, and were of brave and warlike spirit. They confided in the strength of their walls, and the certainty of speedy relief from Granada, which was but about eight leagues distant. Manning the battlements and towers, they discharged showers of stones and arrows, whenever the part of the Christian army, without the walls, attempted to approach. They barricadoed the entrances of their streets, also, which opened towards the castle; stationing men expert at the cross-bow and arquebuse. These kept up a constant fire upon the gate of the castle, so that no one could sally forth without being instantly shot down. Two valiant cavaliers, who attempted to lead forth a party in defiance of this fatal tempest, were shot dead at the very portal.

The Christians now found themselves in a situation of great peril. Reinforcements must soon arrive to the enemy from Granada; unless, therefore, they gained possession of the town in the course of the day, they were likely to be surrounded and beleaguered, without provisions, in the castle. Some observed that, even if they took the town, they should not be able to maintain possession of it. They proposed, therefore, to make booty of everything valuable, to sack the castle, set it on fire, and make good their retreat to Seville.

The marques of Cadiz was of different counsel. "God has given the citadel into Christian hands," said he, "he will no doubt strengthen them to maintain it. We have gained the place with difficulty and bloodshed; it would be a stain upon our honor to abandon it through fear of imaginary dangers." The adelantado and Don Diego de Merlo joined in his opinion; but without their earnest and united remonstrances, the place would have been abandoned; so exhausted were the troops by forced marches and hard fighting, and so apprehensive of the approach of the Moors of Granada.

The strength and spirits of the party within the castle were in some degree restored by the provisions which they found. The Christian army beneath the town, being also refreshed by a morning's repast, advanced vigorously to the attack of the walls. They planted their scaling-ladders, and, swarming up, sword in hand, fought fiercely with the Moorish soldiery upon the ramparts.

In the meantime, the marques of Cadiz, seeing that the gate of the castle, which opened toward the city, was completely commanded by the artillery of the enemy, ordered a large breach to be made in the wall, through which he might lead his troops to the attack: animating them, in this perilous moment, by assuring them that the place should be given up to plunder, and its inhabitants made captives.

The breach being made, the marques put himself at the head of his troops, and entered sword in hand. A simultaneous attack was made by the Christians in every part — by the ramparts, by the gate, by the roofs and walls which connected the castle with the town. The Moors fought valiantly in their streets, from their windows, and from the tops of their houses. They were not equal to the Christians in bodily strength, for they were for the most part peaceful men, of industrious callings, and enervated by the frequent use of the warm bath; but they were superior in number, and unconquerable in spirit; old and young, strong and weak, fought with the same desperation. The Moors fought for property, for liberty, for life. They fought at their thresholds and their hearths, with the shrieks of their wives and children ringing in their ears, and they fought in the hope that each moment would bring aid from Granada. They regarded neither their own wounds nor the death of their companions; but continued fighting until they fell, and seemed as if, when they could no longer contend, they would block up the thresholds of their beloved homes with their mangled bodies. The Christians fought for glory, for revenge, for the holy faith, and for the spoil of these wealthy infidels. Success would place a rich town at their mercy; failure would deliver them into the hands of the tyrant of Granada.

The contest raged from morning until night, when the Moors began to yield. Retreating to a large mosque near the walls, they kept up so galling a fire from it with lances, cross-bows, and arquebuses, that for some time the Christians dared not approach. Covering themselves, at length, with bucklers and mantelets,* to protect them from the deadly shower, the latter made their way to the mosque, and set fire to the doors. When the smoke and flames rolled in upon them, the Moors gave up all as lost. Many rushed forth desperately upon the enemy, but were immediately slain; the rest surrendered themselves captives.

The struggle was now at an end; the town remained at the mercy of the Christians; and the inhabitants, both male and female, became the slaves of those who made them prisoners. Some few escaped by a mine or subterranean way, which led to the river, and concealed themselves, their wives and children, in caves and secret places; but in three or four days were compelled to surrender themselves through hunger.

The town was given up to plunder, and the booty was immense. There were found prodigious quantities of gold and silver, and jewels, and rich silks, and costly stuffs of all kinds; together with horses and beeves, and abundance of grain and oil, and honey, and all other productions of this fruitful kingdom; for in Alhama were

* Mantelet—a movable parapet, made of thick planks, to protect troops when advancing to sap or assault a walled place.

collected the royal rents and tributes of the surrounding country; it was the richest town in the Moorish territory, and, from its great strength and its peculiar situation, was called the key to Granada.

Great waste and devastation were committed by the Spanish soldiery; for, thinking it would be impossible to keep possession of the place, they began to destroy whatever they could not take away. Immense jars of oil were broken, costly furniture shattered to pieces, and magazines of grain broken open, and their contents scattered to the winds. Many Christian captives, who had been taken at Zahara, were found buried in a Moorish dungeon, and were triumphantly restored to light and liberty; and a renegado Spaniard, who had often served as guide to the Moors in their incursions into the Christian territories, was hanged on the highest part of the battlements, for the edification of the army.

# CHAPTER VI.

 MOORISH horseman had spurred across the vega, nor reined his panting steed until he alighted at the gate of the Alhambra. He brought tidings to Muley Abul Hassan of the attack upon Alhama. "The Christians," said he, "are in the land. They came upon us, we know not whence or how, and scaled the walls of the castle in the night. There has been dreadful fighting and carnage in its towers and courts; and when I spurred my steed from the gate of Alhama, the castle was in possession of the unbelievers."

Muley Abul Hassan felt for a moment as if swift retribution had come upon him for the woes he had inflicted upon Zahara. Still he flattered himself that this had only been some transient inroad of a party of marauders, intent upon plunder; and that a little succor, thrown into the town, would be sufficient to expel them from the castle, and drive them from the land. He ordered out, therefore, a thousand of his chosen cavalry, and sent

59

them in all speed to the assistance of Alhama. They arrived before its walls the morning after its capture; the Christian standards floated upon its towers, and a body of cavalry poured forth from its gates and came wheeling down into the plain to receive them.

The Moorish horsemen turned the reins of their steeds, and galloped back for Granada. They entered its gates in tumultuous confusion, spreading terror and lamentation by their tidings. "Alhama is fallen! Alhama is fallen!" exclaimed they; "the Christians garrison its walls; the key of Granada is in the hands of the enemy!"

When the people heard these words, they remembered the denunciation of the santon. His prediction seemed still to resound in every ear, and its fulfillment to be at hand. Nothing was heard throughout the city but sighs and wailings. "Woe is me, Alhama!" was in every mouth; and this ejaculation of deep sorrow and doleful foreboding, came to be the burthen of a plaintive ballad, which remains until the present day.*

Many aged men, who had taken refuge in Granada from other Moorish dominions which had fallen into the power of the Christians, now groaned in despair at the thoughts that war was to follow them into this last retreat, to lay waste this pleasant land, and to bring trouble and sorrow

* The mournful little Spanish romance of *Ay de mi Alhama!* is supposed to be of Moorish origin, and to embody the grief of the people of Granada on this occasion.

upon their declining years. The women were more loud
and vehement in their grief; for they beheld the evils
impending over their children, and what can restrain the
agony of a mother's heart? Many of them made their
way through the halls of the Alhambra into the presence
of the king, weeping, and wailing, and tearing their hair.
"Accursed be the day," cried they, "that thou hast lit
the flame of war in our land! May the holy Prophet
bear witness before Allah that we and our children are
innocent of this act! Upon thy head, and upon the
heads of thy posterity, until the end of the world, rest
the sin of the desolation of Zahara!"*

Muley Abul Hassan remained unmoved amidst all
this storm; his heart was hardened (observes Fray
Antonio Agapida) like that of Pharaoh, to the end that,
through his blind violence and rage, he might produce
the deliverance of the land from its heathen bondage.
In fact, he was a bold and fearless warrior, and trusted
soon to make this blow recoil upon the head of the enemy. He had ascertained that the captors of Alhama
were but a handful: they were in the centre of his dominions, within a short distance of his capital. They
were deficient in munitions of war and provisions for
sustaining a siege. By a rapid movement he might surround them with a powerful army, cut off all aid from
their countrymen, and entrap them in the fortress they
had taken.

* Garibay, lib. 40, c. 29.

To think was to act, with Muley Abul Hassan; but he was prone to act with too much precipitation. He immediately set forth in person, with three thousand horse and fifty thousand foot, and, in his eagerness to arrive at the scene of action, would not wait to provide artillery and the various engines required in a siege. "The multitude of my forces," said he, confidently, "will be sufficient to overwhelm the enemy."

The marques of Cadiz, who thus held possession of Alhama, had a chosen friend and faithful companion in arms, among the most distinguished of the Christian chivalry. This was Don Alonzo de Cordova, senior and lord of the house of Aguilar, and brother of Gonsalvo of Cordova, afterwards renowned as Grand Captain of Spain. As yet, Alonzo de Aguilar was the glory of his name and race—for his brother was but young in arms. He was one of the most hardy, valiant, and enterprising of the Spanish knights, and foremost in all service of a perilous and adventurous nature. He had not been at hand, to accompany his friend, Ponce de Leon, marques of Cadiz, in his inroad into the Moorish territory; but he hastily assembled a number of retainers, horse and foot, and pressed forward to join the enterprise. Arriving at the river Yeguas, he found the baggage of the army still upon its banks, and took charge of it to carry it to Alhama. The marques of Cadiz heard of the approach of his friend, whose march was slow in consequence of being encumbered by the baggage. He was within but a few leagues of Alhama, when scouts came hurrying into the place, with intelligence that the Moorish king was at hand with a powerful army. The marques of Cadiz was filled with alarm lest De Aguilar should fall into the hands of the enemy. Forgetting his own danger, and thinking only of that of his friend, he dispatched a well-mounted messenger to ride full speed, and warn him not to approach.

The first determination of Alonzo de Aguilar, when he heard that the Moorish king was at hand, was to take a strong position in the mountains, and await his coming. The madness of an attempt with his handful of men to oppose an immense army, was represented to him with such force as to induce him to abandon the idea; he then thought of throwing himself into Alhama, to share the fortunes of his friend: but it was now too late. The Moor would infallibly intercept him, and he should only give the marques the additional distress of beholding him captured beneath his walls. It was even urged upon him that he had no time for delay, if he would consult his own safety, which could only be insured by an immediate retreat into the Christian territory. This last opinion was confirmed by the return of scouts, who brought information that Muley Abul Hassan had received notice of his movements, and was rapidly advancing in quest of him. It was with infinite reluctance that Don Alonzo de Aguilar yielded to these united and powerful reasons. Proudly and sullenly he drew off his forces, laden with the baggage of the army, and made an unwilling retreat towards Antiquera. Muley Abul Hassan pursued him for some distance through the mountains, but soon gave up the chase, and turned with his forces upon Alhama.

As the army approached the town, they beheld the fields strewn with the dead bodies of their countrymen, who had fallen in defense of the place, and had been cast forth and left unburied by the Christians. There they lay, mangled and exposed to every indignity; while droves of half-famished dogs were preying upon them, and fighting and howling over their hideous repast.* Furious at the sight, the Moors, in the first transports of their rage, attacked those ravenous animals: their next measure was to vent their fury upon the Christians. They rushed like madmen to the walls, applied scaling-ladders in all parts, without waiting for the necessary mantelets and other protections,—thinking, by attacking suddenly and at various points, to distract the enemy, and overcome them by the force of numbers.

The marques of Cadiz, with his confederate commanders, distributed themselves along the walls, to direct and animate their men in the defense. The Moors, in their blind fury, often assailed the most difficult and dangerous places. Darts, stones, and all kinds of missiles, were hurled down upon their defenseless heads. As fast as

---

* Pulgar, *Cronica.*

they mounted, they were cut down, or dashed from the battlements, their ladders overturned, and all who were on them precipitated headlong below.

Muley Abul Hassan stormed with passion at the sight; he sent detachment after detachment to scale the walls— but in vain; they were like waves rushing upon a rock, only to dash themselves to pieces. The Moors lay in heaps beneath the wall, and among them many of the bravest cavaliers of Granada. The Christians, also, sallied frequently from the gates, and made great havoc in the irregular multitude of assailants.

Muley Abul Hassan now became sensible of his error in hurrying from Granada without the proper engines for a siege. Destitute of all means to batter the fortifications, the town remained uninjured, defying the mighty army which raged and roamed before it. Incensed at being thus foiled, Muley Abul Hassan gave orders to undermine the walls. The Moors advanced with shouts to the attempt. They were received with a deadly fire from the ramparts, which drove them from their works. Repeatedly were they repulsed, and repeatedly did they return to the charge. The Christians not merely galled them from the battlements, but issued forth and cut them down in the excavations they were attempting to form. The contest lasted throughout a whole day, and by evening two thousand Moors were either killed or wounded.

Muley Abul Hassan now abandoned all hope of carrying the place by assault, and attempted to distress it into terms by turning the channel of the river which runs by its walls. On this stream the inhabitants depended for their supply of water; the place being destitute of fountains and cisterns, from which circumstances it is called Alhama *la seca,* or "the dry."

A desperate conflict ensued on the banks of the river, the Moors endeavoring to plant palisades in its bed to divert the stream, and the Christians striving to prevent them. The Spanish commanders exposed themselves to the utmost danger to animate their men, who were repeatedly driven back into the town. The marques of Cadiz was often up to his knees in the stream, fighting hand to hand with the Moors. The water ran red with blood, and was encumbered with dead bodies. At length, the overwhelming numbers of the Moors gave them the advantage, and they succeeded in diverting the greater part of the water. The Christians had to struggle severely, to supply themselves from the feeble rill which remained. They sallied to the river by a subterraneous passage; but the Moorish cross-bowmen stationed themselves on the opposite bank, keeping up a heavy fire upon the Christians, whenever they attempted to fill their vessels from the scanty and turbid stream. One party of the Christians had, therefore, to fight, while another drew water. At all hours of the day and night, this deadly strife was maintained, until it seemed as if every drop of water were purchased with a drop of blood.

In the meantime the sufferings of the town became intense. None but the soldiery and their horses were allowed the precious beverage so dearly earned, and even that in quantities that only tantalized their wants. The wounded, who could not sally to procure it, were almost destitute; while the unhappy prisoners, shut up in the mosques, were reduced to frightful extremities. Many perished raving mad, fancying themselves swimming in boundless seas, yet unable to assuage their thirst. Many of the soldiers lay parched and panting along the battlements, no longer able to draw a bowstring or hurl a stone; while above five thousand Moors, stationed upon a rocky height which overlooked part of the town, kept up a galling fire into it with slings and cross-bows; so that the marques of Cadiz was obliged to heighten the battlements, by using the doors from the private dwellings.

The Christian cavaliers, exposed to this extreme peril, and in imminent danger of falling into the hands of the enemy, dispatched fleet messengers to Seville and Cordova, entreating the chivalry of Andalusia to hasten to their aid. They sent likewise, imploring assistance from the king and queen, who at that time held their court in Medina del Campo. In the midst of their distress, a tank or cistern of water was fortunately discovered in the city, which gave temporary relief to their sufferings.

# CHAPTER VII.

### HOW THE DUKE OF MEDINA SIDONIA, AND THE CHIVALRY OF ANDALUSIA,
### HASTENED TO THE RELIEF OF ALHAMA.

THE perilous situation of the Christian cavaliers pent up and beleaguered within the walls of Alhama, spread terror among their friends, and anxiety throughout all Andalusia. Nothing, however, could equal the anguish of the marchioness of Cadiz, the wife of the gallant Roderigo Ponce de Leon. In her deep distress, she looked round for some powerful noble, who had the means of rousing the country to the assistance of her husband. No one appeared more competent for the purpose than Don Juan de Guzman, the duke of Medina Sidonia. He was one of the most wealthy and puissant grandees of Spain; his possessions extended over some of the most fertile parts of Andalusia, embracing towns, and sea-ports, and numerous villages. Here he reigned in feudal state, like a petty sovereign, and could at any time bring into the field an immense force of vassals and retainers.

The duke of Medina Sidonia and the marques of Cadiz, however, were at this time deadly foes. An hereditary feud existed between them, which had often arisen to bloodshed and open war; for as yet the fierce contests between the proud and puissant Spanish nobles had not been completely quelled by the power of the crown, and in this respect they exerted a right of sovereignty, in leading their vassals against each other in open field.

The duke of Medina Sidonia would have appeared, to many, the very last person to whom to apply for aid of the marques of Cadiz; but the marchioness judged of him by the standard of her own high and generous mind. She knew him to be a gallant and courteous knight, and had already experienced the magnanimity of his spirit, having been relieved by him when besieged by the Moors in her husband's fortress of Arcos. To the duke, therefore, she applied in this moment of sudden calamity, imploring him to furnish succor to her husband. The event showed how well noble spirits understand each other. No sooner did the duke receive this appeal from the wife of his enemy, than he generously forgot all feeling of animosity, and determined to go in person to his succor. He immediately dispatched a courteous letter to the marchioness, assuring her that in consideration of the request of so honorable and estimable a lady, and to rescue from peril so valiant a cavalier as her husband, whose loss would be great, not only to Spain, but to all Christendom, he would forego the recollection of all past grievances, and hasten to his relief with all the forces he could raise.

The duke wrote at the same time to the alcaydes of his towns and fortresses, ordering them to join him forthwith at Seville, with all the forces they could spare from their garrisons. He called on all the chivalry of Andalusia to make a common cause in the rescue of those Christian cavaliers, and he offered large pay to all volunteers who would resort to him with horses, armor, and provisions. Thus all who could be incited by honor, religion, patriotism, or thirst of gain, were induced to hasten to his standard, and he took the field with an army of five thousand horse and fifty thousand foot.* Many cavaliers of distinguished name accompanied him in this generous enterprise. Among these was the redoubtable Alonzo de Aguilar, the chosen friend of the marques of Cadiz, and with him his younger brother, Gonsalvo Fernandez de Cordova, afterwards renowned as the Grand Captain; Don Roderigo Giron, also, Master of the order of Calatrava, together with Martin Alonzo de Montemayor, and the marques De Villena, esteemed the best lance in Spain. It was a gallant and splendid army, comprising the flower of Spanish chivalry, and poured forth in brilliant array from the gates of Seville, bearing the great standard of that ancient and renowned city.

Ferdinand and Isabella were at Medina del Campo, when tidings came of the capture of Alhama. The king was at mass when he received the news, and ordered

* *Cronica de Los Duques de Medina Sidonia*, por Pedro de Medina, MS.

*Te Deum* to be chanted for this signal triumph of the holy faith. When the first flush of triumph had subsided, and the king learnt the imminent peril of the valorous Ponce de Leon and his companions, and the great danger that this stronghold might again be wrested from their grasp, he resolved to hurry in person to the scene of action. So pressing appeared to him the emergency, that he barely gave himself time to take a hasty repast while horses were providing, and then departed at furious speed for Andalusia, leaving a request for the queen to follow him.* He was attended by Don Beltram de la Cueva, duke of Albuquerque, Don Inigo Lopez de Mendoza, count of Tendilla, and Don Pedro Mauriques, count of Treviño, with a few more cavaliers of prowess and distinction. He travelled by forced journeys, frequently changing his jaded horses, being eager to arrive in time to take command of the Andalusian chivalry. When he arrived within five leagues of Cordova, the duke of Albuquerque remonstrated with him upon entering, with such incautious haste, into the enemy's country. He represented to him that there were troops enough assembled to succor Alhama, and that it was not for him to venture his royal person in doing what could be done by his subjects, especially as he had such valiant and experienced captains to act for him. "Besides, sire," added the duke, "your majesty should bethink you that the troops

* Illescas, *Hist. Pontifical.*

about to take the field are mere men of Andalusia, whereas your illustrious predecessors never made an inroad into the territory of the Moors, without being accompanied by a powerful force of the stanch and iron warriors of old Castile."

"Duke," replied the king, "your counsel might have been good, had I not departed from Medina with the avowed determination of succoring these cavaliers in person. I am now near the end of my journey, and it would be beneath my dignity to change my intention, before even I had met with an impediment. I shall take the troops of this country who are assembled, without waiting for those of Castile, and with the aid of God, shall prosecute my journey." *

As King Ferdinand approached Cordova, the principal inhabitants came forth to receive him. Learning, however, that the duke of Medina Sidonia was already on the march, and pressing forward into the territory of the Moors, the king was all on fire to overtake him, and to lead in person the succor to Alhama. Without entering Cordova, therefore, he exchanged his weary horses for those of the inhabitants who had come forth to meet him, and pressed forward for the army. He dispatched fleet couriers in advance, requesting the duke of Medina Sidonia to await his coming, that he might take command of the forces.

* Pulgar, *Cronica*, p. 3, cap. 3.

Neither the duke nor his companions in arms, however, felt inclined to pause in their generous expedition, and gratify the inclinations of the king. They sent back missives, representing that they were far within the enemies' frontier, and it was dangerous either to pause or turn back. They had likewise received pressing entreaties from the besieged to hasten their speed, setting forth their great sufferings, and their hourly peril of being overwhelmed by the enemy.

The king was at Ponton del Maestre, when he received these missives. So inflamed was he with zeal for the success of this enterprise, that he would have penetrated into the kingdom of Granada with the handful of cavaliers who accompanied him, but they represented the rashness of such a journey, through the mountainous defiles of a hostile country, thickly beset with towns and castles. With some difficulty, therefore, he was dissuaded from his inclination, and prevailed upon to await tidings from the army, in the frontier city of Antiquera.

## CHAPTER VIII.

### SEQUEL OF THE EVENTS AT ALHAMA.

HILE all Andalusia was thus in arms and pouring its chivalry through the mountain passes of
the Moorish frontiers, the garrison of Alhama
was reduced to great extremity, and in danger of sinking
under its sufferings before the promised succor could
arrive. The intolerable thirst that prevailed in consequence of the scarcity of water, the incessant watch that
had to be maintained over the vast force of enemies
without, and the great number of prisoners within, and
the wounds which almost every soldier had received in
the incessant skirmishes and assaults, had worn grievously both flesh and spirit. The noble Ponce de Leon,
marques of Cadiz, still animated the soldiery, however,
by word and example, sharing every hardship, and being
foremost in every danger; exemplifying that a good commander is the vital spirit of an army.

When Muley Abul Hassan heard of the vast force that
was approaching under the command of the duke of
Medina Sidonia, and that Ferdinand was coming in person with additional troops, he perceived that no time

was to be lost: Alhama must be carried by one powerful attack, or abandoned entirely to the Christians.

A number of Moorish cavaliers, some of the bravest youth of Granada, knowing the wishes of the king, proposed to undertake a desperate enterprise, which, if successful, must put Alhama in his power. Early one morning, when it was scarcely the gray of the dawn, about the time of changing the watch, these cavaliers approached the town, at a place considered inaccessible, from the steepness of the rocks on which the wall was founded; which it was supposed, elevated the battlements beyond the reach of the longest scaling-ladder. The Moorish knights, aided by a number of the strongest and most active escaladors, mounted these rocks, and applied the ladders, without being discovered; for, to divert attention from them, Muley Abul Hassan made a false attack upon the town in another quarter.

The scaling party mounted with difficulty, and in small numbers; the sentinel was killed at his post, and seventy of the Moors made their way into the streets before an alarm was given. The guards rushed to the walls, to stop the hostile throng that was still pouring in. A sharp conflict, hand to hand and man to man, took place on the battlements, and many on both sides fell. The Moors, whether wounded or slain, were thrown headlong without the walls; the scaling-ladders were overturned, and those who were mounting were dashed upon the rocks, and from thence tumbled upon the plain. Thus, in a little while, the ramparts were cleared by Christian prowess, led on by that valiant knight Don Alonzo Ponce, the uncle, and that brave esquire Pedro Pineda, nephew of the marques of Cadiz.

The walls being cleared, these two kindred cavaliers now hastened with their forces in pursuit of the seventy Moors, who had gained an entrance into the town. The main party of the garrison being engaged at a distance resisting the feigned attack of the Moorish king, this fierce band of infidels had ranged the streets almost without opposition, and were making their way to the gates to throw them open to the army.* They were chosen men from among the Moorish forces, several of them gallant knights, of the proudest families of Granada. Their footsteps through the city were in a manner printed in blood, and they were tracked by the bodies of those they had killed and wounded. They had attained the gate; most of the guard had fallen beneath their scimetars; a moment more, and Alhama would have been thrown open to the enemy.

Just at this juncture, Don Alonzo Ponce and Pedro de Pineda reached the spot with their forces. The Moors had the enemy in front and rear; they placed themselves back to back, with their banner in the centre. In this way they fought with desperate and deadly determination, making a rampart around them with the slain.

* Zurita, lib. 20, c. 43.

More Christian troops arrived, and hemmed them in; but still they fought, without asking for quarter. As their numbers decreased, they serried their circle still closer; defending their banner from assault; and the last Moor died at his post, grasping the standard of the prophet. This standard was displayed from the walls, and the turbaned heads of the Moors were thrown down to the besiegers.*

Muley Abul Hassan tore his beard with rage at the failure of this attempt, and at the death of so many of his chosen cavaliers. He saw that all further effort was in vain; his scouts brought word that they had seen from the heights the long columns and flaunting banners of the Christian army approaching through the mountains. To linger, would be to place himself between two bodies of the enemy. Breaking up his camp, therefore, in all haste, he gave up the siege of Alhama, and hastened back to Granada; and the last clash of his cymbals scarce died upon the ear from the distant hills, before the standard of the duke of Medina Sidonia was seen emerging in another direction from the defiles of the mountains.

When the Christians in Alhama beheld their enemies retreating on one side, and their friends advancing on the other, they uttered shouts of joy and hymns of

* Pedro de Pineda received the honor of knighthood from the hand of king Ferdinand, for his valor on this occasion (Alonzo Ponce was already knight).—See Zuñiga, *Annals of Seville,* lib. 12, an 1482.

thanksgiving, for it was as a sudden relief from present
death. Harassed by several weeks of incessant vigil
and fighting, suffering from scarcity of provisions and
almost continual thirst, they resembled skeletons rather
than living men. It was a noble and gracious spectacle—the meeting of those hitherto inveterate foes, the
duke of Medina Sidonia and the marques of Cadiz. At
sight of his magnanimous deliverer the marques melted
into tears: all past animosities only gave the greater
poignancy to present feelings of gratitude and admiration. The late deadly rivals clasped each other in their
arms, and from that time forward were true and cordial
friends.

While this generous scene took place between the
commanders, a sordid contest arose among their troops.
The soldiers who had come to the rescue claimed a portion of the spoils of Alhama ; and so violent was the dispute, that both parties seized their arms. The duke of
Medina Sidonia interfered, and settled the question with
his characteristic magnanimity. He declared that the
spoil belonged to those who had captured the city.
"We have taken the field," said he, "only for honor, for
religion, and for the rescue of our countrymen and fellow
Christians ; and the success of our enterprise is a sufficient and a glorious reward. If we desire booty, there
are sufficient Moorish cities yet to be taken, to enrich
us all." The soldiers were convinced by the frank and
chivalrous reasoning of the duke ; they replied to his

speech by acclamations, and the transient broil was happily appeased.

The marchioness of Cadiz, with the forethought of a loving wife, had dispatched her major-domo with the army, with a large supply of provisions. Tables were immediately spread beneath the tents, where the marques gave a banquet to the duke and the cavaliers who had accompanied him, and nothing but hilarity prevailed in this late scene of suffering and death.

A garrison of fresh troops was left at Alhama, and the veterans who had so valiantly captured and maintained it, returned to their homes, burdened with precious booty. The marques and duke, and their confederate cavaliers, repaired to Antiquera, where they were received with great distinction by the king, who honored the marques of Cadiz with signal marks of favor. The duke then accompanied his late enemy, but now most zealous and grateful friend, the marques of Cadiz, to his town of Marchena, where he received the reward of his generous conduct, in the thanks and blessings of the marchioness. The marques celebrated a sumptuous feast, in honor of his guest; for a day and night his palace was thrown open, and was the scene of continual revel and festivity. When the duke departed for his estates at St. Lucar, the marques attended him for some distance on his journey; and when they separated, it was as the parting scene of brothers. Such was the noble spectacle exhibited to the chivalry of Spain, by these two illustri-

ous rivals.   Each reaped universal renown from the part
he had performed in the campaign ; the marques, from
having surprised and captured one of the most important
and formidable fortresses of the kingdom of Granada ;
and the duke, from having subdued his deadliest foe, by
a great act of magnanimity.

# CHAPTER IX.

EVENTS AT GRANADA, AND RISE OF THE MOORISH KING BOABDIL EL CHICO.

HE Moorish king, Abul Hassan, returned, baffled and disappointed, from before the walls of Alhama, and was received with groans and smothered execrations by the people of Granada. The prediction of the santon was in every mouth, and appeared to be rapidly fulfilling; for the enemy was already strongly fortified in Alhama, in the very heart of the kingdom. At the same time the nobles who had secretly conspired to depose the old king and elevate his son Boabdil to the throne, had matured their plans, in concert with the prince, who had been joined in Guadix by hosts of adherents. An opportunity soon presented to carry their plans into operation.

Muley Abul Hassan had a royal country palace, with gardens and fountains, called the Alixares, situated on the Cerro del Sol, or Mountain of the Sun; a height, the ascent to which leads up from the Alhambra, but which towers far above that fortress, and looks down as from the clouds upon it, and upon the subjacent city of Granada. It was a favorite retreat of the Moorish kings, to

6

inhale the pure mountain breezes, and leave far below the din and turmoil of the city. Muley Abul Hassan had passed a day among its bowers, in company with his favorite wife, Zoraya, when towards evening he heard a strange sound rising from the city, like the gathering of a storm, or the sulien roar of the ocean. Apprehensive of evil, he ordered the officers of his guard to descend with all speed to the city, and reconnoitre. The intelligence brought back was astounding. A civil war was raging in the city. Boabdil had been brought from Guadix by the conspirators, the foremost of whom were the gallant race of the Abencerrages. He had entered the Albaycin in triumph, and been hailed with rapture, and proclaimed king in that populous quarter of the city. Abul Cacim Vanegas, the vizier, at the head of the royal guards, had attacked the rebels ; and the noise which had alarmed the king, was the din of fighting in the streets and squares.

Muley Abul Hassan hastened to descend to the Alhambra, confident that, ensconced in that formidable fortress, he could soon put an end to the rash commotion. To his surprise and dismay he found the battlements lined with hostile troops ; Aben Comixa, the alcayde, had declared in favor of Boabdil, and elevated his standard on the towers ; thus, cut off from his stronghold, the old monarch was fain to return to the Alixares.

The conflict lasted throughout the night with carnage on both sides. In the morning Abul Cacim, driven out of the city, appeared before the old king with his broken squadrons, and told him there was no safety but in flight. "Allah Achbar, (God is great!)" exclaimed old Muley, "it is in vain to contend against what is written in the book of fate. It was predestined that my son should sit upon the throne—Allah forfend the rest of the prediction." So saying he made a hasty retreat, escorted by Abul Cacim Vanegas and his troops, who conducted him to the castle of Mondujar, in the Valley of Locrin. Here he was joined by many powerful cavaliers, relatives of Abul Cacim and partisans of Zoraya; among whom were Cid Hiaya, Aben Jamy, and Reduan Vanegas, men who had alcaydes, vassals at their command, and possessed great influence in Almeria and Baza. He was joined, also, by his brother Abdallah, commonly called El Zagal, or the Valiant; who was popular in many parts of the kingdom. All these offered to aid him with their swords in suppressing the rebellion.

Thus reinforced, Muley Abul Hassan determined on a sudden blow for the recovery of his throne and the punishment of the rebels. He took his measures with that combination of dexterity and daring which formed his character, and arrived one night under the walls of Granada, with five hundred chosen followers. Scaling the walls of the Alhambra, he threw himself with sanguinary fury into its silent courts. The sleeping inmates were roused from their repose only to fall by the exterminating scimetar. The rage of Abul Hassan spared neither age, nor rank, nor sex; the halls resounded with shrieks and yells, and the fountains ran red with blood. The alcayde, Aben Comixa, retreated to a strong tower, with a few of the garrison and inhabitants. The furious Abul Hassan did not lose time in pursuing him; he was anxious to secure the city, and to wreak his vengeance on its rebellious inhabitants. Descending with his bloody band into the streets, he cut down the defenseless inhabitants, as, startled from their sleep, they rushed forth to learn the cause of the alarm. The city was soon completely roused; the people flew to arms; lights blazed in every street, revealing the scanty number of this band, that had been dealing such fatal vengeance in the dark. Muley Abul Hassan had been mistaken in his conjectures; the great mass of the people, incensed by his tyranny, were zealous in favor of his son. A violent, but transient conflict took place in the streets and squares: many of the followers of Abul Hassan were slain: the rest driven out of the city; and the old monarch, with the remnant of his band, retreated to his loyal city of Malaga.

Such was the commencement of those great internal feuds and divisions, which hastened the downfall of Granada. The Moors became separated into two hostile factions, headed by the father and the son, the latter of whom was called by the Spaniards *El Rey Chico*, or the young king; but though bloody encounters took place between them, they never failed to act with all their separate force against the Christians as a common enemy, whenever an opportunity occurred.

## CHAPTER X.

ING FERDINAND held a council of war at Cordova, where it was deliberated what was to be done with Alhama. Most of the council advised that it should be demolished, inasmuch as being in the centre of the Moorish kingdom, it would be at all times liable to attack, and could only be maintained by a powerful garrison and at a vast expense. Queen Isabella arrived at Cordova in the midst of these deliberations, and listened to them with surprise and impatience. "What!" said she, "destroy the first fruits of our victories? Abandon the first place we have wrested from the Moors? Never let us suffer such an idea to occupy our minds. It would argue fear or feebleness, and give new courage to the enemy. You talk of the toil and expense of maintaining Alhama. Did we doubt, on undertaking this war, that it was to be one of infinite cost, labor, and bloodshed? And shall we shrink from the cost, the moment a victory is obtained, and the question is merely to guard or abandon its glorious trophy? Let us hear no more about the destruction of Alhama; let us

85

maintain its walls sacred, as a stronghold granted us by Heaven, in the centre of this hostile land; and let our only consideration be how to extend our conquest, and capture the surrounding cities."

The language of the queen infused a more lofty and chivalrous spirit into the royal council. Preparations were made to maintain Alhama at all risk and expense; and King Ferdinand appointed, as alcayde, Luis Fernandez Puerto Carrero, Senior of the house of Palma, supported by Diego Lopez de Ayala, Pero Ruiz de Alarcon, and Alonzo Ortis, captains of four hundred lances, and a body of one thousand foot, supplied with provisions for three months.

Ferdinand resolved also to lay siege to Loxa, or Loja, a city of great strength, at no great distance from Alhama, and all-important to its protection. It was, in fact, a military point, situated in a pass of the mountains, between the kingdoms of Granada and Castile, and commanded a main entrance to the vega. The Xenil flowed by its walls, and it had a strong castle or citadel, built on a rock. In preparing for the siege of this formidable place, Ferdinand called upon all the cities and towns of Andalusia and Estramadura, and the domains of the orders of Santiago, Calatrava, and Alcantara, and of the priory of St. Juan and the kingdom of Toledo, and beyond to the cities of Salamanca, Toro, and Valladolid, to furnish, according to their repartimientos or allotments, a certain quantity of bread, wine, and cattle, to be deliv-

ered at the royal camp before Loxa, one half at the end
of June, and one half in July. These lands, also, together with Biscay and Guipiscoa, were ordered to send
reinforcements of horse and foot, each town furnishing
its quota; and great diligence was used in providing
bombards, powder, and other warlike munitions.

The Moors were no less active in their preparations,
and sent missives into Africa, entreating supplies, and
calling upon the Barbary princes to aid them in this war
of the faith. To intercept all succor, the Castilian sovereigns stationed an armada of ships and galleys in the
Straits of Gibraltar, under the command of Martin Diaz
de Mina and Carlos de Valera, with orders to scour the
Barbary coast, and sweep every Moorish sail from the sea.

While these preparations were making, Ferdinand
made an incursion, at the head of his army, into the
kingdom of Granada, and laid waste the vega, destroying
its hamlets and villages, ravaging its fields of grain, and
driving away the cattle.

It was about the end of June that King Ferdinand departed from Cordova, to sit down before the walls of
Loxa. So confident was he of success, that he left a great
part of the army at Ecija, and advanced with but five
thousand cavalry and eight thousand infantry. The marques of Cadiz, a warrior as wise as he was valiant, remonstrated against employing so small a force, and, indeed, was opposed to the measure altogether, as being
undertaken precipitately, and without sufficient prepa-

ration. King Ferdinand, however, was influenced by the counsel of Don Diego de Merlo, and was eager to strike a brilliant and decided blow. A vainglorious confidence prevailed, about this time, among the Spanish cavaliers; they overrated their own prowess, or rather they undervalued and despised their enemy. Many of them believed that the Moors would scarcely remain in their city when they saw the Christian troops advancing to assail it. The Spanish chivalry, therefore, marched gallantly and fearlessly, and almost carelessly, over the border, scantily supplied with the things needful for a besieging army, in the heart of an enemy's country. In the same negligent and confident spirit, they took up their station before Loxa.

The country around was broken and hilly, so that it was extremely difficult to form a combined camp. The river Xenil, which runs by the town, was compressed between high banks, and so deep as to be fordable with extreme difficulty; and the Moors had possession of the bridge. The king pitched his tents in a plantation of olives, on the banks of the river; the troops were distributed in different encampments on the heights, but separated from each other by deep rocky ravines, so as to be incapable of yielding each other prompt assistance. There was no room for the operation of the cavalry. The artillery, also, was so injudiciously placed as to be almost entirely useless. Alonzo of Aragon, duke of Villahermosa, and illegitimate brother of the king, was present at the siege, and disapproved of the whole arrangement. He was one of the most able generals of his time, and especially renowned for his skill in battering fortified places. He recommended that the whole disposition of the camp should be changed, and that several bridges should be thrown across the river. His advice was adopted, but slowly and negligently followed, so that it was rendered of no avail. Among other oversights in this hasty and negligent expedition, the army had no supply of baked bread; and, in the hurry of encampment, there was no time to erect furnaces. Cakes were therefore hastily made, and baked on the coals, and for two days the troops were supplied in this irregular way.

King Ferdinand felt, too late, the insecurity of his position, and endeavored to provide a temporary remedy. There was a height near the city, called by the Moors Santo Albohacen, which was in front of the bridge. He ordered several of his most valiant cavaliers to take possession of this height, and to hold it as a check upon the enemy and a protection to the camp. The cavaliers chosen for this distinguished and perilous post were the Marques of Cadiz, the Marques of Villena, Don Roderigo Tellez Giron, master of Calatrava, his brother the Count of Ureña, and Don Alonzo de Aguilar. These valiant warriors and tried companions in arms led their troops with alacrity to the height, which soon glittered with the array of arms, and was graced by several of the most redoubtable pennons of warlike Spain.

Loxa was commanded at this time by an old Moorish alcayde, whose daughter was the favorite wife of Boabdil. The name of this Moor was Ibrahim Ali Atar, but he was generally known among the Spaniards as Alatar. He had grown gray in border warfare, was an implacable enemy of the Christians, and his name had long been the terror of the frontier. Lord of Zagra, and in the receipt of rich revenues, he expended them all in paying scouts and spies, and maintaining a small but chosen force with which to foray into the Christian territories; and so straitened was he at times by these warlike expenses, that when his daughter married Boabdil, her bridal dress and jewels had to be borrowed. He was now in the ninetieth year of his age, yet indomitable in spirit, fiery in his passions, sinewy and powerful in frame, deeply versed in warlike stratagem, and accounted the best lance in all Mauritania. He had three thousand horsemen under his command, veteran troops, with whom he had often scoured the borders; and he daily expected the old Moorish king with reinforcements.

Old Ali Atar had watched from his fortress every movement of the Christian army, and had exulted in all the errors of its commanders: when he beheld the flower of Spanish chivalry, glittering about the height of Albohacen, his eye flashed with exultation. "By the aid of Allah," said he, "I will give those pranking cavaliers a rouse."

Ali Atar, privately and by night, sent forth a large

body of his chosen troops, to lie in ambush near one of the skirts of Albohacen. On the fourth day of the siege he sallied across the bridge, and made a feint attack upon the height. The cavaliers rushed impetuously forth to meet him, leaving their encampment almost unprotected. Ali Atar wheeled and fled, and was hotly pursued. When the Christian cavaliers had been drawn a considerable distance from their encampment, they heard a vast shout behind them, and, looking round, beheld their encampment assailed by the Moorish force which had been placed in ambush, and which had ascended a different side of the hill. The cavaliers desisted from the pursuit, and hastened to prevent the plunder of their tents. Ali Atar, in his turn, wheeled and pursued them; and they were attacked in front and rear on the summit of the hill. The contest lasted for an hour; the height of Albohacen was red with blood; many brave cavaliers fell, expiring among heaps of the enemy. The fierce Ali fought with the fury of a demon, until the arrival of more Christian forces compelled him to retreat into the city. The severest loss to the Christians, in this skirmish, was that of Roderigo Tellez Giron, grand master of Calatrava, whose burnished armor, emblazoned with the red cross of his order, made him a mark for the missiles of the enemy. As he was raising his arm to make a blow, an arrow pierced him, just beneath the shoulder, at the open part of the corselet. The lance and bridle fell from his hands, he faltered in his saddle,

and would have fallen to the ground, but was caught by
Pedro Gasca, a cavalier of Avila, who conveyed him to
his tent, where he died.  The king and queen, and the
whole kingdom, mourned his death, for he was in the
freshness of his youth, being but twenty-four years of
age, and had proved himself a gallant and high-minded
cavalier.  A melancholy group collected about his corse,
on the bloody height of Albohacen ; the knights of Calatrava mourned him as a commander; the cavaliers who
were encamped on the height lamented him as their companion in arms, in a service of peril; while the Count de
Ureña grieved over him with the tender affection of a
brother.

King Ferdinand now perceived the wisdom of the
opinion of the marques of Cadiz, and that his force was
quite insufficient for the enterprise.  To continue his
camp in its present unfortunate position would cost him
the lives of his bravest cavaliers, if not a total defeat, in
case of reinforcements to the enemy.  He called a council of war, late in the evening of Saturday ; and it was
determined to withdraw the army, early the next morning, to Rio Frio, a short distance from the city, and there
wait for additional troops from Cordova.

The next morning, early, the cavaliers on the height of
Albohacen began to strike their tents.  No sooner did
Ali Atar behold this, than he sallied forth to attack
them.  Many of the Christian troops, who had not heard
of the intention to change the camp, seeing the tents

struck and the Moors sallying forth, supposed that the enemy had been reinforced in the night, and that the army was on the point of retreating. Without stopping to ascertain the truth or to receive orders, they fled in dismay, spreading confusion through the camp; nor did they halt until they had reached the Rock of the Lovers, about seven leagues from Loxa.*

The king and his commanders saw the imminent peril of the moment, and made face to the Moors, each commander guarding his quarter and repelling all assaults, while the tents were struck and the artillery and ammunition conveyed away. The king, with a handful of cavaliers, galloped to a rising ground, exposed to the fire of the enemy, calling upon the flying troops and endeavoring in vain to rally them. Setting upon the Moors, he and his cavaliers charged them so vigorously, that they put a squadron to flight, slaying many with their swords and lances, and driving others into the river, where they were drowned. The Moors, however, were soon reinforced, and returned in great numbers. The king was in danger of being surrounded, and twice owed his safety to the valor of Don Juan de Ribera, Senior of Montemayor.

The marques of Cadiz beheld, from a distance, the peril of his sovereign. Summoning about seventy horsemen to follow him, he galloped to the spot, threw him-

* Pulgar, *Cronica.*

self between the king and the enemy, and, hurling his
lance, transpierced one of the most daring of the Moors.
For some time he remained with no other weapon than
his sword; his horse was wounded by an arrow, and
many of his followers were slain; but he succeeded in
beating off the Moors, and rescuing the king from imminent jeopardy, whom he then prevailed upon to retire to
less dangerous ground.

The marques continued, throughout the day, to expose
himself to the repeated assaults of the enemy; he was
ever found in the place of the greatest danger, and
through his bravery a great part of the army and camp
was preserved from destruction.*

It was a perilous day for the commanders; for in a
retreat of the kind, it is the noblest cavaliers who most
expose themselves to save their people. The duke of
Medina Celi was struck to the ground, but rescued
by his troops. The count de Tendilla, whose tents
were nearest to the city, received several wounds, and
various other cavaliers of the most distinguished note
were exposed to fearful jeopardy. The whole day was
passed in bloody skirmishings, in which the hidalgos and cavaliers of the royal household distinguished
themselves by their bravery; at length, the encampments being all broken up, and most of the artillery and
baggage removed, the bloody height of Albohacen was

* *Cura de los Palacios, c. 58.*

abandoned, and the neighborhood of Loxa evacuated. Several tents, a quantity of provisions, and a few pieces of artillery, were left upon the spot, from the want of horses and mules to carry them off.

Ali Atar hung upon the rear of the retiring army, and harassed it until it reached Rio Frio. Ferdinand returned thence to Cordova, deeply mortified though greatly benefited by the severe lesson he had received, which served to render him more cautious in his campaigns and more diffident of fortune. He sent letters to all parts, excusing his retreat, imputing it to the small number of his forces, and the circumstance that many of them were quotas sent from various cities, and not in royal pay; in the meantime, to console his troops for their disappointment, and to keep up their spirits, he led them upon another inroad to lay waste the vega of Granada.

# CHAPTER XI.

HOW MULEY ABUL HASSAN MADE A FORAY INTO THE LANDS OF MEDINA
SIDONIA, AND HOW HE WAS RECEIVED.

ULEY ABUL HASSAN had mustered an army,
and marched to the relief of Loxa; but arrived
too late—the last squadron of Ferdinand had
already passed over the border. "They have come and
gone," said he, "like a summer cloud, and all their
vaunting has been mere empty thunder." He turned to
make another attempt upon Alhama, the garrison of
which was in the utmost consternation at the retreat of
Ferdinand, and would have deserted the place, had it not
been for the courage and perseverance of the alcayde,
Luis Fernandez Puerto Carrero. That brave and loyal
commander cheered up the spirits of his men, and kept
the old Moorish king at bay, until the approach of Ferdinand, on his second incursion into the vega, obliged him
to make an unwilling retreat to Malaga.

Muley Abul Hassan felt that it would be in vain, with
his inferior force, to oppose the powerful army of the
Christian monarch; but to remain idle and see his territories laid waste, would ruin him in the estimation of his

people. "If we cannot parry," said he, "we can strike; if we cannot keep our own lands from being ravaged, we can ravage the lands of the enemy." He inquired and learned that most of the chivalry of Andalusia, in their eagerness for a foray, had marched off with the king, and left their own country almost defenseless. The territories of the duke of Medina Sidonia were particularly unguarded: here were vast plains of pasturage, covered with flocks and herds—the very country for a hasty inroad. The old monarch had a bitter grudge against the duke for having foiled him at Alhama. "I'll give this cavalier a lesson," said he, exultingly, "that will cure him of his love of campaigning." So he prepared in all haste for a foray into the country about Medina Sidonia.

Muley Abul Hassan sallied out of Malaga with fifteen hundred horse and six thousand foot, and took the way by the sea-coast, marching through Estiponia, and entering the Christian country between Gibraltar and Castellar. The only person that was likely to molest him on this route, was one Pedro de Vargas, a shrewd, hardy, and vigilant soldier, alcayde of Gibraltar, and who lay ensconced in his old warrior rock as in a citadel. Muley Abul Hassan knew the watchful and daring character of the man, but had ascertained that his garrison was too small to enable him to make a sally, or at least to insure him any success. Still he pursued his march with great silence and caution; sent parties in advance, to explore every pass where a foe might lie in ambush; cast many

7

an anxious eye towards the old rock of Gibraltar, as its cloud-capped summit was seen towering in the distance on his left, nor did he feel entirely at ease, until he had passed through the broken and mountainous country of Castellar, and descended into the plains. Here he encamped on the banks of the Celemin, and sent four hundred corredors, or fleet horsemen, armed with lances, to station themselves near Algeziras, and keep a strict watch across the bay, upon the opposite fortress of Gibraltar. If the alcayde attempted to sally forth, they were to waylay and attack him, being almost four times his supposed force; and were to send swift tidings to the camp. In the meantime, two hundred corredors were sent to scour that vast plain called the Campiña de Tarifa, abounding with flocks and herds; and two hundred more were to ravage the lands about Medina Sidonia. Muley Abul Hassan remained with the main body of the army, as a rallying point, on the banks of the Celemin.

The foraging parties scoured the country to such effect, that they came driving vast flocks and herds before them, enough to supply the place of all that had been swept from the vega of Granada. The troops which had kept watch upon the rock of Gibraltar, returned with word that they had not seen a Christian helmet stirring. The old king congratulated himself upon the secrecy and promptness with which he had conducted his foray, and upon having baffled the vigilance of Pedro de Vargas.

He had not been so secret, however, as he imagined;

the watchful alcayde of Gibraltar had received notice of his movements; but his garrison was barely sufficient for the defense of his post. Luckily there arrived at this juncture a squadron of the armed galleys, under Carlos de Valera, recently stationed in the Straits. Pedro de Vargas prevailed upon him to take charge of Gibraltar during his temporary absence, and forthwith sallied out at midnight, at the head of seventy chosen horsemen. By his command alarm fires were lighted on the mountains, signals that the Moors were on the ravage, at sight of which the peasants were accustomed to drive their flocks and herds to places of refuge. He sent couriers also spurring in every direction, summoning all capable of bearing arms to meet him at Castellar. This was a town strongly posted on a steep height, by which the Moorish king would have to return.

Muley Abul Hassan saw by the fires blazing on the mountains, that the country was rising. He struck his tents, and pushed forward as rapidly as possible for the border; but he was encumbered with booty, and with the vast cavalgada swept from the pastures of the Campiña de Tarifa. His scouts brought him word that there were troops in the field, but he made light of the intelligence, knowing that they could only be those of the alcayde of Gibraltar, and that he had not more than a hundred horsemen in his garrison. He threw in advance two hundred and fifty of his bravest troops, and with them the alcaydes of Marabella and Casares. Behind this vanguard followed a great cavalgada of cattle; and in the rear marched the king, with the main force of his little army.

It was near the middle of a sultry summer day, when they approached Castellar. De Vargas was on the watch, and beheld, by an immense cloud of dust, that they were descending one of the heights of that wild and broken country. The vanguard and rear-guard were above half a league asunder, with the cavalgada between them; and a long and close forest hid them from each other. De Vargas saw that they could render but little assistance to each other in case of a sudden attack, and might be easily thrown into confusion. He chose fifty of his bravest horsemen, and, making a circuit, took his post secretly in a narrow glen opening into a defile between two rocky heights, through which the Moors had to pass. It was his intention to suffer the vanguard and the cavalgada to pass, and to fall upon the rear.

While thus lying perdue, six Moorish scouts, well mounted and well armed, entered the glen, examining every place that might conceal an enemy. Some of the Christians advised that they should slay these six men, and retreat to Gibraltar. "No," said De Vargas, "I have come out for higher game than these; and I hope, by the aid of God and Santiago, to do good work this day. I know these Moors well, and doubt not but that they may readily be thrown into confusion."

By this time, the six horsemen approached so near

that they were on the point of discovering the Christian ambush. De Vargas gave the word, and ten horsemen rushed upon them; in an instant, four of the Moors rolled in the dust; the other two put spurs to their steeds, and fled towards their army, pursued by the ten Christians. About eighty of the Moorish vanguard came galloping to the relief of their companions; the Christians turned, and fled towards their ambush. De Vargas kept his men concealed, until the fugitives and their pursuers came clattering pell-mell into the glen. At a signal trumpet his men sallied forth with great heat and in close array. The Moors almost rushed upon their weapons, before they perceived them; forty of the infidels were overthrown, the rest turned their backs. "Forward!" cried De Vargas; "let us give the vanguard a brush, before it can be joined by the rear." So saying, he pursued the flying Moors down hill, and came with such force and fury upon the advance guard as to overturn many of them at the first encounter. As he wheeled off with his men the Moors discharged their lances; upon which he turned to the charge, and made great slaughter. The Moors fought valiantly for a short time, until the alcaydes of Marabella and Casares were slain, when they gave way and fled for the rear-guard. In their flight, they passed through the cavalgada of cattle, threw the whole in confusion, and raised such a cloud of dust that the Christians could no longer distinguish objects. Fearing that the king and the main body might be at hand, and

finding that De Vargas was badly wounded, they contented themselves with despoiling the slain and taking about
twenty-eight horses, and then retreated to Castellar.

When the routed Moors came flying back upon the
rear-guard, Muley Abul Hassan feared that the people of
Xeres were in arms. Several of his followers advised
him to abandon the cavalgada, and retreat by another
road. "No," said the old king, "he is no true soldier
who gives up his booty without fighting." Putting spurs
to his horse, he galloped forward through the centre of
the cavalgada, driving the cattle to the right and left.
When he reached the field of battle, he found it strewed with the bodies of upwards of one hundred Moors,
among which were those of the two alcaydes. Enraged
at the sight, he summoned all his cross-bowmen and
cavalry, pushed on to the very gates of Castellar, and set
fire to two houses close to the walls. Pedro de Vargas
was too severely wounded to sally forth in person; but
he ordered out his troops, and there was brisk skirmishing under the walls, until the king drew off and returned
to the scene of the recent encounter. Here he had the
bodies of the principal warriors laid across mules, to be
interred honorably at Malaga; the rest of the slain were
buried on the field of battle. Then, gathering together
the scattered cavalgada, he paraded it slowly, in an immense line, past the walls of Castellar, by way of taunting his foe.

With all his fierceness, old Muley Abul Hassan had a

gleam of warlike courtesy, and admired the hardy and soldier-like character of Pedro de Vargas. He summoned two Christian captives, and demanded what were the revenues of the alcayde of Gibraltar. They told him that, among other things, he was entitled to one out of every drove of cattle that passed his boundaries. " Allah forbid," cried the old monarch, " that so brave a cavalier should be defrauded of his dues."

He immediately chose twelve of the finest cattle, from the twelve droves which formed the cavalgada. These he gave in charge to an alfaqui, to deliver to Pedro de Vargas. "Tell him," said he, "that I crave his pardon for not having sent these cattle sooner; but I have this moment learnt the nature of his rights, and I hasten to satisfy them, with the punctuality due to so worthy a cavalier. Tell him, at the same time, that I had no idea the alcayde of Gibraltar was so active and vigilant in collecting his tolls."

The brave alcayde relished the stern soldier-like pleasantry of the old Moorish monarch. He ordered a rich silken vest, and a scarlet mantle, to be given to the alfaqui, and dismissed him with great courtesy. "Tell his majesty," said he, " that I kiss his hands for the honor he has done me, and regret that my scanty force has not permitted me to give him a more signal reception, on his coming into these parts. Had three hundred horsemen, whom I have been promised from Xeres, arrived in time, I might have served up an entertainment more befitting such a monarch. I trust, however, they will arrive in the course of the night, in which case his majesty may be sure of a royal regale in the dawning."

Muley Abul Hassan shook his head, when he received the reply of De Vargas. "Allah preserve us," said he, "from any visitation of these hard riders of Xeres! a handful of troops, acquainted with the wild passes of these mountains, may destroy an army encumbered as ours is with booty."

It was some relief to the king, however, to learn that the hardy alcayde of Gibraltar was too severely wounded to take the field in person. He immediately beat a retreat, with all speed, before the close of the day, hurrying with such precipitation, that the cavalgada was frequently broken, and scattered among the rugged defiles of the mountains; and above five thousand of the cattle turned back, and were regained by the Christians. Muley Abul Hassan returned triumphantly with the residue to Malaga, glorying in the spoils of the duke of Medina Sidonia.

King Ferdinand was mortified at finding his incursion into the vega of Granada counterbalanced by this inroad into his dominions, and saw that there were two sides to the game of war, as to all other games. The only one who reaped real glory, in this series of inroads and skirmishings, was Pedro de Vargas, the stout alcayde of Gibraltar.*

* Alonzo de Palencia, lib. 28, c. 3, MS.

# CHAPTER XII.

### FORAY OF SPANISH CAVALIERS AMONG THE MOUNTAINS OF MALAGA.

HE foray of old Muley Abul Hassan had touched the pride of the Andalusian chivalry, and they determined on retaliation. For this purpose, a number of the most distinguished cavaliers assembled at Antiquera, in the month of March, 1483. The leaders of the enterprise were, the gallant marques of Cadiz; Don Pedro Henriquez, adelantado of Andalusia; Don Juan de Silva, count of Cifuentes, and bearer of the royal standard, who commanded in Seville; Don Alonzo de Cardenas, master of the religious and military order of Santiago; and Don Alonzo de Aguilar. Several other cavaliers of note hastened to take part in the enterprise; and in a little while, about twenty-seven hundred horse, and several companies of foot, were assembled within the old warlike city of Antiquera, comprising the very flower of Andalusian chivalry.

A council of war was held by the chiefs, to determine in what quarter they should strike a blow. The rival Moorish kings were waging civil war with each other, in the vicinity of Granada: and the whole country lay open to inroads. Various plans were proposed by the different cavaliers. The marques of Cadiz was desirous of scaling the walls of Zahara, and regaining possession of that important fortress. The master of Santiago, however, suggested a wider range and a still more important object. He had received information from his adalides, who were apostate Moors, that an incursion might be safely made into a mountainous region near Malaga, called the Axarquia. Here were valleys of pasture land, well stocked with flocks and herds; and there were numerous villages and hamlets, which would be an easy prey. The city of Malaga was too weakly garrisoned, and had too few cavalry, to send forth any force in opposition; nay, he added, they might even extend their ravages to its very gates, and peradventure carry that wealthy place by sudden assault.

The adventurous spirits of the cavaliers were inflamed by this suggestion; in their sanguine confidence, they already beheld Malaga in their power, and they were eager for the enterprise. The marques of Cadiz endeavored to interpose a little cool caution. He likewise had apostate adalides, the most intelligent and experienced on the borders; among these, he placed especial reliance on one named Luis Amar, who knew all the mountains and valleys of the country. He had received from him a particular account of these mountains of the Axarquia.* Their

* Pulgar, in his Chronicle, reverses the case, and makes the marques of Cadiz recommend the expedition to the Axarquia; but Fray Antonio

savage and broken nature was a sufficient defense for the
fierce people who inhabited them, who, manning their
rocks, and their tremendous passes, which were often
nothing more than the deep dry beds of torrents, might
set whole armies at defiance. Even if vanquished, they
afforded no spoil to the victor. Their houses were little
better than bare walls, and they would drive off their
scanty flocks and herds to the fastnesses of the mountains.

The sober counsel of the marques, however, was over-
ruled. The cavaliers, accustomed to mountain warfare,
considered themselves and their horses equal to any
wild and rugged expedition, and were flushed with the
idea of terminating their foray by a brilliant assault upon
Malaga.

Leaving all heavy baggage at Antiquera, and all such
as had horses too weak for this mountain scramble, they
set forth, full of spirit and confidence. Don Alonzo de
Aguilar, and the adelantado of Andalusia, led the squadron of advance. The count of Cifuentes followed, with
certain of the chivalry of Seville. Then came the battalion of the most valiant Roderigo Ponce de Leon, marques of Cadiz; he was accompanied by several of his
brothers and nephews, and many cavaliers, who sought
distinction under his banner; and this family band attracted universal attention and applause, as they paraded

Agapida is supported in his statement by that most veracious and contemporary chronicler, Andres Bernaldes, curate of Los Palacios.

in martial state through the streets of Antiquera. The rear-guard was led by Don Alonzo Cardenas, master of Santiago, and was composed of the knights of his order, and the cavaliers of Ecija, with certain men-at-arms of the Holy Brotherhood, whom the king had placed under his command. The army was attended by a great train of mules, laden with provisions for a few days' supply, until they should be able to forage among the Moorish villages. Never did a more gallant and self-confident little army tread the earth. It was composed of men full of health and vigor, to whom war was a pastime and delight. They had spared no expense in their equipments, for never was the pomp of war carried to a higher pitch than among the proud chivalry of Spain. Cased in armor richly inlaid and embossed, with rich surcoats and waving plumes, and superbly mounted on Andalusian steeds, they pranced out of Antiquera with banners flying, and their various devices and armorial bearings ostentatiously displayed; and in the confidence of their hopes, promised the inhabitants to enrich them with the spoils of Malaga.

In the rear of this warlike pageant followed a peaceful band, intent on profiting by the anticipated victories. They were not the customary wretches that hover about armies to plunder and strip the dead, but goodly and substantial traders from Seville, Cordova, and other cities of traffic. They rode sleek mules, and were clad in goodly raiment, with long leather purses at their girdles, well filled with pistoles and other golden coin. They had heard of the spoils wasted by the soldiery at the capture of Alhama, and were provided with moneys to buy up the jewels and precious stones, the vessels of gold and silver, and the rich silks and cloths, that should form the plunder of Malaga. The proud cavaliers eyed these sons of traffic with great disdain, but permitted them to follow for the convenience of the troops, who might otherwise be overburdened with booty.

It had been intended to conduct this expedition with great celerity and secrecy; but the noise of their preparations had already reached the city of Malaga. The garrison, it is true, was weak; but it possessed a commander who was himself a host. This was Muley Abdallah, commonly called El Zagal, or the Valiant. He was younger brother of Muley Abul Hassan, and general of the few forces which remained faithful to the old monarch. He possessed equal fierceness of spirit with his brother, and surpassed him in craft and vigilance. His very name was a war-cry among his soldiery, who had the most extravagant opinion of his prowess.

El Zagal suspected that Malaga was the object of this noisy expedition. He consulted with old Bexir, a veteran Moor, who governed the city. "If this army of marauders should reach Malaga," said he, "we should hardly be able to keep them without its walls. I will throw myself, with a small force, into the mountains; rouse the peasantry, take possession of the passes, and

endeavor to give these Spanish cavaliers sufficient entertainment upon the road."

It was on a Wednesday, that the pranking army of
high-mettled warriors issued forth from the ancient gates
of Antiquera. They marched all day and night, making
their way, secretly as they supposed, through the passes
of the mountains. As the tract of country they intended
to maraud was far in the Moorish territories near the
coast of the Mediterranean, they did not arrive there until late in the following day. In passing through these
stern and lofty mountains, their path was often along the
bottom of a barranco, or deep rocky valley, with a scanty
stream dashing along it, among the loose rocks and
stones, which it had broken and rolled down, in the time
of its autumnal violence. Sometimes their road was a
mere rambla, or dry bed of a torrent, cut deep into the
mountains, and filled with their shattered fragments.
These barrancos and ramblas were overhung by immense
cliffs and precipices; forming the lurking-places of ambuscades, during the wars between the Moors and Spaniards, as in after times they have become the favorite
haunts of robbers to waylay the unfortunate traveller.

As the sun went down, the cavaliers came to a lofty
part of the mountains, commanding to the right a distant
glimpse of a part of the fair vega of Malaga, with the
blue Mediterranean beyond; and they hailed it with
exultation, as a glimpse of the promised land. As the
night closed in, they reached the chain of little valleys

and hamlets, locked up among these rocky heights, and known among the Moors by the name of the Axarquia. Here their vaunting hopes were destined to meet with the first disappointment. The inhabitants had heard of their approach; they had conveyed away their cattle and effects, and, with their wives and children, had taken refuge in the towers and fastnesses of the mountains.

Enraged at their disappointment, the troops set fire to the deserted houses, and pressed forward, hoping for better fortune as they advanced. Don Alonzo de Aguilar, and the other cavaliers in the vanguard, spread out their forces to lay waste the country; capturing a few lingering herds of cattle, with the Moorish peasants who were driving them to some place of safety.

While this marauding party carried fire and sword in the advance, and lit up the mountain cliffs with the flames of the hamlets, the master of Santiago, who brought up the rear-guard, maintained strict order, keeping his knights together in martial array, ready for attack or defense, should an enemy appear. The men-at-arms of the Holy Brotherhood attempted to roam in quest of booty; but he called them back, and rebuked them severely.

At length they came to a part of the mountain completely broken up by barrancos and ramblas, of vast depth, and shagged with rocks and precipices. It was impossible to maintain the order of march; the horses had no room for action, and were scarcely manageable, having to scramble from rock to rock, and up and down frightful declivities, where there was scarce footing for a mountain goat. Passing by a burning village, the light of the flames revealed their perplexed situation. The Moors, who had taken refuge in a watch-tower on an impending height, shouted with exultation, when they looked down upon these glistening cavaliers struggling and stumbling among the rocks. Sallying forth from their tower, they took possession of the cliffs which over-hung the ravine, and hurled darts and stones upon the enemy. It was with the utmost grief of heart that the good master of Santiago beheld his brave men falling like helpless victims around him, without the means of resistance or revenge. The confusion of his followers was increased by the shouts of the Moors, multiplied by the echoes of every crag and cliff, as if they were sur-rounded by innumerable foes. Being entirely ignorant of the country, in their struggles to extricate themselves they plunged into other glens and defiles, where they were still more exposed to danger. In this extremity, the master of Santiago dispatched messengers in search of succor. The marques of Cadiz, like a loyal companion in arms, hastened to his aid with his cavalry; his approach checked the assaults of the enemy, and the master was at length enabled to extricate his troops from the defile.

In the meantime, Don Alonzo de Aguilar and his com-panions, in their eager advance, had likewise got entan-gled in deep glens and the dry beds of torrents, where they had been severely galled by the insulting attacks of a handful of Moorish peasants posted on the impending precipices. The proud spirit of De Aguilar was incensed at having the game of war thus turned upon him, and his gallant forces domineered over by mountain boors, whom he had thought to drive, like their own cattle, to Antiquera. Hearing, however, that his friend the marques of Cadiz, and the master of Santiago, were engaged with the enemy, he disregarded his own danger, and, calling together his troops, returned to assist them, or rather to partake their perils. Being once more together, the cavaliers held a hasty council, amidst the hurling of stones and the whistling of arrows; and their resolves were quickened by the sight, from time to time, of some gallant companion in arms laid low. They determined that there was no spoil in this part of the country, to repay for the extraordinary peril; and that it was better to abandon the herds they had already taken, which only embarrassed their march, and to retreat with all speed to less dangerous ground.

The adalides, or guides, were ordered to lead the way out of this place of carnage. These, thinking to conduct them by the most secure route, led them by a steep and rocky pass, difficult for the foot-soldiers, but almost impracticable to the cavalry. It was overhung with precipices, from whence showers of stones and arrows were poured upon them, accompanied by savage yells, which appalled the stoutest heart. In some places, they could

8

pass but one at a time, and were often transpierced, horse and rider, by the Moorish darts, impeding the progress of their comrades by their dying struggles. The surrounding precipices were lit up by a thousand alarm-fires; every crag and cliff had its flame, by the light of which they beheld their foes, bounding from rock to rock, and looking more like fiends than mortal men.

Either through terror and confusion, or through real ignorance of the country, their guides, instead of conducting them out of the mountains, led them deeper into their fatal recesses. The morning dawned upon them in a narrow rambla, its bottom formed of broken rocks, where once had raved along the mountain torrent; while above, there beetled great arid cliffs, over the brows of which they beheld the turbaned heads of their fierce and exulting foes. What a different appearance did the unfortunate cavaliers present, from that of the gallant band that marched so vauntingly out of Antiquera! Covered with dust, and blood, and wounds, and haggard with fatigue and horror, they looked like victims rather than like warriors. Many of their banners were lost, and not a trumpet was heard to rally up their sinking spirits. The men turned with imploring eyes to their commanders; while the hearts of the cavaliers were ready to burst with rage and grief at the merciless havoc made among their faithful followers.

All day they made ineffectual attempts to extricate themselves from the mountains. Columns of smoke rose from the heights, where, in the preceding night, had blazed the alarm-fire. The mountaineers assembled from every direction; they swarmed at every pass, getting in the advance of the Christians, and garrisoning the cliffs like so many towers and battlements.

Night closed again upon the Christians, when they were shut up in a narrow valley traversed by a deep stream, and surrounded by precipices which seemed to reach the skies, and on which blazed and flared the alarm-fires. Suddenly a new cry was heard resounding along the valley: "El Zagal! El Zagal!" echoed from cliff to cliff. "What cry is that?" said the master of Santiago. "It is the war-cry of El Zagal, the Moorish general," said an old Castilian soldier: "he must be coming in person, with the troops of Malaga."

The worthy master turned to his knights: "Let us die," said he, "making a road with our hearts, since we cannot with our swords. Let us scale the mountain, and sell our lives dearly, instead of staying here to be tamely butchered."

So saying, he turned his steed against the mountain, and spurred him up its flinty side. Horse and foot followed his example, eager, if they could not escape, to have at least a dying blow at the enemy. As they struggled up the height, a tremendous storm of darts and stones were showered upon them by the Moors. Sometimes a fragment of rock came bounding and thundering down, ploughing its way through the centre of their host. The foot-soldiers, faint with weariness and hunger, or crippled by wounds, held by the tails and manes of the horses to aid them in their ascent; while the horses, losing their foothold among the loose stones, or receiving some sudden wound, tumbled down the steep declivity, steed, rider, and soldier, rolling from crag to crag until they were dashed to pieces in the valley. In this desperate struggle, the alferez or standard-bearer of the master, with his standard, was lost; as were many of his relations and his dearest friends. At length he succeeded in attaining the crest of the mountain; but it was only to be plunged in new difficulties. A wilderness of rocks and rugged dells lay before him, beset by cruel foes. Having neither banner nor trumpet by which to rally his troops, they wandered apart, each intent upon saving himself from the precipices of the mountains, and the darts of the enemy. When the pious master of Santiago beheld the scattered fragments of his late gallant force, he could not restrain his grief. "O God!" exclaimed he, "great is thine anger this day against thy servants. Thou hast converted the cowardice of these infidels into desperate valor, and hast made peasants and boors victorious over armed men of battle."

He would fain have kept with his foot-soldiers, and, gathering them together, have made head against the enemy; but those around him entreated him to think only of his personal safety. To remain was to perish, without striking a blow; to escape was to preserve a life that might be devoted to vengeance on the Moors. The master reluctantly yielded to the advice. "O Lord of hosts!" exclaimed he again, "from thy wrath do I fly; not from these infidels: they are but instruments in thy hands, to chastise us for our sins." So saying, he sent the guides in the advance, and putting spurs to his horse, dashed through a defile of the mountains before the Moors could intercept him. The moment the master put his horse to speed, his troops scattered in all directions. Some endeavored to follow his traces, but were confounded among the intricacies of the mountain. They fled hither and thither, many perishing among the precipices, others being slain by the Moors, and others taken prisoners.

The gallant marques of Cadiz, guided by his trusty adalid, Luis Amar, had ascended a different part of the mountain. He was followed by his friend, Don Alonzo de Aguilar, the adelantado, and the count of Cifuentes; but, in the darkness and confusion, the bands of these commanders became separated from each other. When the marques attained the summit, he looked around for his companions in arms; but they were no longer following him, and there was no trumpet to summon them. It was a consolation to the marques, however, that his brothers and several of his relations, with a number of his retainers, were still with him; he called his brothers by name, and their replies gave comfort to his heart.

His guide now led the way into another valley, where

he would be less exposed to danger; when he had reached the bottom of it, the marques paused to collect his scattered followers, and to give time for his fellow-commanders to rejoin him. Here he was suddenly assailed by the troops of El Zagal, aided by the mountaineers from the cliffs. The Christians, exhausted and terrified, lost all presence of mind: most of them fled, and were either slain or taken captive. The marques and his valiant brothers, with a few tried friends, made a stout resistance. His horse was killed under him; his brothers, Don Diego and Don Lope, with his two nephews, Don Lorenzo and Don Manuel, were one by one swept from his side, either transfixed with darts and lances by the soldiers of El Zagal, or crushed by stones from the heights. The marques was a veteran warrior, and had been in many a bloody battle; but never before had death fallen so thick and close around him. When he saw his remaining brother, Don Beltram, struck out of his saddle by a fragment of a rock, and his horse running wildly about without his rider, he gave a cry of anguish, and stood bewildered and aghast. A few faithful followers surrounded him, and entreated him to fly for his life. He would still have remained, to have shared the fortunes of his friend, Don Alonzo de Aguilar, and his other companions in arms; but the forces of El Zagal were between him and them, and death was whistling by on every wind. Reluctantly, therefore, he consented to fly. Another horse was brought him: his faithful adalid guided him by one of the steepest paths, which lasted for four leagues ; the enemy still hanging on his traces, and thinning the scanty ranks of his followers. At length the marques reached the extremity of the mountain defiles, and, with a haggard remnant of his men, escaped by dint of hoof to Antiquera.

The count of Cifuentes, with a few of his retainers, in attempting to follow the marques of Cadiz, wandered into a narrow pass, where they were completely surrounded by the band of El Zagal. The count himself was assailed by six of the enemy, against whom he was defending himself with desperation, when their leader, struck with the inequality of the fight, ordered the others to desist, and continued the combat alone. The count, already exhausted, was soon compelled to surrender ; his brother, Don Pedro de Silva, and the few of his retainers who survived, were likewise taken prisoners. The Moorish cavalier who had manifested such a chivalric spirit in encountering the count singly, was Raduan Vanegas, brother of the former vizier of Muley Abul Hassan, and one of the leaders of the faction of the sultana Zoraya.

The dawn of day found Don Alonzo de Aguilar, with a handful of his followers, still among the mountains. They had attempted to follow the marques of Cadiz, but had been obliged to pause and defend themselves against the thickening forces of the enemy. They at length traversed the mountain, and reached the same valley where the marques had made his last disastrous stand.

Wearied and perplexed, they sheltered themselves in a natural grotto, under an overhanging rock, which kept off the darts of the enemy; while a bubbling fountain gave them the means of slaking their raging thirst, and refreshing their exhausted steeds. As day broke, the scene of slaughter unfolded its horrors. There lay the noble brothers and nephews of the gallant marques, transfixed with darts, or gashed and bruised with unseemly wounds; while many other gallant cavaliers lay stretched out dead and dying around, some of them partly stripped and plundered by the Moors. De Aguilar was a pious knight, but his piety was not humble and resigned, like that of the worthy master of Santiago. He imprecated holy curses upon the infidels for having thus laid low the flower of Christian chivalry; and he vowed in his heart bitter vengeance upon the surrounding country.

By degrees, the little force of De Aguilar was augmented by numbers of fugitives, who issued from caves and chasms, where they had taken refuge in the night. A little band of mounted knights was gradually formed; and the Moors having abandoned the heights to collect the spoils of the slain, this gallant but forlorn squadron was enabled to retreat to Antiquera.

This disastrous affair lasted from Thursday evening, throughout Friday, the twenty-first of March, the festival of St. Benedict. It is still recorded in Spanish calendars as the defeat of the mountains of Malaga; and the spot where the greatest slaughter took place is called *la Cuesta de la Matanza,* or The Hill of the Massacre. The principal leaders who survived returned to Antiquera. Many of the knights took refuge in Alhama and other towns; many wandered about the mountains for eight days, living on roots and herbs, hiding themselves during the day, and sallying forth at night. So enfeebled and disheartened were they, that they offered no resistance if attacked. Three or four soldiers would surrender to a Moorish peasant; and even the women of Malaga sallied forth and made prisoners. Some were thrown into the dungeons of frontier towns, others led captive to Granada; but by far the greater number were conducted to Malaga, the city they had threatened to attack. Two hundred and fifty principal cavaliers, alcaydes, commanders, and hidalgos, of generous blood, were confined in the Alcazaba, or citadel of Malaga, to await their ransom; and five hundred and seventy of the common soldiery were crowded in an inclosure or court-yard of the Alcazaba, to be sold as slaves.*

Great spoils were collected of splendid armor and weapons taken from the slain, or thrown away by the cavaliers in their flight; and many horses, magnificently caparisoned, together with numerous standards — all which were paraded in triumph in the Moorish towns.

The merchants, also, who had come with the army, in-

* *Cura de los Palacios.*

tending to traffic in the spoils of the Moors, were themselves made objects of traffic. Several of them were driven like cattle before the Moorish viragoes, to the market of Malaga; and in spite of all their adroitness in trade, and their attempts to buy themselves off at a cheap ransom, they were unable to purchase their freedom without such draughts upon their money-bags at home as drained them to the very bottom.

# CHAPTER XIII.

EFFECTS OF THE DISASTERS AMONG THE MOUNTAINS OF MALAGA.

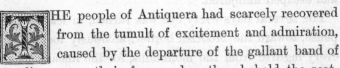HE people of Antiquera had scarcely recovered from the tumult of excitement and admiration, caused by the departure of the gallant band of cavaliers upon their foray, when they beheld the scattered wrecks flying for refuge to their walls. Day after day, and hour after hour, brought some wretched fugitive, in whose battered plight, and haggard, woebegone demeanor, it was almost impossible to recognize the warrior who had lately issued so gayly and gloriously from their gates.

The arrival of the marques of Cadiz, almost alone, covered with dust and blood, his armor shattered and defaced, his countenance the picture of despair, filled every heart with sorrow, for he was greatly beloved by the people. The multitude asked of his companions, where was the band of brothers which had rallied round him as he went forth to the field; and when told that one by one they had been slaughtered at his side, they hushed their voices, or spake to each other only in whispers as he passed, gazing at him in silent sympathy. No one at-

tempted to console him in so great an affliction, nor did
the good marques speak ever a word, but, shutting himself up, brooded in lonely anguish over his misfortune.
It was only the arrival of Don Alonzo de Aguilar that
gave him a gleam of consolation, rejoicing to find that
amidst the shafts of death which had fallen so thickly
among his family his chosen friend and brother in arms
had escaped uninjured.

For several days every eye was turned, in fearful suspense, toward the Moorish border, anxiously looking, in
every fugitive from the mountains, for the lineaments of
some friend or relative, whose fate was yet a mystery.
At length every hope and doubt subsided into certainty;
the whole extent of this great calamity was known,
spreading grief and consternation throughout the land,
and laying desolate the pride and hopes of palaces. It
was a sorrow that visited the marble hall and silken
pillow. Stately dames mourned over the loss of their
sons, the joy and glory of their age; and many a fair
cheek was blanched with woe, which had lately mantled
with secret admiration. "All Andalusia," says a historian of the time, "was overwhelmed by a great affliction; there was no drying of the eyes which wept in
her." *

Fear and trembling reigned, for a time, along the frontier. Their spear seemed broken, their buckler cleft in

* *Cura de los Palacios.*

twain: every border town dreaded an attack, and the mother caught her infant to her bosom when the watch-dog howled in the night, fancying it the war-cry of the Moor. All, for a time, seemed lost; and despondency even found its way to the royal breasts of Ferdinand and Isabella, amidst the splendors of their court.

Great, on the other hand, was the joy of the Moors, when they saw whole legions of Christian warriors brought captive into their towns, by rude mountain peas-antry. They thought it the work of Allah in favor of the faithful. But when they recognized, among the captives thus dejected and broken down, some of the proudest of Christian chivalry; when they saw several of the banners and devices of the noblest houses of Spain, which they had been accustomed to behold in the foremost of the battle, now trailed ignominiously through their streets; when, in short, they witnessed the arrival of the count of Cifuentes, the royal standard-bearer of Spain, with his gallant brother Don Pedro de Silva, brought prisoners into the gates of Granada, there were no bounds to their exultation. They thought that the days of their ancient glory were about to return, and that they were to renew their career of triumph over the unbelievers.

The Christian historians of the time are sorely per-plexed to account for this misfortune; and why so many Christian knights, fighting in the cause of the holy faith, should thus miraculously, as it were, be given captive to a handful of infidel boors; for we are assured, that all this rout and destruction was effected by five hundred foot and fifty horse, and those mere mountaineers, without science or discipline.* "It was intended," observes one historiographer, " as a lesson to their confidence and vainglory ; overrating their own prowess and thinking that so chosen a band of chivalry had but to appear in the land of the enemy, and conquer. It was to teach them that the race is not to the swift, nor the battle to the strong, but that God alone giveth the victory."

The worthy father Fray Antonio Agapida, however, asserts it to be a punishment for the avarice of the Spanish warriors. They did not enter the kingdom of the infidels with the pure spirit of Christian knights, zealous only for the glory of the faith, but rather as greedy men of traffic, to enrich themselves by vending the spoils of the infidels. Instead of preparing themselves by confession and communion, and executing their testaments, and making donations and bequests to churches and convents, they thought only of arranging bargains and sales of their anticipated booty. Instead of taking with them holy monks to aid them with their prayers, they were followed by a train of trading men, to keep alive their worldly and sordid ideas, and to turn what ought to be holy triumphs into scenes of brawling traffic. Such is the opinion of the excellent Agapida, in which he is joined by that most worthy and upright of chroniclers,

* *Cura de los Palacios.*

the curate of Los Palacios.  Agapida comforts himself, however, with the reflection, that this visitation was meant in mercy, to try the Castilian heart, and to extract, from its present humiliation, the elements of future success, as gold is extracted from amidst the impurities of earth ; and in this reflection he is supported by the venerable historian Pedro Abarca, of the society of Jesuits.*

* Abarca.  *Anales de Aragon*, Rey 30, cap. 2, § 7.

## CHAPTER XIV.

HOW KING BOABDIL EL CHICO MARCHED OVER THE BORDER.

HE defeat of the Christian cavaliers among the mountains of Malaga, and the successful inroad of Muley Abul Hassan into the lands of Medina Sidonia, had produced a favorable effect on the fortunes of the old monarch. The inconstant populace began to shout forth his name in the streets, and to sneer at the inactivity of his son Boabdil el Chico. The latter, though in the flower of his age, and distinguished for vigor and dexterity in jousts and tournaments, had never yet fleshed his weapon in the field of battle; and it was murmured that he preferred the silken repose of the cool halls of the Alhambra to the fatigue and danger of the foray, and the hard encampments of the mountains.

The popularity of these rival kings depended upon their success against the Christians, and Boabdil el Chico found it necessary to strike some signal blow to counterbalance the late triumph of his father. He was further incited by his father-in-law, Ali Atar, alcayde of Loxa, with whom the coals of wrath against the Christians still burned among the ashes of age, and had lately been blown into a flame by the attack made by Ferdinand on the city under his command.

Ali Atar informed Boabdil that the late discomfiture of the Christian knights had stripped Andalusia of the prime of her chivalry, and broken the spirit of the country. All the frontier of Cordova and Ecija now lay open to inroad; but he especially pointed out the city of Lucena as an object of attack, being feebly garrisoned, and lying in a country rich in pasturage, abounding in cattle and grain, in oil and wine. The fiery old Moor spoke from thorough information; for he had made many an incursion into these parts, and his very name was a terror throughout the country. It had become a by-word in the garrison of Loxa to call Lucena the garden of Ali Atar, for he was accustomed to forage its fertile territories for all his supplies.

Boabdil el Chico listened to the persuasions of this veteran of the borders. He assembled a force of nine thousand foot and seven hundred horse, most of them his own adherents, but many the partisans of his father; for both factions, however they might fight among themselves, were ready to unite in any expedition against the Christians. Many of the most illustrious and valiant of the Moorish nobility assembled round his standard, magnificently arrayed in sumptuous armor and rich embroidery, as though for a festival or a tilt of canes, rather than an enterprise of iron war. Boabdil's mother, the sultana Ayxa la Horra, armed him for the field, and gave him her

9

benediction as she girded his scimetar to his side. His favorite wife Morayma wept, as she thought of the evils that might befall him. "Why dost thou weep, daughter of Ali Atar?" said the high-minded Ayxa: "these tears become not the daughter of a warrior, nor the wife of a king. Believe me, there lurks more danger for a monarch within the strong walls of a palace than within the frail curtains of a tent. It is by perils in the field that thy husband must purchase security on his throne."

But Morayma still hung upon his neck, with tears and sad forebodings ; and when he departed from the Alhambra, she betook herself to her mirador, overlooking the vega, whence she watched the army, as it went, in shining order, along the road leading to Loxa; and every burst of warlike melody that came swelling on the breeze was answered by a gush of sorrow.

As the royal cavalcade issued from the palace and descended through the streets of Granada, the populace greeted their youthful sovereign with shouts, anticipating deeds of prowess that would wither the laurels of his father. The appearance of Boabdil was well calculated to captivate the public eye, if we may judge from the description given by the abbot of Rute, in his manuscript history of the House of Cordova. He was mounted on a superb white charger, magnificently caparisoned. His corselets were of polished steel, richly ornamented; studded with gold nails, and lined with crimson velvet. He wore a steel casque, exquisitely chiseled and embossed; his scimetar and dagger of Damascus were of highest temper; he had a round buckler at his shoulder, and bore a ponderous lance. In passing through the gate of Elvira, however, he accidentally broke his lance against the arch. At this, certain of his nobles turned pale, and entreated him to turn back, for they regarded it as an evil omen. Boabdil scoffed at their fears as idle fancies. He refused to take another spear, but drew forth his scimetar, and led the way (adds Agapida) in an arrogant and haughty style, as though he would set both heaven and earth at defiance. Another evil omen was sent to deter him from his enterprise: arriving at the rambla, or dry ravine of Beyro, which is scarcely a bow-shot from the city, a fox ran through the whole army, and close by the person of the king; and, though a thousand bolts were discharged at it, escaped uninjured to the mountains. The principal courtiers now reiterated their remonstrances against proceeding; the king, however, was not to be dismayed by these portents, but continued to march forward.*

At Loxa the army was reinforced by old Ali Atar, with the chosen horsemen of his garrison, and many of the bravest warriors of the border towns. The people of Loxa shouted with exultation when they beheld Ali Atar, armed at all points, and mounted on his Barbary steed, which had often borne him over the borders. The

---

* Marmol. *Rebel. de los Moros*, lib. 1, c. 12, fol. 14.

veteran warrior, with nearly a century of years upon his head, had all the fire and animation of youth at the prospect of a foray, and careered from rank to rank with the velocity of an Arab of the desert. The populace watched the army, as it paraded over the bridge, and wound into the passes of the mountains; and still their eyes were fixed upon the pennon of Ali Atar, as if it bore with it an assurance of victory.

The Moorish army entered the Christian frontier by forced marches, hastily ravaging the country, driving off the flocks and herds, and making captives of the inhabitants. They pressed on furiously, and made the latter part of their march in the night, to elude observation, and come upon Lucena by surprise. Boabdil was inexperienced in warfare, but had a veteran counselor in his old father-in-law; for Ali Atar knew every secret of the country, and, as he prowled through it, his eye ranged over the land, uniting in its glare the craft of the fox with the sanguinary ferocity of the wolf. He had flattered himself that their march had been so rapid as to outstrip intelligence, and that Lucena would be an easy capture; when suddenly he beheld alarm-fires blazing upon the mountains. "We are discovered," said he to Boabdil; "the country will be up in arms; we have nothing left but to strike boldly for Lucena; it is but slightly garrisoned, and we may carry it by assault before we can receive assistance." The king approved of his counsel, and they marched rapidly for the gate of Lucena.

## CHAPTER XV.

ON DIEGO DE CORDOVA, count of Cabra, was in the castle of Vaena, which, with the town of the same name, is situated on a lofty, sun-burnt hill, on the frontier of the kingdom of Cordova, and but a few leagues from Lucena. The range of mountains of Horquera lie between them. The castle of Vaena was strong, and well furnished with arms, and the count had a numerous band of vassals and retainers; for it behooved the noblemen of the frontiers, in those times, to be well prepared with man and horse, with lance and buckler, to resist the sudden incursions of the Moors. The count of Cabra was a hardy and experienced warrior, shrewd in council, prompt in action, rapid and fearless in the field. He was one of the bravest of cavaliers for an inroad, and had been quickened and sharpened, in thought and action, by living on the borders.

On the night of the 20th of April, 1483, the count was about to retire to rest, when the watchman from the turret brought him word that there were alarm-fires on the

133

mountains of Horquera, and that they were made on the signal-tower overhanging the defile through which the road passes to Cabra and Lucena.

The count ascended the battlement, and beheld five lights blazing on the tower—a sign that there was a Moorish army attacking some place on the frontier. The count instantly ordered the alarm-bells to be sounded, and dispatched couriers to rouse the commanders of the neighboring towns. He called upon his retainers to prepare for action, and sent a trumpet through the town, summoning the men to assemble at the castle-gate at daybreak, armed and equipped for the field.

Throughout the remainder of the night, the castle resounded with the din of preparation. Every house in the town was in equal bustle; for in these frontier towns every house had its warrior, and the lance and buckler were ever hanging against the wall, ready to be snatched down for instant service. Nothing was heard but the din of armorers, the shoeing of studs, and furbishing up of weapons, and, all night long, the alarm fires kept blazing on the mountains.

When the morning dawned the count of Cabra sallied forth, at the head of two hundred and fifty cavaliers, of the best families of Vaena, all well appointed, exercised in arms, and experienced in the warfare of the borders. There were, besides, twelve hundred foot soldiers, brave and well-seasoned men of the same town. The count ordered them to hasten forward, whoever could make most speed, taking the road to Cabra, which was three leagues distant. That they might not loiter on the road, he allowed none of them to break their fast until they arrived at that place. The provident count dispatched couriers in advance, and the little army, on reaching Cabra, found tables spread with food and refreshments, at the gates of the town. Here they were joined by Don Alonzo de Cordova, senior of Zuheros.

Having made a hearty repast, they were on the point of resuming their march, when the count discovered that, in the hurry of his departure from home, he had forgotten to bring the standard of Vaena, which for upwards of eighty years had always been borne to battle by his family. It was noon, and there was not time to return: he took, therefore, the standard of Cabra, the device of which is a goat, and which had not been seen in the wars for the last half century. When about to depart, a courier came galloping at full speed, bringing missives to the count from his nephew, Don Diego Fernandez de Cordova, senior of Lucena and alcayde de los Donzeles,* entreating him to hasten to his aid, as his town was beset by the Moorish king, Boabdil el Chico, with a powerful army, who were actually setting fire to the gates.

The count put his little army instantly in movement for Lucena, which is only one league from Cabra; he

---

* The Donzeles were young cavaliers who had been pages in the royal household, but now formed an élite corps in the army.

was fired with the idea of having the Moorish king in person to contend with. By the time he reached Lucena, the Moors had desisted from the attack, and were ravaging the surrounding country. He entered the town with a few of his cavaliers, and was received with joy by his nephew, whose whole force consisted but of eighty horse and three hundred foot. Don Diego Fernandez de Cordova was a young man, yet he was a prudent, careful, and capable officer. Having learnt, the evening before, that the Moors had passed the frontiers, he had gathered within his walls all the women and children from the environs; had armed the men, sent couriers in all directions for succor, and had lighted alarm-fires on the mountains.

Boabdil had arrived with his army at daybreak, and had sent in a message threatening to put the garrison to the sword if the place were not instantly surrendered. The messenger was a Moor of Granada, named Hamet, whom Don Diego had formerly known: he contrived to amuse him with negotiation, to gain time for succor to arrive. The fierce Ali Atar, losing all patience, had made an assault upon the town, and stormed like a fury at the gate; but had been repulsed. Another and more serious attack was expected in the course of the night.

When the count de Cabra had heard this account of the situation of affairs, he turned to his nephew, with his usual alacrity of manner, and proposed that they should immediately sally forth in quest of the enemy. The prudent Don Diego remonstrated at the rashness of attacking so great a force with a mere handful of men. "Nephew," said the count, "I came from Vaena with a determination to fight this Moorish king, and I will not be disappointed."

"At any rate," replied Don Diego, "let us wait but two hours, and we shall have reinforcements which have been promised me from Rambla, Santaella, Montilla, and other places in the neighborhood." "If we await these," said the hardy count, "the Moors will be off, and all our trouble will have been in vain. You may await them, if you please; I am resolved on fighting."

The count paused for no reply, but, in his prompt and rapid manner, sallied forth to his men. The young alcayde de los Donzeles, though more prudent than his ardent uncle, was equally brave; he determined to stand by him in his rash enterprise, and, summoning his little force, marched forth to join the count, who was already on the move. They then proceeded together in quest of the enemy.

The Moorish army had ceased ravaging the country, and were not to be seen—the neighborhood being hilly, and broken with deep ravines. The count dispatched six scouts on horseback to reconnoitre, ordering them to return with all speed on discovering the enemy, and by no means to engage in skirmishing with stragglers. The scouts, ascending a high hill, beheld the Moorish army in a valley behind it, the cavalry ranged in five battalions keeping guard, while the foot soldiers were seated on the grass making a repast. They returned immediately with the intelligence.

The count now ordered the troops to march in the direction of the enemy. He and his nephew ascended the hill, and saw that the five battalions of Moorish cavalry had been formed into two, one of about nine hundred lances, the other of about six hundred. The whole force seemed prepared to march for the frontier. The foot soldiers were already under way, with many prisoners, and a great train of mules and beasts of burden, laden with booty. At a distance was Boabdil el Chico: they could not distinguish his person, but they knew him by his superb black and white charger, magnificently caparisoned, and by his being surrounded by a numerous guard, sumptuously armed and attired. Old Ali Atar was careering about the valley with his usual impatience, hurrying the march of the loitering troops.

The eyes of the count de Cabra glistened with eager joy, as he beheld the royal prize within his reach. The immense disparity of their forces never entered into his mind. "By Santiago!" said he to his nephew, as they hastened down the hill, "had we waited for more forces, the Moorish king and his army would have escaped us!"

The count now harangued his men, to inspirit them to this hazardous encounter. He told them not to be dismayed at the number of the Moors, for God often permitted the few to conquer the many: and he had great confidence, that, through the divine aid, they were that day to achieve a signal victory, which should win them both riches and renown. He commanded that no man should hurl his lance at the enemy, but should keep it in his hands, and strike as many blows with it as he could. He warned them, also, never to shout except when the Moors did; for when both armies shouted together, there was no perceiving which made the most noise and was the strongest. He desired his uncle Lope de Mendoza, and Diego de Cabrera, alcayde of Doña Mencia, to alight and enter on foot in the battalion of infantry, to animate them to the combat. He appointed also the alcayde of Vaena and Diego de Clavijo, a cavalier of his household, to remain in the rear, and not to permit any one to lag behind, either to despoil the dead, or for any other purpose.

Such were the orders given by this most adroit, active, and intrepid cavalier, to his little army, supplying by admirable sagacity and subtile management, the want of a more numerous force. His orders being given, and all arrangements made, he threw aside his lance, drew his sword, and commanded his standard to be advanced against the enemy.

# CHAPTER XVI.

### THE BATTLE OF LUCENA.

HE Moorish king had descried the Spanish forces at a distance, although a slight fog prevented his seeing them distinctly, and ascertaining their numbers. His old father-in-law, Ali Atar, was by his side, who, being a veteran marauder, was well acquainted with all the standards and armorial bearings of the frontiers. When the king beheld the ancient and long-disused banner of Cabra emerging from the mist, he turned to Ali Atar, and demanded whose ensign it was. The old borderer was for once at a loss, for the banner had not been displayed in battle in his time. "In truth," replied he, after a pause, "I have been considering that standard for some time, but I confess, I do not know it. It cannot be the ensign of any single commander or community, for none would venture single-handed to attack you. It appears to be a dog, which device is borne by the towns of Baeza and Ubeda. If it be so, all Andalusia is in movement against you, and I would advise you to retire."

The count de Cabra, in winding down the hill towards

the Moors, found himself on much lower ground than the
enemy; he ordered in all haste that his standard should
be taken back, so as to gain the vantage ground. The
Moors, mistaking this for a retreat, rushed impetuously
towards the Christians. The latter having gained the
height proposed, charged upon them at the same moment, with the battle-cry of "Santiago!" and dealing the
first blows, laid many of the Moorish cavaliers in the
dust.

The Moors, thus checked in their tumultuous assault,
were thrown into confusion, and began to give way, the
Christians following hard upon them. Boabdil el Chico
endeavored to rally them. "Hold! hold! for shame!"
cried he; "let us not fly, at least until we know our
enemy." The Moorish chivalry were stung by this re-
proof, and turned to make front, with the valor of men
who feel that they are fighting under their monarch's
eye.

At this moment, Lorenzo de Porres, alcayde of Luque,
arrived with fifty horse and one hundred foot, sounding
an Italian trumpet from among a copse of oak trees,
which concealed his force. The quick ear of old Ali
Atar caught the note. "That is an Italian trumpet,"
said he to the king; "the whole world seems in arms
against your highness!"

The trumpet of Lorenzo de Porres was answered by
that of the count de Cabra, in another direction, and it
seemed to the Moors as if they were between two armies.

Don Lorenzo, sallying from among the oaks, now charged upon the enemy: the latter did not wait to ascertain the force of this new foe ; the confusion, the variety of alarms, the attacks from opposite quarters, the obscurity of the fog, all conspired to deceive them as to the number of their adversaries. Broken and dismayed, they retreated fighting; and nothing but the presence and remonstrances of the king prevented their retreat from becoming a headlong flight. If Boabdil had displayed little of the talents of a general in the outset of his enterprise, he manifested courage and presence of mind amid the disasters of its close. Seconded by a small body of cavalry, the choicest and most loyal of his guards, he made repeated stand against the press of the foe, in a skirmishing retreat of about three leagues; and the way was strewn with the flower of his chivalry. At length, they came to the brook of Martin Gonzales, or Mingozales, as it is called by the Moorish chroniclers; which, swollen by recent rain, was now a deep and turbid torrent. Here a scene of confusion ensued. Horse and foot precipitated themselves into the stream. Some of the horses stuck fast in the mire and blocked up the ford; others trampled down the foot-soldiers; many were drowned and more carried down the stream. Such of the foot-soldiers as gained the opposite side, immediately took to flight; the horsemen, too, who had struggled through the stream, gave reins to their steeds and scoured for the frontier.

The little band of devoted cavaliers about the king serried their forces, to keep the enemy in check, fighting with them hand to hand, until he should have time to cross. In the tumult, his horse was shot down, and he became environed in the throng of foot-soldiers, struggling forward to the ford, and in peril from the lances of their pursuers. Conscious that his rich array made him a conspicuous object, he retreated along the bank of the river, and endeavored to conceal himself in a thicket of willows and tamarisks. Thence, looking back, he beheld his loyal band at length give way, supposing, no doubt, he had effected his escape. They crossed the ford, followed pell-mell by the enemy, and several of them were struck down in the stream.

While Boabdil was meditating to throw himself into the water, and endeavor to swim across, he was discovered by Martin Hurtado, regidor of Lucena, a brave cavalier, who had been captive in the prisons of Granada, and exchanged for a Christian knight. Hurtado attacked the king with a pike, but was kept at bay; until seeing other soldiers approaching, Boabdil cried for quarters; proclaiming himself a person of high rank, who would pay a noble ransom. At this moment came up several men of Vaena, of the troop of the count de Cabra. Hearing the talk of ransom and noticing the splendid attire of the Moor, they endeavored to secure for themselves so rich a prize. One of them seized hold of Boabdil, but the latter resented the indignity, by striking him to the earth with a blow of his poniard.   Others of Hurtado's townsmen coming up, a contest arose between the men of Lucena and Vaena, as to who had a right to the prisoner. The noise brought Don Diego Fernandez de Cordova to the spot, who, by his authority, put an end to the altercation.   Boabdil, finding himself unknown by all present, concealed his quality, giving himself out as the son of Aben Alnayer, a cavalier of the royal household.*   Don Diego treated him with great courtesy; put a red band round his neck in sign of his being a captive, and sent him under an escort to the castle of Lucena, where his quality would be ascertained, his ransom arranged, and the question settled as to who had made him prisoner.

This done, the count put spurs to his horse, and hastened to rejoin the count de Cabra, who was in hot pursuit of the enemy.   He overtook him at a stream called Reanaul; and they continued together to press on the skirts of the flying army during the remainder of the day. The pursuit was almost as hazardous as the battle; for, had the enemy at any time recovered from their panic, they might, by a sudden reaction, have overwhelmed the small force of their pursuers.   To guard against this peril, the wary count kept his battalion always in close order, and had a body of a hundred chosen lancers in the advance.   The Moors kept up a Parthian retreat; several times they turned to make battle; but, seeing this solid

* Garibay, lib. 40, cap. 31.

body of steeled warriors pressing upon them, they again took to flight.

The main retreat of the army was along the valley watered by the Xenil, and opening through the mountains of Algaringo to the city of Loxa. The alarm-fires of the preceding night had aroused the country; every man snatched sword and buckler from the wall, and the towns and villages poured forth their warriors to harass the retreating foe. Ali Atar kept the main force of the army together, and turned fiercely from time to time upon his pursuers; he was like a wolf, hunted through the country he had often made desolate by his maraudings.

The alarm of this invasion had reached the city of Antiquera, where were several of the cavaliers who had escaped from the carnage in the mountains of Malaga. Their proud minds were festering with their late disgrace, and their only prayer was for vengeance on the infidels. No sooner did they hear of the Moor being over the border, than they were armed and mounted for action. Don Alonzo de Aguilar led them forth;—a small body of but forty horsemen, but all cavaliers of prowess, and thirsting for revenge. They came upon the foe on the banks of the Xenil, where it winds through the valleys of Cordova. The river, swelled by the late rains, was deep and turbulent, and only fordable at certain places. The main body of the army was gathered in confusion on the banks, endeavoring to ford the stream, protected by the cavalry of Ali Atar.

10

No sooner did the little band of Alonzo de Aguilar come in sight of the Moors, than fury flashed from their eyes. "Remember the mountains of Malaga!" cried they to each other, as they rushed to combat. Their charge was desperate, but was gallantly resisted. A scrambling and bloody fight ensued, hand to hand and sword to sword, sometimes on land, sometimes in the water. Many were lanced on the banks; others, throwing themselves into the river, sank with the weight of their armor, and were drowned; some, grappling together, fell from their horses, but continued their struggle in the waves, and helm and turban rolled together down the stream. The Moors were far greater in number, and among them were many warriors of rank; but they were disheartened by defeat, while the Christians were excited even to desperation.

Ali Atar alone preserved all his fire and energy, amid his reverses. He had been enraged at the defeat of the army, and the ignominious flight he had been obliged to make through a country which had so often been the scene of his exploits; but to be thus impeded in his flight, and harassed and insulted by a mere handful of warriors, roused the violent passions of the old Moor to perfect frenzy. He had marked Don Alonzo de Aguilar dealing his blows (says Agapida), with the pious vehemence of a righteous knight, who knows that in every wound inflicted upon the infidels, he is doing God service. Ali Atar spurred his steed along the bank of the river, to come upon Don Alonzo by surprise. The back of the warrior was toward him; and, collecting all his force, the Moor hurled his lance to transfix him on the spot. The lance was not thrown with the usual accuracy of Ali Atar: it tore away a part of the cuirass of Don Alonzo, but failed to inflict a wound. The Moor rushed upon Don Alonzo with his scimetar; but the latter was on the alert, and parried his blow. They fought desperately upon the borders of the river, alternately pressing each other into the stream, and fighting their way again up the bank. Ali Atar was repeatedly wounded; and Don Alonzo, having pity on his age, would have spared his life: he called upon him to surrender. "Never," cried Ali Atar, "to a Christian dog!" The words were scarce out of his mouth, when the sword of Don Alonzo clove his turbaned head, and sank deep into the brain. He fell dead without a groan; his body rolled into the Xenil, nor was it ever found nor recognized.* Thus fell Ali Atar, who had long been the terror of Andalusia. As he had hated and warred upon the Christians all his life, so he died in the very act of bitter hostility.

The fall of Ali Atar put an end to the transient stand of the cavalry. Horse and foot mingled together, in the desperate struggle across the Xenil; and many were trampled down and perished beneath the waves. Don Alonzo and his band continued to harass them until they

---

* *Cura de los Palacios.*

crossed the frontier; and every blow struck home to the Moors seemed to lighten the load of humiliation and sorrow which had weighed heavy on their hearts.

In this disastrous rout, the Moors lost upwards of five thousand killed and made prisoners; many of whom were of the most noble lineages of Granada: numbers fled to rocks and mountains, where they were subsequently taken.

Boabdil remained a prisoner in the state tower of the citadel of Lucena, under the vigilance of Alonzo de Rueda, esquire of the alcayde of the Donzeles; his quality was still unknown, until the 24th of April, three days after the battle. On that day some prisoners, natives of Granada, just brought in, caught sight of the unfortunate Boabdil, despoiled of his royal robes. Throwing themselves at his feet, they broke forth in loud lamentations; apostrophizing him as their lord and king.

Great was the astonishment and triumph of the count de Cabra and Don Diego Fernandez de Cordova on learning the rank of the supposed cavalier. They both ascended to the castle to see that he was lodged in a style befitting his quality. When the good count beheld, in the dejected captive before him, the monarch who had so recently appeared in royal splendor, surrounded by an army, his generous heart was touched by sympathy. He said everything to comfort him that became a courteous and Christian knight, observing that the same mutability of things which had suddenly brought him low, might as rapidly restore him to prosperity, since in this world nothing is stable, and sorrow, like joy, has its allotted term.

The action here recorded was called by some the battle of Lucena, by others the battle of the Moorish king, because of the capture of Boabdil. Twenty-two banners, taken on the occasion, were borne in triumph into Vaena on the 23d of April, St. George's day, and hung up in the church. There they remain (says a historian of after times) to this day. Once a year, on the festival of St. George, they are borne about in procession by the inhabitants, who, at the same time, give thanks to God for this signal victory granted to their forefathers.*

---

* Several circumstances relative to the capture of Boabdil vary in this from the first edition, in consequence of later light thrown on the subject by Don Miguel Lafuente Alcantara in his history of Granada. He has availed himself much of various ancient documents relative to the battle, especially the history of the House of Cordova, by the Abbot of Rute, a descendant of that family; a rare manuscript, of which few copies exist.

The question as to the person entitled to the honor and reward for having captured the king, long continued a matter of dispute between the people of Lucena and Vaena. On the 20th of October, 1520, about thirty-seven years after the event, an examination of several witnesses to the fact took place before the chief justice of the fortress of Lucena, at the instance of Bartolomy Hurtado, the son of Martin, when the claim of his father was established by Doña Lenora Hernandez, lady in attendance on the mother of the alcayde of los Donzeles, who testified being present when Boabdil signalized Martin Hurtado as his captor.

The chief honor of the day, and of course of the defeat and capture of the Moorish monarch, was given by the sovereign to the count de Cabra: the second to his nephew, Don Diego Fernandez de Cordova.

Among the curious papers cited by Alcantara, is one existing in the archives of the House of Medina Celi, giving the account of the treasurer of Don Diego Fernandez, as to the sums expended by his lord in the capture of the king; the reward given to some soldiers for a standard of the king's which they had taken; to others for wounds they had received, etc.

Another paper speaks of an auction at Lucena on the 28th of April, of horses and mules taken in the battle. Another paper states the gratuities of the alcayde of los Donzeles to the soldiery—four fanegas, or about four hundred weight of wheat and a lance to each horseman, two fanegas of wheat and a lance to each foot-soldier.

# CHAPTER XVII.

THE sentinels looked out from the watch-towers of Loxa, along the valley of the Xenil, which passes through the mountains of Algaringo. They looked to behold the king returning in triumph, at the head of his shining host, laden with the spoil of the unbeliever. They looked to behold the standard of their warlike idol, the fierce Ali Atar, borne by the chivalry of Loxa, ever foremost in the wars of the border.

In the evening of the 21st of April, they descried a single horseman urging his faltering steed along the banks of the Xenil. As he drew near, they perceived, by the flash of arms, that he was a warrior; and on nearer approach, by the richness of his armor and the caparison of his steed, they knew him to be a warrior of rank.

He reached Loxa, faint and aghast; his courser covered with foam, and dust, and blood, panting and staggering with fatigue, and gashed with wounds. Having brought his master in safety, he sank down and died before the gate of the city. The soldiers at the gate gathered round the cavalier, as he stood by his expiring steed; they knew him to be Cidi Caleb, nephew of the chief alfaqui of the mosque in the Albaycin, and their hearts were filled with fearful forebodings.

"Cavalier," said they, "how fares it with the king and army?"

He cast his hand mournfully towards the land of the Christians. "There they lie!" exclaimed he. "The Heavens have fallen upon them. All are lost! all dead!"[*]

Upon this, there was a great cry of consternation among the people, and loud wailings of women: for the flower of the youth of Loxa were with the army.

An old Moorish soldier, scarred in many a border battle, stood leaning on his lance by the gateway. "Where is Ali Atar?" demanded he eagerly. "If he lives, the army cannot be lost."

"I saw his helm cleft by the Christian sword; his body is floating in the Xenil."

When the soldier heard these words, he smote his breast and threw dust upon his head; for he was an old follower of Ali Atar.

Cidi Caleb gave himself no repose, but, mounting another steed, hastened towards Granada. As he passed through the villages and hamlets, he spread sorrow around; for their chosen men had followed the king to the wars.

[*] Bernaldez (*Cura de los Palacios*) *Hist. de los Reyes Catol.*, MS. cap. 61.

When he entered the gates of Granada, and announced the loss of the king and army, a voice of horror went throughout the city. Every one thought but of his own share in the general calamity, and crowded round the bearer of ill tidings. One asked after a father, another after a brother, some after a lover, and many a mother after her son. His replies all spoke of wounds and death. To one he replied, "I saw thy father pierced with a lance, as he defended the person of the king." To another, "Thy brother fell wounded under the hoofs of the horses; but there was no time to aid him, for the Christian cavalry were upon us." To another, "I saw the horse of thy lover, covered with blood and galloping without his rider." To another, "Thy son fought by my side, on the banks of the Xenil: we were surrounded by the enemy, and driven into the stream. I heard him cry upon Allah, in the midst of the waters: when I reached the other bank, he was no longer by my side."

Cidi Caleb passed on, leaving all Granada in lamentation; he urged his steed up the steep avenue of trees and fountains that leads to the Alhambra, nor stopped until he arrived before the gate of Justice. Ayxa, the mother of Boabdil, and Morayma, his beloved and tender wife, had daily watched from the tower of Gomeres, to behold his triumphant return. Who shall describe their affliction, when they heard the tidings of Cidi Caleb? The sultana Ayxa spake not much, but sat as one entranced. Every now and then, a deep sigh burst forth, but she raised her eyes to Heaven: "It is the will of Allah!" said she, and with these words endeavored to repress the agonies of a mother's sorrow. The tender Morayma threw herself on the earth, and gave way to the full turbulence of her feelings, bewailing her husband and her father. The high-minded Ayxa rebuked the violence of her grief: "Moderate these transports, my daughter," said she; "remember magnanimity should be the attribute of princes; it becomes not them to give way to clamorous sorrow, like common and vulgar minds." But Morayma could only deplore her loss, with the anguish of a tender woman. She shut herself up in her mirador, and gazed all day, with streaming eyes, upon the vega. Every object recalled the causes of her affliction. The river Xenil, which ran shining amidst groves and gardens, was the same on whose banks had perished her father, Ali Atar; before her lay the road to Loxa, by which Boabdil had departed, in martial state, surrounded by the chivalry of Granada. Ever and anon, she would burst into an agony of grief. "Alas! my father!" she would exclaim; "the river runs smiling before me, that covers thy mangled remains; who will gather them to an honored tomb, in the land of the unbeliever? And thou, O Boabdil, light of my eyes! joy of my heart! life of my life! woe the day, and woe the hour, that I saw thee depart from these walls. The road by which thou hast departed is solitary; never will it be gladdened by thy return! the mountain thou hast traversed lies like a cloud in the distance, and all beyond is darkness."

The royal minstrels were summoned to assuage her sorrows; they attuned their instruments to cheerful strains; but in a little while the anguish of their hearts prevailed, and turned their songs to lamentations.

"Beautiful Granada!" exclaimed they, "how is thy glory faded! The flower of thy chivalry lies low in the land of the stranger; no longer does the Vivarrambla echo to the tramp of steed and sound of trumpet; no longer is it crowded with thy youthful nobles, gloriously arrayed for the tilt and tourney. Beautiful Granada! the soft note of the lute no longer floats through thy moonlit streets; the serenade is no more heard beneath thy balconies; the lively castanet is silent upon thy hills; the graceful dance of the Zambra is no more seen beneath thy bowers! Beautiful Granada! why is the Alhambra so lorn and desolate! The orange and myrtle still breathe their perfumes into its silken chambers; the nightingale still sings within its groves; its marble halls are still refreshed with the plash of fountains and the gush of limpid rills. Alas! alas! the countenance of the king no longer shines within those halls. The light of the Alhambra is set forever!"

Thus all Granada, say the Arabian chroniclers, gave itself up to lamentation; there was nothing but the voice of wailing, from the palace to the cottage. All joined to deplore their youthful monarch, cut down in the fresh-

ness and promise of his youth; many feared that the
prediction of the astrologers was about to be fulfilled,
and that the downfall of the kingdom would follow the
death of Boabdil; while all declared, that had he survived, he was the very sovereign calculated to restore the
realm to its ancient prosperity and glory.

## CHAPTER XVIII.

### HOW MULEY ABUL HASSAN PROFITED BY THE MISFORTUNES OF HIS SON BOABDIL.

N unfortunate death atones, with the world, for
a multitude of errors. While the populace
thought their youthful monarch had perished
in the field, nothing could exceed their grief for his loss,
and their adoration of his memory: when, however, they
learnt that he was still alive, and had surrendered himself captive to the Christians, their feelings underwent
an instant change. They decried his talents as a commander, his courage as a soldier; they railed at his expedition, as rash and ill-conducted; and they reviled him
for not having dared to die on the field of battle, rather
than surrender to the enemy.

The alfaquis, as usual, mingled with the populace, and
artfully guided their discontents. "Behold," exclaimed
they, "the prediction is accomplished, which was pronounced at the birth of Boabdil. He has been seated on
the throne, and the kingdom has suffered downfall and
disgrace by his defeat and captivity. Comfort yourselves, O Moslems! The evil day has passed by; the

prophecy is fulfilled : the sceptre which has been broken
in the feeble hand of Boabdil, is destined to resume its
former sway in the vigorous grasp of Abul Hassan."

The people were struck with the wisdom of these
words : they rejoiced that the baleful prediction, which
had so long hung over them, was at an end ; and declared, that none but Muley Abul Hassan had the valor
and capacity necessary for the protection of the kingdom,
in this time of trouble.

The longer the captivity of Boabdil continued, the
greater grew the popularity of his father. One city after
another renewed allegiance to him ; for power attracts
power, and fortune creates fortune. At length he was
enabled to return to Granada, and establish himself once
more in the Alhambra. At his approach, his repudiated
spouse, the sultana Ayxa, gathered together the family
and treasures of her captive son, and retired, with a
handful of the nobles, into the Albaycin, the rival quarter of the city, the inhabitants of which still retained
feelings of loyalty to Boabdil. Here she fortified herself,
and held the semblance of a court in the name of her
son. The fierce Muley Abul Hassan would have willing-
ly carried fire and sword into this factious quarter of the
capital ; but he dared not confide in his new and uncertain popularity. Many of the nobles detested him for his
past cruelty ; and a large portion of the soldiery, besides
many of the people of his own party, respected the virtues
of Ayxa la Horra, and pitied the misfortunes of Boabdil.

Granada therefore presented the singular spectacle of two sovereignties within the same city. The old king fortified himself in the lofty towers of the Alhambra, as much against his own subjects as against the Christians; while Ayxa, with the zeal of a mother's affection, which waxes warmer and warmer towards her offspring when in adversity, still maintained the standard of Boabdil on the rival fortress of the Alcazaba, and kept his powerful faction alive within the walls of the Albaycin.

# CHAPTER XIX.

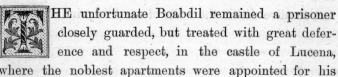HE unfortunate Boabdil remained a prisoner closely guarded, but treated with great deference and respect, in the castle of Lucena, where the noblest apartments were appointed for his abode. From the towers of his prison, he beheld the town below filled with armed men; and the lofty hill on which it was built, girdled by massive walls and ramparts, on which a vigilant watch was maintained night and day. The mountains around were studded with watch-towers, overlooking the lonely roads which led to Granada, so that a turban could not stir over the border without the alarm being given, and the whole country put on the alert. Boabdil saw that there was no hope of escape from such a fortress, and that any attempt to rescue him would be equally in vain. His heart was filled with anxiety, as he thought on the confusion and ruin which his captivity must cause in his affairs; while sorrows of a softer kind overcame his fortitude, as he thought on the evils it might bring upon his family.

A few days only had passed away, when missives

arrived from the Castilian sovereigns. Ferdinand had been transported with joy at hearing of the capture of the Moorish monarch, seeing the deep and politic uses that might be made of such an event; but the magnanimous spirit of Isabella was filled with compassion for the unfortunate captive. Their messages to Boabdil were full of sympathy and consolation, breathing that high and gentle courtesy which dwells in noble minds.

This magnanimity in his foe cheered the dejected spirit of the captive monarch. "Tell my sovereigns, the king and queen," said he to the messenger, "that I cannot be unhappy, being in the power of such high and mighty princes, especially since they partake so largely of that grace and goodness which Allah bestows upon the monarchs whom he greatly loves. Tell them further, that I had long thought of submitting myself to their sway, to receive the kingdom of Granada from their hands, in the same manner that my ancestor received it from king John II., father to the gracious queen. My greatest sorrow, in this my captivity, is, that I must appear to do that from force, which I would fain have done from inclination."

In the meantime, Muley Abul Hassan, finding the faction of his son still formidable in Granada, was anxious to consolidate his power, by gaining possession of the person of Boabdil. For this purpose he sent an embassy to the Catholic monarchs, offering large terms for the ransom, or rather the purchase of his son; proposing,

11

among other conditions, to release the count of Cifuentes and nine other of his most distinguished captives, and to enter into a treaty of confederacy with the sovereigns. Neither did the implacable father make any scruple of testifying his indifference whether his son were delivered up alive or dead, so that his person were placed assuredly within his power.

The humane heart of Isabella revolted at the idea of giving up the unfortunate prince into the hands of his most unnatural and inveterate enemy; a disdainful refusal was therefore returned to the old monarch, whose message had been couched in a vaunting spirit. He was informed that the Castilian sovereigns would listen to no proposals of peace from Muley Abul Hassan, until he should lay down his arms, and offer them in all humility.

Overtures in a different spirit were made by the mother of Boabdil, the sultana Ayxa la Horra, with the concurrence of the party which still remained faithful to him. It was thereby proposed, that Mahomet Abdallah, otherwise called Boabdil, should hold his crown as vassal to the Castilian sovereigns, paying an annual tribute, and releasing seventy Christian captives annually, for five years; that he should, moreover, pay a large sum, upon the spot, for his ransom, and at the same time give freedom to four hundred Christians to be chosen by the king: that he should also engage to be always ready to render military aid, and should come to the Cortes, or assemblage of nobles and distinguished vassals of the crown, whenever summoned. His only son, and the sons of twelve distinguished Moorish houses, were to be delivered as hostages.

An embassy, composed of the alcayde Aben Comixa, Muley the royal standard-bearer, and other distinguished cavaliers, bore this proposition to the Spanish Court at Cordova, where they were received by King Ferdinand. Queen Isabella was absent at the time. He was anxious to consult her in so momentous an affair; or rather, he was fearful of proceeding too precipitately, and not drawing from this fortunate event all the advantage of which it was susceptible. Without returning any reply, therefore, to the mission, he ordered that the captive monarch should be brought to Cordova.

The alcayde of the Donzeles was the bearer of this mandate, and summoned all the hidalgos of Lucena and of his own estates, to form an honorable escort for the illustrious prisoner. In this style he conducted him to the capital. The cavaliers and authorities of Cordova came forth to receive the captive king with all due ceremony; and especial care was taken to prevent any taunt or insult from the multitude, or anything that might remind him of his humiliation. In this way he entered the once proud capital of the Abda'rahmans, and was lodged in the house of the king's major-domo. Ferdinand, however, declined seeing the Moorish monarch. He was still undetermined what course to pursue,—whether to retain him prisoner, set him at liberty on ransom, or treat him with politic magnanimity; and each course would require a different kind of reception. Until this point should be resolved, therefore, he gave him in charge to Martin de Alarcon, alcayde of the ancient fortress of Porcuna, with orders to guard him strictly, but to treat him with the distinction and deference due unto a prince. These commands were strictly obeyed; he was escorted, as before, in royal state, to the fortress which was to form his prison; and, with the exception of being restrained in his liberty, was as nobly entertained there as he could have been in his regal palace at Granada.

In the meantime, Ferdinand availed himself of this critical moment, while Granada was distracted with factions and dissensions, and before he had concluded any treaty with Boabdil, to make a puissant and ostentatious inroad into the very heart of the kingdom, at the head of his most illustrious nobles. He sacked and destroyed several towns and castles, and extended his ravages to the very gates of Granada. Muley Abul Hassan did not venture to oppose him. His city was filled with troops, but he was uncertain of their affection. He dreaded that, should he sally forth, the gates of Granada might be closed against him by the faction of the Albaycin.

The old Moor stood on the lofty tower of the Alhambra (says Antonio Agapida), grinding his teeth, and foaming like a tiger shut up in his cage, as he beheld the glittering battalions of the Christians wheeling about the vega, and the standard of the cross shining forth from among the smoke of infidel villages and hamlets. The most Catholic king (continues Agapida) would gladly have continued this righteous ravage, but his munitions began to fail. Satisfied, therefore, with having laid waste the country of the enemy, and insulted Muley Abul Hassan in his very capital, he returned to Cordova covered with laurels, and his army laden with spoils; and now bethought himself of coming to an immediate decision, in regard to his royal prisoner.

# CHAPTER XX.

### OF THE TREATMENT OF BOABDIL BY THE CASTILIAN SOVEREIGNS.

 STATELY convention was held by King Ferdinand in the ancient city of Cordova, composed
of several of the most reverend prelates and
renowned cavaliers of the kingdom, to determine upon
the fate of the unfortunate Boabdil.

Don Alonzo de Cárdenas, the worthy master of Santiago, was one of the first who gave his counsel. He was
a pious and zealous knight, rigid in his devotion to
the faith; and his holy zeal had been inflamed to peculiar vehemence, since his disastrous crusade among the
mountains of Malaga. He inveighed with ardor against
any compromise or compact with the infidels; the object
of this war, he observed, was not the subjection of the
Moors, but their utter expulsion from the land; so that
there might no longer remain a single stain of Mohamme-
danism throughout Christian Spain. He gave it as his
opinion, therefore, that the captive king ought not to be
set at liberty.

Roderigo Ponce de Leon, marques of Cadiz, on the
contrary, spoke warmly for the release of Boabdil. He

pronounced it a measure of sound policy, even if done without conditions. It would tend to keep up the civil war in Granada, which was as a fire consuming the entrails of the enemy, and effecting more for the interests of Spain, without expense, than all the conquests of its arms.

The grand cardinal of Spain, Don Pedro Gonzalez de Mendoza, coincided in opinion with the marques of Cadiz. Nay (added that pious prelate and politic statesman), it would be sound wisdom to furnish the Moor with men and money, and all other necessaries, to promote the civil war in Granada : by this means would be produced great benefit to the service of God, since we are assured by his infallible word, that "a kingdom divided against itself cannot stand." *

Ferdinand weighed these counsels in his mind, but was slow in coming to a decision; he was religiously attentive to his own interests (observes Fray Antonio Agapida), knowing himself to be but an instrument of Providence in this holy war, and that, therefore, in consulting his own advantage he was promoting the interests of the faith. The opinion of queen Isabella relieved him from his perplexity. That high-minded princess was. zealous for the promotion of the faith, but not for the extermination of the infidels. The Moorish kings had held their thrones as vassals to her progenitors; she was con-

* Salazar. *Cronica del Gran Cardinal,* p. 188.

tent at present to accord the same privilege, and that the
royal prisoner should be liberated on condition of becoming a vassal to the crown. By this means might be
effected the deliverance of many Christian captives, who
were languishing in Moorish chains.

King Ferdinand adopted the magnanimous measure
recommended by the queen; but he accompanied it with
several shrewd conditions; exacting tribute, military services, and safe passages and maintenance for Christian
troops, throughout the places which should adhere to
Boabdil. The captive king readily submitted to these
stipulations, and swore, after the manner of his faith, to
observe them with exactitude. A truce was arranged for
two years, during which the Castilian sovereigns engaged
to maintain him on his throne, and to assist him in recovering all places which he had lost during his captivity.

When Boabdil el Chico had solemnly agreed to this
arrangement, in the castle of Porcuna, preparations were
made to receive him in Cordova in regal style. Superb
steeds richly caparisoned, and raiments of brocade, and
silk, and the most costly cloths, with all other articles of
sumptuous array, were furnished to him and to fifty
Moorish cavaliers, who had come to treat for his ransom,
that he might appear in state befitting the monarch of
Granada, and the most distinguished vassal of the Castilian sovereigns. Money was also advanced to maintain
him in suitable grandeur, during his residence at the Castilian court, and his return to his dominions. Finally,

it was ordered by the sovereigns, that when he came to Cordova, all the nobles and dignitaries of the court should go forth to receive him.

A question now arose among certain of those ancient and experienced men, who grow gray about a court in the profound study of forms and ceremonials, with whom a point of punctilio is as a vast political right, and who contract a sublime and awful idea of the external dignity of the throne. Certain of these court sages propounded the momentous question, whether the Moorish monarch, coming to do homage as a vassal, ought not to kneel and kiss the hand of the king. This was immediately decided in the affirmative, by a large number of ancient cavaliers, accustomed (says Antonio Agapida) to the lofty punctilio of our most dignified court and transcendent sovereigns. The king, therefore, was informed by those who arranged the ceremonials, that when the Moorish king appeared in his presence, he was expected to extend his royal hand to receive the kiss of homage.

" I should certainly do so," replied king Ferdinand, " were he at liberty, and in his own kingdom; but I certainly shall not do so, seeing that he is a prisoner and in mine."

The courtiers loudly applauded the magnanimity of this reply; though many condemned it in secret, as savoring of too much generosity towards an infidel; and the worthy Jesuit, Fray Antonio Agapida, fully concurs in their opinion.

The Moorish king entered Cordova with his little train of faithful knights, and escorted by all the nobility and chivalry of the Castilian court. He was conducted, with great state and ceremony, to the royal palace. When he came in presence of Ferdinand, he knelt and offered to kiss his hand, not merely in homage as his subject, but in gratitude for his liberty. Ferdinand declined the token of vassalage, and raised him graciously from the earth. An interpreter began, in the name of Boabdil, to laud the magnanimity of the Castilian monarch, and to promise the most implicit submission. "Enough," said king Ferdinand, interrupting the interpreter in the midst of his harangue : "there is no need of these compliments. I trust in his integrity, that he will do everything becoming a good man and a good king." With these words he received Boabdil el Chico into his royal friendship and protection.

# CHAPTER XXI.

### RETURN OF BOABDIL FROM CAPTIVITY.

IN the month of August, a noble Moor, of the race of the Abencerrages, arrived with a splendid retinue at the city of Cordova, bringing with him the son of Boabdil el Chico, and other of the noble youth of Granada, as hostages for the fulfillment of the terms of ransom. When the Moorish king beheld his son, his only child, who was to remain in his stead, a sort of captive in a hostile land, he folded him in his arms and wept over him. "Woe the day that I was born!" exclaimed he, "and evil the stars that presided at my birth! Well was I called El Zogoybi, or the Unlucky; for sorrow is heaped upon me by my father, and sorrow do I transmit to my son!" The afflicted heart of Boabdil, however, was soothed by the kindness of the Christian sovereigns, who received the hostage prince with a tenderness suited to his age, and a distinction worthy of his rank. They delivered him in charge to the worthy alcayde Martin de Alarcon, who had treated his father with such courtesy during his confinement in the castle of Porcuna, giving orders, that, after the depar-

171

ture of the latter, his son should be entertained, with great honor and princely attention, in the same fortress.

On the 2d of September, a guard of honor assembled at the gate of the mansion of Boabdil, to escort him to the frontiers of his kingdom. He pressed his child to his heart at parting, but he uttered not a word; for there were many Christian eyes, to behold his emotion. He mounted his steed, and never turned his head to look again upon the youth; but those who were near him observed the vehement struggle that shook his frame, wherein the anguish of the father had well-nigh subdued the studied equanimity of the king.

Boabdil el Chico and king Ferdinand sallied forth, side by side, from Cordova, amidst the acclamations of a prodigious multitude. When they were a short distance from the city, they separated, with many gracious expressions on the part of the Castilian monarch, and many thankful acknowledgments from his late captive, whose heart had been humbled by adversity. Ferdinand departed for Guadalupe, and Boabdil for Granada. The latter was accompanied by a guard of honor; and the viceroys of Andalusia, and the generals on the frontier, were ordered to furnish him with escorts, and to show him all possible honor on his journey. In this way he was conducted in royal state through the country he had entered to ravage, and was placed in safety in his own dominions.

He was met on the frontier by the principal nobles

and cavaliers of his court, who had been secretly sent by his mother, the sultana Ayxa, to escort him to the capital. The heart of Boabdil was lifted up for a moment, when he found himself on his own territories, surrounded by Moslem knights, with his own banners waving over his head; and he began to doubt the prediction of the astrologers: he soon found cause, however, to moderate his exultation. The royal train which had come to welcome him, was but scanty in number, and he missed many of his most zealous and obsequious courtiers. He had returned, indeed, to his kingdom, but it was no longer the devoted kingdom he had left. The story of his vassalage to the Christian sovereigns had been made use of by his father to ruin him with the people. He had been represented as a traitor to his country, a renegado to his faith, and as leagued with the enemies of both, to subdue the Moslems of Spain to the yoke of Christian bondage. In this way the mind of the public had been turned from him; the greater part of the nobility had thronged round the throne of his father in the Alhambra; and his mother, the resolute sultana Ayxa, with difficulty maintained her faction in the opposite towers of the Alcazaba.

Such was the melancholy picture of affairs given to Boabdil by the courtiers who had come forth to meet him. They even informed him that it would be an enterprise of difficulty and danger to make his way back to the capital, and regain the little court which still remained faithful to him in the heart of the city. The old tiger, Muley Abul Hassan, lay couched within the Alhambra, and the walls and gates of the city were strongly guarded by his troops. Boabdil shook his head at these tidings. He called to mind the ill omen of his breaking his lance against the gate of Elvira, when issuing forth so vaingloriously with his army, which he now saw clearly had foreboded the destruction of that army on which he had so confidently relied. "Henceforth," said he, "let no man have the impiety to scoff at omens."

Boabdil approached his capital by stealth, and in the night, prowling about its walls like an enemy seeking to destroy, rather than a monarch returning to his throne. At length he seized upon a postern-gate of the Albaycin—that part of the city which had always been in his favor; he passed rapidly through the streets before the populace were aroused from their sleep, and reached in safety the fortress of the Alcazaba. Here he was received into the embraces of his intrepid mother, and his favorite wife Morayma. The transports of the latter, on the safe return of her husband, were mingled with tears; for she thought of her father, Ali Atar, who had fallen in his cause, and of her only son, who was left a hostage in the hand of the Christians.

The heart of Boabdil, softened by his misfortunes, was moved by the changes in everything round him; but his mother called up his spirits. "This," said she, "is no time for tears and fondness. A king must think of his sceptre and his throne, and not yield to softness like common men. Thou hast done well, my son, in throwing thyself resolutely into Granada : it must depend upon thyself whether thou remain here a king or a captive."

The old king, Muley Abul Hassan, had retired to his couch that night, in one of the strongest towers of the Alhambra; but his restless anxiety kept him from repose. In the first watch of the night, he heard a shout faintly rising from the quarter of the Albaycin, which is on the opposite side of the dark valley of the Darro. Shortly afterwards, horsemen came galloping up the hill that leads to the main gate of the Alhambra, spreading the alarm that Boabdil had entered the city and possessed himself of the Alcazaba.

In the first transports of his rage, the old king would have struck the messenger to earth. He hastily summoned his counselors and commanders, exhorting them to stand by him in this critical moment ; and, during the night, made every preparation to enter the Albaycin sword in hand in the morning.

In the meantime, the sultana Ayxa had taken prompt and vigorous measures to strengthen her party. The Albaycin was the part of the city filled by the lower orders. The return of Boabdil was proclaimed throughout the streets, and large sums of money were distributed among the populace. The nobles, assembled in the Alcazaba, were promised honors and rewards by

Boabdil, as soon as he should be firmly seated on the throne. These well-timed measures had the customary effect; and, by daybreak, all the motley populace of the Albaycin were in arms.

A doleful day succeeded. All Granada was a scene of tumult and horror. Drums and trumpets resounded in every part; all business was interrupted; the shops were shut, the doors barricadoed. Armed bands paraded the streets, some shouting for Boabdil, and some for Muley Abul Hassan. When they encountered each other, they fought furiously and without mercy; every public square became a scene of battle. The great mass of the lower orders was in favor of Boabdil, but it was a multitude without discipline or lofty spirit; part of the people were regularly armed, but the greater number had sallied forth with the implements of their trade. The troops of the old king, among whom were many cavaliers of pride and valor, soon drove the populace from the squares. They fortified themselves, however, in the streets and lanes, which they barricadoed. They made fortresses of their houses, and fought desperately from the windows and the roofs, and many a warrior of the highest blood of Granada was laid low by plebeian hands and plebeian weapons in this civic brawl.*

It was impossible that such violent convulsions should last long in the heart of a city. The people soon long

* Conde, *Domin. de los Arabes.*, p. 4, c. 37.

for repose, and a return to their peaceful occupations; and the cavaliers detested these conflicts with the multitude, in which were all the horrors of war without its laurels. By the interference of the alfaquis, an armistice was at length effected. Boabdil was persuaded that there was no dependence upon the inconstant favor of the multitude, and was prevailed upon to quit a capital where he could only maintain a precarious seat upon his throne by a perpetual and bloody struggle. He fixed his court at the city of Almeria, which was entirely devoted to him, and which at that time vied with Granada in splendor and importance. This compromise of grandeur for tranquillity, however, was sorely against the counsels of his proud-spirited mother, the sultana Ayxa. Granada appeared, in her eyes, the only legitimate seat of dominion; and she observed, with a smile of disdain, that he was not worthy of being called a monarch, who was not master of his capital.

12

## CHAPTER XXII.

HOUGH Muley Abul Hassan had regained undivided sway over the city of Granada, and the alfaquis, by his command, had denounced his son Boabdil as an apostate, doomed by Heaven to misfortune, still the latter had many adherents among the common people. Whenever, therefore, any act of the old monarch was displeasing to the turbulent multitude, they were prone to give him a hint of the slippery nature of his standing by shouting out the name of Boabdil el Chico. Long experience had instructed Muley Abul Hassan in the character of the inconstant people over whom he ruled. "A successful inroad into the country of the unbelievers," said he, "will make more converts to my cause than a thousand texts of the Koran, expounded by ten thousand alfaquis."

At this time king Ferdinand was absent from Andalusia on a distant expedition, with many of his troops. The moment was favorable for a foray, and Muley Abul Hassan cast about his thoughts for a leader to conduct it. Ali Atar, the terror of the border, the scourge of

178

Andalusia, was dead; but there was another veteran general, scarce inferior to him for predatory warfare. This was old Bexir, the gray and crafty alcayde of Malaga; and the people under his command were ripe for an expedition of the kind. The signal defeat and slaughter of the Spanish knights in the neighboring mountains had illed the people of Malaga with vanity and self-conceit. They had attributed to their own valor the defeat caused by the nature of the country. Many of them wore the armor and paraded in public with the horses of the unfortunate cavaliers slain on that occasion, vauntingly displaying them as trophies of their boasted victory. They had talked themselves into a contempt for the chivalry of Andalusia, and were impatient for an opportunity to overrun a country defended by such troops. This, Muley Abul Hassan considered a favorable state of mind for a daring inroad, and sent orders to old Bexir to gather together the choicest warriors of the borders, and carry fire and sword into the very heart of Andalusia. Bexir immediately dispatched his emissaries among the alcaydes of the border towns, calling upon them to assemble with their troops at the city of Ronda.

Ronda was the most virulent nest of Moorish depredators in the whole border country. It was situated in the midst of the wild Serrania, or chain of mountains of the same name, which are uncommonly lofty, broken, and precipitous. It stood on an almost isolated rock, nearly encircled by a deep valley, or rather chasm, through which ran the beautiful river called Rio Verde. The Moors of this city were the most active, robust, and warlike of all the mountaineers, and their very children discharged the crossbow with unerring aim. They were incessantly harassing the rich plains of Andalusia; their city abounded with Christian captives, who might sigh in vain for deliverance from this impregnable fortress. Such was Ronda in the time of the Moors; and it has ever retained something of the same character, even to the present day. Its inhabitants continue to be among the boldest, fiercest, and most adventurous of the Andalusian mountaineers; and the Serrania de Ronda is famous as the most dangerous resort of the bandit and the contrabandista.

Hamet Zeli, surnamed El Zegri, was the commander of this belligerent city and its fierce inhabitants. He was of the tribe of the Zegries, and one of the most proud and daring of that warlike race. Beside the inhabitants of Ronda and some of his own tribe, he had a legion of African Moors in his immediate service. They were of the tribe of the Gomeres, so called from their native mountains, mercenary troops, whose hot African blood had not yet been tempered by the softer living of Spain, and whose whole business was to fight. These he kept always well armed and well appointed. The rich pasturage of the Valley of Ronda produced a breed of horses famous for strength and speed; no cavalry, therefore, was better mounted than the band of Gomeres.

Rapid on the march, fierce in the attack, it would sweep down upon the Andalusian plains like a sudden blast from the mountains, and pass away as suddenly, before there was time for pursuit.

There was nothing that stirred up the spirit of the Moors of the frontiers more thoroughly than the idea of a foray. The summons of Bexir was gladly obeyed by the alcaydes of the border towns, and in a little while there was a force of fifteen hundred horse and four thousand foot, the very pith and marrow of the surrounding country, assembled within the walls of Ronda. The people of the place anticipated with eagerness the rich spoils of Andalusia, soon to crowd their gates; throughout the day, the city resounded with the noise of kettle-drum and trumpet; the high-mettled steeds stamped and neighed in their stalls, as if they shared the impatience for the foray; while the Christian captives sighed, as the varied din of preparation reached their rocky dungeons, denoting a fresh expedition against their countrymen.

The infidel host sallied forth full of spirits, anticipating an easy ravage and abundant booty. They encouraged each other in a contempt for the prowess of the foe. Many of the warriors of Malaga, and of some of the mountain towns, had insultingly arrayed themselves in the splendid armor of the Christian knights slain or taken prisoners in the famous massacre, and some of them rode the Andalusian steeds captured on that occasion.

The wary Bexir concerted his plans so secretly and expeditiously, that the Christian towns of Andalusia had not the least suspicion of the storm gathering beyond the mountains. The vast and rocky range of the Serrania de Ronda extended like a screen, covering all their movements from observation.

The army made its way as rapidly as the rugged nature of the mountains would permit, guided by Hamet el Zegri, the bold alcayde of Ronda, who knew every pass and defile: not a drum, nor the clash of a cymbal, nor the blast of a trumpet, was permitted to be heard. The mass of war rolled quietly on as the gathering cloud to the brow of the mountains, intending to burst down like the thunderbolt upon the plain.

Never let the most wary commander fancy himself secure from discovery; for rocks have eyes, and trees have ears, and the birds of the air have tongues, to betray the most secret enterprise. There chanced at this time to be six Christian scouts, prowling about the savage heights of the Serrania de Ronda. They were of that kind of lawless ruffians who infest the borders of belligerent countries, ready at any time to fight for pay, or prowl for plunder. The wild mountain passes of Spain have ever abounded with loose rambling vagabonds of the kind—soldiers in war, robbers in peace; guides, guards, smugglers, or cut-throats, according to the circumstances of the case.

These six marauders (says Fray Antonio Agapida)

were on this occasion chosen instruments, sanctified by the righteousness of their cause. They were lurking among the mountains, to entrap Moorish cattle or Moorish prisoners, both of which were equally saleable in the Christian market. They had ascended one of the loftiest cliffs, and were looking out like birds of prey, ready to pounce upon anything that might offer in the valley, when they descried the Moorish army emerging from a mountain glen. They watched it as it wound below them, remarking the standards of the various towns and the pennons of the commanders. They hovered about it on its march, skulking from cliff to cliff, until they saw the route by which it intended to enter the Christian country. They then dispersed, each making his way by the secret passes of the mountains to some different alcayde, that they might spread the alarm far and wide, and each get a separate reward.

One hastened to Luis Fernandez Puerto Carrero, the same valiant alcayde who had repulsed Muley Abul Hassan from the walls of Alhama, and who now commanded at Ecija, in the absence of the master of Santiago. Others roused the town of Utrera, and the places of that neighborhood, putting them all on the alert.[*]

Puerto Carrero was a cavalier of consummate vigor and activity. He immediately sent couriers to the alcaydes of the neighboring fortresses; to Herman Carrello, cap-

---

[*] Pulgar, p. 3, c. 24. *Cura de los Palacios,* cap. 67.

tain of a body of the Holy Brotherhood, and to certain knights of the order of Alcantara. Puerto Carrero was the first to take the field. Knowing the hard and hungry service of these border scampers, he made every man take a hearty repast, and see that his horse was well shod and perfectly appointed. Then all being refreshed and in valiant heart, he sallied forth to seek the Moors. He had but a handful of men, the retainers of his household and troops of his captaincy; but they were well armed and mounted, and accustomed to the rouses of the border; men whom the cry of "Arm and out! to horse and to the field!" was sufficient at any time to put in a fever of animation.

While the northern part of Andalusia was thus on the alert, one of the scouts had hastened southward to the city of Xeres, and given the alarm to the valiant marques of Cadiz. When the marques heard that the Moor was over the border, and that the standard of Malaga was in the advance, his heart bounded with a momentary joy; for he remembered the massacre in the mountains, where his valiant brothers had been mangled before his eyes. The very authors of his calamity were now at hand, and he flattered himself that the day of vengeance had arrived. He made a hasty levy of his retainers and of the fighting men of Xeres, and hurried off with three hundred horse and two hundred foot, all resolute men and panting for revenge.

In the meantime the veteran Bexir had accomplished

his march, as he imagined, undiscovered. From the openings of the craggy defiles, he pointed out the fertile plains of Andalusia, and regaled the eyes of his soldiery with the rich country they were about to ravage. The fierce Gomeres of Ronda were flushed with joy at the sight; and even their steeds seemed to prick up their ears and snuff the breeze, as they beheld the scenes of their frequent forays.

When they came to where the mountain defile opened into the low land, Bexir divided his force into three parts : one composed of foot-soldiers and such as were weakly mounted, he left to guard the pass, being too experienced a veteran not to know the importance of securing a retreat; a second body he placed in ambush, among the groves and thickets on the banks of the river Lopera ; the third, consisting of light cavalry, he sent forth to ravage the Campiña, or great plain of Utrera. Most of this latter force was composed of the Gomeres of Ronda, mounted on the fleet steeds bred among the mountains. It was led by Hamet el Zegri, ever eager to be foremost in the forage. Little suspecting that the country on both sides was on the alarm, and rushing from all directions to close upon them in the rear, this fiery troop dashed forward until they came within two leagues of Utrera. Here they scattered themselves about the plain, careering round the great herds of cattle and flocks of sheep, and sweeping them into droves, to be hurried to the mountains.

While thus dispersed, a troop of horse and body of foot from Utrera came suddenly upon them. The Moors rallied together in small parties, and endeavored to defend themselves; but they were without a leader, for Hamet el Zegri was at a distance, having, like a hawk, made a wide circuit in pursuit of prey. The marauders soon gave way and fled towards the ambush on the banks of the Lopera, being hotly pursued by the men of Utrera.

When they reached the Lopera, the Moors in ambush rushed forth with furious cries; and the fugitives, recovering courage from this reinforcement, rallied and turned upon their pursuers. The Christians stood their ground, though greatly inferior in number. Their lances were soon broken, and they came to sharp work with sword and scimetar. The Christians fought valiantly, but were in danger of being overwhelmed. The bold Hamet collected a handful of his scattered Gomeres, left his prey, and galloped towards the scene of action. His little troop of horsemen had reached the crest of a rising ground at no great distance, when trumpets were heard in another direction, and Luis Fernandez Puerto Carrero and his followers came galloping into the field, and charged upon the infidels in flank.

The Moors were astounded at finding war thus breaking upon them from various quarters of what they had expected to find an unguarded country. They fought for a short time with desperation, and resisted a vehement assault from the knights of Alcantara, and the men-at-arms of the Holy Brotherhood. At length the veteran Bexir was struck from his horse by Puerto Carrero, and taken prisoner, and the whole force gave way and fled. In their flight, they separated, and took two roads to the mountains, thinking, by dividing their forces, to distract the enemy. The Christians were too few to separate. Puerto Carrero kept them together, pursuing one division of the enemy with great slaughter. This battle took place at the fountain of the fig-tree, near to the Lopera. Six hundred Moorish cavaliers were slain, and many taken prisoners. Much spoil was collected on the field, with which the Christians returned in triumph to their homes.

The larger body of the enemy had retreated along a road leading more to the south, by the banks of the Guadalete. When they reached that river the sound of pursuit had died away, and they rallied to breathe and refresh themselves on the margin of the stream. Their force was reduced to about a thousand horse, and a confused multitude of foot. While they were scattered and partly dismounted on the banks of the Guadalete, a fresh storm of war burst upon them from an opposite direction. It was the marques of Cadiz, leading on his household troops and the fighting men of Xeres. When the Christian warriors came in sight of the Moors, they were roused to fury at beholding many of them arrayed in the armor of the cavaliers who had been slain among the mountains of Malaga. Nay, some who had been in that defeat beheld their own armor, which they had cast away in their flight, to enable themselves to climb the mountains. Exasperated at the sight, they rushed upon the foe with the ferocity of tigers, rather than the temperate courage of cavaliers. Each man felt as if he were avenging the death of a relative, or wiping out his own disgrace. The good marques, himself, beheld a powerful Moor bestriding the horse of his brother Beltran: giving a cry of rage and anguish at the sight, he rushed through the thickest of the enemy, attacked the Moor with resistless fury, and after a short combat, hurled him breathless to the earth.

The Moors, already vanquished in spirit, could not withstand the assault of men thus madly excited. They soon gave way, and fled for the defile of the Serrania de Ronda, where the body of troops had been stationed to secure a retreat. These, seeing them come galloping wildly up the defile, with Christian banners in pursuit, and the flash of weapons at their deadly work, thought all Andalusia was upon them, and fled without awaiting an attack. The pursuit continued among glens and defiles; for the Christian warriors, eager for revenge, had no compassion on the foe.

When the pursuit was over, the marques of Cadiz and his followers reposed themselves upon the banks of the Guadalete, where they divided the spoil. Among this were found many rich corselets, helmets, and weapons— the Moorish trophies of the defeat in the mountains of

Malaga. Several were claimed by their owners; others were known to have belonged to noble cavaliers, who had been slain or taken prisoners. There were several horses, also, richly caparisoned, which had pranced proudly with the unfortunate warriors, as they sallied out of Antiquera upon that fatal expedition. Thus the exultation of the victors was dashed with melancholy, and many a knight was seen lamenting over the helmet or corselet of some loved companion in arms.

The good marques of Cadiz was resting under a tree on the banks of the Guadalete, when the horse which had belonged to his slaughtered brother Beltran was brought to him. He laid his hand upon the mane, and looked wistfully at the empty saddle. His bosom heaved with violent agitation, and his lip quivered and was pale. "Ay de mi! hermano!" (woe is me! my brother!) was all that he said; for the grief of a warrior has not many words. He looked round on the field strewn with the bodies of the enemy, and in the bitterness of his woe felt consoled by the idea that his brother had not been un-revenged.

NOTE.—"En el despojo de la Batalla se vieron muchas ricas corazas e capacetes, e barberas de las que se habian perdido en el Axarquia, e otras muchas armas, e algunes fueron conocidas de sus dueños que las habian dejado por fuir, e otras fueron conocidas, que eran mui señaladas de hombres principales que habian quedado muertos e cautivos, i fueron tornados muchos de los mismos Caballos con sus ricas sillas, de los que quedaron en la Axarquia e fueron conocidos cuios eran."—*Cura de los Palacios*, cap. 67.

# CHAPTER XXIII.

THE bold alcayde of Ronda, Hamet el Zegri, had careered wide over the Campiña of Utrera, encompassing the flocks and herds, when he heard the burst of war at a distance. There were with him but a handful of his Gomeres. He saw the scamper and pursuit afar off, and beheld the Christian horsemen spurring madly towards the ambuscade on the banks of the Lopera. Hamet tossed his hand triumphantly aloft, for his men to follow him. "The Christian dogs are ours!" said he, as he put spurs to his horse, to take the enemy in rear. The little band which followed Hamet scarcely amounted to thirty horsemen. They spurred across the plain, and reached a rising ground, just as the force of Puerto Carrero had charged, with sound of trumpet, upon the flank of the party in ambush. Hamet beheld the headlong rout of the army with rage and consternation. He found the country was pouring forth its legions from every quarter, and perceived that there was no safety but in precipitate flight.

But which way to fly? An army was between him and

190

the mountain pass; all the forces of the neighborhood were rushing to the borders; the whole route by which he had come was by this time occupied by the foe. He checked his steed, rose in the stirrups, and rolled a stern and thoughtful eye over the country; then sinking into his saddle, he seemed to commune a moment with himself. Turning quickly to his troop, he singled out a renegado Christian, a traitor to his religion and his king. "Come hither," said Hamet. "Thou knowest all the secret passes of the country." "I do," replied the renegado. "Dost thou know any circuitous route, solitary and untravelled, by which we can pass wide within these troops, and reach the Serrania?" The renegado paused: "Such a route I know, but it is full of peril, for it leads through the heart of the Christian land." "'Tis well," said Hamet; "the more dangerous in appearance, the less it will be suspected. Now hearken to me. Ride by my side. Thou seest this purse of gold and this scimetar. Take us, by the route thou hast mentioned, safe to the pass of the Serrania, and this purse shall be thy reward; betray us, and this scimetar shall cleave thee to the saddle-bow." *

The renegado obeyed, trembling. They turned off from the direct road to the mountains, and struck southward toward Lebrixa, passing by the most solitary roads, and along those deep ramblas and ravines by which the

* *Cura de los Palacios,* ubi sup.

country is intersected. It was indeed a daring course. Every now and then they heard the distant sound of trumpets, and the alarm-bells of towns and villages, and found that the war was still hurrying to the borders. They hid themselves in thickets and in dry beds of rivers, until the danger had passed by, and then resumed their course. Hamet el Zegri rode on in silence, his hand upon his scimetar and his eye upon the renegado guide, prepared to sacrifice him on the least sign of treachery; while his band followed, gnawing their lips with rage, at having thus to skulk through a country they had come to ravage.

When night fell, they struck into more practicable roads, always keeping wide of the villages and hamlets, lest the watch-dogs should betray them. In this way they passed in deep midnight by Arcos, crossed the Guadalete, and effected their retreat to the mountains. The day dawned as they made their way up the savage defiles. Their comrades had been hunted up these very glens by the enemy. Every now and then they came to where there had been a partial fight, or a slaughter of the fugitives; and the rocks were red with blood, and strewed with mangled bodies. The alcayde of Ronda was almost frantic with rage, at seeing many of his bravest warriors lying stiff and stark, a prey to the hawks and vultures of the mountains. Now and then some wretched Moor would crawl out of a cave or glen, whither he had fled for refuge; for in the retreat many of the horsemen had abandoned their steeds, thrown away their armor, and clambered up the cliffs, where they could not be pursued by the Christian cavalry.

The Moorish army had sallied forth from Ronda, amidst shouts and acclamations; but wailings were heard within its walls as the alcayde and his broken band returned without banner or trumpet, and haggard with famine and fatigue. The tidings of their disaster had preceded them, borne by the fugitives of the army. No one ventured to speak to the stern Hamet, as he entered the city; for they saw a dark cloud upon his brow.

It seemed (says the pious Antonio Agapida) as if Heaven meted out this defeat in exact retribution for the ills inflicted upon the Christian warriors in the heights of Malaga. It was equally signal and disastrous. Of the brilliant array of Moorish chivalry, which had descended so confidently into Andalusia, not more than two hundred escaped. The choicest troops of the frontier were either taken or destroyed; the Moorish garrisons enfeebled; and many alcaydes and cavaliers of noble lineage carried into captivity, who were afterwards obliged to redeem themselves with heavy ransoms.

This was called the battle of Lopera, and was fought on the 17th of September, 1483. Ferdinand and Isabella were at Vittoria, in Old Castile, when they received news of the victory, and the standards taken from the enemy. They celebrated the event with processions, illuminations, and other festivities. Ferdinand sent to the mar-

13

ques of Cadiz the royal raiment which he had worn on that day, and conferred on him, and all those who should inherit his title, the privilege of wearing royal robes on our Lady's day, in September, in commemoration of this victory.*

Queen Isabella was equally mindful of the great services of Don Luis Fernandez Puerto Carrero. Besides many encomiums and favors, she sent to his wife the royal vestments and robe of brocade which she had worn on the same day, to be worn by her, during her life, on the anniversary of that battle.*

Mariana, Abarca, Zurita, Pulgar, etc.

## CHAPTER XXIV.

IN the midst of the bustle of warlike affairs, the worthy chronicler Fray Antonio Agapida pauses to note, with curious accuracy, the distinguished reception given to the count de Cabra and his nephew, the alcayde de los Donceles, at the stately and ceremonious court of the Castilian sovereigns, in reward for the capture of the Moorish king Boabdil. The court (he observes) was held at the time in the ancient Moorish palace of the city of Cordova, and the ceremonials were arranged by that venerable prelate, Don Pedro Gonzales de Mendoza, bishop of Toledo and grand cardinal of Spain.

It was on Wednesday, the 14th of October (continues the precise Antonio Agapida), that the good count de Cabra, according to arrangement, appeared at the gate of Cordova. Here he was met by the grand cardinal, and the duke of Villahermosa, illegitimate brother of the king, together with many of the first grandees and prelates of the kingdom. By this august train was he attended to the palace, amidst strains of martial music, and the shouts of a prodigious multitude.

When the count arrived in the presence of the sovereigns, who were seated in state on a dais or raised part of the hall of audience, they both arose. The king advanced exactly five steps toward the count, who knelt and kissed his royal hand; however, the king would not receive him as a mere vassal, but embraced him with affectionate cordiality. The queen also advanced two steps, and received the count with a countenance full of sweetness and benignity: after he had kissed her hand, the king and queen returned to their thrones, and, cushions being brought, they ordered the count de Cabra to be seated in their presence. This last circumstance is written in large letters, and followed by several notes of admiration, in the manuscript of the worthy Fray Antonio Agapida, who considers the extraordinary privilege of sitting in presence of the Catholic sovereigns an honor well worth fighting for.

The good count took his seat at a short distance from the king, and near him was seated the duke of Najera, then the bishop of Palencia, then the count of Aguilar, the count Luna, and Don Gutierre de Cardenas, senior commander of Leon.

On the side of the queen were seated the grand cardinal of Spain, the duke of Villahermosa, the count of Monte Rey, and the bishops of Jaen and Cuenca, each in the order in which they are named. The infanta Isabella was prevented, by indisposition, from attending the ceremony.

And now festive music resounded through the hall, and twenty ladies of the queen's retinue entered, magnificently attired; upon which twenty youthful cavaliers, very gay and galliard in their array, stepped forth, and, each seeking his fair partner, they commenced a stately dance. The court, in the meantime (observes Fray Antonio Agapida), looked on with lofty and becoming gravity.

When the dance was concluded, the king and queen rose to retire to supper, and dismissed the count with many gracious expressions. He was then attended by all the grandees present to the palace of the grand cardinal, where they partook of a sumptuous banquet.

On the following Saturday, the alcayde de los Donceles was received, likewise, with great honors; but the ceremonies were so arranged, as to be a degree less in dignity than those shown to his uncle; the latter being considered the principal actor in this great achievement. Thus the grand cardinal and the duke of Villahermosa did not meet him at the gate of the city, but received him in the palace, and entertained him in conversation until summoned to the sovereigns.

When the alcayde de los Donceles entered the presence chamber, the king and queen rose from their chairs, but without advancing. They greeted him graciously, and commanded him to be seated next to the count de Cabra.

The infanta Isabella came forth to this reception, and took her seat beside the queen. When the court were all seated, the music again sounded through the hall, and the twenty ladies came forth as on the preceding occasion, richly attired, but in different raiment. They danced as before; and the infanta Isabella, taking a young Portuguese damsel for a partner, joined in the dance. When this was concluded, the king and queen dismissed the alcayde de los Donceles with great courtesy, and the court broke up.

The worthy Fray Antonio Agapida here indulges in a long eulogy on the scrupulous discrimination of the Castilian court, in the distribution of its honors and rewards, by which means every smile, and gesture, and word of the sovereigns, had its certain value, and conveyed its equivalent of joy to the heart of the subject;—a matter well worth the study (says he) of all monarchs, who are too apt to distribute honors with a heedless caprice that renders them of no avail.

On the following Sunday both the count de Cabra and the alcayde de los Donceles were invited to sup with the sovereigns. The court that evening was attended by the highest nobility, arrayed with that cost and splendor for which the Spanish nobility of those days were renowned.

Before supper, there was a stately and ceremonious dance, befitting the dignity of so august a court. The king led forth the queen, in grave and graceful measure;

the count de Cabra was honored with the hand of the infanta Isabella; and the alcayde de los Donceles danced with a daughter of the marques de Astorga.

The dance being concluded, the royal party repaired to the supper-table, which was placed on an elevated part of the saloon. Here, in full view of the court, the count de Cabra and the alcayde de los Donceles supped at the same table with the king, the queen, and the infanta. The royal family were served by the marques of Villena. The cupbearer to the king was his nephew, Fadrique de Toledo, son to the duke of Alva. Don Alexis de Estañiga had the honor of fulfilling that office for the queen, and Tello de Aguilar for the infanta. Other cavaliers of rank and distinction waited on the count and the alcayde de los Donceles. At one o'clock, the two distinguished guests were dismissed with many courteous expressions by the sovereigns.

Such (says Fray Antonio Agapida) were the great honors paid at our most exalted and ceremonious court to these renowned cavaliers; but the gratitude of the sovereigns did not end here. A few days afterwards, they bestowed upon them large revenues for life, and others to descend to their heirs, with the privilege for them and their descendants to prefix the title of Don to their names. They gave them, moreover, as armorial bearings, a Moor's head crowned, with a golden chain round the neck, in a sanguine field, and twenty-two banners round the margin of the escutcheon. Their descend-

ants, of the houses of Cabra and Cordova, continue to
bear these arms at the present day, in memorial of the
victory of Lucena and the capture of Boabdil el Chico.*

* The account given by Fray Antonio Agapida of this ceremonial, so
characteristic of the old Spanish court, agrees in almost every particular
with an ancient manuscript, made up from the chronicles of the Curate
of los Palacios and other old Spanish writers

# CHAPTER XXV.

HOW THE MARQUES OF CADIZ CONCERTED TO SURPRISE ZAHARA, AND THE
RESULT OF HIS ENTERPRISE.

HE valiant Roderigo Ponce de Leon, marques
of Cadiz, was one of the most vigilant of commanders. He kept in his pay a number of
converted Moors, to serve as adalides, or armed guides.
These mongrel Christians were of great service in procuring information. Availing themselves of their Moorish character and tongue, they penetrated into the enemy's country, prowled about the castles and fortresses,
noticed the state of the walls, the gates and towers, the
strength of their garrison, and the vigilance or negligence
of their commanders. All this they reported minutely to
the marques, who thus knew the state of every fortress
upon the frontier, and when it might be attacked with
advantage. Besides the various towns and cities over
which he held feudal sway, he had always an armed force
about him, ready for the field. A host of retainers fed in
his hall, who were ready to follow him to danger and
death itself, without inquiring who or why they fought.
The armories of his castles were supplied with helms and

201

cuirasses, and weapons of all kinds, ready burnished for use; and his stables were filled with hardy steeds, that could stand a mountain scamper.

The marques was aware that the late defeat of the Moors on the banks of the Lopera had weakened their whole frontier; for many of the castles and fortresses had lost their alcaydes, and their choicest troops. He sent out his war-hounds, therefore, upon the range, to ascertain where a successful blow might be struck; and they soon returned, with word that Zahara was weakly garrisoned and short of provisions.

This was the very fortress, which, about two years before, had been stormed by Muley Abul Hassan; and its capture had been the first blow of this eventful war. It had ever since remained a thorn in the side of Andalusia. All the Christians had been carried away captive, and no civil population had been introduced in their stead. There were no women or children in the place. It was kept up as a mere military post, commanding one of the most important passes of the mountains, and was a stronghold of Moorish marauders. The marques was animated by the idea of regaining this fortress for his sovereigns and wresting from the old Moorish king this boasted trophy of his prowess. He sent missives, therefore, to the brave Luis Fernandez Puerto Carrero, who had distinguished himself in the late victory, and to Juan Almaraz, captain of the men-at-arms of the Holy Brotherhood, informing them of his designs, and inviting them to meet him with their forces on the banks of the Guadalete.

It was on the day (says Fray Antonio Agapida) of the glorious apostles St. Simon and Judas, the twenty-eighth of October, in the year of grace one thousand four hundred and eighty-three, that this chosen band of Christian soldiers assembled suddenly and secretly at the appointed place. Their forces, when united, amounted to six hundred horse and fifteen hundred foot. Their gathering place was at the entrance of the defile leading to Zahara. That ancient town, renowned in Moorish warfare, is situated in one of the roughest passes of the Serrania de Ronda. It is built round the craggy cone of a hill, on the lofty summit of which is a strong castle. The country around is broken into deep barrancas or ravines, some of which approach its very walls. The place had until recently been considered impregnable; but (as the worthy Fray Antonio Agapida observes) the walls of impregnable fortresses, like the virtue of self-confident saints, have their weak points of attack.

The marques of Cadiz advanced with his little army in the dead of the night, marching silently into the deep and dark defiles of the mountains, and stealing up the ravines which extended to the walls of the town. Their approach was so noiseless that the Moorish sentinels upon the walls heard not a voice or a footfall. The marques was accompanied by his old escalador, Ortega de Prado, who had distinguished himself at the scaling of

Alhama. This hardy veteran was stationed, with ten men, furnished with scaling-ladders, in a cavity among the rocks, close to the walls. At a little distance, seventy men were hid in a ravine, to be at hand to second him, when he should have fixed his ladders. The rest of the troops were concealed in another ravine, commanding a fair approach to the gate of the fortress. A shrewd and wary adalid, well acquainted with the place, was appointed to give signals, and so stationed, that he could be seen by the various parties in ambush, but not by the garrison.

The remainder of the night passed away in profound quiet. The Moorish sentinels could be heard tranquilly patrolling the walls, in perfect security. The day dawned, and the rising sun began to shine against the lofty peaks of the Serrania de Ronda. The sentinels looked from their battlements over a savage but quiet mountain country, where not a human being was stirring; they little dreamt of the mischief lurking in every ravine and chasm of the rocks around them. Apprehending no danger of surprise in broad day, the greater part of the soldiers abandoned the walls and towers, and descended into the city.

By orders of the marques, a small body of light cavalry passed along the glen, and, turning round a point of rock, showed themselves before the town : they skirred the fields almost to the gates, as if by way of bravado, and to defy the garrison to a skirmish. The Moors were not slow in replying to it. About seventy horse, and a number of foot who had guarded the walls, sallied forth impetuously, thinking to make easy prey of these insolent marauders. The Christian horsemen fled for the ravine, the Moors pursued them down the hill, until they heard a great shouting and tumult behind them. Looking round towards the town, they beheld a scaling party mounting the walls sword in hand. Wheeling about, they galloped for the gate; the marques of Cadiz and Luis Fernandez Puerto Carrero rushed forth at the same time with their ambuscade, and endeavored to cut them off; but the Moors succeeded in throwing themselves within the walls.

While Puerto Carrero stormed at the gate, the marques put spurs to his horse and galloped to the support of Ortega de Prado and his scaling party. He arrived at a moment of imminent peril, when the party was assailed by fifty Moors, armed with cuirasses and lances, who were on the point of thrusting them from the walls. The marques sprang from his horse, mounted a ladder, sword in hand, followed by a number of his troops, and made a vigorous attack upon the enemy.* They were soon driven from the walls, and the gates and towers remained in possession of the Christians. The Moors defended themselves for a short time in the streets, but at length took refuge in the castle, the walls of which

* *Cura de los Palacios,* c. 68.

were strong, and capable of holding out until relief should arrive. The marques had no desire to carry on a siege, and he had not provisions sufficient for many prisoners; he granted them, therefore, favorable terms. They were permitted, on leaving their arms behind them, to march out with as much of their effects as they could carry; and it was stipulated that they should pass over to Barbary. The marques remained in the place until both town and castle were put in a perfect state of defense, and strongly garrisoned.

Thus did Zahara return once more in possession of the Christians, to the great confusion of old Muley Abul Hassan, who, having paid the penalty of his ill-timed violence, was now deprived of its vaunted fruits. The Castilian sovereigns were so gratified by this achievement of the valiant Ponce de Leon, that they authorized him thenceforth to entitle himself duke of Cadiz and marques of Zahara. The warrior, however, was so proud of the original title, under which he had so often signalized himself, that he gave it the precedence, and always signed himself marques, duke of Cadiz. As the reader may have acquired the same predilection, we shall continue to call him by his ancient title.

# CHAPTER XXVI.

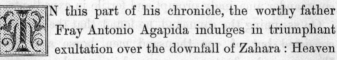N this part of his chronicle, the worthy father Fray Antonio Agapida indulges in triumphant exultation over the downfall of Zahara : Heaven sometimes speaks (says he) through the mouths of false prophets, for the confusion of the wicked.   By the fall of this fortress was the prediction of the santon of Granada in some measure fulfilled, that "the ruins of Zahara should fall upon the heads of the infidels."

Our zealous chronicler scoffs at the Moorish alcayde, who lost his fortress by surprise in broad daylight; and contrasts the vigilance of the Christian governor of Alhama, the town taken in retaliation for the storming of Zahara.

The important post of Alhama was at this time confided by King Ferdinand to Don Inigo Lopez de Mendoza, count of Tendilla, a cavalier of noble blood, brother to the grand cardinal of Spain.   He had been instructed by the king, not merely to maintain his post, but also to make sallies and lay waste the surrounding country.   His fortress was critically situated. It was within seven leagues of Granada, and at no great distance from the warlike city of Loxa. It was nestled in the lap of the mountains, commanding the high-road to Malaga and a view over the extensive vega. Thus situated, in the heart of the enemy's country, surrounded by foes ready to assail him, and a rich country for him to ravage, it behooved this cavalier to be forever on the alert. He was in fact an experienced veteran, a shrewd and wary officer, and a commander amazingly prompt and fertile in expedients.

On assuming the command, he found that the garrison consisted but of one thousand men, horse and foot. They were hardy troops, seasoned in rough mountain campaigning, but reckless and dissolute, as soldiers are apt to be when accustomed to predatory warfare. They would fight hard for booty, and then gamble it heedlessly away, or squander it in licentious reveling. Alhama abounded with hawking, sharping, idle hangers-on, eager to profit by the vices and follies of the garrison. The soldiers were oftener gambling and dancing beneath the walls, than keeping watch upon the battlements; and nothing was heard, from morning till night, but the noisy contest of cards and dice, mingled with the sound of the bolero or fandango, the drowsy strumming of the guitar, and the rattling of the castanets; while often the whole was interrupted by the loud brawl, and fierce and bloody contest.

The count of Tendilla set himself vigorously to reform

these excesses; he knew that laxity of morals is generally attended by neglect of duty, and that the least breach of discipline in the exposed situation of his fortress might be fatal. "Here is but a handful of men," said he; "it is necessary that each man should be a hero."

He endeavored to awaken a proper ambition in the minds of his soldiers, and to instill into them the high principles of chivalry. "A just war," he observed, "is often rendered wicked and disastrous by the manner in which it is conducted; for the righteousness of the cause is not sufficient to sanction the profligacy of the means, and the want of order and subordination among the troops may bring ruin and disgrace upon the best concerted plans." But we cannot describe the character and conduct of this renowned commander in more forcible language than that of Fray Antonio Agapida, excepting that the pious father places in the foreground of his virtues his hatred of the Moors. "The count de Tendilla," says he, "was a mirror of Christian knighthood—watchful, abstemious, chaste, devout, and thoroughly filled with the spirit of the cause. He labored incessantly and strenuously for the glory of the faith, and the prosperity of their most Catholic majesties; and, above all, he hated the infidels with a pure and holy hatred. This worthy cavalier discountenanced all idleness, rioting, chambering, and wantonness, among his soldiery. He kept them constantly to the exercise of arms, making

14

them adroit in the use of their weapons and management
of their steeds, and prompt for the field at a moment's
notice.  He permitted no sound of lute or harp, or song,
or other loose minstrelsy, to be heard in his fortress,
debauching the ear and softening the valor of the soldier ; no other music was allowed but the wholesome
rolling of the drum and braying of the trumpet, and such
like spirit-stirring instruments, as fill the mind with
thoughts of iron-war.  All wandering minstrels, sharping pedlars, sturdy trulls, and other camp trumpery,
were ordered to pack up their baggage, and were
drummed out of the gates of Alhama.  In place of such
lewd rabble, he introduced a train of holy friars to inspirit his people by exhortation, and prayer, and choral
chanting, and to spur them on to fight the good fight of
faith.  All games of chance were prohibited, except the
game of war ; and this he labored, by vigilance and
vigor, to reduce to a game of certainty.  Heaven smiled
upon the efforts of this righteous cavalier.  His men
became soldiers at all points, and terrors to the Moors.
The good count never set forth on a ravage, without
observing the rites of confession, absolution, and communion, and obliging his followers to do the same.
Their banners were blessed by the holy friars whom he
maintained in Alhama ; and in this way success was
secured to his arms, and he was enabled to lay waste the
land of the heathen."

"The fortress of Alhama," continues Fray Antonio

Agapida, "overlooked from its lofty site a great part of the fertile vega, watered by the Cazin and the Xenil; from this he made frequent sallies, sweeping away the flocks and herds from the pasture, the laborer from the field, and the convoy from the road; so that it was said by the Moors, that a beetle could not crawl across the vega without being seen by count Tendilla. The peasantry, therefore, were fain to betake themselves to watch-towers and fortified hamlets, where they shut up their cattle, garnered their corn, and sheltered their wives and children. Even there they were not safe; the count would storm these rustic fortresses with fire and sword; make captives of their inhabitants; carry off the corn, the oil, the silks, and cattle; and leave the ruins blazing and smoking, within the very sight of Granada."

"It was a pleasing and refreshing sight," continues the good father, "to behold this pious knight and his followers returning from one of these crusades, leaving the rich land of the infidel in smoking desolation behind them; to behold the long line of mules and asses, laden with the plunder of the Gentiles—the hosts of captive Moors, men, women, and children—droves of sturdy beeves, lowing kine, and bleating sheep; all winding up the steep acclivity to the gates of Alhama, pricked on by the Catholic soldiery. His garrison thus thrived on the fat of the land and the spoil of the infidel; nor was he unmindful of the pious fathers, whose blessings crowned his enterprises with success. A large portion of the spoil was always dedicated to the church; and the good friars were ever ready at the gate to hail him on his return, and receive the share allotted them. Beside these allotments, he made many votive offerings, either in time of peril or on the eve of a foray; and the chapels of Alhama were resplendent with chalices, crosses, and other precious gifts made by this Catholic cavalier."

Thus eloquently does the venerable Fray Antonio Agapida dilate in praise of the good count de Tendilla; and other historians of equal veracity, but less unction, agree in pronouncing him one of the ablest of Spanish generals. So terrible in fact did he become in the land, that the Moorish peasantry could not venture a league from Granada or Loxa to labor in the fields, without peril of being carried into captivity. The people of Granada clamored against Muley Abul Hassan, for suffering his lands to be thus outraged and insulted, and demanded to have this bold marauder shut up in his fortress. The old monarch was roused by their remonstrances. He sent forth powerful troops of horse, to protect the country, during the season that the husbandmen were abroad in the fields. These troops patrolled in formidable squadrons in the neighborhood of Alhama, keeping strict watch upon its gates; so that it was impossible for the Christians to make a sally, without being seen and intercepted.

While Alhama was thus blockaded by a roving force of Moorish cavalry, the inhabitants were awakened one night by a tremendous crash, that shook the fortress to its foundations. The garrison flew to arms, supposing it some assault of the enemy. The alarm proved to have been caused by the rupture of a portion of the wall, which, undermined by heavy rains, had suddenly given way, leaving a large chasm yawning towards the plain.

The count de Tendilla was for a time in great anxiety. Should this breach be discovered by the blockading horsemen, they would arouse the country, Granada and Loxa would pour out an overwhelming force, and they would find his walls ready sapped for an assault. In this fearful emergency, the count displayed his noted talent for expedients. He ordered a quantity of linen cloth to be stretched in front of the breach, painted in imitation of stone, and indented with battlements, so as at a distance to resemble the other parts of the walls: behind this screen he employed workmen, day and night, in repairing the fracture. No one was permitted to leave the fortress, lest information of its defenseless plight should be carried to the Moor. Light squadrons of the enemy were seen hovering about the plain, but never approached near enough to discover the deception; and thus, in the course of a few days, the wall was rebuilt stronger than before.

There was another expedient of this shrewd veteran, which greatly excites the marvel of Agapida. "It happened," he observes, "that this Catholic cavalier at one time was destitute of gold and silver, wherewith to pay the wages of his troops; and the soldiers murmured greatly, seeing that they had not the means of purchasing necessaries from the people of the town. In this dilemma, what does this most sagacious commander? He takes me a number of little morsels of paper, on the which he inscribes various sums, large and small, according to the nature of the case, and signs me them with his own hand and name. These did he give to the soldiery, in earnest of their pay. 'How!' you will say, 'are soldiers to be paid with scraps of paper?' Even so, I answer, and well paid too, as I will presently make manifest : for the good count issued a proclamation, ordering the inhabitants of Alhama to take these morsels of paper for the full amount thereon inscribed, promising to redeem them at a future time with silver and gold, and threatening severe punishment to all who should refuse. The people, having full confidence in his word, and trusting that he would be as willing to perform the one promise as he certainly was able to perform the other, took those curious morsels of paper without hesitation or demur. Thus, by a subtle and most miraculous kind of alchemy, did this Catholic cavalier turn worthless paper into precious gold, and make his late impoverished garrison abound in money!"

It is but just to add, that the count de Tendilla redeemed his promises, like a loyal knight; and this miracle as it appeared in the eyes of Fray Antonio Agapida, is the first instance on record of paper money, which has since inundated the civilized world with unbounded opulence.

## CHAPTER XXVII.

THE Spanish cavaliers who had survived the memorable massacre among the mountains of Malaga, although they had repeatedly avenged the death of their companions, could not forget the horror and humiliation of their defeat. Nothing would satisfy them but a second expedition of the kind, to carry fire and sword throughout a wide part of the Moorish territories, and leave the region which had triumphed in their disaster a black and burning monument of their vengeance. Their wishes accorded with the policy of the king, to destroy the resources of the enemy; every assistance was therefore given to their enterprise.

In the spring of 1484, the ancient city of Antiquera again resounded with arms; numbers of the same cavaliers who had assembled there so gayly the preceding year, came wheeling into the gates with their steeled and shining warriors, but with a more dark and solemn brow than on that disastrous occasion, for they had the recollection of their slaughtered friends present to their minds, whose deaths they were to avenge.

215

In a little while there was a chosen force of six thousand horse and twelve thousand foot assembled in Antiquera, many of them the very flower of Spanish chivalry, troops of the established military and religious orders, and of the Holy Brotherhood.

Precautions had been taken to furnish this army with all things needful for its perilous inroad. Numerous surgeons accompanied it, who were to attend upon the sick and wounded, without charge, being paid for their services by the queen. Isabella also, in her considerate humanity, provided six spacious tents furnished with beds and all things needful for the wounded and infirm. These continued to be used in all great expeditions throughout the war, and were called the Queen's Hospital. The worthy father, Fray Antonio Agapida, vaunts this benignant provision of the queen, as the first introduction of a regular camp hospital in campaigning service.

Thus thoroughly prepared, the cavaliers issued forth from Antiquera in splendid and terrible array, but with less exulting confidence and vaunting ostentation than on their former foray; and this was the order of the army. Don Alonzo de Aguilar led the advance guard, accompanied by Don Diego Fernandez de Cordova, the alcayde de los Donceles, and Luis Fernandez Puerto Carrero, count of Palma, with their household troops. They were followed by Juan de Merlo, Juan de Almara, and Carlos de Biezman, of the Holy Brotherhood, with the men-at-arms of their captaincies.

The second battalion was commanded by the marques of Cadiz and the Master of Santiago, with the cavaliers of Santiago and the troops of the house of Ponce Leon; with these also went the senior commander of Calatrava and the knights of that order, and various other cavaliers and their retainers.

. The right wing of this second battalion was led by Gonsalvo de Cordova, afterwards renowned as grand captain of Spain; the left by Diego Lopez de Avila. They were accompanied by several distinguished cavaliers, and certain captains of the Holy Brotherhood, with their men-at-arms.

The duke of Medina Sidonia and the count de Cabra commanded the third battalion, with the troops of their respective houses. They were accompanied by other commanders of note, with their forces.

The rear-guard was brought up by the senior commander and knights of Alcantara, followed by the Andalusian chivalry from Xeres, Ecija, and Carmona.

Such was the army that issued forth from the gates of Antiquera, on one of the most extensive *talas*, or devastating inroads, that ever laid waste the kingdom of Granada.

The army entered the Moorish territory by the way of Alora, destroying all the corn-fields, vineyards, and orchards, and plantations of olives, round that city. It then proceeded through the rich valleys and fertile uplands of Coin, Cazarabonela, Almexia, and Cartama; and in ten days all those fertile regions were a smoking and frightful desert. Hence it pursued its slow and destructive course, like the stream of lava of a volcano, through the regions of Pupiana and Alhendin, and so on to the vega of Malaga, laying waste the groves of olives and almonds, and the fields of grain, and destroying every green thing. The Moors of some of those places interceded in vain for their groves and fields, offering to deliver up their Christian captives. One part of the army blockaded the towns, while the other ravaged the surrounding country. Sometimes the Moors sallied forth desperately to defend their property, but were driven back to their gates with slaughter and their suburbs pillaged and burnt. It was an awful spectacle at night to behold the volumes of black smoke mingled with lurid flames rising from the burning suburbs, and the women on the walls of the town wringing their hands and shrieking at the desolation of their dwellings.

The destroying army, on arriving at the sea-coast, found vessels lying off shore laden with all kinds of provisions and munitions sent from Seville and Xeres, and was thus enabled to continue its desolating career. Advancing to the neighborhood of Malaga, it was bravely assailed by the Moors of that city, and there was severe skirmishing for a whole day; but while the main part of the army encountered the enemy, the rest ravaged the whole vega and destroyed all the mills. As the object of the expedition was not to capture places, but merely to burn, ravage, and destroy, the host, satisfied with the mischief they had done in the vega, turned their backs upon Malaga, and again entered the mountains. They passed by Coin, and through the regions of Allazayna, and Gatero, and Alhaurin; all which were likewise desolated. In this way did they make the circuit of a chain of rich and verdant valleys, the glory of those mountains and the pride and delight of the Moors. For forty days did they continue on like a consuming fire, leaving a smoking and howling waste to mark their course, until, weary with the work of destruction, and having fully sated their revenge for the massacre of the Axarquia, they returned in triumph to the meadows of Antiquera.

In the month of June, King Ferdinand took command in person of this destructive army; he increased its force, and added to its means of mischief several lombards and other heavy artillery, intended for the battering of towns, and managed by engineers from France and Germany. With these, the marques of Cadiz assured the king, he would soon be able to reduce the Moorish fortresses, which were only calculated for defense against the engines anciently used in warfare. Their walls and towers were high and thin, depending for security on their rough and rocky situations. The stone and iron balls thundered from the lombards would soon tumble them in ruins upon the heads of their defenders.

The fate of Alora speedily proved the truth of this opinion. It was strongly posted on a rock washed by a

river. The artillery soon battered down two of the
towers and a part of the wall. The Moors were thrown
into consternation at the vehemence of the assault, and
the effect of those tremendous engines upon their vaunted bulwarks. The roaring of the artillery and the tumbling of the walls terrified the women, who beset the
alcayde with vociferous supplications to surrender. The
place was given up on the 20th of June, on condition that
the inhabitants might depart with their effects. The
people of Malaga, as yet unacquainted with the power of
this battering ordnance, were so incensed at those of
Alora for what they considered a tame surrender, that
they would not admit them into their city.

A similar fate attended the town of Setenil, built on a
lofty rock, and esteemed impregnable. Many times had
it been besieged under former Christian kings, but never
taken. Even now, for several days the artillery was directed against it without effect, and many of the cavaliers
murmured at the marques of Cadiz for having counseled
the king to attack this unconquerable place.*

On the same night that these reproaches were uttered,
the marques directed the artillery himself: he leveled the
lombards at the bottom of the walls and at the gates. In
a little while the gates were battered to pieces, a great
breach was effected in the walls, and the Moors were fain
to capitulate. Twenty-four Christian captains, who had

* *Cura de los Palacios.*

been taken in the defeat of the mountains of Malaga, were rescued from the dungeons of this fortress, and hailed the marques as their deliverer.

Needless is it to mention the capture of various other places, which surrendered without waiting to be attacked. The Moors had always shown great bravery and perseverance in defending their towns; they were formidable in their sallies and skirmishes, and patient in enduring hunger and thirst when besieged; but this terrible ordnance, which demolished their walls with such ease and rapidity, overwhelmed them with dismay, and rendered vain all resistance. King Ferdinand was so struck with the effect of this artillery, that he ordered the number of lombards to be increased; and these potent engines had henceforth a great influence on the fortunes of this war.

The last operation of this year, so disastrous to the Moors, was an inroad by Ferdinand, in the latter part of summer, into the vega, in which he ravaged the country, burned two villages near to Granada, and destroyed the mills near the very gates of the city.

Old Muley Abul Hassan was overwhelmed with dismay at the desolation which, during the whole year, had raged throughout his territories, and had now reached the walls of his capital. His fierce spirit was broken by misfortunes and infirmity; he offered to purchase a peace, and to hold his crown as a tributary vassal. Ferdinand would listen to no propositions: the absolute conquest of Granada was the great object of this war, and he was resolved never to rest content without its complete fulfillment. Having supplied and strengthened the garrisons of the places taken in the heart of the Moorish territories, he enjoined their commanders to render every assistance to the younger Moorish king, in the civil war against his father. He then returned with his army to Cordova, in great triumph, closing a series of ravaging campaigns, which had filled the kingdom of Granada with grief and consternation.

# CHAPTER XXVIII.

URING this year of sorrow and disaster to the Moors, the younger king Boabdil, most truly called the Unfortunate, held a diminished and feeble court in the maritime city of Almeria. He retained little more than the name of king, and was supported in even this shadow of royalty by the countenance and treasures of the Castilian sovereigns. Still he trusted that, in the fluctuation of events, the inconstant nation might once more return to his standard, and replace him on the throne of the Alhambra.

His mother, the high-spirited sultana, Ayxa la Horra, endeavored to rouse him from this passive state. "It is a feeble mind," said she, "that waits for the turn of fortune's wheel; the brave mind seizes upon it, and turns it to its purpose. Take the field, and you may drive danger before you; remain cowering at home, and it besieges you in your dwelling. By a bold enterprise, you may regain your splendid throne in Granada; by passive forbearance, you will forfeit even this miserable throne in Almeria."

223

Boabdil had not the force of soul to follow these courageous counsels, and in a little time the evils his mother had predicted fell upon him.

Old Muley Abul Hassan was almost extinguished by age and paralysis. He had nearly lost his sight, and was completely bed-ridden. His brother, Abdallah, surnamed El Zagal, or the Valiant, the same who had assisted in the massacre of the Spanish chivalry among the mountains of Malaga, was commander-in-chief of the Moorish armies, and gradually took upon himself most of the cares of sovereignty. Among other things, he was particularly zealous in espousing his brother's quarrel with his son; and he prosecuted it with such vehemence, that many affirmed there was something more than mere fraternal sympathy at the bottom of his zeal.

The disasters and disgraces inflicted on the country by the Christians during this year had wounded the national feelings of the people of Almeria; and many felt indignant that Boabdil should remain passive at such a time, or rather, should appear to make a common cause with the enemy. His uncle, Abdallah, diligently fomented this feeling by his agents. The same arts were made use of that had been successful in Granada. Boabdil was secretly but actively denounced by the alfaquis as an apostate, leagued with the Christians against his country and his early faith; the affections of the populace and soldiery were gradually alienated from him, and a deep conspiracy concerted for his destruction.

In the month of February, 1485, El Zagal suddenly appeared before Almeria, at the head of a troop of horse. The alfaquis were prepared for his arrival, and the gates were thrown open to him. He entered with his band, and galloped to the citadel. The alcayde would have made resistance; but the garrison put him to death, and received El Zagal with acclamations. The latter rushed through the apartments of the Alcazar, but he sought in vain for Boabdil. He found the sultana, Ayxa la Horra, in one of the saloons, with Aben Haxig, a younger brother of the monarch, and several Abencerrages, who rallied round them to protect them. "Where is the traitor Boabdil?" exclaimed El Zagal. "I know no traitor more perfidious than thyself," exclaimed the intrepid sultana; "and I trust my son is in safety, to take vengeance on thy treason." The rage of El Zagal was without bounds when he learned that his intended victim had escaped. In his fury he slew the prince Aben Haxig, and his followers fell upon and massacred the Abencerrages. As to the proud sultana, she was borne away prisoner, and loaded with revilings, as having upheld her son in his rebellion, and fomented a civil war.

The unfortunate Boabdil had been apprised of his danger by a faithful soldier, just in time to make his escape. Throwing himself on one of his fleetest horses, and followed by a handful of adherents, he galloped in the confusion out of the gates of Almeria. Several of the cavalry of El Zagal, stationed without the walls, perceived

15

his flight, and attempted to pursue him : their horses were jaded with travel, and he soon left them far behind. But whither was he to fly?  Every fortress and castle in the kingdom of Granada was closed against him; he knew not whom among the Moors to trust, for they had been taught to detest him as a traitor and an apostate. He had no alternative but to seek refuge among the Christians, his hereditary enemies.  With a heavy heart, he turned his horse's head towards Cordova.  He had to lurk, like a fugitive, through a part of his own dominions; nor did he feel himself secure until he had passed the frontier, and beheld the mountain barrier of his country towering behind him.  Then it was that he became conscious of his humiliating state—a fugitive from his throne, an outcast from his nation, a king without a kingdom.  He smote his breast, in an agony of grief: "Evil indeed," exclaimed he, "was the day of my birth, and truly was I named El Zogoybi, the Unlucky."

He entered the gates of Cordova with downcast countenance, and with a train of but forty followers.  The sovereigns were absent; but the cavaliers of Andalusia manifested that sympathy in the misfortunes of the monarch which becomes men of lofty and chivalrous souls. They received him with great distinction, attended him with the utmost courtesy, and he was honorably entertained by the civil and military commanders of that ancient city.

In the meantime, El Zagal put a new alcayde over

Almeria, to govern in the name of his brother; and, having strongly garrisoned the place, repaired to Malaga, where an attack of the Christians was apprehended. The young monarch being driven out of the land, and the old monarch blind and bed-ridden, El Zagal, at the head of the armies, was virtually the sovereign of Granada. He was supported by the brave and powerful family of the Alnayans and Venegas; the people were pleased with having a new idol to look up to, and a new name to shout forth; and El Zagal was hailed with acclamations, as the main hope of the nation.

## CHAPTER XXIX.

THE recent effect of the battering ordnance in demolishing the Moorish fortresses, induced king Ferdinand to procure a powerful train for the campaign of 1485, intending to assault some of the most formidable holds of the enemy. An army of nine thousand cavalry and twenty thousand infantry assembled at Cordova, early in the spring ; and the king took the field on the 5th of April. It had been determined in secret council, to attack the city of Malaga, that ancient and important seaport, on which Granada depended for foreign aid and supplies. It was thought proper previously, however, to get possession of various towns and fortresses in the valleys of Santa Maria and Cartama, through which pass the roads to Malaga.

The first place assailed was the town of Benamexi or Bonameji. It had submitted to the Catholic sovereigns in the preceding year, but had since renounced its allegiance. King Ferdinand was enraged at the rebellion of the inhabitants. " I will make their punishment," said

228

he, "a terror to others: they shall be loyal through force, if not through faith." The place was carried by storm: one hundred and eight of the principal inhabitants were either put to the sword or hanged on the battlements: the rest were carried into captivity.*

The towns of Coin and Cartama were besieged on the same day; the first by a division of the army led on by the marques of Cadiz, the second by another division commanded by Don Alonzo de Aguilar and Louis Fernandez Puerto Carrero, the brave senior of Palma. The king, with the rest of the army, remained posted between the two places, to render assistance to either division. The batteries opened upon both places at the same time, and the thunder of the lombards was mutually heard from one camp to the other. The Moors made frequent sallies and a valiant defense; but they were confounded by the tremendous uproar of the batteries, and the destruction of their walls. In the mean time, the alarm fires gathered together the Moorish mountaineers of all the Serrania, who assembled in great numbers in the city of Monda, about a league from Coin. They made several attempts to enter the besieged town, but in vain: they were each time intercepted and driven back by the Christians, and were reduced to gaze at a distance in despair on the destruction of the place. While thus situated, there rode one day into Monda a fierce and

* Pulgar, Garibay, *Cura de los Palacios.*

haughty Moorish chieftain, at the head of a band of swarthy African horsemen : it was Hamet el Zegri, the fiery spirited alcayde of Ronda, at the head of his band of Gomeres. He had not yet recovered from the rage and mortification of his defeat on the banks of the Lopera, in the disastrous foray of old Bexir, when he had been obliged to steal back furtively to his mountains, with the loss of the bravest of his followers. He had ever since panted for revenge. He now rode among the host of warriors assembled at Monda. "Who among you," cried he, "feels pity for the women and children of Coin, exposed to captivity and death ? Whoever he is, let him follow me, who am ready to die as a Moslem for the relief of Moslems." So saying, he seized a white banner, and, waving it over his head, rode forth from the town, followed by the Gomeres. Many of the warriors, roused by his words and his example, spurred resolutely after his banner. The people of Coin, being prepared for this attempt, sallied forth as they saw the white banner, and made an attack upon the Christian camp ; and in the confusion of the moment, Hamet and his followers galloped into the gates. This reinforcement animated the besieged, and Hamet exhorted them to hold out obstinately in defense of life and town. As the Gomeres were veteran warriors, the more they were attacked the harder they fought.

At length, a great breach was made in the walls, and Ferdinand, who was impatient of the resistance of the place, ordered the duke of Naxara and the count of Benavente to enter with their troops; and as their forces were not sufficient, he sent word to Louis de Cerda, duke of Medina Celi, to send a part of his people to their assistance.

The feudal pride of the duke was roused at this demand. "Tell my lord the king," said the haughty grandee, "that I have come to succor him with my household troops: if my people are ordered to any place, I am to go with them; but if I am to remain in the camp, my people must remain with me. For the troops cannot serve without their commander, nor their commander without his troops."

The reply of the high-spirited grandee perplexed the cautious Ferdinand, who knew the jealous pride of his powerful nobles. In the meantime, the people of the camp, having made all preparations for the assault, were impatient to be led forward. Upon this, Pero Ruyz de Alarcon put himself at their head, and, seizing their mantas, or portable bulwarks, and their other defenses, they made a gallant assault, and fought their way in at the breach. The Moors were so overcome by the fury of their assault, that they retreated, fighting, to the square of the town. Pero Ruyz de Alarcon thought the place was carried, when suddenly Hamet and his Gomeres came scouring through the streets with wild war-cries, and fell furiously upon the Christians. The latter were in their turn beaten back, and, while attacked in the front by the

Gomeres, were assailed by the inhabitants with all kinds of missiles from their roofs and windows. They at length gave way and retreated through the breach. Pero Ruyz de Alarcon still maintained his ground in one of the principal streets—the few cavaliers that stood by him urged him to fly : "No," said he ; "I came here to fight, and not to fly." He was presently surrounded by the Gomeres; his companions fled for their lives ; the last they saw of him, he was covered with wounds, but still fighting desperately for the fame of a good cavalier.[*]

The resistance of the inhabitants, though aided by the valor of the Gomeres, was of no avail. The battering artillery of the Christians demolished their walls ; combustibles thrown into their town, set it on fire in various places ; and they were at length compelled to capitulate. They were permitted to depart with their effects, and the Gomeres with their arms. Hamet el Zegri and his African band rode proudly through the Christian camp ; nor could the Spanish cavaliers refrain from regarding with admiration that haughty warrior and his devoted and dauntless followers.

The capture of Coin was accompanied by that of Cartama : the fortifications of the latter were repaired and garrisoned ; but Coin, being too extensive to be defended by a moderate force, its walls were demolished. The siege of these places struck such terror into the

[*] Pulgar, pt. 3, cap. 42.

surrounding country, that the Moors of many of the neighboring towns abandoned their homes, and fled with such of their effects as they could carry away; upon which the king gave order to demolish their walls and towers.

King Ferdinand now left his camp and his heavy artillery near Cartama, and proceeded with his lighter troops to reconnoitre Malaga. By this time, the secret plan of attack, arranged in the council of war at Cordova, was known to all the world. The vigilant warrior, El Zagal, had thrown himself into the place, put all the fortifications, which were of vast strength, into a state of defense, and sent orders to the alcaydes of the mountain towns, to hasten with their forces to his assistance.

The very day that Ferdinand appeared before the place, El Zagal sallied forth to receive him, at the head of a thousand cavalry, the choicest warriors of Granada. A sharp skirmish took place among the gardens and olive-trees near the city. Many were killed on both sides; and this gave the Christians a foretaste of what they might expect, if they attempted to besiege the place.

When the skirmish was over, the marques of Cadiz had a private conference with the king. He represented the difficulty of besieging Malaga with their present force, especially as their plans had been discovered and anticipated, and the whole country was marching to oppose them. The marques, who had secret intelligence

from all quarters, had received a letter from Juceph
Xerife, a Moor of Ronda, of Christian lineage, apprising
him of the situation of that important place and its garrison, which at that moment laid it open to attack; and
the marques was urgent with the king to seize upon this
critical moment, and secure a place which was one of the
most powerful Moorish fortresses on the frontiers, and in
the hands of Hamet el Zegri had been the scourge of
Andalusia. The good marques had another motive for
his advice, becoming of a true and loyal knight. In the
deep dungeons of Ronda languished several of his companions in arms, who had been captured in the defeat in
the Axarquia. To break their chains, and restore them
to liberty and light, he felt to be his peculiar duty, as
one of those who had most promoted that disastrous
enterprise.

King Ferdinand listened to the advice of the marques.
He knew the importance of Ronda, which was considered
one of the keys to the kingdom of Granada; and he was
disposed to punish the inhabitants, for the aid they had
rendered to the garrison of Coin. The siege of Malaga,
therefore, was abandoned for the present, and preparations made for a rapid and secret move against the city
of Ronda.

# CHAPTER XXX.

### SIEGE OF RONDA.

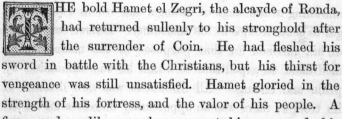

THE bold Hamet el Zegri, the alcayde of Ronda, had returned sullenly to his stronghold after the surrender of Coin. He had fleshed his sword in battle with the Christians, but his thirst for vengeance was still unsatisfied. Hamet gloried in the strength of his fortress, and the valor of his people. A fierce and warlike populace was at his command; his signal-fires could summon all the warriors of the Serrania; his Gomeres almost subsisted on the spoils of Andalusia; and in the rock on which his fortress was built, were hopeless dungeons, filled with Christian captives, carried off by these war-hawks of the mountains.

Ronda was considered as impregnable. It was situated in the heart of wild and rugged mountains, and perched upon an isolated rock, crested by a strong citadel, with triple walls and towers. A deep ravine, or rather a perpendicular chasm of the rocks, of frightful depth, surrounded three parts of the city; through this flowed the Rio Verde, or Green River. There were two suburbs to the city, fortified by walls and towers, and almost inaccessible, from the natural asperity of the rocks. Around this rugged city were deep, rich valleys, sheltered by the mountains, refreshed by constant streams, abounding with grain and the most delicious fruits, and yielding verdant meadows, in which was reared a renowned breed of horses, the best in the whole kingdom for a foray.

Hamet el Zegri had scarcely returned to Ronda, when he received intelligence that the Christian army was marching to the siege of Malaga, and orders from El Zagal to send troops to his assistance. Hamet sent a part of his garrison for that purpose; in the meantime, he meditated an expedition to which he was stimulated by pride and revenge. All Andalusia was now drained of its troops; there was an opportunity therefore for an inroad, by which he might wipe out the disgrace of his defeat at the battle of Lopera. Apprehending no danger to his mountain city, now that the storm of war had passed down into the vega of Malaga, he left but a remnant of his garrison to man its walls, and, putting himself at the head of his band of Gomeres, swept down suddenly into the plains of Andalusia. He careered, almost without resistance, over those vast campiñas or pasture lands, which formed a part of the domains of the duke of Medina Sidonia. In vain the bells were rung, and the alarm fires kindled—the band of Hamet had passed by, before any force could be assembled, and was only to be traced, like a hurricane, by the devastation it had made.

Hamet regained in safety the Serrania de Ronda, exulting in his successful inroad. The mountain glens were filled with long droves of cattle and flocks of sheep, from the campiñas of Medina Sidonia. There were mules, too, laden with the plunder of the villages; and every warrior had some costly spoil of jewels, for his favorite mistress.

As the Zegri drew near to Ronda, he was roused from his dream of triumph by the sound of heavy ordnance bellowing through the mountain defiles. His heart misgave him—he put spurs to his horse, and galloped in advance of his lagging cavalgada. As he proceeded, the noise of the ordnance increased, echoing from cliff to cliff. Spurring his horse up a craggy height which commanded an extensive view, he beheld, to his consternation, the country about Ronda white with the tents of a besieging army. The royal standard, displayed before a proud encampment, showed that Ferdinand himself was present; while the incessant blaze and thunder of artillery, and the volumes of overhanging smoke, told the work of destruction that was going on.

The royal army had succeeded in coming upon Ronda by surprise, during the absence of its alcayde and most of its garrison; but its inhabitants were warlike, and defended themselves bravely, trusting that Hamet and his Gomeres would soon return to their assistance.

The fancied strength of their bulwarks had been of little avail against the batteries of the besiegers. In the space of four days, three towers, and great masses of the walls which defended the suburbs, were battered down, and the suburbs taken and plundered. Lombards and other heavy ordnance were now leveled at the walls of the city, and stones and missiles of all kinds hurled into the streets. The very rock on which the city stood shook with the thunder of the artillery; and the Christian captives, deep within its dungeons, hailed the sound as the promise of deliverance.

When Hamet el Zegri beheld his city thus surrounded and assailed, he called upon his men to follow him, and cut their way through to its relief. They proceeded stealthily through the mountains, until they came to the nearest heights above the Christian camp. When night fell, and part of the army was sunk in sleep, they descended the rocks, and, rushing suddenly upon the weakest part of the camp, endeavored to break their way through and gain the city. The camp was too strong to be forced; they were driven back to the crags of the mountains, whence they defended themselves by showering down darts and stones upon their pursuers.

Hamet now lit alarm-fires about the heights; his standard was joined by the neighboring mountaineers, and by troops from Malaga. Thus reinforced, he made repeated assaults upon the Christians, cutting off all stragglers from the camp. All his attempts to force his way into the city, however, were fruitless; many of his bravest men were slain, and he was obliged to retreat into the fastnesses of the mountains.

In the meanwhile, the distress of Ronda increased

hourly. The marques of Cadiz, having possession of the suburbs, was enabled to approach to the very foot of the perpendicular precipice rising from the river, on the summit of which the city is built. At the foot of this rock is a living fountain of limpid water, gushing into a great natural basin. A secret mine led down from within the city to this fountain, by several hundred steps cut in the solid rock. Hence the city obtained its chief supply of water; and these steps were deeply worn by the weary feet of Christian captives, employed in this painful labor. The marques of Cadiz discovered this subterraneous passage, and directed his pioneers to countermine in the side of the rock; they pierced to the shaft, and, stopping it up, deprived the city of the benefit of this precious fountain.

While the marques was thus pressing the siege with the generous thought of soon delivering his companions in arms from the Moorish dungeons, far other were the feelings of the alcayde, Hamet el Zegri. He smote his breast and gnashed his teeth in impotent fury, as he beheld from the mountain cliffs the destruction of the city. Every thunder of the Christian ordnance seemed to batter against his heart. He saw tower after tower tumbling by day, and various parts of the city in a blaze at night. "They fired not merely stones from their ordnance," says a chronicler of the times, "but likewise great balls of iron, cast in moulds, which demolished everything they struck." They threw also balls of tow, steeped in pitch and oil and gunpowder, which, when once on fire, were not to be extinguished, and which set the houses in flames. Great was the horror of the inhabitants: they knew not where to fly for refuge: their houses were in a blaze, or shattered by the ordnance; the streets were perilous from the falling ruins and the bounding balls, which dashed to pieces everything they encountered. At night, the city looked like a fiery furnace; the cries and wailings of the women between the thunders of the ordnance, reached even to the Moors on the opposite mountains, who answered them by yells of fury and despair.

All hope of external succor being at an end, the inhabitants of Ronda were compelled to capitulate. Ferdinand was easily prevailed upon to grant them favorable terms. The place was capable of longer resistance; and he feared for the safety of his camp, as the forces were daily augmenting on the mountains, and making frequent assaults. The inhabitants were permitted to depart with their effects, either to Barbary, Granada, or elsewhere; and those who chose to reside in Spain had lands assigned them, and were indulged in the practice of their religion.

No sooner did the place surrender, than detachments were sent to attack the Moors who hovered about the neighboring mountains. Hamet el Zegri, however, did not remain to make a fruitless battle. He gave up the game as lost, and retreated with his Gomeres, filled with grief and rage, but trusting to fortune to give him future vengeance.

The first care of the good marques of Cadiz, on entering Ronda, was to deliver his unfortunate companions in arms from the dungeons of the fortress. What a difference in their looks from the time when, flushed with health and hope, and arrayed in military pomp, they had sallied forth upon the mountain foray! Many of them were almost naked, with irons at their ankles, and beards reaching to their waists. Their meeting with the marques was joyful; yet it had the look of grief, for their joy was mingled with many bitter recollections. There was an immense number of other captives, among whom were several young men of noble families, who, with filial piety, had surrendered themselves prisoners in place of their fathers.

The captives were all provided with mules, and sent to the queen at Cordova. The humane heart of Isabella melted at the sight of the piteous cavalcade. They were all supplied by her with food and raiment, and money to pay their expenses to their homes. Their chains were hung as pious trophies against the exterior of the church of St. Juan de los Reyes, in Toledo, where the Christian traveller may regale his eyes with the sight of them at this very day.*

Among the Moorish captives was a young infidel maiden,

* Seen by the author in 1826.

16

of great beauty, who desired to become a Christian and to remain in Spain. She had been inspired with the light of the true faith through the ministry of a young man who had been a captive in Ronda. He was anxious to complete his good work by marrying her. The queen consented to their pious wishes, having first taken care that the young maiden should be properly purified by the holy sacrament of baptism.

"Thus this pestilent nest of warfare and infidelity, the city of Ronda," says the worthy Fray Antonio Agapida, "was converted to the true faith by the thunder of our artillery—an example which was soon followed by Casarabonela, Marbella, and other towns in these parts, insomuch that in the course of this expedition no less than seventy-two places were rescued from the vile sect of Mahomet, and placed under the benignant domination of the cross."

## CHAPTER XXXI.

HOW THE PEOPLE OF GRANADA INVITED EL ZAGAL TO THE THRONE, AND
HOW HE MARCHED TO THE CAPITAL.

HE people of Granada were a versatile, unsteady race, and exceedingly given to make and
unmake kings. They had, for a long time, va-
cillated between old Muley Abul Hassan and his son, Boabdil el Chico; sometimes setting up the one, sometimes
the other, and sometimes both at once, according to the
pinch and pressure of external evils. They found, however, that the evils still went on increasing, in defiance of
every change, and were at their wits' end to devise some
new combination or arrangement, by which an efficient
government might be wrought out of two bad kings.
When the tidings arrived of the fall of Ronda, and the
consequent ruin of the frontier, a tumultuous assemblage
took place in one of the public squares. As usual, the
people attributed the misfortunes of the country to the
faults of their rulers; for the populace never imagine
that any part of their miseries can originate with themselves. A crafty alfaqui, named Alyme Mazer, who had
watched the current of their discontents, rose and ha-

243

rangued them: "You have been choosing and changing,"
said he, "between two monarchs—and who and what are
they? Muley Abul Hassan, for one; a man worn out by
age and infirmities, unable to sally forth against the foe,
even when ravaging to the very gates of the city: and
Boabdil el Chico, for the other; an apostate, a traitor, a
deserter from his throne, a fugitive among the enemies of
his nation, a man fated to misfortune, and proverbially
named 'the unlucky.' In a time of overwhelming war,
like the present, he only is fit to sway a sceptre who can
wield a sword. Would you seek such a man? You need
not look far. Allah has sent such a one, in this time of
distress, to retrieve the fortunes of Granada. You already know whom I mean. You know that it can be no
other than your general, the invincible Abdallah, whose
surname of El Zagal has become a watchword in battle,
rousing the courage of the faithful, and striking terror
into the unbelievers."

The multitude received the words of the alfaqui with
acclamations; they were delighted with the idea of a
third king over Granada; and Abdallah el Zagal being
of the royal family, and already in the virtual exercise of
royal power, the measure had nothing in it that appeared
either rash or violent. A deputation was therefore sent
to El Zagal at Malaga, inviting him to repair to Granada
to receive the crown.

El Zagal expressed great surprise and repugnance,
when the mission was announced to him; and nothing

but his patriotic zeal for the public safety, and his fraternal eagerness to relieve the aged Abul Hassan from the cares of government, prevailed upon him to accept the offer. Leaving, therefore, Reduax Vanegas, one of the bravest Moorish generals, in command of Malaga, he departed for Granada, attended by three hundred trusty cavaliers.

Muley Abul Hassan did not wait for the arrival of his brother. Unable any longer to buffet with the storms of the times, his only solicitude was to seek some safe and quiet harbor of repose. In one of the deep valleys which indent the Mediterranean coast, and which are shut up on the land side by stupendous mountains, stood the little city of Almunecar. The valley was watered by the limpid river Frio, and abounded with fruits, with grain and pasturage. The city was strongly fortified, and the garrison and alcayde were devoted to the old monarch. This was the place chosen by Muley Abul Hassan for his asylum. His first care was to send thither all his treasures; his next care was to take refuge there himself; his third, that his sultana Zoraya, and their two sons, should follow him.

In the meantime, Muley Abdallah el Zagal pursued his journey towards the capital, attended by his three hundred cavaliers. The road from Malaga to Granada winds close by Alhama, and is dominated by that lofty fortress. This had been a most perilous pass for the Moors, during the time that Alhama was commanded by

the count de Tendilla: not a traveller could escape his
eagle eye, and his garrison was ever ready for a sally.
The count de Tendilla, however, had been relieved from
this arduous post, and it had been given in charge to
Don Gutiere de Padilla, clavero, or treasurer of the
order of Calatrava; an easy, indulgent man, who had
with him three hundred gallant knights of his order,
besides other mercenary troops. The garrison had
fallen off in discipline; the cavaliers were hardy in fight
and daring in foray, but confident in themselves and negligent of proper precautions. Just before the journey of
El Zagal, a number of these cavaliers, with several soldiers of fortune of the garrison, in all about one hundred
and seventy men, had sallied forth to harass the Moorish
country during its present distracted state, and, having
ravaged the valleys of the Sierra Nevada, or Snowy
Mountains, were returning to Alhama in gay spirits and
laden with booty.

As El Zagal passed through the neighborhood of Alhama, he recollected the ancient perils of the road, and
sent light cerradors in advance, to inspect each rock
and ravine where a foe might lurk in ambush. One of
these scouts, overlooking a narrow valley which opened
upon the road, descried a troop of horsemen on the
banks of a little stream. They were dismounted, and
had taken the bridles from their steeds, that they might
crop the fresh grass on the banks of the river. The
horsemen were scattered about, some reposing in the

shades of rocks and trees, others gambling for the spoil they had taken: not a sentinel was posted to keep guard; everything showed the perfect security of men who consider themselves beyond the reach of danger.

These careless cavaliers were in fact the knights of Calatrava returning from their foray. A part of their force had passed on with the cavalgada; ninety of the principal cavaliers had halted to refresh themselves in this valley. El Zagal smiled with ferocious joy, when he heard of their negligent security. "Here will be trophies," said he, "to grace our entrance into Granada."

Approaching the valley with cautious silence, he wheeled into it at full speed at the head of his troop, and attacked the Christians so suddenly, that they had not time to put the bridles upon their horses, or even to leap into the saddles. They made a confused but valiant defense, fighting among the rocks, and in the rugged bed of the river. Their defense was useless; seventy-nine were slain, and the remaining eleven were taken prisoners.

A party of the Moors galloped in pursuit of the cavalgada: they soon overtook it, winding slowly up a hill. The horsemen who conveyed it, perceiving the enemy at a distance, made their escape, and left the spoil to be retaken by the Moors. El Zagal gathered together his captives and his booty, and proceeded, elate with success, to Granada.

He paused before the gate of Elvira, for as yet he had

not been proclaimed king. This ceremony was immediately performed; for the fame of his recent exploit had preceded him, and intoxicated the minds of the giddy populace. He entered Granada in a sort of triumph. The eleven captive knights of Calatrava walked in front: next were paraded the ninety captured steeds, bearing the armor and weapons of their late owners, and led by as many mounted Moors: then came seventy Moorish horsemen, with as many Christian heads hanging at their saddle-bows: Muley Abdallah followed, surrounded by a number of distinguished cavaliers splendidly attired; and the pageant was closed by a long cavalgada of the flocks and herds, and other booty recovered from the Christians.*

The populace gazed with almost savage triumph at these captive cavaliers and the gory heads of their companions, knowing them to have been part of the formidable garrison at Alhama, so long the scourge of Granada and the terror of the vega. They hailed this petty triumph as an auspicious opening of the reign of their new monarch; for several days, the names of Muley Abul Hassan and Boabdil el Chico were never mentioned but with contempt, and the whole city resounded with the praises of El Zagal, or the Valiant.

* Zurita, lib. 20, c. 62. Mariana, *Hist. de Espana.* Abarca, *Anales de Aragon.*

# CHAPTER XXXII.

HOW THE COUNT DE CABRA ATTEMPTED TO CAPTURE ANOTHER KING, AND
HOW HE FARED IN HIS ATTEMPT.

HE elevation of a bold and active veteran to
the throne of Granada, in place of its late
bed-ridden king, made an important difference
in the aspect of the war, and called for some blow
that should dash the confidence of the Moors in their
new monarch, and animate the Christians to fresh exertions.

Don Diego de Cordova, the brave count de Cabra, was
at this time in his castle of Vaena, where he kept a wary
eye upon the frontier. It was now the latter part of
August, and he grieved that the summer should pass
away without an inroad into the country of the foe. He
sent out his scouts on the prowl, and they brought him
word that the important post of Moclin was but weakly
garrisoned. This was a castellated town, strongly situated upon a high mountain, partly surrounded by thick
forests, and partly girdled by a river. It defended one
of the rugged and solitary passes, by which the Christians were wont to make their inroads ; insomuch that

249

the Moors, in their figurative way, denominated it the shield of Granada.

The count de Cabra sent word to the monarchs of the feeble state of the garrison, and gave it as his opinion, that, by a secret and rapid expedition, the place might be surprised. King Ferdinand asked the advice of his counselors. Some cautioned him against the sanguine temperament of the count, and his heedlessness of danger; Moclin, they observed, was near to Granada, and might be promptly reinforced. The opinion of the count, however, prevailed; the king considering him almost infallible, in matters of border warfare, since his capture of Boabdil el Chico.

The king departed, therefore, from Cordova, and took post at Alcala la Real, for the purpose of being near to Moclin. The queen also proceeded to Vaena, accompanied by her children, prince Juan and the princess Isabella, and her great counselor in all matters, public and private, spiritual and temporal, the venerable grand cardinal of Spain.

Nothing could exceed the pride and satisfaction of the loyal count de Cabra, when he saw this stately train winding along the dreary mountain roads, and entering the gates of Vaena. He received his royal guests with all due ceremony, and lodged them in the best apartments that the warrior castle afforded.

King Ferdinand had concerted a wary plan to insure the success of the enterprise. The count de Cabra and

Don Martin Alonzo de Montemayor were to set forth with their troops, so as to reach Moclin by a certain hour, and to intercept all who should attempt to enter, or should sally from the town. The master of Calatrava, the troops of the grand cardinal, commanded by the count of Buendia, and the forces of the bishop of Jaen, led by that belligerent prelate, amounting in all to four thousand horse and six thousand foot, were to set off in time to coöperate with the count de Cabra, so as to surround the town. The king was to follow with his whole force, and encamp before the place.

And here the worthy padre Fray Antonio Agapida breaks forth into a triumphant eulogy of the pious prelates, who thus mingled personally in these scenes of warfare. As this was a holy crusade (says he), undertaken for the advancement of the faith and the glory of the church, so was it always countenanced and upheld by saintly men; for the victories of their most Catholic majesties were not followed, like those of mere worldly sovereigns, by erecting castles and towers, and appointing alcaydes and garrisons; but by the founding of convents and cathedrals, and the establishment of wealthy bishoprics. Wherefore their majesties were always surrounded, in court or camp, in the cabinet or in the field, by a crowd of ghostly advisers, inspiriting them to the prosecution of this most righteous war. Nay, the holy men of the church did not scruple, at times, to buckle on the cuirass over the cassock, to exchange the crosier for the lance, and thus, with corporal hands and temporal weapons, to fight the good fight of the faith.

But to return from this rhapsody of the worthy friar. The count de Cabra, being instructed in the complicated arrangements of the king, marched forth at midnight, to execute them punctually. He led his troops by the little river that winds below Vaena, and so up to the wild defiles of the mountains, marching all night, and stopping only in the heat of the following day, to repose under the shadowy cliffs of a deep barranca, calculating to arrive at Moclin exactly in time to coöperate with the other forces.

The troops had scarcely stretched themselves on the earth to take repose, when a scout arrived, bringing word that El Zagal had suddenly sallied out of Granada with a strong force, and had encamped in the vicinity of Moclin. It was plain that the wary Moor had received information of the intended attack. This, however, was not the idea that presented itself to the mind of the count de Cabra. He had captured one king—here was a fair opportunity to secure another. What a prisoner to deliver into the hands of his royal mistress! Fired with the thoughts, the good count forgot all the arrangements of the king; or rather, blinded by former success, he trusted everything to courage and fortune, and thought that, by one bold sweep, he might again bear off the royal prize, and wear his laurels without competition.*

* Mariana, lib. 25, c. 17. Abarca, Zurita, etc.

His only fear was that the master of Calatrava, and the belligerent bishop might come up in time to share the glory of the victory; so ordering every one to horse, this hot-spirited cavalier pushed on for Moclin without allowing his troops the necessary time for repose.

The evening closed, as the count arrived in the neighborhood of Moclin. It was the full of the moon, and a bright and cloudless night. The count was marching through one of those deep valleys or ravines, worn in the Spanish mountains by the brief but tremendous torrents which prevail during the autumnal rains. It was walled on each side by lofty and almost perpendicular cliffs, but great masses of moonlight were thrown into the bottom of the glen, glittering on the armor of the shining squadrons, as they silently passed through it. Suddenly the war-cry of the Moors rose in various parts of the valley; "El Zagal! El Zagal!" was shouted from every cliff, accompanied by showers of missiles, that struck down several of the Christian warriors. The count lifted up his eyes, and beheld, by the light of the moon, every cliff glistening with Moorish soldiery. The deadly shower fell thickly round him, and the shining armor of his followers made them fair objects for the aim of the enemy. The count saw his brother Gonzalo struck dead by his side; his own horse sank under him, pierced by four Moorish lances; and he received a wound in the hand from an arquebuse. He remembered the horrible massacre of the mountains of Malaga, and feared a similar catastrophe. There was no time to pause. His brother's horse, freed from his slaughtered rider, was running at large; seizing the reins, he sprang into the saddle, called upon his men to follow him, and wheeling round, retreated out of the fatal valley.

The Moors, rushing down from the heights, pursued the retreating Christians. The chase endured for a league, but it was a league of rough and broken road, where the Christians had to turn and fight at almost every step. In these short but fierce combats, the enemy lost many cavaliers of note; but the loss of the Christians was infinitely more grievous, comprising numbers of the noblest warriors of Vaena and its vicinity. Many of the Christians, disabled by wounds or exhausted by fatigue, turned aside and endeavored to conceal themselves among rocks and thickets, but never more rejoined their companions, being slain or captured by the Moors, or perishing in their wretched retreats.

The arrival of the troops, led by the master of Calatrava and the bishop of Jaen, put an end to the rout. El Zagal contented himself with the laurels he had gained, and, ordering the trumpets to call off his men from the pursuit, returned in great triumph to Moclin.*

Queen Isabella was at Vaena, awaiting with great anxiety the result of the expedition. She was in a stately apartment of the castle, looking towards the road that

* Zurita, lib. 20, c. 4.    Pulgar, *Cronica.*

winds through the mountains from Moclin, and regarding the watch-towers on the neighboring heights, in hopes of favorable signals. The prince and princess, her children, were with her, and her venerable counselor, the grand cardinal. All shared in the anxiety of the moment. At length couriers were seen riding toward the town. They entered its gates, but before they reached the castle, the nature of their tidings was known to the queen, by the shrieks and wailings from the streets below. The messengers were soon followed by wounded fugitives, hastening home to be relieved, or to die among their friends and families. The whole town resounded with lamentations; for it had lost the flower of its youth, and its bravest warriors. Isabella was a woman of courageous soul, but her feelings were overpowered by spectacles of woe on every side; her maternal heart mourned over the death of so many loyal subjects, who shortly before had rallied round her with devoted affection; and, losing her usual self-command, she sank into deep despondency.

In this gloomy state of mind, a thousand apprehensions crowded upon her. She dreaded the confidence which this success would impart to the Moors; she feared also for the important fortress of Alhama, the garrison of which had not been reinforced, since its foraging party had been cut off by this same El Zagal. On every side she saw danger and disaster, and feared that a general reverse was about to attend the Castilian arms.

The grand cardinal comforted her with both spiritual and worldly counsel. He told her to recollect that no country was ever conquered without occasional reverses to the conquerors; that the Moors were a warlike people, fortified in a rough and mountainous country where they never could be conquered by her ancestors,—and that in fact her armies had already, in three years, taken more cities than those of any of her predecessors had been able to do in twelve. He concluded by offering to take the field himself, with three thousand cavalry, his own retainers, paid and maintained by himself, and either hasten to the relief of Alhama, or undertake any other expedition her majesty might command. The discreet words of the cardinal soothed the spirit of the queen, who always looked to him for consolation; and she soon recovered her usual equanimity.

Some of the counselors of Isabella, of that politic class who seek to rise by the faults of others, were loud in their censures of the rashness of the count. The queen defended him with prompt generosity. "The enterprise," said she, "was rash, but not more rash than that of Lucena, which was crowned with success, and which we have applauded as the height of heroism. Had the count de Cabra succeeded in capturing the uncle, as he did the nephew, who is there that would not have praised him to the skies?"

The magnanimous words of the queen put a stop to all invidious remarks in her presence; but certain of the courtiers, who had envied the count the glory gained by his former achievements, continued to magnify, among themselves, his present imprudence; and we are told by Fray Antonio Agapida, that they sneeringly gave the worthy cavalier the appellation of count de Cabra, the king-catcher.

Ferdinand had reached the place on the frontier called the Fountain of the King, within three leagues of Moclin, when he heard of the late disaster. He greatly lamented the precipitation of the count, but forbore to express himself with severity, for he knew the value of that loyal and valiant cavalier.* He held a council of war, to determine what course was to be pursued. Some of his cavaliers advised him to abandon the attempt upon Moclin, the place being strongly reinforced, and the enemy inspirited by his recent victory. Certain old Spanish hidalgos reminded him that he had but few Castilian troops in his army, without which stanch soldiery his predecessors never presumed to enter the Moorish territory; while others remonstrated that it would be beneath the dignity of the king to retire from an enterprise on account of the defeat of a single cavalier and his retainers. In this way the king was distracted by a multitude of counselors, when fortunately a letter from the queen put an end to his perplexities. Proceed we, in the next chapter, to relate what was the purport of that letter.

* Abarca, *Anales de Aragon.*

17

# CHAPTER XXXIII.

### EXPEDITION AGAINST THE CASTLES OF CAMBIL AND ALBAHAR.

APPY are those princes," exclaims the worthy padre, Fray Antonio Agapida, " who have women and priests to advise them, for in these dwelleth the spirit of counsel." While Ferdinand and his captains were confounding each other in their deliberations at the Fountain of the King, a quiet but deep little council of war was held in the state apartment of the old castle of Vaena, between Queen Isabella, the venerable Pedro Gonzalez de Mendoza, grand cardinal of Spain, and Don Garcia Osorio, the belligerent bishop of Jaen. This last worthy prelate, who had exchanged his mitre for a helm, no sooner beheld the defeat of the enterprise against Moclin, than he turned the reins of his sleek, stall-fed steed, and hastened back to Vaena, full of a project for the employment of the army, the advancement of the faith, and the benefit of his own diocese. He knew that the actions of the king were influenced by the opinions of the queen, and that the queen always inclined a listening ear to the counsels of saintly men: he laid his plans, therefore, with the customary wisdom of his cloth, to turn the ideas of the queen into the proper channel; and this was the purport of the worthy bishop's suggestions.

The bishopric of Jaen had for a long time been harassed by two Moorish castles, the scourge and terror of all that part of the country. They were situated on the frontiers of the kingdom of Granada, about four leagues from Jaen, in a deep, narrow, and rugged valley, surrounded by lofty mountains. Through this valley runs the Rio Frio (or Cold River), in a deep channel, worn between high, precipitous banks. On each side of the stream rise two vast rocks, nearly perpendicular, within a stone's throw of each other, blocking up the gorge of the valley. On the summits of these rocks stood the two formidable castles, Cambil and Albahar, fortified with battlements and towers of great height and thickness. They were connected together by a bridge, thrown from rock to rock across the river. The road, which passed through the valley, traversed this bridge, and was completely commanded by these castles. They stood like two giants of romance, guarding the pass, and dominating the valley.

The kings of Granada, knowing the importance of these castles, kept them always well garrisoned, and victualled to stand a siege, with fleet steeds and hard riders, to forage the country of the Christians. The warlike race of the Abencerrages, the troops of the royal household, and others of the choicest chivalry of Granada, made them their strongholds or posts of arms, whence to sally forth on those predatory and roving enterprises in which they delighted. As the wealthy bishopric of Jaen lay immediately at hand, it suffered more peculiarly from these marauders. They drove off the fat beeves and the flocks of sheep from the pastures, and swept the laborers from the field; they scoured the country to the very gates of Jaen, so that the citizens could not venture from their walls without the risk of being borne off captive to the dungeons of these castles.

The worthy bishop, like a good pastor, beheld with grief of heart his fat bishopric daily waxing leaner and leaner and poorer and poorer; and his holy ire was kindled at the thoughts that the possessions of the church should thus be at the mercy of a crew of infidels. It was the urgent counsel of the bishop, therefore, that the military force, thus providentially assembled in the neighborhood, since it was apparently foiled in its attempt upon Moclin, should be turned against these insolent castles, and the country delivered from their domination. The grand cardinal supported the suggestion of the bishop, and declared that he had long meditated the policy of a measure of the kind. Their united opinions found favor with the queen, and she dispatched a letter on the subject to the king. It came just in time to relieve him from the distraction of a multitude of counselors, and he immediately undertook the reduction of those castles.

The marques of Cadiz was accordingly sent in advance, with two thousand horse, to keep a watch upon the garrisons, and prevent all entrance or exit until the king should arrive with the main army and the battering artillery. The queen, to be near at hand in case of need, moved her quarters to the city of Jaen, where she was received with martial honors by the belligerent bishop, who had buckled on his cuirass and girded on his sword, to fight in the cause of his diocese.

In the meantime, the marques of Cadiz arrived in the valley, and completely shut up the Moors within their walls. The castles were under the command of Mahomet Lentin Ben Usef, an Abencerrage, and one of the bravest cavaliers of Granada. In his garrisons were many troops of the fierce African tribe of the Gomeres. Mahomet Lentin, confident in the strength of his fortresses, smiled as he looked down from his battlements upon the Christian cavalry, perplexed in the rough and narrow valley. He sent forth skirmishing parties to harass them, and there were many sharp combats between small parties and single knights; but the Moors were driven back to their castles, and all attempts to send intelligence of their situation to Granada were frustrated by the vigilance of the marques of Cadiz.

At length the legions of the royal army came pouring, with vaunting trumpet and fluttering banner, along the defiles of the mountains. They halted before the castles, but the king could not find room in the narrow and rugged valley to form his camp; he had to divide it into three parts, which were posted on different heights; and his tents whitened the sides of the neighboring hills. When the encampment was formed, the army remained gazing idly at the castles. The artillery was upwards of four leagues in the rear, and without artillery all attack would be in vain.

The alcayde Mahomet Lentin knew the nature of the road by which the artillery had to be brought. It was merely a narrow and rugged path, at times scaling almost perpendicular crags and precipices, up which it was utterly impossible for wheel carriages to pass; neither was it in the power of man or beast to draw up the lombards, and other ponderous ordnance. He felt assured, therefore, that they never could be brought to the camp; and, without their aid, what could the Christians effect against his rock-built castles? He scoffed at them, therefore, as he saw their tents by day and their fires by night covering the surrounding heights. "Let them linger here a little while longer," said he, "and the autumnal torrents will wash them from the mountains."

While the alcayde was thus closely mewed up within his walls, and the Christians remained inactive in their camp, he noticed, one calm autumnal day, the sound of implements of labor echoing among the mountains, and now and then the crash of a falling tree, or a thundering report, as if some rock had been heaved from its bed and hurled into the valley. The alcayde was on the battlements of his castle, surrounded by his knights. "Methinks," said he, "these Christians are making war upon the rocks and trees of the mountains, since they find our castles unassailable."

The sounds did not cease even during the night: every now and then, the Moorish sentinel, as he paced the battlements, heard some crash echoing among the heights. The return of day explained the mystery. Scarcely did the sun shine against the summits of the mountains, than shouts burst from the cliffs opposite to the castles, and were answered from the camp, with joyful sound of kettle-drums and trumpets.

The astonished Moors lifted up their eyes, and beheld, as it were, a torrent of war breaking out of a narrow defile. There was a multitude of men, with pickaxes, spades, and bars of iron, clearing away every obstacle; while behind them slowly moved along great teams of oxen, dragging heavy ordnance, and all the munitions of battering artillery.

"What cannot women and priests effect, when they unite in council?" exclaims again the worthy Antonio Agapida. The queen had held another consultation with the grand cardinal and the belligerent bishop of Jaen. It was clear that the heavy ordnance could never be conveyed to the camp by the regular road of the country; and without battering artillery, nothing could be effected. It was suggested, however, by the zealous bishop, that another road might be opened through a more practicable part of the mountains. It would be an undertaking extravagant and chimerical, with ordinary means; and, therefore, unlooked for by the enemy: but what could not kings effect, who had treasures and armies at command?

The project struck the enterprising spirit of the queen. Six thousand men, with pickaxes, crowbars, and every other necessary implement, were set to work day and night, to break a road through the very centre of the mountains. No time was to be lost, for it was rumored that El Zagal was about to march with a mighty host to the relief of the castles. The bustling bishop of Jaen acted as pioneer, to mark the route and superintend the laborers; and the grand cardinal took care that the work should never languish through lack of means.*

"When kings' treasures," says Fray Antonio Agapida, "are dispensed by priestly hands, there is no stint, as the glorious annals of Spain bear witness. Under the guidance of these ghostly men, it seemed as if miracles were effected. Almost an entire mountain was leveled, valleys were filled up, trees hewn down, rocks broken and overturned; in short, all the obstacles which nature had heaped around, entirely and promptly vanished. In little more than twelve days, this gigantic work was effected, and the ordnance dragged to the camp, to the great triumph of the Christians and confusion of the Moors."†

* Zurita, *Anales de Aragon*, lib. 20, c. 64.   Pulgar, part 3, cap. 51.
† *Idem.*

No sooner was the heavy artillery arrived, than it was mounted, in all haste, upon the neighboring heights: Francisco Ramirez de Madrid, the first engineer in Spain, superintended the batteries and soon opened a destructive fire upon the castles.

When the alcayde, Mahomet Lentin, found his towers tumbling about him, and his bravest men dashed from the walls, without the power of inflicting a wound upon the foe, his haughty spirit was greatly exasperated. "Of what avail," said he, bitterly, "is all the prowess of knighthood against these cowardly engines that murder from afar?"

For a whole day, a tremendous fire kept thundering upon the castle of Albahar. The lombards discharged large stones, which demolished two of the towers, and all the battlements which guarded the portal. If any Moors attempted to defend the walls or repair the breaches, they were shot down by ribadoquines, and other small pieces of artillery. The Christian soldiery issued from the camp, under cover of this fire; and, approaching the castles, discharged flights of arrows and stones through the openings made by the ordnance.

At length, to bring the siege to a conclusion, Francisco Ramirez elevated some of the heaviest artillery on a mount that rose in form of a cone or pyramid, on the side of the river near to Albahar, and commanded both castles. This was an operation of great skill and excessive labor, but it was repaid by complete success; for the

Moors did not dare to wait until this terrible battery should discharge its fury. Satisfied that all further resistance was vain, the valiant alcayde made signal for a parley. The articles of capitulation were soon arranged. The alcayde and his garrisons were permitted to return in safety to the city of Granada, and the castles were delivered into the possession of King Ferdinand, on the day of the festival of St. Matthew, in the month of September. They were immediately repaired, strongly garrisoned, and delivered in charge of the city of Jaen.

The effects of this triumph were immediately apparent. Quiet and security once more settled upon the bishopric. The husbandmen tilled their fields in peace, the herds and flocks fattened unmolested in the pastures, and the vineyards yielded corpulent skinsful of rosy wine. The good bishop enjoyed, in the gratitude of his people, the approbation of his conscience, the increase of his revenues, and the abundance of his table, a reward for all his toils and perils. "This glorious victory," exclaims Fray Antonio Agapida, "achieved by such extraordinary management and infinite labor, is a shining example of what a bishop can effect, for the promotion of the faith and the good of his diocese."

# CHAPTER XXXIV.

ENTERPRISE OF THE KNIGHTS OF CALATRAVA AGAINST ZALEA.

HILE these events were taking place on the northern frontier of the kingdom of Granada, the important fortress of Alhama was neglected, and its commander, Don Gutiere de Padilla, clavero of Calatrava, reduced to great perplexity. The remnant of the foraging party, which had been surprised and massacred by El Zagal when on his way to Granada to receive the crown, had returned in confusion and dismay to the fortress. They could only speak of their own disgrace, being obliged to abandon their cavalgada and fly, pursued by a superior force: of the flower of their party, the gallant knights of Calatrava, who had remained behind in the valley, they knew nothing. A few days cleared up the mystery of their fate: tidings were brought that their bloody heads had been borne in triumph into Granada. The surviving knights of Calatrava, who formed a part of the garrison, burned to revenge the death of their comrades, and to wipe out the stigma of this defeat; but the clavero had been rendered cautious by disaster—he resisted all their entreaties for a foray.

His garrison was weakened by the loss of so many of its bravest men; the vega was patrolled by numerous and powerful squadrons, sent forth by El Zagal; above all, the movements of the garrison were watched by the warriors of Zalea, a strong town, only two leagues distant, on the road towards Loxa. This place was a continual check upon Alhama, when in its most powerful state, placing ambuscades to entrap the Christian cavaliers in the course of their sallies. Frequent and bloody skirmishes had taken place, in consequence; and the troops of Alhama, when returning from their forays, had often to fight their way back through the squadrons of Zalea. Thus surrounded by dangers, Don Gutiere de Padilla restrained the eagerness of his troops for a sally, knowing that any additional disaster might be followed by the loss of Alhama.

In the meanwhile provisions began to grow scarce; they were unable to forage the country as usual for supplies, and depended for relief upon the Castilian sovereigns. The defeat of the count de Cabra filled the measure of their perplexities, as it interrupted the intended reinforcements and supplies. To such extremity were they reduced, that they were compelled to kill some of their horses for provisions.

The worthy clavero, Don Gutiere de Padilla, was pondering one day on this gloomy state of affairs, when a Moor was brought before him who had surrendered himself at the gate of Alhama, and claimed an audience.

Don Gutiere was accustomed to visits of the kind from renegado Moors, who roamed the country as spies and adalides; but the countenance of this man was quite unknown to him. He had a box strapped to his shoulders, containing divers articles of traffic, and appeared to be one of those itinerant traders, who often resorted to Alhama and the other garrison towns, under pretext of vending trivial merchandise, such as amulets, perfumes, and trinkets, but who often produced rich shawls, golden chains and necklaces, and valuable gems and jewels.

The Moor requested a private conference with the clavero: "I have a precious jewel," said he, "to dispose of."

"I want no jewels," replied Don Gutiere.

"For the sake of Him who died on the cross, the great prophet of your faith," said the Moor, solemnly, "refuse not my request; the jewel I speak of you alone can purchase, but I can only treat about it in secret."

Don Gutiere perceived there was something hidden under these mystic and figurative terms, in which the Moors were often accustomed to talk. He motioned his attendants to retire. When they were alone, the Moor looked cautiously around the apartment, and then, approaching close to the knight, demanded in a low voice, "What will you give me, if I deliver the fortress of Zalea into your hands?"

Don Gutiere looked with surprise at the humble individual that made such a suggestion.

"What means have you," said he, "of effecting such a proposition?"

"I have a brother in the garrison of Zalea," replied the Moor, "who, for a proper compensation, would admit a body of troops into the citadel."

Don Gutiere turned a scrutinizing eye upon the Moor. "What right have I to believe," said he, "that thou wilt be truer to me, than to those of thy blood and thy religion?"

"I renounce all ties to them, either of blood or religion," replied the Moor; "my mother was a Christian captive; her country shall henceforth be my country, and her faith, my faith."*

The doubts of Don Gutiere were not dispelled by this profession of mongrel Christianity. "Granting the sincerity of thy conversion," said he, "art thou under no obligations of gratitude or duty to the alcayde of the fortress thou wouldst betray?"

The eyes of the Moor flashed fire at the words; he gnashed his teeth with fury. "The alcayde," cried he, "is a dog! He has deprived my brother of his just share of booty; he has robbed me of my merchandise, treated me worse than a Jew when I murmured at his injustice, and ordered me to be thrust forth ignominiously from his walls. May the curse of God fall upon my head, if I rest content until I have full revenge!"

* *Cura de los Palacios.*

"Enough," said Don Gutiere: "I trust more to thy revenge than thy religion."

The good clavero called a council of his officers. The knights of Calatrava were unanimous for the enterprise—zealous to appease the manes of their slaughtered comrades. Don Gutiere reminded them of the state of the garrison, enfeebled by their late loss, and scarcely sufficient for the defense of the walls. The cavaliers replied, that there was no achievement without risk, and that there would have been no great actions recorded in history, had there not been daring spirits ready to peril life to gain renown.

Don Gutiere yielded to the wishes of his knights, for to have resisted any further might have drawn on him the imputation of timidity; he ascertained by trusty spies that everything in Zalea remained in the usual state, and he made all the requisite arrangements for the attack.

When the appointed night arrived, all the cavaliers were anxious to engage in the enterprise; but the individuals were decided by lot. They set out, under the guidance of the Moor; and when they had arrived in the vicinity of Zalea, they bound his hands behind his back, and their leader pledged his knightly word to strike him dead, on the first sign of treachery. He then bade him to lead the way.

It was near midnight when they reached the walls of the fortress. They passed silently along until they found themselves below the citadel. Here their guide made a low and preconcerted signal : it was answered from above, and a cord let down from the wall. The knights attached to it a ladder, which was drawn up and fastened. Gutiere Muñoz was the first that mounted, followed by Pedro de Alvarado, both brave and hardy soldiers. A handful succeeded; they were attacked by a party of guards, but held them at bay until more of their comrades ascended; with their assistance they gained possession of a tower and part of the wall. The garrison, by this time, was aroused; but before they could reach the scene of action, most of the cavaliers were within the battlements. A bloody contest raged for about an hour —several of the Christians were slain, but many of the Moors; at length the citadel was carried, and the town submitted without resistance.

Thus did the gallant knights of Calatrava gain the strong town of Zalea with scarcely any loss, and atone for the inglorious defeat of their companions by El Zagal. They found the magazines of the place well stored with provisions, and were enabled to carry a seasonable supply to their own famishing garrison.

The tidings of this event reached the sovereigns, just after the surrender of Cambil and Albahar. They were greatly rejoiced at this additional success of their arms, and immediately sent strong reinforcements and ample supplies for both Alhama and Zalea. They then dismissed the army for the winter. Ferdinand and Isabella retired to Alcala de Henares, where the queen, on the 16th of December, 1485, gave birth to the princess Catharine, afterwards wife of Henry VIII., of England. Thus prosperously terminated the checkered campaign of this important year.

18

# CHAPTER XXXV.

ULEY ABDALLAH EL ZAGAL had been received with great acclamations at Granada, on his return from defeating the count de Cabra. He had endeavored to turn his victory to the greatest advantage with his subjects; giving tilts and tournaments, and other public festivities, in which the Moors delighted. The loss of the castles of Cambil and Albahar, and of the fortress of Zalea, however, checked this sudden tide of popularity; and some of the fickle populace began to doubt whether they had not been rather precipitate in deposing his brother, Muley Abul Hassan.

That superannuated monarch remained in his faithful town of Almuñecar, on the border of the Mediterranean, surrounded by a few adherents, together with his wife Zoraya and his children; and he had all his treasures safe in his possession. The fiery heart of the old king was almost burnt out, and all his powers of doing either harm or good seemed at an end.

While in this passive and helpless state, his brother El Zagal manifested a sudden anxiety for his health. He

274

had him removed, with all tenderness and care, to Salobreña, another fortress on the Mediterranean coast, famous for its pure and salubrious air; and the alcayde, who was a devoted adherent to El Zagal, was charged to have especial care that nothing was wanting to the comfort and solace of his brother.

Salobreña was a small town, situated on a lofty and rocky hill, in the midst of a beautiful and fertile vega, shut up on three sides by mountains, and opening on the fourth to the Mediterranean. It was protected by strong walls and a powerful castle, and, being deemed impregnable, was often used by the Moorish kings as a place of deposit for their treasures. They were accustomed also to assign it as a residence for such of their sons and brothers as might endanger the security of their reign. Here the princes lived, in luxurious repose : they had delicious gardens, perfumed baths, a harem of beauties, at their command—nothing was denied them but the liberty to depart; that alone was wanting to render this abode an earthly paradise.

Such was the delightful place appointed by El Zagal for the residence of his brother; but notwithstanding its wonderful salubrity, the old monarch had not been removed thither many days before he expired. There was nothing extraordinary in his death : life with him had long been glimmering in the socket, and for some time past he might rather have been numbered with the dead than with the living. The public, however, are fond of seeing things in a sinister and mysterious point of view, and there were many dark surmises as to the cause of this event. El Zagal acted in a manner to heighten these suspicions: he caused the treasures of his deceased brother to be packed on mules and brought to Granada, where he took possession of them, to the exclusion of the children of Abul Hassan. The sultana Zoraya and her two sons were lodged in the Alhambra, in the tower of Comares. This was a residence in a palace—but it had proved a royal prison to the sultana Ayxa la Horra, and her youthful son Boabdil. There the unhappy Zoraya had time to meditate upon the disappointment of all those ambitious schemes for herself and children, for which she had stained her conscience with so many crimes.

The corpse of old Muley was also brought to Granada, not in state becoming the remains of a once powerful sovereign, but transported on a mule, like the corpse of the poorest peasant. It received no honor or ceremonial from El Zagal, and appears to have been interred obscurely, to prevent any popular sensation, and it is recorded by an ancient and faithful chronicler of the time, that the body of the old monarch was deposited by two Christian captives in his osario or charnel-house.* Such was the end of the turbulent Muley Abul Hassan, who, after passing his life in constant contests for em-

---

* *Cura de los Palacios*, c. 77.

pire, could scarce gain quiet admission into the corner of
a sepulchre.

No sooner were the populace well assured that old
Muley Abul Hassan was dead, and beyond recovery, than
they all began to extol his memory, and deplore his loss.
They admitted that he had been fierce and cruel, but
then he had been brave ; he had, to be sure, pulled this
war upon their heads, but he had likewise been crushed
by it. In a word, *he was dead ;* and his death atoned for
every fault ; for a king, recently dead, is generally either
a hero or a saint.

In proportion as they ceased to hate old Muley, they
began to hate his brother. The circumstances of the old
king's death, the eagerness to appropriate his treasures,
the scandalous neglect of his corpse, and the imprisonment of his sultana and children, all filled the public
mind with gloomy suspicions ; and the epithet of Fratri-
cide ! was sometimes substituted for that of El Zagal, in
the low murmurings of the people.

As the public must always have some object to like as
well as to hate, there began once more to be an inquiry
after their fugitive king, Boabdil el Chico. That unfortunate monarch was still at Cordova, existing on the cool
courtesy and meagre friendship of Ferdinand ; which had
waned exceedingly, ever since Boabdil had ceased to
have any influence in his late dominions. The reviving
interest expressed in his fate by the Moorish public, and
certain secret overtures made to him, once more aroused

the sympathy of Ferdinand: he advised Boabdil again to set up his standard within the frontiers of Granada, and furnished him with money and means for the purpose. Boabdil advanced but a little way into his late territories; he took up his post at Velez el Blanco, a strong town on the confines of Murcia; there he established the shadow of a court, and stood, as it were, with one foot over the border, and ready to draw that back upon the least alarm. His presence in the kingdom, however, and his assumption of royal state, gave life to his faction in Granada. The inhabitants of the Albaycin, the poorest but most warlike part of the populace, were generally in his favor: the more rich, courtly, and aristocratical inhabitants of the quarter of the Alhambra, rallied round what appeared to be the most stable authority, and supported the throne of El Zagal. So it is, in the admirable order of sublunary affairs: everything seeks its kind; the rich befriend the rich, the powerful stand by the powerful, the poor enjoy the patronage of the poor—and thus a universal harmony prevails!

# CHAPTER XXXVI.

REAT and glorious was the style with which the Catholic sovereigns opened another year's campaign of this eventful war. It was like commencing another act of a stately and heroic drama, where the curtain rises to the inspiring sound of martial melody and the whole stage glitters with the array of warriors and the pomp of arms. The ancient city of Cordova was the place appointed by the sovereigns for the assemblage of the troops; and early in the spring of 1486, the fair valley of the Guadalquivir resounded with the shrill blast of trumpet, and the impatient neighing of the war-horse. In this splendid era of Spanish chivalry, there was a rivalship among the nobles who most should distinguish himself by the splendor of his appearance, and the number and equipments of his feudal followers. Every day beheld some cavalier of note, the representative of some proud and powerful house, entering the gates of Cordova with sound of trumpet, and displaying his banner and device, renowned in many a contest. He would appear in sumptuous array, surrounded

279

by pages and lackeys no less gorgeously attired, and followed by a host of vassals and retainers, horse and foot, all admirably equipped in burnished armor.

Such was the state of Don Inigo Lopez de Mendoza, duke of Infantado; who may be cited as a picture of a warlike noble of those times. He brought with him five hundred men-at-arms of his household, armed and mounted *à la gineta* and *à la guisa*. The cavaliers who attended him were magnificently armed and dressed. The housings of fifty of his horses were of rich cloth, embroidered with gold; and others were of brocade. The sumpter mules had housings of the same, with halters of silk; while the bridles, head-pieces, and all the harnessing, glittered with silver.

The camp equipage of these noble and luxurious warriors was equally magnificent. Their tents were gay pavilions, of various colors, fitted up with silken hangings and decorated with fluttering pennons. They had vessels of gold and silver for the service of their tables, as if they were about to engage in a course of stately feasts and courtly revels, instead of the stern encounters of rugged and mountainous warfare. Sometimes they passed through the streets of Cordova at night, in splendid cavalcade, with great numbers of lighted torches, the rays of which, falling upon polished armor and nodding plumes, and silken scarfs, and trappings of golden embroidery, filled all beholders with admiration.*

* Pulgar, part 3, cap. 41, 56.

But it was not the chivalry of Spain, alone, which thronged the streets of Cordova. The fame of this war had spread throughout Christendom : it was considered a kind of crusade ; and Catholic knights from all parts hastened to signalize themselves in so holy a cause. There were several valiant chevaliers from France, among whom the most distinguished was Gaston du Leon, seneschal of Toulouse. With him came a gallant train, well armed and mounted, and decorated with rich sur-coats and panaches of feathers. These cavaliers, it is said, eclipsed all others in the light festivities of the court: they were devoted to the fair, but not after the solemn and passionate manner of the Spanish lovers ; they were gay, gallant, and joyous in their amours, and captivated by the vivacity of their attacks. They were at first held in light estimation by the grave and stately Spanish knights, until they made themselves to be respected by their wonderful prowess in the field.

The most conspicuous of the volunteers, however, who appeared in Cordova on this occasion, was an English knight of royal connection. This was the lord Scales, earl of Rivers, brother to the queen of England, wife of Henry VII. He had distinguished himself in the preceding year, at the battle of Bosworth field, where Henry Tudor, then earl of Richmond, overcame Richard III. That decisive battle having left the country at peace, the earl of Rivers, having conceived a passion for warlike scenes, repaired to the Castilian court, to keep his arms in exercise in a campaign against the Moors. He brought with him a hundred archers, all dexterous with the long-bow and the cloth-yard arrow; also two hundred yeomen, armed cap-a-pie, who fought with pike and battle-axe—men robust of frame, and of prodigious strength. The worthy padre Fray Antonio Agapida describes this stranger knight and his followers with his accustomed accuracy and minuteness.

"This cavalier," he observes, "was from the far island of England, and brought with him a train of his vassals; men who had been hardened in certain civil wars which raged in their country. They were a comely race of men, but too fair and fresh for warriors, not having the sunburnt, warlike hue of our old Castilian soldiery. They were huge feeders also, and deep carousers, and could not accommodate themselves to the sober diet of our troops, but must fain eat and drink after the manner of their own country. They were often noisy and unruly, also, in their wassail; and their quarter of the camp was prone to be a scene of loud revel and sudden brawl. They were, withal, of great pride, yet it was not like our inflammable Spanish pride: they stood not much upon the *pundonor*, the high punctilio, and rarely drew the stiletto in their disputes; but their pride was silent and contumelious. Though from a remote and somewhat barbarous island, they believed themselves the most perfect men upon earth, and magnified their chieftain, the lord Scales, beyond the greatest of their grandees. With all this, it must be said of them that they were marvelous good men in the field, dexterous archers, and powerful with the battle-axe. In their great pride and self-will, they always sought to press in the advance and take the post of danger, trying to outvie our Spanish chivalry. They did not rush on fiercely to the fight, nor make a brilliant onset like the Moorish and Spanish troops, but they went into the fight deliberately, and persisted obstinately, and were slow to find out when they were beaten. Withal they were much esteemed, yet little liked by our soldiery, who considered them stanch companions in the field, yet coveted but little fellowship with them in the camp.

"Their commander, the lord Scales, was an accomplished cavalier, of gracious and noble presence and fair speech; it was a marvel to see so much courtesy in a knight brought up so far from our Castilian court. He was much honored by the king and queen, and found great favor with the fair dames about the court, who indeed are rather prone to be pleased with foreign cavaliers. He went always in costly state, attended by pages and esquires, and accompanied by noble young cavaliers of his country, who had enrolled themselves under his banner, to learn the gentle exercise of arms. In all pageants and festivals, the eyes of the populace were attracted by the singular bearing and rich array of the English earl and his train, who prided themselves in always appearing in the garb and manner of their country

—and were indeed something very magnificent, delectable, and strange to behold."

The worthy chronicler is no less elaborate in his description of the masters of Santiago, Calatrava, and Alcantara, and their valiant knights, armed at all points, and decorated with the badges of their orders. These, he affirms, were the flower of Christian chivalry; being constantly in service, they became more steadfast and accomplished in discipline than the irregular and temporary levies of the feudal nobles. Calm, solemn, and stately, they sat like towers upon their powerful chargers. On parades, they manifested none of the show and ostentation of the other troops: neither, in battle, did they endeavor to signalize themselves by any fiery vivacity, or desperate and vainglorious exploit—everything, with them, was measured and sedate; yet it was observed, that none were more warlike in their appearance in the camp, or more terrible for their achievements in the field.

The gorgeous magnificence of the Spanish nobles found but little favor in the eyes of the sovereigns. They saw that it caused a competition in expense, ruinous to cavaliers of moderate fortune: and they feared that a softness and effeminacy might thus be introduced, incompatible with the stern nature of the war. They signified their disapprobation to several of the principal noblemen, and recommended a more sober and soldierlike display while in actual service.

"These are rare troops for a tourney, my lord," said Ferdinand to the duke of Infantado, as he beheld his retainers glittering in gold and embroidery; "but gold, though gorgeous, is soft and yielding: iron is the metal for the field."

"Sire," replied the duke, "if my men parade in gold, your majesty will find they fight with steel." The king smiled, but shook his head, and the duke treasured up his speech in his heart.

It remains now to reveal the immediate object of this mighty and chivalrous preparation, which had, in fact, the gratification of a royal pique at bottom. The severe lesson which Ferdinand had received from the veteran Ali Atar, before the walls of Loxa, though it had been of great service in rendering him wary in his attacks upon fortified places, yet rankled sorely in his mind; and he had ever since held Loxa in peculiar odium. It was, in truth, one of the most belligerent and troublesome cities on the borders, incessantly harassing Andalusia by its incursions. It also intervened between the Christian territories and Alhama, and other important places gained in the kingdom of Granada. For all these reasons King Ferdinand had determined to make another grand attempt upon this warrior city; and for this purpose, had summoned to the field his most powerful chivalry.

It was in the month of May, that the king sallied from Cordova, at the head of his army. He had twelve thou-

sand cavalry and forty thousand foot-soldiers, armed
with cross-bows, lances, and arquebuses. There were
six thousand pioneers, with hatchets, pickaxes, and crowbars, for leveling roads. He took with him, also, a great
train of lombards and other heavy artillery, with a body
of Germans skilled in the service of ordnance, and the
art of battering walls.

It was a glorious spectacle (says Fray Antonio Agapida) to behold this pompous pageant issuing forth from
Cordova, the pennons and devices of the proudest houses
of Spain, with those of gallant stranger knights, fluttering above a sea of crests and plumes; to see it slowly
moving, with flash of helm, and cuirass, and buckler,
across the ancient bridge, and reflected in the waters of
the Guadalquivir, while the neigh of steed and blast of
trumpet vibrated in the air, and resounded to the distant
mountains. "But above all," concludes the good father,
with his accustomed zeal, "it was triumphant to behold
the standard of the faith everywhere displayed, and to
reflect that this was no worldly-minded army, intent upon
some temporal scheme of ambition or revenge; but a
Christian host, bound on a crusade to extirpate the vile
seed of Mahomet from the land, and to extend the pure
dominion of the church."

# CHAPTER XXXVII.

HILE perfect unity of object and harmony of operation gave power to the Christian arms, the devoted kingdom of Granada continued a prey to internal feuds. The transient popularity of El Zagal had declined ever since the death of his brother, and the party of Boabdil was daily gaining strength ; the Albaycin and the Alhambra were again arrayed against each other in deadly strife, and the streets of unhappy Granada were daily dyed in the blood of her children. In the midst of these dissensions, tidings arrived of the formidable army assembling at Cordova. The rival factions paused in their infatuated brawls, and were roused to a temporary sense of the common danger. They forthwith resorted to their old expedient of new-modeling their government, or rather of making and unmaking kings. The elevation of El Zagal to the throne had not produced the desired effect—what then was to be done ? Recall Boabdil el Chico, and acknowledge him again as sovereign? While they were in a popular tumult of de-

287

liberation, Hamet Aben Zarrax, surnamed El Santo, rose among them. This was the same wild, melancholy man, who had predicted the woes of Granada. He issued from one of the caverns of the adjacent height which overhangs the Darro, and has since been called the Holy Mountain. His appearance was more haggard than ever; for the unheeded spirit of prophecy seemed to have turned inwardly, and preyed upon his vitals. "Beware, O Moslems," exclaimed he, "of men who are eager to govern, yet are unable to protect. Why slaughter each other for El Chico or El Zagal? Let your kings renounce their contests, unite for the salvation of Granada, or let them be deposed."

Hamet Aben Zarrax had long been revered as a saint— he was now considered an oracle. The old men and the nobles immediately consulted together, how the two rival kings might be brought to accord. They had tried most expedients; it was now determined to divide the kingdom between them; giving Granada, Malaga, Velez Malaga, Almera, Almuñecar, and their dependencies to El Zagal—and the residue to Boabdil el Chico. Among the cities granted to the latter, Loxa was particularly specified, with a condition that he should immediately take command of it in person; for the council thought the favor he enjoyed with the Castilian monarchs might avert the threatened attack.

El Zagal readily agreed to this arrangement; he had been hastily elevated to the throne by an ebullition of the people, and might be as hastily cast down again. It secured him one half of a kingdom to which he had no hereditary right, and he trusted to force or fraud to gain the other half hereafter. The wily old monarch even sent a deputation to his nephew, making a merit of offering him cheerfully the half which he had thus been compelled to relinquish, and inviting him to enter into an amicable coalition for the good of the country.

The heart of Boabdil shrank from all connection with a man who had sought his life, and whom he regarded as the murderer of his kindred. He accepted one half of the kingdom as an offer from the nation, not to be rejected by a prince who scarcely held possession of the ground he stood on. He asserted, nevertheless, his absolute right to the whole, and only submitted to the partition out of anxiety for the present good of his people. He assembled his handful of adherents, and prepared to hasten to Loxa. As he mounted his horse to depart, Hamet Aben Zarrax stood suddenly before him. "Be true to thy country and thy faith," cried he : "hold no further communication with these Christian dogs. Trust not the hollow-hearted friendship of the Castilian king; he is mining the earth beneath thy feet. Choose one of two things ; be a sovereign or a slave—thou canst not be both."

Boabdil ruminated on these words ; he made many wise resolutions, but he was prone always to act from the impulse of the moment, and was unfortunately given to

19

temporize in his policy. He wrote to Ferdinand, informing him that Loxa and certain other cities had returned
to their allegiance, and that he held them as vassal to
the Castilian crown, according to their convention. He
conjured him, therefore, to refrain from any meditated
attack, offering free passage to the Spanish army to
Malaga, or any other place under the dominion of his
uncle.*

Ferdinand turned a deaf ear to the entreaty, and to all
professions of friendship and vassalage. Boabdil was
nothing to him, but as an instrument for stirring up the
flames of civil war. He now insisted that he had entered
into a hostile league with his uncle, and had consequently forfeited all claims to his indulgence; and he
prosecuted, with the greater earnestness, his campaign
against the city of Loxa.

"Thus," observes the worthy Fray Antonio Agapida,
"thus did this most sagacious sovereign act upon the
text in the eleventh chapter of the Evangelist St. Luke,
that 'a kingdom divided against itself cannot stand.' He
had induced these infidels to waste and destroy themselves by internal dissensions, and finally cast forth the
survivor; while the Moorish monarchs, by their ruinous
contests, made good the old Castilian proverb in cases of
civil war, 'El vencido vencido, y el vencidor perdido,'
(the conquered conquered, and the conqueror undone)." †

* Zurita, lib. 20, c. 68.　　　　　† Garibay, lib. 40, c. 38.

# CHAPTER XXXVIII.

HE royal army, on its march against Loxa, lay
encamped, one pleasant evening in May, in a
meadow on the banks of the river Yeguas,
around the foot of a lofty cliff called the Rock of the
Lovers. The quarters of each nobleman formed, as it
were, a separate little encampment; his stately pavilion,
surmounted by his fluttering pennon, rising above the
surrounding tents of his vassals and retainers. A little
apart from the others, as it were in proud reserve, was
the encampment of the English earl. It was sumptuous in its furniture, and complete in all its munitions.
Archers, and soldiers armed with battle-axes, kept
guard around it; while above, the standard of England
rolled out its ample folds, and flapped in the evening
breeze.

The mingled sounds of various tongues and nations
were heard from the soldiery, as they watered their
horses in the stream, or busied themselves round the
fires which began to glow, here and there, in the twi-

light : the gay chanson of the Frenchman, singing of his amours on the pleasant banks of the Loire, or the sunny regions of the Garonne ; the broad guttural tones of the German, chanting some doughty *krieger lied*, or extolling the vintage of the Rhine ; the wild romance of the Spaniard, reciting the achievements of the Cid, and many a famous passage of the Moorish wars ; and the long and melancholy ditty of the Englishman, treating of some feudal hero or redoubtable outlaw of his distant island.

On a rising ground, commanding a view of the whole encampment, stood the ample and magnificent pavilion of the king, with the banner of Castile and Aragon, and the holy standard of the cross, erected before it.  In this tent were assembled the principal commanders of the army, having been summoned by Ferdinand to a council of war, on receiving tidings that Boabdil had thrown himself into Loxa with a considerable reinforcement. After some conclusion, it was determined to invest Loxa on both sides : one part of the army should seize upon the dangerous but commanding height of Santo Albohacen, in front of the city ; while the remainder, making a circuit, should encamp on the opposite side.

No sooner was this resolved upon, than the marques of Cadiz stood forth and claimed the post of danger in behalf of himself and those cavaliers, his companions in arms, who had been compelled to relinquish it by the general retreat of the army on the former siege.  The enemy had exulted over them, as if driven from it in disgrace. To regain that perilous height, to pitch their tents upon it, and to avenge the blood of their valiant compeer, the master of Calatrava, who had fallen upon it, was due to their fame; the marques demanded, therefore, that they might lead the advance and secure that height, engaging to hold the enemy employed until the main army should take its position on the opposite side of the city.

King Ferdinand readily granted his permission; upon which the count de Cabra entreated to be admitted to a share of the enterprise. He had always been accustomed to serve in the advance; and now that Boabdil was in the field, and a king was to be taken, he could not content himself with remaining in the rear. Ferdinand yielded his consent, for he was disposed to give the good count every opportunity to retrieve his late disaster.

The English earl, when he heard there was an enterprise of danger in question, was hot to be admitted to the party; but the king restrained his ardor. "These cavaliers," said he, "conceive that they have an account to settle with their pride; let them have the enterprise to themselves, my lord; if you follow these Moorish wars long, you will find no lack of perilous service."

The marques of Cadiz, and his companions in arms, struck their tents before daybreak; they were five thousand horse and twelve thousand foot, and marched rapidly along the defiles of the mountains; the cavaliers being anxious to strike the blow, and get possession of

the height of Albohacen, before the king with the main
army should arrive to their assistance.

The city of Loxa stands on a high hill, between two
mountains, on the banks of the Xenil. To attain the
height of Albohacen, the troops had to pass over a tract
of rugged and broken country, and a deep valley, intersected by those canals and watercourses with which the
Moors irrigated their lands : they were extremely embarrassed in this part of their march, and in imminent risk
of being cut up in detail before they could reach the
height.

The count de Cabra, with his usual eagerness, endeavored to push across this valley, in defiance of every
obstacle; he, in consequence, soon became entangled with
his cavalry among the canals; but his impatience would
not permit him to retrace his steps, and choose a more
practicable but circuitous route. Others slowly crossed
another part of the valley, by the aid of pontoons ; while
the marques of Cadiz, Don Alonzo de Aguilar, and the
count de Ureña, being more experienced in the ground
from their former campaign, made a circuit round the
bottom of the height, and, winding up it, began to display their squadrons and elevate their banners on the
redoubtable post, which, in their former siege, they had
been compelled so reluctantly to abandon.

# CHAPTER XXXIX.

THE advance of the Christian army upon Loxa, threw the wavering Boabdil el Chico into one of his usual dilemmas; and he was greatly perplexed between his oath of allegiance to the Spanish sovereigns, and his sense of duty to his subjects. His doubts were determined by the sight of the enemy glittering upon the height of Albohacen, and by the clamors of the people to be led forth to battle. "Allah!" exclaimed he, "thou knowest my heart: thou knowest I have been true in my faith to this Christian monarch. I have offered to hold Loxa as his vassal, but he has preferred to approach it as an enemy—on his head be the infraction of our treaty."

Boabdil was not wanting in courage; he only needed decision. When he had once made up his mind, he acted vigorously; the misfortune was, he either did not make it up at all, or he made it up too late. He who decides tardily generally acts rashly, endeavoring to make up by

295

hurry of action for slowness of deliberation. Boabdil hastily buckled on his armor, and sallied forth, surrounded by his guards, and at the head of five hundred horse and four thousand foot, the flower of his army. Some he detached to skirmish with the Christians, who were scattered and perplexed in the valley, and to prevent their concentrating their forces; while, with his main body, he pressed forward to drive the enemy from the height of Albohacen, before they had time to collect there in any number, or to fortify themselves in that important position.

The worthy count de Cabra was yet entangled with his cavalry among the watercourses of the valley, when he heard the war-cries of the Moors, and saw their army rushing over the bridge. He recognized Boabdil himself, by his splendid armor, the magnificent caparison of his steed, and the brilliant guard which surrounded him. The royal host swept on toward the height of Albohacen: an intervening hill hid it from his sight; but loud shouts and cries, the din of drums and trumpets, and the reports of arquebuses, gave note that the battle had begun.

Here was a royal prize in the field, and the count de Cabra unable to get into the action! The good cavalier was in an agony of impatience; every attempt to force his way across the valley only plunged him into new difficulties. At length, after many eager but ineffectual efforts, he was obliged to order his troops to dismount, and slowly and carefully to lead their horses back, along slippery paths, and amid plashes of mire and water, where often there was scarce a foothold. The good count groaned in spirit, and sweat with mere impatience as he went, fearing the battle might be fought, and the prize won or lost, before he could reach the field. Having at length toilfully unraveled the mazes of the valley, and arrived at firmer ground, he ordered his troops to mount, and led them full gallop to the height. Part of the good count's wishes were satisfied, but the dearest were disappointed ; he came in season to partake of the very hottest of the fight, but the royal prize was no longer in the field.

Boabdil had led on his men with impetuous valor, or rather with hurried rashness. Heedlessly exposing himself in the front of the battle, he received two wounds in the very first encounter. His guards rallied round him, defended him with matchless valor, and bore him, bleeding, out of the action. The count de Cabra arrived just in time to see the loyal squadron crossing the bridge, and slowly conveying their disabled monarch towards the gate of the city.

The departure of Boabdil made no difference in the fury of the battle. A Moorish warrior, dark and terrible in aspect, mounted on a black charger and followed by a band of savage Gomeres, rushed forward to take the lead. It was Hamet el Zegri, the fierce alcayde of Ronda, with the remnant of his once redoubtable garrison. Animated by his example, the Moors renewed their assaults upon the height. It was bravely defended on one side by the marques of Cadiz, on another by Don Alonzo de Aguilar; and as fast as the Moors ascended, they were driven back and dashed down the declivities. The count de Ureña took his stand upon the fatal spot where his brother had fallen; his followers entered with zeal into the feelings of their commander, and heaps of the enemy sunk beneath their weapons—sacrifices to the manes of the lamented master of Calatrava.

The battle continued with incredible obstinacy. The Moors knew the importance of the height to the safety of the city; the cavaliers felt their honors staked to maintain it. Fresh supplies of troops were poured out of the city; some battled on the height, while some attacked the Christians who were still in the valley and among the orchards and gardens, to prevent their uniting their forces. The troops in the valley were gradually driven back, and the whole host of the Moors swept around the height of Albohacen. The situation of the marques de Cadiz and his companions was perilous in the extreme : they were a mere handful; and, while fighting hand to hand with the Moors who assailed the height, were galled from a distance by the cross-bows and arquebuses of a host that augmented each moment in number. At this critical juncture, King Ferdinand emerged from the mountains with the main body of the army, and advanced to an eminence commanding a full view of the field of action. By his side was the noble English cavalier, the earl of Rivers. This was the first time he had witnessed a scene of Moorish warfare. He looked with eager interest at the chance-medley fight before him, where there was the wild career of cavalry, the irregular and tumultuous rush of infantry, and where Christian and Moor were intermingled in deadly struggle. The high blood of the English knight mounted at the sight, and his soul was stirred within him, by the confused war-cries, the clangor of drums and trumpets, and the reports of arquebuses. Seeing that the king was sending a reinforcement to the field, he entreated permission to mingle in the affray, and fight according to the fashion of his country. His request being granted, he alighted from his steed: he was merely armed *en blanco*, that is to say, with morion, back-piece, and breastplate ; his sword was girded by his side, and in his hand he wielded a powerful battle-axe. He was followed by a body of his yeomen, armed in like manner, and by a band of archers with bows made of the tough English yew-tree. The earl turned to his troops, and addressed them briefly and bluntly, according to the manner of his country. "Remember, my merry men all," said he, "the eyes of strangers are upon you ; you are in a foreign land, fighting for the glory of God, and the honor of merry old England!" A loud shout was the reply. The earl waved his battle-axe over his head ; "St. George for England!" cried he ; and to the inspiring sound of this old

English war-cry, he and his followers rushed down to the battle with manly and courageous hearts.* They soon made their way into the midst of the enemy; but when engaged in the hottest of the fight, they made no shouts nor outcries. They pressed steadily forward, dealing their blows to right and left, hewing down the Moors, and cutting their way, with their battle-axes, like woodmen in a forest; while the archers, pressing into the opening they had made, plied their bows vigorously, and spread death on every side.

When the Castilian mountaineers beheld the valor of the English yeomanry, they would not be outdone in hardihood. They could not vie with them in weight or bulk, but for vigor and activity they were surpassed by none. They kept pace with them, therefore, with equal heart and rival prowess, and gave a brave support to the stout Englishmen.

The Moors were confounded by the fury of these assaults, and disheartened by the loss of Hamet el Zegri, who was carried wounded from the field. They gradually fell back upon the bridge; the Christians followed up their advantage, and drove them over it tumultuously. The Moors retreated into the suburb; and Lord Rivers and his troops entered with them pell-mell, fighting in the streets and in the houses. King Ferdinand came up to the scene of action with his royal guard, and

* *Cura de los Palacios.*

the infidels were driven within the city walls. Thus were the suburbs gained by the hardihood of the English lord, without such an event having been premeditated.*

The earl of Rivers, notwithstanding he had received a wound, still urged forward in the attack. He penetrated almost to the city gate, in defiance of a shower of missiles that slew many of his followers. A stone, hurled from the battlements, checked his impetuous career: it struck him in the face, dashed out two of his front teeth, and laid him senseless on the earth. He was removed to a short distance by his men; but, recovering his senses, refused to permit himself to be taken from the suburb.

When the contest was over, the streets presented a piteous spectacle—so many of their inhabitants had died in the defense of their thresholds, or been slaughtered without resistance. Among the victims was a poor weaver, who had been at work in his dwelling at this turbulent moment. His wife urged him to fly into the city. "Why should I fly?" said the Moor—"to be reserved for hunger and slavery? I tell you, wife, I will await the foe here; for better is it to die quickly by the steel, than to perish piecemeal in chains and dungeons." He said no more, but resumed his occupation of weaving; and, in the indiscriminate fury of the assault, was slaughtered at his loom.†

The Christians remained masters of the field, and pro-

* *Cura de los Palacios*, MS.          † Pulgar, part 3, c. 58.

ceeded to pitch three encampments for the prosecution of the siege. The king, with the great body of the army, took a position on the side of the city next to Granada: the marques of Cadiz and his brave companions once more pitched their tents upon the height of Santo Albohacen: but the English earl planted his standard sturdily within the suburbs he had taken.

# CHAPTER XL.

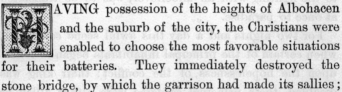AVING possession of the heights of Albohacen and the suburb of the city, the Christians were enabled to choose the most favorable situations for their batteries. They immediately destroyed the stone bridge, by which the garrison had made its sallies; and they threw two wooden bridges across the river, and others over the canals and streams, so as to establish an easy communication between the different camps.

When all was arranged, a heavy fire was opened upon the city from various points. They threw not only balls of stone and iron, but great carcasses of fire, which burst like meteors on the houses, wrapping them instantly in a blaze. The walls were shattered, and the towers toppled down, by tremendous discharges from the lombards. Through the openings thus made, they could behold the interior of the city—houses tumbling or in flames — men, women, and children, flying in terror through the streets, and slaughtered by the shower of missiles, sent through the openings from smaller artillery, and from cross-bows and arquebuses.

303

The Moors attempted to repair the breaches, but fresh discharges from the lombards buried them beneath the ruins of the walls they were mending.  In their despair, many of the inhabitants rushed forth into the narrow streets of the suburbs, and assailed the Christians with darts, scimetars, and poniards, seeking to destroy rather than defend, and heedless of death, in the confidence that to die fighting with an unbeliever, was to be translated at once to paradise.

For two nights and a day this awful scene continued; when certain of the principal inhabitants began to reflect upon the hopelessness of the conflict: their king was disabled, their principal captains were either killed or wounded, their fortifications little better than heaps of ruins.  They had urged the unfortunate Boabdil to the conflict: they now clamored for a capitulation.  A parley was procured from the Christian monarch, and the terms of surrender were soon adjusted.  They were to yield up the city immediately, with all their Christian captives, and to sally forth with as much of their property as they could take with them.  The marques of Cadiz, on whose honor and humanity they had great reliance, was to escort them to Granada, to protect them from assault or robbery: such as chose to remain in Spain were to be permitted to reside in Castile, Aragon, or Valencia.  As to Boabdil el Chico, he was to do homage as a vassal to King Ferdinand, but no charge was to be urged against him of having violated his former pledge. If he should yield up all pretensions to Granada, the title of duke of Guadix was to be assigned to him, and the territory thereto annexed, provided it should be recovered from El Zagal within six months.

The capitulation being arranged, they gave as hostages the alcayde of the city, and the principal officers, together with the sons of their late chieftain, the veteran Ali Atar. The warriors of Loxa then issued forth, humbled and dejected at having to surrender those walls which they had so long maintained with valor and renown; and the women and children filled the air with lamentations, at being exiled from their native homes.

Last came forth Boabdil, most truly called El Zogoybi, the unlucky. Accustomed, as he was, to be crowned and uncrowned, to be ransomed and treated as a matter of bargain, he had acceded of course to the capitulation. He was enfeebled by his wounds, and had an air of dejection; yet it is said, his conscience acquitted him of a breach of faith towards the Castilian sovereigns, and the personal valor he had displayed had caused a sympathy for him among many of the Christian cavaliers. He knelt to Ferdinand according to the forms of vassalage, and then departed, in melancholy mood, for Priego, a town about three leagues distant.

Ferdinand immediately ordered Loxa to be repaired, and strongly garrisoned. He was greatly elated at the capture of this place, in consequence of his former defeat before its walls. He passed great encomiums upon

20

the commanders who had distinguished themselves; and historians dwell particularly upon his visit to the tent of the English earl. His majesty consoled him for the loss of his teeth, by the consideration that he might otherwise have lost them by natural decay; whereas the lack of them would now be esteemed a beauty, rather than a defect, serving as a trophy of the glorious cause in which he had been engaged.

The earl replied, that he gave thanks to God and to the holy Virgin, for being thus honored by a visit from the most potent king in Christendom ; that he accepted with all gratitude his gracious consolation for the loss of his teeth, though he held it little to lose two teeth in the service of God, who had given him all: "A speech," says Fray Antonio Agapida, "full of most courtly wit and Christian piety ; and one only marvels that it should have been made by a native of an island so far distant from Castile."

ING FERDINAND followed up his victory at Loxa, by laying siege to the strong town of Illora. This redoubtable fortress was perched upon a high rock, in the midst of a spacious valley. It was within four leagues of the Moorish capital; and its lofty castle, keeping vigilant watch over a wide circuit of country, was termed the right eye of Granada.

The alcayde of Illora was one of the bravest of the Moorish commanders, and made every preparation to defend his fortress to the last extremity. He sent the women and children, the aged and infirm, to the metropolis. He placed barricades in the suburbs, opened doors of communication from house to house, and pierced their walls with loop-holes for the discharge of crossbows, arquebuses, and other missiles.

King Ferdinand arrived before the place, with all his forces; he stationed himself upon the hill of Encinilla, and distributed the other encampments in various situations, so as to invest the fortress. Knowing the valiant character of the alcayde, and the desperate courage of

307

the Moors, he ordered the encampments to be fortified with trenches and palisadoes, the guards to be doubled, and sentinels to be placed in all the watch-towers of the adjacent heights.

When all was ready, the duke del Infantado demanded the attack; it was his first campaign, and he was anxious to disprove the royal insinuation made against the hardihood of his embroidered chivalry. King Ferdinand granted his demand, with a becoming compliment to his spirit; he ordered the count de Cabra to make a simultaneous attack upon a different quarter. Both chiefs led forth their troops; those of the duke in fresh and brilliant armor, richly ornamented, and as yet uninjured by the service of the field; those of the count were weather-beaten veterans, whose armor was dented and hacked in many a hard-fought battle. The youthful duke blushed at the contrast. "Cavaliers," cried he, " we have been reproached with the finery of our array : let us prove that a trenchant blade may rest in a gilded sheath. Forward! to the foe! and I trust in God, that as we enter this affray knights well accoutred, so we shall leave it cavaliers well proved." His men responded by eager acclamations, and the duke led them forward to the assault. He advanced under a tremendous shower of stones, darts, balls, and arrows; but nothing could check his career; he entered the suburb sword in hand; his men fought furiously, though with great loss, for every dwelling had been turned into a fortress. After a severe conflict, they succeeded in driving the Moors into the town, about the same time that the other suburb was carried by the count de Cabra and his veterans.

The troops of the duke del Infantado came out of the contest thinned in number, and covered with blood, and dust, and wounds; they received the highest encomiums of the king, and there was never afterwards any sneer at their embroidery.

The suburbs being taken, three batteries, each furnished with eight huge lombards, were opened upon the fortress. The damage and havoc were tremendous, for the fortifications had not been constructed to withstand such engines. The towers were overthrown, the walls battered to pieces; the interior of the place was all exposed, houses were demolished, and many people slain. The Moors were terrified by the tumbling ruins, and the tremendous din. The alcayde had resolved to defend the place until the last extremity; he beheld it a heap of rubbish; there was no prospect of aid from Granada; his people had lost all spirit to fight, and were vociferous for a surrender; with a reluctant heart, he capitulated. The inhabitants were permitted to depart with all their effects, excepting their arms; and were escorted in safety by the duke del Infantado and the count de Cabra, to the bridge of Pinos, within two leagues of Granada.

King Ferdinand gave directions to repair the fortifications of Illora, and to place it in a strong state of defense. He left, as alcayde of the town and fortress, Gon-

salvo de Cordova, younger brother of Don Alonzo de
Aguilar. This gallant cavalier was captain of the royal
guards of Ferdinand and Isabella, and gave already
proofs of that prowess which afterwards rendered him
so renowned.

# CHAPTER XLII.

OF THE ARRIVAL OF QUEEN ISABELLA AT THE CAMP BEFORE MOCLIN, AND
OF THE PLEASANT SAYINGS OF THE ENGLISH EARL.

THE war of Granada, however poets may em-
broider it with the flowers of their fancy, was
certainly one of the sternest of those iron conflicts which have been celebrated under the name of holy
wars. The worthy Fray Antonio Agapida dwells with
unsated delight upon the succession of rugged mountain
enterprises, bloody battles, and merciless sackings and
ravages, which characterized it; yet we find him on
one occasion pausing in the full career of victory over
the infidels, to detail a stately pageant of the Catholic
sovereigns.

Immediately on the capture of Loxa, Ferdinand had
written to Isabella, soliciting her presence at the camp,
that he might consult with her as to the disposition of
their newly-acquired territories.

It was in the early part of June, that the queen
departed from Cordova, with the princess Isabella and
numerous ladies of her court. She had a glorious attendance of cavaliers and pages, with many guards and do-

mestics. There were forty mules for the use of the queen, the princess, and their train.

As this courtly cavalcade approached the Rock of the Lovers, on the banks of the river Yeguas, they beheld a splendid train of knights advancing to meet them. It was headed by that accomplished cavalier the marques duke de Cadiz, accompanied by the adelantado of Andalusia. He had left the camp the day after the capture of Illora, and advanced thus far to receive the queen and escort her over the borders. The queen received the marques with distinguished honor; for he was esteemed the mirror of chivalry. His actions in this war had become the theme of every tongue, and many hesitated not to compare him in prowess with the immortal Cid.*

Thus gallantly attended, the queen entered the vanquished frontier of Granada; journeying securely along the pleasant banks of the Xenel, so lately subject to the scourings of the Moors. She stopped at Loxa, where she administered aid and consolation to the wounded, distributing money among them for their support, according to their rank.

The king, after the capture of Illora, had removed his camp before the fortress of Moclin, with an intention of besieging it. Thither the queen proceeded, still escorted through the mountain roads by the marques of Cadiz. As Isabella drew near to the camp, the duke del Infan-

* *Cura de los Palacios.*

tado issued forth a league and a half to receive her, magnificently arrayed, and followed by all his chivalry in glorious attire. With him came the standard of Seville, borne by the men-at-arms of that renowned city; and the Prior of St. Juan, with his followers. They ranged themselves in order of battle, on the left of the road by which the queen was to pass.

The worthy Agapida is loyally minute in his description of the state and grandeur of the Catholic sovereigns. The queen rode a chestnut mule, seated in a magnificent saddle-chair, decorated with silver gilt. The housings of the mule were of fine crimson cloth; the borders embroidered with gold; the reins and head-piece were of satin, curiously embossed with needlework of silk, and wrought with golden letters. The queen wore a brial or regal skirt of velvet, under which were others of brocade; a scarlet mantle, ornamented in the Moresco fashion; and a black hat, embroidered round the crown and brim.

The infanta was likewise mounted on a chestnut mule, richly caparisoned: she wore a brial or skirt of black brocade, and a black mantle ornamented like that of the queen.

When the royal cavalcade passed by the chivalry of the duke del Infantado, which was drawn out in battle array, the queen made a reverence to the standard of Seville, and ordered it to pass to the right hand. When she approached the camp, the multitude ran forth to meet her, with great demonstrations of joy; for she was universally beloved by her subjects.  All the battalions sallied forth in military array, bearing the various standards and banners of the camp, which were lowered in salutation as she passed.

The king now came forth in royal state, mounted on a superb chestnut horse, and attended by many grandees of Castile.  He wore a jubon or close vest of crimson cloth, with cuisses or short skirts of yellow satin, a loose cassock of brocade, a rich Moorish scimetar, and a hat with plumes.  The grandees who attended him were arrayed with wonderful magnificence, each according to his taste and invention.

These high and mighty princes (says Antonio Agapida) regarded each other with great deference, as allied sovereigns, rather than with connubial familiarity, as mere husband and wife.  When they approached each other, therefore, before embracing, they made three profound reverences, the queen taking off her hat, and remaining in a silk net or cawl, with her face uncovered.  The king then approached and embraced her, and kissed her respectfully on the cheek.  He also embraced his daughter the princess; and, making the sign of the cross, he blessed her, and kissed her on the lips.*

The good Agapida seems scarcely to have been more struck with the appearance of the sovereigns than with that of the English earl.  He followed (says he) immedi-

* *Cura de los Palacios.*

ately after the king, with great pomp, and, in an extraordinary manner, taking precedence of all the rest. He was mounted "*a la guisa*," or with long stirrups, on a superb chestnut horse, with trappings of azure silk which reached to the ground. The housings were of mulberry, powdered with stars of gold. He was armed in proof, and wore over his armor a short French mantle of black brocade; he had a white French hat with plumes, and carried on his left arm a small round buckler, banded with gold. Five pages attended him, appareled in silk and brocade, and mounted on horses sumptuously caparisoned; he had also a train of followers, bravely attired after the fashion of his country.

He advanced in a chivalrous and courteous manner, making his reverences first to the queen and infanta, and afterwards to the king. Queen Isabella received him graciously, complimenting him on his courageous conduct at Loxa, and condoling with him on the loss of his teeth. The earl, however, made light of his disfiguring wound, saying that "our blessed Lord, who had built all that house, had opened a window there, that he might see more readily what passed within;"* whereupon the worthy Fray Antonio Agapida is more than ever astonished at the pregnant wit of this island cavalier. The earl continued some little distance by the side of the royal family, complimenting them all with courteous speeches, his horse curveting and caracoling, but being

* Pietro Martyr, *Epist.* 61.

managed with great grace and dexterity; leaving the grandees and the people at large not more filled with admiration at the strangeness and magnificence of his state than at the excellence of his horsemanship.*

To testify her sense of the gallantry and services of this noble English knight, who had come from so far to assist in their wars, the queen sent him the next day presents of twelve horses, with stately tents, fine linen, two beds with coverings of gold brocade, and many other articles of great value.

Having refreshed himself, as it were, with the description of this progress of Queen Isabella to the camp, and the glorious pomp of the Catholic sovereigns, the worthy Antonio Agapida returns with renewed relish to his pious work of discomfiting the Moors.

The description of this royal pageant, and the particulars concerning the English earl, thus given from the manuscript of Fray Antonio Agapida, agree precisely with the chronicle of Andres Bernaldes, the curate of los Palacios. The English earl makes no further figure in this war. It appears from various histories that he returned in the course of the year to England. In the following year his passion for fighting took him to the Continent, at the head of four hundred adventurers, in aid of Francis, duke of Brittany, against Louis XI. of France. He was killed in the same year [1488] in the battle of St. Alban's, between the Bretons and the French.

* *Cura de los Palacios.*

# CHAPTER XLIII.

"THE Catholic sovereigns," says Fray Antonio Agapida, "had by this time closely clipped the right wing of the Moorish vulture." In other words, most of the strong fortresses along the western frontier of Granada had fallen beneath the Christian artillery. The army now lay encamped before the town of Moclin, on the frontier of Jaen, one of the most stubborn fortresses of the border. It stood on a high, rocky hill, the base of which was nearly girdled by a river: a thick forest protected the back part of the town, towards the mountain. Thus strongly situated, it domineered, with its frowning battlements and massive towers, all the mountain passes into that part of the country, and was called "the shield of Granada." It had a double arrear of blood to settle with the Christians; two hundred years before, a master of Santiago and all his cavaliers had been lanced by the Moors before its gates. It had recently made terrible slaughter among the troops of the good count de Cabra, in his precipitate attempt to entrap

317

the old Moorish monarch. The pride of Ferdinand had been piqued by being obliged on that occasion to recede from his plan, and abandon his concerted attack on the place; he was now prepared to take a full revenge.

El Zagal, the old warrior king of Granada, anticipating a second attempt, had provided the place with ample ammunitions and provisions; had ordered trenches to be digged, and additional bulwarks thrown up; and caused all the old men, the women, and the children to be removed to the capital.

Such was the strength of the fortress, and the difficulties of its position, that Ferdinand anticipated much trouble in reducing it, and made every preparation for a regular siege. In the centre of his camp were two great mounds, one of sacks of flour, the other of grain, which were called the royal granary. Three batteries of heavy ordnance were opened against the citadel and principal towers, while smaller artillery, engines for the discharge of missiles, arquebuses, and cross-bows were distributed in various places, to keep up a fire into any breaches that might be made, and upon those of the garrison who should appear on the battlements.

The lombards soon made an impression on the works, demolishing a part of the wall, and tumbling down several of those haughty towers, which from their height had been impregnable before the invention of gunpowder. The Moors repaired their walls as well as they were able, and, still confiding in the strength of their situation, kept up a resolute defense, firing down from their lofty battlements and towers upon the Christian camp. For two nights and a day an incessant fire was kept up, so that there was not a moment in which the roaring of ordnance was not heard, or some damage sustained by the Christians or the Moors. It was a conflict, however, more of engineers and artillerists than of gallant cavaliers; there was no sally of troops, nor shock of armed men, nor rush and charge of cavalry. The knights stood looking on with idle weapons, waiting until they should have an opportunity of signalizing their prowess by scaling the walls or storming the breaches. As the place, however, was assailable only in one part, there was every prospect of a long and obstinate resistance.

The engineers, as usual, discharged not merely balls of stone and iron, to demolish the walls, but flaming balls of inextinguishable combustibles, designed to set fire to the houses. One of these, which passed high through the air like a meteor, sending out sparks and crackling as it went, entered the window of a tower which was used as a magazine of gunpowder. The tower blew up with a tremendous explosion; the Moors who were upon its battlements were hurled into the air, and fell mangled in various parts of the town; and the houses in its vicinity were rent and overthrown as with an earthquake.

The Moors, who had never witnessed an explosion of the kind, ascribed the destruction of the tower to a miracle. Some who had seen the descent of the flaming ball, imagined that fire had fallen from heaven to punish them for their pertinacity. The pious Agapida, himself, believes that this fiery missive was conducted by divine agency to confound the infidels; an opinion in which he is supported by other Catholic historians.*

Seeing heaven and earth as it were combined against them, the Moors lost all heart: they capitulated, and were permitted to depart with their effects, leaving behind all arms and munitions of war.

The Catholic army (says Antonio Agapida) entered Moclin in solemn state, not as a licentious host, intent upon plunder and desolation, but as a band of Christian warriors, coming to purify and regenerate the land. The standard of the cross, that ensign of this holy crusade, was borne in the advance, followed by the other banners of the army. Then came the king and queen, at the head of a vast number of armed cavaliers. They were accompanied by a band of priests and friars, with the choir of the royal chapel, chanting the canticle " *Te Deum laudamus.*" As they were moving through the streets in this solemn manner, every sound hushed excepting the anthem of the choir, they suddenly heard, issuing as it were from underground, a chorus of voices chanting in solemn response, " *Benedictum qui venit in nomine domini.*" † The procession paused in wonder. The sounds rose from Christian captives, and among

---

* Pulgar, Garibay, Lucio Marino Siculo, *Cosas Memoral. de Hispan.* lib. 20.                                          † Marino Siculo.

them several priests who were confined in subterranean dungeons.

The heart of Isabella was greatly touched. She ordered the captives to be drawn forth from their cells, and was still more moved at beholding, by their wan, discolored, and emaciated appearance, how much they had suffered. Their hair and beards were overgrown and shagged; they were wasted by hunger, half naked, and in chains. She ordered that they should be clothed and cherished, and money furnished them to bear them to their homes.*

Several of the captives were brave cavaliers, who had been wounded and made prisoners, in the defeat of the count de Cabra by El Zagal, in the preceding year. There were also found other melancholy traces of that disastrous affair. On visiting the narrow pass where the defeat had taken place, the remains of several Christian warriors were found in thickets, or hidden behind rocks, or in the clefts of the mountains. These were some who had been struck from their horses, and wounded too severely to fly. They had crawled away from the scene of action, and concealed themselves to avoid falling into the hands of the enemy, and had thus perished miserably and alone. The remains of those of note were known by their armor and devices, and were mourned over by their companions who had shared the disasters of that day.†

---

* Illecas, *Hist. Pontif.* lib. 6, c. 20, § 1.     † Pulgar, part 3, cap. 61.

The queen had these remains piously collected, as the relics of so many martyrs, who had fallen in the cause of the faith. They were interred with great solemnity in the mosques of Moclin, which had been purified and consecrated to Christian worship. "There," says Antonio Agapida, "rest the bones of those truly Catholic knights, in the holy ground which in a manner had been sanctified by their blood; and all pilgrims passing through those mountains offer up prayers and masses for the repose of their souls."

The queen remained for some time at Moclin, administering comfort to the wounded and the prisoners, bringing the newly acquired territory into order, and founding churches and monasteries and other pious institutions. "While the king marched in front, laying waste the land of the Philistines," says the figurative Antonio Agapida, "Queen Isabella followed his traces as the binder follows the reaper, gathering and garnering the rich harvest that has fallen beneath his sickle. In this she was greatly assisted by the counsels of that cloud of bishops, friars, and other saintly men, which continually surrounded her, garnering the first fruits of this infidel land into the granaries of the church." Leaving her thus piously employed, the king pursued his career of conquest, determined to lay waste the vega, and carry fire and sword to the very gates of Granada.

# CHAPTER XLIV.

HOW KING FERDINAND FORAGED THE VEGA; AND OF THE BATTLE OF THE
BRIDGE OF PINOS, AND THE FATE OF THE TWO MOORISH BROTHERS.

ULEY ABDALLAH EL ZAGAL had been
under a spell of ill fortune, ever since the
suspicious death of the old king his brother.
Success had deserted his standard; and, with his fickle
subjects, want of success was one of the greatest crimes
in a sovereign. He found his popularity declining, and
he lost all confidence in his people. The Christian army
marched in open defiance through his territories and sat
down deliberately before his fortresses; yet he dared not
lead forth his legions to oppose them, lest the inhabitants of the Albaycin, ever ripe for a revolt, should rise
and shut the gates of Granada against his return.

Every few days, some melancholy train entered the
metropolis, the inhabitants of some captured town, bearing the few effects spared them, and weeping and bewailing the desolation of their homes. When the tidings arrived that Illora and Moclin had fallen, the people were
seized with consternation. "The right eye of Granada is
extinguished," exclaimed they; "the shield of Granada is

broken: what shall protect us from the inroad of the foe?" When the survivors of the garrisons of those towns arrived, with downcast looks, bearing the marks of battle, and destitute of arms and standards, the populace reviled them in their wrath; but they answered, "We fought as long as we had force to fight, or walls to shelter us; but the Christians laid our town and battlements in ruins, and we looked in vain for aid from Granada."

The alcaydes of Illora and Moclin were brothers; they were alike in prowess, and the bravest among the Moorish cavaliers. They had been the most distinguished in those tilts and tourneys which graced the happier days of Granada, and had distinguished themselves in the sterner conflicts of the field. Acclamation had always followed their banners, and they had long been the delight of the people. Yet now, when they returned after the capture of their fortresses, they were followed by the unsteady populace with execrations. The hearts of the alcaydes swelled with indignation; they found the ingratitude of their countrymen still more intolerable than the hostility of the Christians.

Tidings came, that the enemy was advancing with his triumphant legions, to lay waste the country about Granada. Still El Zagal did not dare to take the field. The two alcaydes of Illora and Moclin stood before him: "We have defended your fortresses," said they, "until we were almost buried under their ruins, and for our reward we receive scoffings and revilings; give us, O king, an opportunity where knightly valor may signalize itself, not shut up behind stone walls, but in the open conflict of the field. The enemy approaches to lay our country desolate; give us men to meet him in the advance, and let shame light upon our heads if we be found wanting in the battle!"

The two brothers were sent forth, with a large force of horse and foot: El Zagal intended, should they be successful, to issue forth with his whole force, and by a decisive victory, repair the losses he had suffered. When the people saw the well-known standards of the brothers going forth to battle, there was a feeble shout; but the alcaydes passed on with stern countenances, for they knew the same voices would curse them were they to return unfortunate. They cast a farewell look at fair Granada, and upon the beautiful fields of their infancy, as if for these they were willing to lay down their lives, but not for an ungrateful people.

The army of Ferdinand had arrived within two leagues of Granada, at the Bridge of Pinos, a pass famous in the wars of the Moors and Christians for many a bloody conflict. It was the pass by which the Castilian monarchs generally made their inroads, and was capable of great defense, from the ruggedness of the country and the difficulty of the bridge. The king, with the main body of the army, had attained the brow of a hill, when they beheld the advance guard, under the marques of Cadiz and the master of Santiago, furiously attacked by the enemy, in the vicinity of the bridge. The Moors rushed to the assault with their usual shouts, but with more than usual ferocity. There was a hard struggle at the bridge ; both parties knew the importance of that pass.

The king particularly noted the prowess of two Moorish cavaliers, alike in arms and devices, and whom by their bearing and attendance he perceived to be commanders of the enemy. They were the two brothers, the alcaydes of Illora and Moclin. Wherever they turned, they carried confusion and death into the ranks of the Christians; but they fought with desperation, rather than valor. The count de Cabra, and his brother Don Martin de Cordova, pressed forward with eagerness against them ; but having advanced too precipitately, were surrounded by the foe, and in imminent danger. A young Christian knight, seeing their peril, hastened with his followers to their relief. The king recognized him for Don Juan de Arragon, count of Ribargoza, his own nephew ; for he was illegitimate son of the duke of Villahermosa, illegitimate brother of King Ferdinand. The splendid armor of Don Juan, and the sumptuous caparison of his steed, rendered him a brilliant object of attack. He was assailed on all sides, and his superb steed slain under him ; yet still he fought valiantly, bearing for a time the brunt of the fight, and giving the exhausted forces of the count de Cabra time to recover breath.

Seeing the peril of these troops and the general obstinacy of the fight, the king ordered the royal standard to be advanced and hastened, with all his forces, to the relief of the count de Cabra. At his approach, the enemy gave way, and retreated towards the bridge. The two Moorish commanders endeavored to rally their troops, and animate them to defend this pass to the utmost: they used prayers, remonstrances, menaces—but almost in vain. They could only collect a scanty handful of cavaliers; with these they planted themselves at the head of the bridge, and disputed it inch by inch. The fight was hot and obstinate, for but few could contend hand to hand, yet many discharged cross-bows and arquebuses from the banks. The river was covered with the floating bodies of the slain. The Moorish band of cavaliers was almost entirely cut to pieces; the two brothers fell, covered with wounds, upon the bridge they had so resolutely defended. They had given up the battle for lost, but had determined not to return alive to ungrateful Granada.

When the people of the capital heard how devotedly they had fallen, they lamented greatly their deaths, and extolled their memory: a column was erected to their honor in the vicinity of the bridge, which long went by the name of "the Tomb of the Brothers."

The army of Ferdinand now marched on, and established its camp in the vicinity of Granada. The worthy Agapida gives many triumphant details of the ravages committed in the vega, which was again laid waste; the grain, fruits, and other productions of the earth, destroyed—and that earthly paradise rendered a dreary desert. He narrates several fierce but ineffectual sallies and skirmishes of the Moors, in defense of their favorite plain; among which, one deserves to be mentioned, as it records the achievements of one of the saintly heroes of this war.

During one of the movements of the Christian army, near the walls of Granada, a battalion of fifteen hundred cavalry, and a large force of foot, had sallied from the city, and posted themselves near some gardens, which were surrounded by a canal, and traversed by ditches, for the purpose of irrigation.

The Moors beheld the duke del Infantado pass by, with his two splendid battalions; one of men-at-arms, the other of light cavalry, armed *à la gineta.* In company with him, but following as a rear-guard, was Don Garcia Osorio, the belligerent bishop of Jaen, attended by Francisco Bovadillo, the corregidor of his city, and followed by two squadrons of men-at-arms, from Jaen, Anduxar, Ubeda, and Baeza.* The success of last year's campaign had given the good bishop an inclination for warlike affairs, and he had once more buckled on his cuirass.

The Moors were much given to stratagem in warfare. They looked wistfully at the magnificent squadrons of the duke del Infantado; but their martial discipline pre-

---

* Pulgar, part 3, cap. 62.

cluded all attack: the good bishop promised to be a more easy prey. Suffering the duke and his troops to pass unmolested, they approached the squadrons of the bishop, and, making a pretended attack, skirmished slightly, and fled in apparent confusion. The bishop considered the day his own, and, seconded by his corregidor Bovadillo, followed with valorous precipitation. The Moors fled into the *Huerta del Rey*, or orchard of the king; the troops of the bishop followed hotly after them.

When the Moors perceived their pursuers fairly embarrassed among the intricacies of the garden, they turned fiercely upon them, while some of their number threw open the sluices of the Xenel. In an instant, the canal which encircled and the ditches which traversed the garden, were filled with water, and the valiant bishop and his followers found themselves overwhelmed by a deluge.* A scene of great confusion succeeded. Some of the men of Jaen, stoutest of heart and hand, fought with the Moors in the garden, while others struggled with the water, endeavoring to escape across the canal, in which attempt many horses were drowned.

Fortunately, the duke del Infantado perceived the snare into which his companions had fallen, and dispatched his light cavalry to their assistance. The Moors were compelled to flight, and driven along the road of

* Pulgar

Elvira up to the gates of Granada.* Several Christian
cavaliers perished in this affray; the bishop himself
escaped with difficulty, having slipped from his saddle in
crossing the canal, but saving himself by holding on to
the tail of his charger. This perilous achievement seems
to have satisfied the good bishop's belligerent propensities. He retired on his laurels, (says Agapida,) to his
city of Jaen; where, in the fruition of all good things, he
gradually waxed too corpulent for his corselet, which
was hung up in the hall of his episcopal palace; and we
hear no more of his military deeds, throughout the residue of the holy war of Granada.†

King Ferdinand having completed his ravage of the
vega, and kept El Zagal shut up in his capital, conducted
his army back through the pass of Lope to rejoin Queen
Isabella at Moclin. The fortresses lately taken being
well garrisoned and supplied, he gave the command of
the frontier to his cousin, Don Fadrique de Toledo, afterwards so famous in the Netherlands as the duke of Alva.
The campaign being thus completely crowned with success, the sovereigns returned in triumph to the city of
Cordova.

* Pulgar.

† "Don Luis Osorio fue obispo de Jaen desde el año de 1483, y presidio
in esta Iglesia hasta el de 1496 in que murio en Flandes, a donde fue
acompañando a la princesa Doña Juana, esposa del archiduque Don Felipe."—*España Sagrada*, por Fr. M. Risco, tom. 41, trat. 77, cap. 4.

# CHAPTER XLV.

NO sooner did the last squadron of Christian cavalry disappear behind the mountains of Elvira, and the note of its trumpets die away upon the ear, than the long-suppressed wrath of Muley El Zagal burst forth. He determined no longer to be half a king, reigning over a divided kingdom, in a divided capital; but to exterminate, by any means, fair or foul, his nephew Boabdil and his faction. He turned furiously upon those whose factious conduct had deterred him from sallying upon the foe; some he punished by confiscations, others by banishment, others by death. Once undisputed monarch of the entire kingdom, he trusted to his military skill to retrieve his fortunes, and drive the Christians over the frontier.

Boabdil, however, had again retired to Velez el Blanco, on the confines of Murcia, where he could avail himself, in case of emergency, of any assistance or protection afforded him by the policy of Ferdinand. His defeat had blighted his reviving fortunes, for the people considered him as inevitably doomed to misfortune. Still, while he lived, El Zagal knew he would be a rallying point for faction, and liable at any moment to be elevated into power by the capricious multitude. He had recourse, therefore, to the most perfidious means, to compass his destruction. He sent ambassadors to him, representing the necessity of concord for the salvation of the kingdom, and even offering to resign the title of king, and to become subject to his sway, on receiving some estate on which he could live in tranquil retirement. But while the ambassadors bore these words of peace, they were furnished with poisoned herbs, which they were to administer secretly to Boabdil; and if they failed in this attempt, they had pledged themselves to dispatch him openly, while engaged in conversation. They were instigated to this treason by promises of great reward, and by assurances from the alfaquis that Boabdil was an apostate, whose death would be acceptable to Heaven.

The young monarch was secretly apprised of the concerted treason, and refused an audience to the ambassadors. He denounced his uncle as the murderer of his father and his kindred, and the usurper of his throne; and vowed never to relent in hostility to him, until he should place his head on the walls of the Alhambra.

Open war again broke out between the two monarchs, though feebly carried on, in consequence of their mutual embarrassments. Ferdinand again extended his assist-

ance to Boabdil, ordering the commanders of his fortresses to aid him in all enterprises against his uncle,
and against such places as refused to acknowledge him
as king; and Don Juan de Bonavides, who commanded
in Lorca, even made inroads in his name, into the territories of Almeria, Baza, and Guadix, which owned allegiance to El Zagal.

The unfortunate Boabdil had three great evils to contend with—the inconstancy of his subjects, the hostility
of his uncle, and the friendship of Ferdinand. The last
was by far the most baneful; his fortunes withered under
it. He was looked upon as the enemy of his faith and
of his country. The cities shut their gates against him;
the people cursed him; even the scanty band of cavaliers, who had hitherto followed his ill-starred banner,
began to desert him; for he had not wherewithal to reward, nor even to support them. His spirits sank with
his fortune, and he feared that in a little time he should
not have a spot of earth whereon to plant his standard,
nor an adherent to rally under it.

In the midst of his despondency, he received a message from his lion-hearted mother, the sultana Ayxa la
Horra. It was brought by the steadfast adherent to
their fortunes, Aben Comixa. "For shame," said she,
"to linger timorously about the borders of your kingdom, when a usurper is seated in your capital. Why
look abroad for perfidious aid, when you have loyal
hearts beating true to you in Granada? The Albaycin

is ready to throw open its gates to receive you. Strike
home vigorously—a sudden blow may mend all, or make
an end. A throne or a grave!—for a king there is no
honorable medium."

Boabdil was of an undecided character, but there are
circumstances which bring the most wavering to a decision, and when once resolved they are apt to act with
a daring impulse, unknown to steadier judgments. The
message of the sultana roused him from a dream. Granada, beautiful Granada, with its stately Alhambra, its
delicious gardens, its gushing and limpid fountains sparkling among groves of orange, citron, and myrtle, rose
before him. "What have I done," exclaimed he, "that I
should be an exile from this paradise of my forefathers
—a wanderer and fugitive in my own kingdom, while a
murderous usurper sits proudly upon my throne? Surely
Allah will befriend the righteous cause; one blow, and
all may be my own."

He summoned his scanty band of cavaliers. "Who is
ready to follow his monarch unto the death?" said
he: and every one laid his hand upon his scimetar.
"Enough!" said he; "let each man arm himself and
prepare his steed in secret, for an enterprise of toil and
peril: if we succeed, our reward is empire."

## CHAPTER XLVI.

HOW BOABDIL RETURNED SECRETLY TO GRANADA, AND HOW HE WAS RE-
CEIVED.—SECOND EMBASSY OF DON JUAN DE VERA, AND HIS PERILS IN
THE ALHAMBRA.

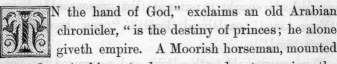N the hand of God," exclaims an old Arabian chronicler, " is the destiny of princes; he alone giveth empire. A Moorish horseman, mounted on a fleet Arabian steed, was one day traversing the mountains which extend between Granada and the frontier of Murcia. He galloped swiftly through the valleys, but paused and looked out cautiously from the summit of every height. A squadron of cavaliers followed warily at a distance. There were fifty lances. The richness of their armor and attire showed them to be warriors of noble rank, and their leader had a lofty and prince-like demeanor." The squadron thus described by the Arabian chronicler, was the Moorish king Boabdil and his devoted followers.

For two nights and a day they pursued their adventurous journey, avoiding all popular parts of the country, and choosing the most solitary passes of the mountains. They suffered severe hardships and fatigues, but suffered without a murmur: they were accustomed to rugged campaigning, and their steeds were of generous and unyielding spirit. It was midnight, and all was dark and silent as they descended from the mountains, and approached the city of Granada. They passed along quietly under the shadow of its walls until they arrived near the gate of the Albaycin. Here Boabdil ordered his followers to halt, and remain concealed. Taking but four or five with him, he advanced resolutely to the gate and knocked with the hilt of his scimetar. The guards demanded who sought to enter at that unseasonable hour. "Your king!" exclaimed Boabdil, "open the gate and admit him!"

The guards held forth a light, and recognized the person of the youthful monarch. They were struck with sudden awe, and threw open the gates ; and Boabdil and his followers entered unmolested. They galloped to the dwellings of the principal inhabitants of the Albaycin, thundering at their portals, and summoning them to rise and take arms for their rightful sovereign. The summons was instantly obeyed : trumpets resounded throughout the streets ; the gleam of torches and the flash of arms showed the Moors hurrying to their gathering-places : by daybreak, the whole force of the Albaycin was rallied under the standard of Boabdil, and Aben Comixa was made alcayde of the fortress. Such was the success of this sudden and desperate act of the young monarch · for we are assured by contemporary historians, that there had been no previous concert or arrangement. "As the guards opened the gates of the city to admit him," observes a pious chronicler, "so God opened the hearts of the Moors to receive him as their king." *

In the morning early, the tidings of this event roused El Zagal from his slumbers in the Alhambra. The fiery old warrior assembled his guard in haste, and made his way sword in hand to the Albaycin, hoping to come upon his nephew by surprise. He was vigorously met by Boabdil and his adherents, and driven back into the quarter of the Alhambra. An encounter took place between the two kings, in the square before the principal mosque ; here they fought hand to hand with implacable fury, as though it had been agreed to decide their competition for the crown by single combat. In the tumult of this chance-medley affray, however, they were separated, and the party of El Zagal was ultimately driven from the square.

The battle raged for some time in the streets and places of the city, but finding their powers of mischief cramped within such narrow limits, both parties sallied forth into the fields, and fought beneath the walls until evening. Many fell on both sides, and at night each party withdrew into its quarter, until the morning gave them light to renew the unnatural conflict. For several days, the two grand divisions of the city remained like

* Pulgar.

hostile powers arrayed against each other. The party of the Alhambra was more numerous than that of the Albaycin, and contained most of the nobility and chivalry ; but the adherents of Boabdil were men hardened and strengthened by labor, and habitually skilled in the exercise of arms.

The Albaycin underwent a kind of siege by the forces of El Zagal ; they effected breaches in the walls, and made repeated attempts to carry it sword in hand, but were as often repulsed. The troops of Boabdil, on the other hand, made frequent sallies ; and in the conflicts which took place, the hatred of the combatants arose to such a pitch of fury, that no quarter was given on either side.

Boabdil perceived the inferiority of his force ; he dreaded also that his adherents, being for the most part tradesmen and artisans, would become impatient of this interruption of their gainful occupations, and disheartened by these continual scenes of carnage. He sent missives, therefore, in all haste, to Don Fadrique de Toledo, who commanded the Christian forces on the frontier, entreating his assistance.

Don Fadrique had received instructions from the politic Ferdinand, to aid the youthful monarch in all his contests with his uncle. He advanced with a body of troops near to Granada. The moment Boabdil discerned, from the towers of the Albaycin, the Christian banners and lances winding round the base of the mountain of

Elvira, he sallied forth to meet them, escorted by a squadron of Abencerrages under Aben Comixa. El Zagal, who was equally on the alert, and apprised that the Christian troops came in aid of his nephew, likewise sallied forth and drew up his troops in battle array. Don Fadrique, wary lest some treachery should be intended, halted among some plantations of olives, retained Boabdil by his side, and signified his wish that Aben Comixa would advance with his squadron and offer battle to the old king. The provocation was given, but El Zagal maintained his position. He threw out some light parties, however, which skirmished with the Abencerrages of Aben Comixa, after which he caused his trumpets to sound a recall, and retired into the city; mortified, it is said, that the Christian cavaliers should witness these fratricidal discords between true believers.

Don Fadrique, still distrustful, drew off to a distance, and encamped for the night near the bridge of Cabillas.

Early in the morning, a Moorish cavalier with an escort approached the advance guard, and his trumpets sounded a parley. He craved an audience, as an envoy from El Zagal, and was admitted to the tent of Don Fadrique. El Zagal had learnt that the Christian troops had come to aid his nephew, and now offered to enter into an alliance with them on terms still more advantageous than those of Boabdil. The wary Don Fadrique listened to the Moor with apparent complacency, but determined to send one of his most intrepid and discreet cavaliers, under the protection of a flag, to hold a conference with the old king within the very walls of the Alhambra. The officer chosen for this important mission was Don Juan de Vera, the same stanch and devout cavalier, who in times preceding the war had borne the message from the Castilian sovereigns, to old Muley Abul Hassan, demanding arrears of tribute. Don Juan was received with great ceremony by the king. No records remain of his diplomatic negotiations, but they extended into the night, and it being too late to return to camp, he was sumptuously lodged in an apartment of the Alhambra. In the morning, one of the courtiers about the palace, somewhat given to jest and raillery, invited Don Juan to a ceremony which some of the alfaquis were about to celebrate in the mosque of the palace. The religious punctilio of this most discreet cavalier immediately took umbrage at what he conceived a banter. "The servants of Queen Isabella of Castile," replied he stiffly and sternly, "who bear on their armor the cross of St. Jago, never enter the temples of Mahomet, but to level them to the earth, and trample on them."

The Moslem courtier retired somewhat disconcerted by this Catholic, but not very courteous reply, and reported it to a renegado of Antiquera. The latter, eager, like all renegadoes, to show devotion to his newly adopted creed, volunteered to return with the courtier and have a tilt of words with the testy diplomatist. They found Don Juan playing a game of chess with the alcayde of the Alhambra, and took occasion to indulge in sportive comments on some of the mysteries of the Christian religion. The ire of this devout knight and discreet ambassador began to kindle; but he restrained it within the limits of lofty gravity. "You would do well," said he, "to cease talking about what you do not understand." This only provoked light attacks of the witlings; until one of them dared to make some degrading and obscene comparison between the Blessed Virgin and Amina, the mother of Mahomet. In an instant Don Juan sprang to his feet, dashed chess-board and chessmen aside, and drawing his sword, dealt, says the curate of los Palacios, such a *fermosa cachillada* (such a handsome slash) across the head of the blaspheming Moor, as felled him to the earth. The renegado, seeing his comrade fall, fled for his life, making the halls and galleries ring with his outcries. Guards, pages, and attendants rushed in, but Don Juan kept them at bay, until the appearance of the king restored order. On inquiring into the cause of the affray, he acted with proper discrimination. Don Juan was held sacred as an ambassador, and the renegado was severely punished for having compromised the hospitality of the royal palace.

The tumult in the Alhambra, however, soon caused a more dangerous tumult in the city. It was rumored that Christians had been introduced into the palace with some treasonable design. The populace caught up arms, and ascended in throngs to the gate of Justice, de-

manding the death of all Christian spies and those who
had introduced them. This was no time to reason with
an infuriate mob, when the noise of their clamors might
bring the garrison of the Albaycin to back them. Nothing was left for El Zagal but to furnish Don Juan with
a disguise, a swift horse, and an escort, and to let him
out of the Alhambra by a private gate. It was a sore
grievance to the stately cavalier to have to submit to
these expedients, but there was no alternative. In
Moorish disguise he passed through crowds that were
clamoring for his head; and once out of the gate of
the city, gave reins to his horse, nor ceased spurring
until he found himself safe under the banners of Don
Fadrique.

Thus ended the second embassy of Don Juan de Vera,
less stately, but more perilous than the first. Don
Fadrique extolled his prowess, whatever he may have
thought of his discretion; and rewarded him with a
superb horse, while at the same time he wrote a letter to
El Zagal, thanking him for the courtesy and protection
he had observed to his ambassador. Queen Isabella also
was particularly delighted with the piety of Don Juan,
and his promptness in vindicating the immaculate character of the Blessed Virgin, and, beside conferring on
him various honorable distinctions, made him a royal
present of three hundred thousand maravadils.*

* Alcantara, *Hist. Granad.* vol. 3, c. 17, apud *De Harro Nobiliaric
Genealogico*, lib. 5, cap. 15.

The report brought by this cavalier of affairs in Granada, together with the preceding skirmishings between the Moorish factions before the walls, convinced Don Fadrique that there was no collusion between the monarchs; on returning to his frontier post, therefore, he sent Boabdil a reinforcement of Christian foot-soldiers and arquebusiers, under Fernan Alvarez de Sotomayer, alcayde of Colomera. This was as a firebrand thrown in to light up anew the flames of war in the city, which remained raging between the Moorish inhabitants for the space of fifty days.

## CHAPTER XLVII.

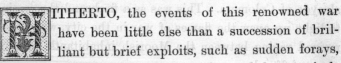

ITHERTO, the events of this renowned war have been little else than a succession of brilliant but brief exploits, such as sudden forays, wild skirmishes among the mountains, and the surprisals of castles, fortresses, and frontier towns. We approach now to more important and prolonged operations, in which ancient and mighty cities, the bulwarks of Granada, were invested by powerful armies, subdued by slow and regular sieges, and thus the capital left naked and alone.

The glorious triumphs of the Christian sovereigns (says Fray Antonio Agapida) had resounded throughout the East, and filled all heathenesse with alarm. The Grand-Turk Bajazet II., and his deadly foe the grand soldan of Egypt, suspending for a time their bloody feuds, entered into a league to protect the religion of Mahomet and the kingdom of Granada from the hostilities of the Christians. It was concerted between them, that Bajazet should send a powerful armada against the island of Sicily, then appertaining to the Spanish crown,

344

for the purpose of distracting the attention of the Castilian sovereigns; while, at the same time, great bodies of
troops should be poured into Granada, from the opposite
coast of Africa.

Ferdinand and Isabella received timely intelligence of
these designs. They resolved at once to carry the war
into the sea-board of Granada, to possess themselves of
its ports, and thus, as it were, to bar the gates of the
kingdom against all external aid. Malaga was to be the
main object of attack: it was the principal sea-port of
the kingdom, and almost necessary to its existence. It
had long been the seat of opulent commerce, sending
many ships to the coasts of Syria and Egypt. It was
also the great channel of communication with Africa,
through which were introduced supplies of money,
troops, arms, and steeds, from Tunis, Tripoli, Fez, Tremezan, and other Barbary powers. It was emphatically
called, therefore, "the hand and mouth of Granada."
Before laying siege to this redoubtable city, however, it
was deemed necessary to secure the neighboring city of
Velez Malaga and its dependent places, which might
otherwise harass the besieging army.

For this important campaign, the nobles of the kingdom were again summoned to take the field with their
forces, in the spring of 1487. The menaced invasion of
the infidel powers of the East, had awakened new ardor
in the bosoms of all true Christian knights; and so zeal-
ously did they respond to the summons of the sovereigns,

that an army of twenty thousand cavalry and fifty thousand foot, the flower of Spanish warriors, led by the bravest of Spanish cavaliers, thronged the renowned city of Cordova, at the appointed time.

On the night before this mighty host set forth upon its march, an earthquake shook the city. The inhabitants, awakened by the shaking of the walls and rocking of the towers, fled to the courts and squares, fearing to be overwhelmed by the ruins of their dwellings. The earthquake was most violent in the quarter of the royal residence, the site of the ancient palace of the Moorish kings. Many looked upon this as an omen of some impending evil; but Fray Antonio Agapida, in that infallible spirit of divination which succeeds an event, plainly reads in it a presage that the empire of the Moors was about to be shaken to its centre.

It was on Saturday, the eve of the Sunday of Palms (says a worthy and loyal chronicler of the time), that the most Catholic monarch departed with his army, to render service to Heaven, and make war upon the Moors.* Heavy rains had swelled all the streams, and rendered the roads deep and difficult. The king, therefore, divided his host into two bodies. In one he put all the artillery, guarded by a strong body of horse, and commanded by the master of Alcantara and Martin Alonzo, senior of Montemayor. This division was to proceed by

---

* Pulgar, *Cronica de los Reyes Catholicos.*

the road through the valleys, where pasturage abounded for the oxen which drew the ordnance.

The main body of the army was led by the king in person. It was divided into numerous battalions, each commanded by some distinguished cavalier. The king took the rough and perilous road of the mountains, and few mountains are more rugged and difficult than those of Andalusia. The roads are mere mule-paths, straggling amidst rocks and along the verge of precipices, clambering vast craggy heights, or descending into frightful chasms and ravines, with scanty and uncertain foothold for either man or steed. Four thousand pioneers were sent in advance, under the alcayde de los Donceles, to conquer, in some degree, the asperities of the road. Some had pickaxes and crowbars to break the rocks, others had implements to construct bridges over the mountain torrents, while it was the duty of others to lay stepping-stones in the smaller streams. As the country was inhabited by fierce Moorish mountaineers, Don Diego de Castrillo was dispatched, with a body of horse and foot, to take possession of the heights and passes. Notwithstanding every precaution, the royal army suffered excessively on its march. At one time there was no place to encamp, for five leagues of the most toilsome and mountainous country; and many of the beasts of burden sank down, and perished on the road.

It was with the greatest joy, therefore, that the royal army emerged from these stern and frightful defiles, and

came to where they looked down upon the vega of Velez
Malaga. The region before them was one of the most
delectable to the eye, that ever was ravaged by an army.
Sheltered from every rude blast by a screen of mountains, and sloping and expanding to the south, this lovely
valley was quickened by the most generous sunshine,
watered by the silver meanderings of the Velez, and refreshed by cooling breezes from the Mediterranean. The
sloping hills were covered with vineyards and olive-trees;
the distant fields waved with grain, or were verdant with
pasturage; while round the city were delightful gardens,
the favorite retreats of the Moors, where their white
pavilions gleamed among groves of oranges, citrons, and
pomegranates, and were surmounted by stately palms—
those plants of southern growth, bespeaking a generous
climate and a cloudless sky.

In the upper part of this delightful valley, the city of
Velez Malaga reared its warrior battlements in stern contrast to the landscape. It was built on the declivity of
a steep and insulated hill, and strongly fortified by walls
and towers. The crest of the hill rose high above the
town, into a mere crag, inaccessible on every other side,
and crowned by a powerful castle, which domineered
over the surrounding country. Two suburbs swept down
into the valley, from the skirts of the town, and were defended by bulwarks and deep ditches. The vast ranges
of gray mountains, often capped with clouds, which rose
to the north, were inhabited by a hardy and warlike

race, whose strong fortresses of Comares, Canillas, Competa, and Benamargosa, frowned down from cragged heights.

When the Christian host arrived in sight of this valley, a squadron was hovering on the smooth sea before it, displaying the banner of Castile. This was commanded by the count of Trevento, and consisted of four armed galleys, conveying a number of caravels, laden with supplies for the army.

After surveying the ground, king Ferdinand encamped on the side of a mountain which advanced close to the city, and was the last of a rugged sierra, or chain of heights, that extended quite to Granada. On the summit of this mountain, and overlooking the camp, was a Moorish town, powerfully fortified, called Bentomiz, considered capable of yielding great assistance to Velez Malaga. Several of the generals remonstrated with the king for choosing a post so exposed to assaults from the mountaineers; but he replied that he should thus cut off all communication between Bentomiz and the city; and that as to the danger, his soldiers must keep the more vigilant guard against surprise.

King Ferdinand rode about, attended by several cavaliers and a small number of cuirassiers, appointing the various stations of the camp. Having directed a body of foot-soldiers to possess themselves, as an advanced guard, of an important height which overlooked the city, he retired to a tent to take refreshment. While at table, he was startled by a sudden uproar, and, looking forth, beheld his soldiers flying before a superior force of the enemy. The king had on no other armor but a cuirass; seizing a lance, however, he sprang upon his horse and galloped to protect the fugitives, followed by his handful of knights and cuirassiers. When the soldiers saw the king hastening to their aid, they turned upon their pursuers. Ferdinand, in his eagerness, threw himself into the midst of the foe. One of his grooms was killed beside him; but, before the Moor who slew him could escape, the king transfixed him with his lance. He then sought to draw his sword, which hung at his saddle-bow, but in vain. Never had he been exposed to such peril; he was surrounded by the enemy, without a weapon wherewith to defend himself.

In this moment of awful jeopardy, the marques of Cadiz, the count de Cabra, the adelantado of Murcia, with two other cavaliers, named Garcilasso de la Vega and Diego de Atayde, came galloping to the scene of action, and, surrounding the king, made a rampart of their bodies against the assaults of the Moors. The horse of the marques was pierced by an arrow, and that worthy cavalier exposed to imminent danger; but, with the aid of his valorous companions, he quickly put the enemy to flight, and pursued them, with slaughter, to the very gates of the city.

When those loyal warriors returned from the pursuit, they remonstrated with the king for exposing his life in personal conflict, seeing that he had so many valiant captains whose business it was to fight. They reminded him that the life of a prince was the life of his people, and that many a brave army was lost by the loss of its commander. They entreated him, therefore, in future to protect them with the force of his mind in the cabinet, rather than of his arm in the field.

Ferdinand acknowledged the wisdom of their advice, but declared that he could not see his people in peril without venturing his person to assist them,—a reply (say the old chroniclers) which delighted the whole army, inasmuch as they saw that he not only governed them as a good king, but protected them as a valiant captain. He, however, was conscious of the extreme peril to which he had been exposed, and made a vow never again to venture into battle without having his sword girt to his side.*

When this achievement of the king was related to Isabella, she trembled amidst her joy at his safety; and afterwards, in memorial of the event, granted to Velez Malaga, as the arms of the city, the figure of the king on horseback, with a groom lying dead at his feet, and the Moors flying.†

The camp was formed, but the artillery was yet on the road, advancing with infinite labor, at the rate of merely a league a day; for heavy rains had converted the

---

\* Illescas, *Hist. Pontif.* lib. 6, c. 20.   Vedmar, *Hist. Velez Malaga.*
† Ibid.

streams of the valleys into raging torrents, and completely broken up the roads. In the meantime, king Ferdinand ordered an assault on the suburbs of the city. They were carried, after a sanguinary conflict of six hours, in which many Christian cavaliers were killed and wounded, and, among the latter, Don Alvaro of Portugal, son of the duke of Braganza. The suburbs were then fortified towards the city with trenches and palisades, and garrisoned by a chosen force, under Don Fadrique de Toledo. Other trenches were digged round the city, and from the suburbs to the royal camp, so as to cut off all communication with the surrounding country.

Bodies of troops were also sent to take possession of the mountain passes, by which the supplies for the army had to be brought. The mountains, however, were so steep and rugged, and so full of defiles and lurking-places, that the Moors could sally forth and retreat in perfect security; frequently swooping down upon Christian convoys, and bearing off both booty and prisoners to their strongholds. Sometimes the Moors would light fires at night, on the sides of the mountains, which would be answered by fires from the watch-towers and fortresses. By these signals they would concert assaults upon the Christian camp, which, in consequence, was obliged to be continually on the alert.

King Ferdinand flattered himself that the manifestation of his force had struck sufficient terror into the city, and that by offers of clemency it might be induced to capitulate. He wrote a letter, therefore, to the commanders, promising, in case of immediate surrender, that all the inhabitants should be permitted to depart with their effects; but threatening them with fire and sword if they persisted in defense. This letter was dispatched by a cavalier named Carvajal, who, putting it on the end of a lance, reached it to the Moors on the walls of the city. Abul Cacim Vanegas, son of Reduan and alcayde of the fortress, replied that the king was too noble and magnanimous to put such a threat in execution, and that he should not surrender, as he knew the artillery could not be brought to the camp, and he was promised succor by the king of Granada.

At the same time that he received this reply, the king learned that at the strong town of Comares, about two leagues distant from the camp, a large number of warriors had assembled from the Axarquia, the same mountains in which the Christian cavaliers had been massacred in the beginning of the war, and that others were daily expected, for this rugged sierra was capable of furnishing fifteen thousand fighting men.

King Ferdinand felt that his army, thus disjointed, and inclosed in an enemy's country, was in a perilous situation, and that the utmost discipline and vigilance were necessary. He put the camp under the strictest regulations, forbidding all gaming, blasphemy, or brawl, and expelling all loose women and their attendant bully ruffians, the usual fomenters of riot and contention among

23

soldiery. He ordered that none should sally forth to skirmish without permission from their commanders; that none should set fire to the woods on the neighboring mountains; and that all word of security given to Moorish places or individuals should be inviolably observed. These regulations were enforced by severe penalties, and had such salutary effect that, though a vast host of various people was collected together, not an opprobrious epithet was heard, nor a weapon drawn in quarrel.

In the meantime, the cloud of war continued to gather about the summits of the mountains, and multitudes of the fierce warriors of the sierra descended to the lower heights of Bentomiz, which overhung the camp, intending to force their way to the city. A detachment was sent against them, which, after sharp fighting, drove them to the higher cliffs, where it was impossible to pursue them.

Ten days had elapsed since the encampment of the army, yet still the artillery had not arrived. The lombards and other heavy ordnance were left in despair, at Antiquera; the rest came groaning slowly through the narrow valleys, which were filled with long trains of artillery, and cars laden with munitions. At length part of the smaller ordnance arrived within half a league of the camp, and the Christians were animated with the hopes of soon being able to make a regular attack upon the fortifications of the city.

# CHAPTER XLVIII.

WHILE the standard of the cross waved on the hills before Velez Malaga, and every height and cliff bristled with hostile arms, the civil war between the factions of the Alhambra and the Albaycin, or rather between El Zagal and El Chico, continued to convulse the city of Granada. The tidings of the investment of Velez Malaga at length roused the attention of the old men and the alfaquis, whose heads were not heated by the daily broils, and they endeavored to arouse the people to a sense of their common danger.

"Why," said they, "continue these brawls between brethren and kindred? what battles are these, where even triumph is ignominious, and the victor blushes and conceals his scars? Behold the Christians ravaging the land won by the valor and blood of your forefathers; dwelling in the houses they built, sitting under the trees they planted, while your brethren wander about, houseless and desolate. Do you wish to seek your real foe?— he is encamped on the mountain of Bentomiz. Do you

355

want a field for the display of your valor?—you will find it before the walls of Velez Malaga."

When they had roused the spirit of the people, they made their way to the rival kings, and addressed them with like remonstrances. Hamet Aben Zarrax, the inspired santon, reproached El Zagal with his blind and senseless ambition: "You are striving to be king," said he, bitterly, "yet suffer the kingdom to be lost!"

El Zagal found himself in a perplexing dilemma. He had a double war to wage,—with the enemy without, and the enemy within. Should the Christians gain possession of the sea-coast, it would be ruinous to the kingdom; should he leave Granada to oppose them, his vacant throne might be seized on by his nephew. He made a merit of necessity, and, pretending to yield to the remonstrances of the alfaquis, endeavored to compromise with Boabdil. He expressed deep concern at the daily losses of the country, caused by the dissensions of the capital; an opportunity now presented to retrieve all by a blow. The Christians had in a manner put themselves in a tomb between the mountains—nothing remained but to throw the earth upon them. He offered to resign the title of king, to submit to the government of his nephew, and fight under his standard; all he desired was to hasten to the relief of Velez Malaga, and to take full vengeance on the Christians.

Boabdil spurned his proposition, as the artifice of a hypocrite and a traitor. "How shall I trust a man," said he, "who has murdered my father and my kindred by treachery, and has repeatedly sought my own life, both by violence and stratagem?"

El Zagal boiled with rage and vexation—but there was no time to be lost. He was beset by the alfaquis and the nobles of his court; the youthful cavaliers were hot for action, the common people loud in their complaints that the richest cities were abandoned to the mercy of the enemy. The old warrior was naturally fond of fighting; he saw also that to remain inactive would endanger both crown and kingdom, whereas a successful blow might secure his popularity in Granada. He had a much more powerful force than his nephew, having lately received reinforcements from Baza, Guadix, and Almeria; he could march with a large force, therefore, to the relief of Velez Malaga, and yet leave a strong garrison in the Alhambra. He took his measures accordingly, and departed suddenly in the night, at the head of one thousand horse and twenty thousand foot, and urged his way rapidly by the most unfrequented roads, along the chain of mountains extending from Granada to the heights above Velez Malaga.

The Christians were alarmed one evening by the sudden blazing of great fires on the mountains about the fortress of Bentomiz. By the ruddy light, they beheld the flash of weapons and the array of troops, and they heard the distant sound of Moorish drums and trumpets. The fires of Bentomiz were answered by fires on the towers of Velez Malaga. The shouts of "El Zagal! El Zagal!" echoed along the cliffs, and resounded from the city; and the Christians found that the old warrior king of Granada was on the mountain above their camp.

The spirits of the Moors were suddenly raised to a pitch of the greatest exultation, while the Christians were astonished to see this storm of war ready to burst upon their heads. The count de Cabra, with his accustomed eagerness when there was a king in the field, would fain have scaled the heights, and attacked El Zagal before he had time to form his camp; but Ferdinand, more cool and wary, restrained him. To attack the height would be to abandon the siege. He ordered every one, therefore, to keep vigilant watch at his post and stand ready to defend it to the utmost, but on no account to sally forth and attack the enemy.

All night the signal-fires kept blazing along the mountains, rousing and animating the whole country. The morning sun rose over the lofty summit of Bentomiz on a scene of martial splendor. As its rays glanced down the mountain, they lighted up the white tents of the Christian cavaliers, cresting its lower prominences, their pennons and ensigns fluttering in the morning breeze. The sumptuous pavilions of the king, with the holy standard of the cross and the royal banners of Castile and Arragon, dominated the encampment. Beyond lay the city, its lofty castle and numerous towers glistening with arms, while above all, and just on the profile of the height, in the full blaze of the rising sun, were descried the tents of the Moor, his troops clustering about them, and his infidel banners floating against the sky. Columns of smoke rose where the night-fires had blazed, and the clash of the Moorish cymbal, the bray of trumpet, and the neigh of steed, were faintly heard from the airy heights. So pure and transparent is the atmosphere in this region, that every object can be distinctly seen at a great distance; and the Christians were able to behold the formidable hosts of foes gathering on the summits of the surrounding mountains.

One of the first measures of the Moorish king was to detach a large force, under Reduan de Vanegas, alcayde of Granada, to fall upon the convoy of ordnance, which stretched, for a great distance, through the mountain defiles. Ferdinand had anticipated this attempt, and sent the commander of Leon, with a body of horse and foot, to reinforce the master of Alcantara. El Zagal, from his mountain height, beheld the detachment issue from the camp, and immediately recalled Reduan. The armies now remained quiet for a time, the Moor looking grimly down upon the Christian camp, like a tiger meditating a bound upon his prey. The Christians were in fearful jeopardy—a hostile city below them, a powerful army above them, and on every side mountains filled with implacable foes.

After El Zagal had maturely considered the situation of the Christian camp, and informed himself of all the passes of the mountain, he conceived a plan to surprise the enemy, which he flattered himself would insure their ruin, and perhaps the capture of King Ferdinand. He wrote a letter to the alcayde of the city, commanding him, in the dead of the night, on a signal-fire being made from the mountain, to sally forth with all his troops, and fall furiously upon the Christian camp. The king would, at the same time, rush down with his army from the mountain, and assail it on the opposite side, thus overwhelming it at the hour of deep repose. This letter he dispatched by a renegado Christian, who knew all the secret roads of the country, and, if taken, could pass himself for a Christian who had escaped from captivity.

El Zagal, confident in his stratagem, looked down upon the Christians as his devoted victims. As the sun went down, and the long shadows of the mountains stretched across the vega, he pointed with exultation to the camp below, apparently unconscious of the impending danger. "Behold," said he, "the unbelievers are delivered into our hands; their king and choicest chivalry will soon be at our mercy. Now is the time to show the courage of men, and, by one glorious victory, retrieve all that we have lost. Happy he who falls fighting in the cause of the prophet! he will at once be transported to the paradise of the faithful, and surrounded by immortal houris. Happy he who shall survive victorious! he will behold Granada!—an earthly paradise—once more delivered

from its foes, and restored to all its glory." The words
of El Zagal were received with acclamations by his
troops, who waited impatiently for the appointed hour,
to pour down from their mountain-hold upon the Christians.

# CHAPTER XLIX.

RESULT OF THE STRATAGEM OF EL ZAGAL TO SURPRISE KING FERDINAND.

UEEN ISABELLA and her court had remained
at Cordova, in great anxiety for the result of
the royal expedition.  Every day brought tidings of the difficulties which attended the transportation
of the ordnance and munitions, and of the critical state
of the army.

While in this state of anxious suspense, couriers arrived with all speed from the frontiers, bringing tidings
of the sudden sally of El Zagal from Granada, to surprise the camp.  All Cordova was in consternation.  The
destruction of the Andalusian chivalry, among the mountains of this very neighborhood, was called to mind:
it was feared that similar ruin was about to burst
forth, from rocks and precipices, upon Ferdinand and his
army.

Queen Isabella shared in the public alarm, but it
served to rouse all the energies of her heroic mind.  Instead of uttering idle apprehensions, she sought only
how to avert the danger.  She called upon all the men
of Andalusia, under the age of seventy, to arm and has-

ten to the relief of their sovereign; and she prepared to set out with the first levies. The grand cardinal of Spain, old Pedro Gonzalez de Mendoza, in whom the piety of the saint and the wisdom of the counselor were mingled with the fire of the cavalier, offered high pay to all horsemen who would follow him to aid their king and the Christian cause; and, buckling on armor, prepared to lead them to the scene of danger.

The summons of the queen roused the quick Andalusian spirit. Warriors who had long since given up fighting, and had sent their sons to battle, now seized the sword and lance, rusting on the wall, and marshaled forth their gray-headed domestics and their grandchildren for the field. The great dread was, that all aid would arrive too late; El Zagal and his host had passed like a storm through the mountains, and it was feared the tempest had already burst upon the Christian camp.

In the meantime, the night had closed which had been appointed by El Zagal for the execution of his plan. He had watched the last light of day expire, and all the Spanish camp remained tranquil. As the hours wore away, the camp-fires were gradually extinguished. No drum nor trumpet sounded from below. Nothing was heard, but now and then the dull, heavy tread of troops, or the echoing tramp of horses—the usual patrols of the camp, and the changes of the guards. El Zagal restrained his own impatience, and that of his troops, until the night should be advanced, and the camp sunk in that heavy sleep from which men are with difficulty awakened; and, when awakened, prone to be bewildered and dismayed.

At length the appointed hour arrived. By order of the Moorish king, a bright flame sprung up from the height of Bentomiz; but El Zagal looked in vain for the responding light from the city. His impatience would brook no longer delay; he ordered the advance of the army to descend the mountain defile and attack the camp. The defile was narrow, and overhung by rocks; as the troops proceeded, they came suddenly, in a shadowy hollow, upon a dark mass of warriors, who, with a loud shout, rushed to assail them. Surprised and disconcerted, they retreated in confusion to the height. When El Zagal heard of a Christian force in the defile, he doubted some counter-plan of the enemy, and gave orders to light the mountain fires. On a signal given, bright flames sprang up on every height, from pyres of wood, prepared for the purpose: cliff blazed out after cliff, until the whole atmosphere was in a glow of furnace light. The ruddy glare lit up the glens and passes, and fell strongly upon the Christian camp, revealing all its tents, and every post and bulwark. Wherever El Zagal turned his eyes, he beheld the light of his fires flashed back from cuirass, and helm, and sparkling lance; he beheld a grove of spears planted in every pass, every assailable point bristling with arms, and squadrons of horse and foot in battle array, awaiting his attack.

In fact, his letter to the alcayde of Velez Malaga had been intercepted by the vigilant Ferdinand, the renegado messenger hanged, and secret measures taken, after nightfall, to give the Moors a warm reception. El Zagal saw that his plan of surprise was discovered and foiled; furious with disappointment, he ordered his troops forward to the attack. They rushed down the defile, but were again encountered by the mass of Christian warriors, being the advance guard of the army, commanded by Don Hurtado de Mendoza, brother of the grand cardinal. The Moors were again repulsed, and retreated up the height. Don Hurtado would have followed them, but the ascent was steep and rugged, and easily defended. A sharp action was kept up through the night, with cross-bows, darts, and arquebuses. The cliffs echoed with deafening uproar, while the fires blazing upon the mountains threw a lurid and uncertain light upon the scene.

When the day dawned, and the Moors saw that there was no coöperation from the city, they slackened in their ardor: they beheld also every pass of the mountain filled with Christian troops, and began to apprehend an assault in return. Just then king Ferdinand sent the marques of Cadiz, with horse and foot, to seize upon a height occupied by a battalion of the enemy. The marques assailed the Moors with his usual intrepidity, and soon put them to flight. The others, who were above, seeing their comrades fly, threw down their arms, and retreated.

One of those unaccountable panics, which now and then seize upon great bodies of people, and to which the light-spirited Moors were prone, now spread throughout the camp. They were terrified, they knew not why, nor at what, and throwing away swords, lances, breast-plates, cross-bows, everything that could impede their motions, scattered themselves wildly in every direction. They fled without pursuers—from the glimpse of each other's arms, from the sound of each other's footsteps. Reduan de Vanegas, the brave alcayde of Granada, alone succeeded in collecting a body of the fugitives; he made a circuit with them through the passes of the mountain, and forcing his way across a weak part of the Christian lines, galloped towards Velez Malaga. The rest of the Moorish host was completely scattered. In vain did El Zagal and his knights attempt to rally them; they were left almost alone, and had to consult their own security by flight.

The marques of Cadiz, finding no opposition, ascended from height to height, cautiously reconnoitering, and fearful of some stratagem or ambush. All, however, was quiet. He reached with his men the place which the Moorish army had occupied: the heights were abandoned, and strewed with cuirasses, scimetars, cross-bows, and other weapons. His force was too small to pursue the enemy, but returned to the royal camp laden with spoils.

Ferdinand at first could not credit so signal and miraculous a defeat, but suspected some lurking stratagem. He ordered, therefore, that a strict watch should be maintained throughout the camp, and every one be ready for instant action. The following night, a thousand cavaliers and hidalgos kept guard about the royal tent, as they had done for several preceding nights ; nor did the king relax this vigilance, until he received certain intelligence that the enemy was completely scattered, and El Zagal flying in confusion.

The tidings of this rout, and of the safety of the Christian army, arrived at Cordova just as reinforcements were on the point of setting out. The anxiety and alarm of the queen and the public, were turned to transports of joy and gratitude. The forces were disbanded, solemn processions were made, and *Te Deums* chanted in the churches, for so signal a victory.

## CHAPTER L.

THE daring spirit of Muley Abdallah El Zagal, in sallying forth to defend his territories, while he left an armed rival in his capital, struck the people of Granada with admiration. They recalled his former exploits, and again anticipated some hardy achievement from his valor. Couriers from the army reported its formidable position on the height of Bento-miz. For a time, there was a pause in the bloody commotions of the city; all attention was turned to the blow about to be struck at the Christian camp. The same considerations which diffused anxiety and terror through Cordova, swelled every bosom with exulting confidence in Granada. The Moors expected to hear of another massacre, like that in the mountains of Malaga. "El Zagal has again entrapped the enemy!" was the cry. "The power of the unbelievers is about to be struck to the heart. We shall soon see the Christian king led captive to the capital." Thus was the name of El Zagal on every tongue. He was extolled as the savior of the country; the only one worthy of wearing the Moorish crown. Boabdil was reviled as basely remaining passive while his country was invaded; and, so violent became the clamor of the populace, that his adherents trembled for his safety.

While the people of Granada were impatiently looking out for tidings of the anticipated victory, scattered horsemen came spurring across the vega. They were fugitives from the Moorish army, and brought the first incoherent account of its defeat. Every one who attempted to tell the tale of this unaccountable panic and dispersion, was as if bewildered by the broken recollection of some frightful dream. He knew not how or why it came to pass. He talked of a battle in the night, among rocks and precipices, by the glare of bale-fires; of multitudes of armed foes in every pass, seen by gleams and flashes; of the sudden horror that seized upon the army at daybreak; its headlong flight, and total dispersion. Hour after hour, the arrival of other fugitives confirmed the story of ruin and disgrace.

In proportion to their recent vaunting, was the humiliation that now fell upon the people of Granada. There was a universal burst, not of grief, but of indignation. They confounded the leader with the army—the deserted, with those who had abandoned him; and El Zagal, from being their idol, became suddenly the object of their execration. He had sacrificed the army; he had disgraced the nation; he had betrayed the country. He was a dastard, a traitor; he was unworthy to reign.

24

On a sudden, one among the multitude shouted, "Long live Boabdil el Chico!" the cry was echoed on all sides, and every one shouted, "Long live Boabdil el Chico! long live the legitimate king of Granada! and death to all usurpers!" In the excitement of the moment, they thronged to the Albaycin; and those who had lately besieged Boabdil with arms, now surrounded his palace with acclamations. The keys of the city, and of all the fortresses, were laid at his feet; he was borne in state to the Alhambra, and once more seated, with all due ceremony, on the throne of his ancestors.

Boabdil had by this time become so accustomed to be crowned and uncrowned by the multitude, that he put no great faith in the duration of their loyalty. He knew that he was surrounded by hollow hearts, and that most of the courtiers of the Alhambra were secretly devoted to his uncle. He ascended the throne as the rightful sovereign, who had been dispossessed of it by usurpation; and he ordered the heads of four of the principal nobles to be struck off, who had been most zealous in support of the usurper. Executions of the kind were matters of course on any change in Moorish government; and Boabdil was lauded for his moderation and humanity, in being content with so small a sacrifice. The factions were awed into obedience; the populace, delighted with any change, extolled Boabdil to the skies; and the name of Muley Abdallah El Zagal was for a time a by-word of scorn and opprobrium throughout the city.

Never was any commander more astonished and confounded by a sudden reverse of fortune, than El Zagal. The evening had seen him with a powerful army at his command, his enemy within his grasp, and victory about to cover him with glory, and to consolidate his power: the morning beheld him a fugitive among the mountains, his army, his prosperity, his power, all dispelled, he knew not how—gone like a dream of the night. In vain had he tried to stem the headlong flight of the army. He saw his squadrons breaking and dispersing among the cliffs of the mountains, until, of all his host, only a handful of cavaliers remained faithful. With these he made a gloomy retreat towards Granada, but with a heart full of foreboding. As he drew near to the city, he paused on the banks of the Xenil, and sent forth scouts to collect intelligence. They returned with dejected countenances: "The gates of Granada," said they, "are closed against you. The banner of Boabdil floats on the tower of the Alhambra."

El Zagal turned his steed, and departed in silence. He retreated to the town of Almunecar, and thence to Almeria, which places still remained faithful to him. Restless and uneasy at being so distant from the capital, he again changed his abode, and repaired to the city of Guadix, within a few leagues of Granada. Here he remained, endeavoring to rally his forces, and preparing to avail himself of any sudden change in the fluctuating politics of the metropolis.

## CHAPTER LI.

SURRENDER OF VELEZ MALAGA AND OTHER PLACES.

HE people of Velez Malaga had beheld the camp of Muley Abdallah, covering the summit of Bentomiz, and glittering in the last rays of the setting sun. During the night they had been alarmed and perplexed by signal-fires on the mountain, and by the sound of distant battle. When the morning broke, the Moorish army had vanished as if by enchantment. While the inhabitants were lost in wonder and conjecture, a body of cavalry, the fragment of the army saved by Reduan de Vanegas, the brave alcayde of Granada, came galloping to the gates. The tidings of the strange discomfiture of the host filled the city with consternation; but Reduan exhorted the people to continue their resistance. He was devoted to El Zagal, and confident in his skill and prowess; and felt assured that he would soon collect his scattered forces and return with fresh troops from Granada. The people were comforted by the words, and encouraged by the presence of Reduan; and they had still a lingering hope that the heavy artillery of the Christians might be locked up in the impassable defiles of the mountains. This hope was soon at an end. The very next day, they beheld long laborious lines of ordnance slowly moving into the Spanish camp, lombards, ribadoquines, catapults, and cars laden with munitions,—while the escort, under the brave master of Alcantara, wheeled in great battalions into the camp, to augment the force of the besiegers.

The intelligence that Granada had shut its gates against El Zagal, and that no reinforcements were to be expected, completed the despair of the inhabitants; even Reduan himself lost confidence, and advised capitulation.

Ferdinand granted favorable conditions, for he was eager to proceed against Malaga. The inhabitants were permitted to depart with their effects, except their arms, and to reside, if they chose it, in Spain, in any place distant from the sea. One hundred and twenty Christians, of both sexes, were rescued from captivity by the surrender, and were sent to Cordova, where they were received with great tenderness by the queen and her daughter the Infanta Isabella, in the famous cathedral, in the midst of public rejoicings for the victory.

The capture of Velez Malaga was followed by the surrender of Bentomiz, Comares, and all the towns and fortresses of the Axarquia, which were strongly garrisoned, and discreet and valiant cavaliers appointed as their alcaydes. The inhabitants of nearly forty towns of the Alpuxarra mountains, also, sent deputations to the Cas-

tilian sovereigns, taking the oath of allegiance as Mude-
hares, or Moslem vassals.

About the same time came letters from Boabdil el
Chico, announcing to the sovereigns the revolution of
Granada in his favor. He solicited kindness and protection for the inhabitants who had returned to their allegiance, and for those of all other places which should
renounce adherence to his uncle. By this means (he
observed) the whole kingdom of Granada would soon be
induced to acknowledge his sway, and would be held by
him in faithful vassalage to the Castilian crown.

The Catholic sovereigns complied with his request.
Protection was immediately extended to the inhabitants
of Granada, permitting them to cultivate their fields in
peace, and to trade with the Christian territories in all
articles excepting arms; being provided with letters of
surety, from some Christian captain or alcayde. The
same favor was promised to all other places which, within
six months, should renounce El Zagal and come under
allegiance to the younger king. Should they not do so
within that time, the sovereigns threatened to make war
upon them, and conquer them for themselves. This
measure had a great effect, in inducing many to return to
the standard of Boabdil.

Having made every necessary arrangement for the
government and security of the newly conquered territory, Ferdinand turned his attention to the great object
of his campaign, the reduction of Malaga.

## CHAPTER LII.

THE city of Malaga lies in the lap of a fertile
valley, surrounded by mountains, excepting on
the part which lies open to the sea.  As it was
one of the most important, so it was one of the strongest,
cities of the Moorish kingdom.  It was fortified by walls
of prodigious strength, studded with a great number of
huge towers.  On the land side, it was protected by a
natural barrier of mountains ; and on the other, the
waves of the Mediterranean beat against the foundations
of its massive bulwarks.

At one end of the city, near the sea, on a high mound,
stood the Alcazaba or citadel, a fortress of great strength.
Immediately above this, rose a steep and rocky mount,
on the top of which, in old times, had been a pharos or
light-house, from which the height derived its name of
Gibralfaro.*  It was at present crowned by an immense
castle, which, from its lofty and cragged situation, its

---

* A corruption of *Gibel-faro*, the hill of the light-house.

375

vast walls and mighty towers, was deemed impregnable. It communicated with the Alcazaba by a covered way, six paces broad, leading down between two walls, along the profile or ridge of the rock. The castle of Gibralfaro commanded both citadel and city, and was capable, if both were taken, of maintaining a siege. Two large suburbs adjoined the city: in the one towards the sea, were the dwelling-houses of the most opulent inhabitants, adorned with hanging gardens; the other, on the land side, was thickly peopled, and surrounded by strong walls and towers.

Malaga possessed a brave and numerous garrison, and the common people were active, hardy, and resolute; but the city was rich and commercial, and under the habitual control of numerous opulent merchants, who dreaded the ruinous consequences of a siege. They were little zealous for the warlike renown of their city, and longed rather to participate in the enviable security of property, and the lucrative privileges of safe traffic with the Christian territories, granted to all places which declared for Boabdil. At the head of these gainful citizens was Ali Dordux, a mighty merchant of uncounted wealth, connected, it is said, with the royal family of Granada, whose ships traded to every part of the Levant, and whose word was as a law in Malaga. Ali Dordux assembled the most opulent and important of his commercial brethren, and they repaired in a body to the Alcazaba, where they were received by the alcayde, Aben Comixa, with that deference generally shown to men of their great local dignity and power of purse. Ali Dordux was ample and stately in his form, and fluent and emphatic in his discourse; his eloquence had an effect, therefore, upon the alcayde, as he represented the hopelessness of a defense of Malaga, the misery that must attend a siege, and the ruin that must follow a capture by force of arms. On the other hand, he set forth the grace that might be obtained from the Castilian sovereigns, by an early and voluntary acknowledgement of Boabdil as king; the peaceful possession of their property, and the profitable commerce with the Christian ports, that would be allowed them. He was seconded by his weighty and important coadjutors; and the alcayde, accustomed to regard them as the arbiters of the affairs of the place, yielded to their united counsels. He departed, therefore, with all speed, to the Christian camp, empowered to arrange a capitulation with the Castilian monarch; and in the meantime, his brother remained in command of the Alcazaba.

There was at this time, as alcayde, in the old cragbuilt castle of Gibralfaro, a warlike and fiery Moor, an implacable enemy of the Christians. This was no other than Hamet Zeli, surnamed El Zegri, the once formidable alcayde of Ronda, and the terror of its mountains. He had never forgiven the capture of his favorite fortress, and panted for vengeance on the Christians. Notwithstanding his reverses, he had retained the favor of

El Zagal, who knew how to appreciate a bold warrior of the kind, and had placed him in command of this important fortress of Gibralfaro.

Hamet el Zegri had gathered round him the remnant of his band of Gomeres, with others of the same tribe, recently arrived from Morocco. These fierce warriors were nestled, like so many war-hawks, about their lofty cliff. They looked down with martial contempt upon the commercial city of Malaga, which they were placed to protect ; or rather, they esteemed it only for its military importance, and its capability of defense. They held no communion with its trading, gainful inhabitants, and even considered the garrison of the Alcazaba their inferiors. War was their pursuit and passion ; they rejoiced in its turbulent and perilous scenes ; and, confident in the strength of the city, and, above all, of their castle, they set at defiance the menace of Christian invasion. There were among them, also, many apostate Moors, who had once embraced Christianity, but had since recanted, and fled from the vengeance of the Inquisition.* These were desperadoes, who had no mercy to expect, should they again fall into the hands of the enemy.

Such were the fierce elements of the garrison of Gibralfaro ; and its rage may easily be conceived, at hearing that Malaga was to be given up without a blow ; that they were to sink into Christian vassals, under the inter-

* Zurita, lib. 30, cap. 71.

mediate sway of Boabdil el Chico; and that the alcayde
of the Alcazaba had departed, to arrange the terms of
capitulation.

Hamet determined to avert, by desperate means, the
threatened degradation. He knew that there was a large
party in the city faithful to El Zagal, being composed of
warlike men, who had taken refuge from the various
mountain towns which had been captured; their feelings
were desperate as their fortunes, and, like Hamet, they
panted for revenge upon the Christians. With these he
had a secret conference, and received assurance of their
adherence to him in any measures of defense. As to the
counsel of the peaceful inhabitants, he considered it unworthy the consideration of a soldier; and he spurned at
the interference of the wealthy merchant Ali Dordux, in
matters of warfare.

"Still," said Hamet el Zegri, "let us proceed regularly." So he descended with his Gomeres to the citadel,
entered it suddenly, put to death the brother of the
alcayde, and such of the garrison as made any demur,
and then summoned the principal inhabitants of Malaga,
to deliberate on measures for the welfare of the city.*
The wealthy merchants again mounted to the citadel,
excepting Ali Dordux, who refused to obey the summons.
They entered with hearts filled with awe, for they found
Hamet surrounded by his grim African guard, and all

* *Cura de los Palacios*, c. 82.

the stern array of military power, and they beheld the bloody traces of the recent massacre.

Hamet rolled a dark and searching eye upon the assembly. "Who," said he, "is loyal and devoted to Muley Abdallah el Zagal?" Every one present asserted his loyalty. "Good!" said Hamet; "and who is ready to prove his devotion to his sovereign, by defending this his important city to the last extremity?" Every one present declared his readiness. "Enough!" observed Hamet; "the alcayde Aben Comixa has proved himself a traitor to his sovereign, and to you all; for he has conspired to deliver the place to the Christians. It behooves you to choose some other commander, capable of defending your city against the approaching enemy." The assembly declared unanimously, that no one was so worthy of the command as himself. So Hamet was appointed alcayde of Malaga, and immediately proceeded to man the forts and towers with his partisans and to make every preparation for a desperate resistance.

Intelligence of these occurrences put an end to the negotiations between king Ferdinand and the superseded alcayde Aben Comixa, and it was supposed there was no alternative but to lay siege to the place. The marques of Cadiz, however, found at Velez a Moorish cavalier of some note, a native of Malaga, who offered to tamper with Hamet el Zegri for the surrender of the city, or at least of the castle of Gibralfaro. The marques communicated this to the king; "I put this business, and the key of my treasury, into your hands," said Ferdinand; "act, stipulate, and disburse, in my name, as you think proper."

The marques armed the Moor with his own lance, cuirass, and target, and mounted him on one of his own horses. He equipped in similar style, also, another Moor, his companion and relative. They bore secret letters to Hamet from the marques, offering him the town of Coin in perpetual inheritance, and four thousand doblas in gold, if he would deliver up Gibralfaro; together with a farm and two thousand doblas for his lieutenant Ibrahim Zenete, and large sums to be distributed among his officers and soldiers; and he offered unlimited rewards for the surrender of the city.

Hamet had a warrior's admiration of the marques of Cadiz, and received his messengers with courtesy in his fortress of Gibralfaro. He even listened to their propositions with patience, and dismissed them in safety, though with an absolute refusal. The marques thought his reply was not so peremptory as to discourage another effort. The emissaries were dispatched, therefore, a second time, with further propositions. They approached Malaga in the night, but found the guards doubled, patrols abroad, and the whole place on the alert. They were discovered, pursued, and only saved themselves by the fleetness of their steeds, and their knowledge of the passes of the mountains.*

* *Cura de los Palacios*, MS., c. 82.

Finding all attempts to tamper with the faith of Hamet utterly futile, king Ferdinand publicly summoned the city to surrender, offering the most favorable terms in case of immediate compliance; but threatening captivity to all the inhabitants, in case of resistance.

It required a man of nerve to undertake the delivery of such a summons in the present heated and turbulent state of the Moorish community. Such a one stepped forward in the person of a cavalier of the royal guards, Hernan Perez del Pulgar by name, a youth of noble descent, who had already signalized himself by his romantic valor and daring enterprise. Furnished with official papers for Hamet el Zegri and a private letter from the king to Ali Dordux, he entered the gates of Malaga under the protection of a flag, and boldly delivered his summons in presence of the principal inhabitants. The language of the summons, or the tone in which it was delivered, exasperated the fiery spirit of the Moors, and it required all the energy of Hamet and the influence of several of the alfaquis, to prevent an outrage to the person of the ambassador. The reply of Hamet was haughty and decided. "The city of Malaga has been confided to me," said he, "not to be surrendered, but defended, and the king shall witness how I acquit myself of my charge."[*]

His mission at an end, Hernan del Pulgar rode slowly

* Pulgar, pt. 3, cap. 74.

and deliberately through the city, utterly regardless of
the scowls and menaces, and scarcely restrained turbulence of the multitude, and bore to Ferdinand at Velez
the haughty answer of the Moor; but at the same time
gave him a formidable account of the force of the garrison, the strength of the fortifications, and the determined spirit of the commander and his men. The king
immediately sent orders to have the heavy artillery for-
warded from Antiquera; and, on the 7th of May, marched
with his army towards Malaga.

# CHAPTER LIII.

ADVANCE OF KING FERDINAND AGAINST MALAGA.

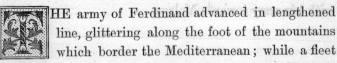

ADVANCE OF KING FERDINAND AGAINST MALAGA.

THE army of Ferdinand advanced in lengthened line, glittering along the foot of the mountains which border the Mediterranean; while a fleet of vessels, freighted with heavy artillery and warlike munitions, kept pace with it at a short distance from the land, covering the sea with a thousand gleaming sails. When Hamet el Zegri saw this force approaching, he set fire to the houses of the suburbs which adjoined the walls, and sent forth three battalions to encounter the advance guard of the enemy.

The Christian army drew near to the city, at that end where the castle and rocky height of Gibralfaro defend the seaboard. Immediately opposite, at about two bow-shots' distance, stood the castle; and between it and the high chain of mountains, was a steep and rocky hill, at present called the hill of St. Christobal, commanding a pass through which the Christians must march to penetrate to the vega and surround the city. Hamet ordered the three battalions to take their stations, one on this hill, another in the pass near the castle, and a third on the side of the mountain near the sea.

A body of Spanish foot-soldiers, of the advance guard, sturdy mountaineers of Galicia, sprang forward to climb the side of the height next the sea; at the same time, a number of cavaliers and hidalgos of the royal household attacked the Moors who guarded the pass below. The Moors defended their posts with obstinate valor. The Galicians were repeatedly overpowered and driven down the hill, but as often rallied, and being reinforced by the hidalgos and cavaliers, returned to the assault. This obstinate struggle lasted for six hours: the strife was of a deadly kind, not merely with cross-bows and arquebuses, but hand to hand, with swords and daggers; no quarter was claimed or given, on either side—they fought not to make captives, but to slay. It was but the advance of the Christian army that was engaged; so narrow was the pass along the coast, that the army could proceed only in file: horse and foot, and beasts of burden, were crowded one upon another, impeding each other, and blocking up the narrow and rugged defile. The soldiers heard the uproar of the battle, the sound of trumpets, and the war-cries of the Moors—but tried in vain to press forward to the assistance of their companions.

At length a body of foot-soldiers of the Holy Brotherhood climbed, with great difficulty, the steep side of the mountain which overhung the pass, and advanced with

25

seven banners displayed. The Moors, seeing this force above them, abandoned the pass in despair. The battle was still raging on the height; the Galicians, though supported by Castilian troops under Don Hurtado de Mendoza and Garcilasso de la Vega, were severely pressed and roughly handled by the Moors; at length a brave standard-bearer, Luys Mazeda by name, threw himself into the midst of the enemy, and planted his banner on the summit. The Galicians and Castilians, stimulated by this noble self-devotion, followed him, fighting desperately, and the Moors were at length driven to their castle of Gibralfaro.*

This important height being taken, the pass lay open to the army; but by this time evening was advancing, and the host was too weary and exhausted to seek proper situations for the encampment. The king, attended by several grandees and cavaliers, went the rounds at night, stationing outposts towards the city, and guards and patrols to give the alarm on the least movement of the enemy. All night the Christians lay upon their arms, lest there should be some attempt to sally forth and attack them.

When the morning dawned, the king gazed with admiration at this city, which he hoped soon to add to his dominions. It was surrounded on one side by vineyards, gardens, and orchards, which covered the hills with verd-

* Pulgar, *Cronica.*

ure; on the other side, its walls were bathed by the smooth and tranquil sea. Its vast and lofty towers and prodigious castles, hoary with age, yet unimpaired in strength, showed the labors of magnanimous men in former times to protect their favorite abode. Hanging gardens, groves of oranges, citrons, and pomegranates, with the cedars and stately palms, were mingled with the stern battlements and towers—bespeaking the opulence and luxury that reigned within.

In the meantime, the Christian army poured through the pass, and throwing out its columns and extending its lines, took possession of every vantage ground around the city. King Ferdinand surveyed the ground, and appointed the stations of the different commanders.

The important mount of St. Christobal, which had cost so violent a struggle, and faced the powerful fortress of Gibralfaro, was given in charge to Roderigo Ponce de Leon, marques of Cadiz, who, in all sieges, claimed the post of danger. He had several noble cavaliers with their retainers in his encampment, which consisted of fifteen hundred horse and fourteen thousand foot; and extended from the summit of the mount to the margin of the sea, completely blocking up the approach to the city on that side. From this post, a line of encampments extended quite round the city to the seaboard, fortified by bulwarks and deep ditches; while a fleet of armed ships and galleys stretched before the harbor; so that the place was completely invested, by sea and land.

The various parts of the valley now resounded with the din of preparation, and were filled with artificers preparing warlike engines and munitions : armorers and smiths, with glowing forges and deafening hammers ; carpenters and engineers, constructing machines wherewith to assail the walls ; stonecutters, shaping stone balls for the ordnance ; and burners of charcoal, preparing fuel for the furnaces and forges.

When the encampment was formed, the heavy ordnance was landed from the ships, and mounted in various parts of the camp. Five huge lombards were placed on the mount commanded by the marques of Cadiz, so as to bear upon the castle of Gibralfaro.

The Moors made strenuous efforts to impede these preparations. They kept up a heavy fire from their ordnance, upon the men employed in digging trenches or constructing batteries, so that the latter had to work principally in the night. The royal tents had been stationed conspicuously, and within reach of the Moorish batteries ; but were so warmly assailed, that they had to be removed behind a hill.

When the works were completed, the Christian batteries opened in return, and kept up a tremendous cannonade ; while the fleet, approaching the land, assailed the city vigorously on the opposite side.

"It was a glorious and delectable sight," observes Fray Antonio Agapida, "to behold this infidel city thus surrounded by sea and land, by a mighty Christian force. Every mound in its circuit was, as it were, a little city of tents, bearing the standard of some renowned Catholic warrior. Beside the warlike ships and galleys which lay before the place, the sea was covered with innumerable sails, passing and repassing, appearing and disappearing, being engaged in bringing supplies for the subsistence of the army. It seemed a vast spectacle contrived to recreate the eye, did not the volleying bursts of flame and smoke from the ships, which seemed to lie asleep on the quiet sea, and the thunder of ordnance from camp and city, from tower and battlement, tell the deadly warfare that was waging.

"At night, the scene was far more direful than in the day. The cheerful light of the sun was gone; there was nothing but the flashes of artillery, or the baleful gleams of combustibles thrown into the city, and the conflagration of the houses. The fire kept up from the Christian batteries was incessant; there were seven great lombards in particular, called The Seven Sisters of Ximenes, which did tremendous execution. The Moorish ordnance replied in thunder from the walls: Gibralfaro was wrapped in volumes of smoke, rolling about its base; and Hamet and his Gomeres looked out with triumph upon the tempest of war they had awaked. Truly they were so many demons incarnate," concludes the pious Fray Antonio Agapida, "who were permitted by Heaven to enter into and possess this infidel city, for its perdition."

390

# CHAPTER LIV.

HE attack on Malaga, by sea and land, was kept up for several days with tremendous violence, but without producing any great impression, so strong were the ancient bulwarks of the city. The count de Cifuentes was the first to signalize himself by any noted achievement. A main tower, protecting what is at present called the suburb of Santa Ana, had been shattered by the ordnance, and the battlements demolished, so as to yield no shelter to its defenders. Seeing this, the count assembled a gallant band of cavaliers of the royal household, and advanced to take it by storm. They applied scaling ladders, and mounted, sword in hand. The Moors, having no longer battlements to protect them, descended to a lower floor, and made furious resistance from the windows and loopholes. They poured down boiling pitch and rosin, and hurled stones, and darts, and arrows, on the assailants. Many of the Christians were slain, their ladders were destroyed by flaming combustibles, and the count was obliged to retreat from before the tower. On the following day he renewed the attack with superior force, and, after a severe combat, succeeded in planting his victorious banner on the tower.

The Moors now assailed the tower in their turn. They undermined the part towards the city, placed props of wood under the foundation, and, setting fire to them, drew off to a distance. In a little while the props gave way, the foundation sunk, and the tower was rent; part of its wall fell, with a tremendous noise; many of the Christians were thrown out headlong, and the rest were laid open to the missiles of the enemy.

By this time, however, a breach had been made in the wall of the suburb adjoining the tower, and troops poured in to the assistance of their comrades. A continued battle was kept up for two days and a night, by reinforcements from camp and city. The parties fought backwards and forwards through the breach of the wall, and in the narrow and winding streets adjacent, with alternate success; and the vicinity of the tower was strewn with the dead and wounded. At length the Moors gradually gave way, disputing every inch of ground, until they were driven into the city; and the Christians remained masters of the greater part of the suburb.

This partial success, though gained with great toil and bloodshed, gave temporary animation to the Christians; they soon found, however, that the attack on the main works of the city was a much more arduous task. The garrison contained veterans who had served in many of the towns captured by the Christians. They were no longer confounded and dismayed by the battering ordnance and other strange engines of foreign invention, and had become expert in parrying their effects, in repairing breaches, and erecting counter-works.

The Christians, accustomed of late to speedy conquests of Moorish fortresses, become impatient of the slow progress of the siege. Many were apprehensive of a scarcity of provisions, from the difficulty of subsisting so numerous a host in the heart of the enemy's country, where it was necessary to transport supplies across rugged and hostile mountains, or subjected to the uncertainties of the sea. Many also were alarmed at a pestilence which broke out in the neighboring villages; and some were so overcome by these apprehensions, as to abandon the camp and return to their homes.

Several of the loose and worthless hangers-on that infest all great armies, hearing these murmurs, thought that the siege would soon be raised, and deserted to the enemy, hoping to make their fortunes. They gave exaggerated accounts of the alarms and discontents of the army, and represented the troops as daily returning home in bands. Above all they declared that the gunpowder was nearly exhausted, so that the artillery would soon be useless. They assured the Moors, therefore, that if they persisted a little longer in their defense, the king would be obliged to draw off his forces and abandon the siege.

The reports of these renegadoes gave fresh courage to the garrison; they made vigorous sallies upon the camp, harassing it by night and day, and obliging every part to be guarded with the most painful vigilance. They fortified the weak parts of their walls with ditches and palisadoes, and gave every manifestation of a determined and unyielding spirit.

Ferdinand soon received intelligence of the reports which had been carried to the Moors; he understood that they had been informed, likewise, that the queen was alarmed for the safety of the camp, and had written repeatedly urging him to abandon the siege. As the best means of disproving all these falsehoods, and destroying the vain hopes of the enemy, he wrote to the queen, entreating her to come and take up her residence in the camp.

# CHAPTER LV.

SIEGE OF MALAGA CONTINUED.—OBSTINACY OF HAMET EL ZEGRI.

REAT was the enthusiasm of the army, when they beheld their patriot queen advancing in state, to share the toils and dangers of her people. Isabella entered the camp, attended by the dignitaries and the whole retinue of her court, to manifest that this was no temporary visit. On one side of her was her daughter, the Infanta; on the other, the grand cardinal of Spain; Hernando de Talavere, the prior of Prado, confessor to the queen, followed, with a great train of prelates, courtiers, cavaliers, and ladies of distinction. The cavalcade moved in calm and stately order through the camp, softening the iron aspect of war by this array of courtly grace and female beauty.

Isabella had commanded, that on her coming to the camp, the horrors of war should be suspended, and fresh offers of peace made to the enemy. On her arrival, therefore, there had been a general cessation of firing throughout the camp. A messenger was, at the same time, dispatched to the besieged, informing them of her being in the camp, and of the determination of the sovereigns to make it their settled residence until the city should be taken. The same terms were offered, in case of immediate surrender, that had been granted to Velez Malaga; but the inhabitants were threatened with captivity and the sword, should they persist in their defense.

Hamet el Zegri received this message with haughty contempt, and dismissed the messenger without deigning a reply, and accompanied by an escort to prevent his holding any communication with the inhabitants in the streets. "The Christian sovereigns," said Hamet to those about him, "have made this offer in consequence of their despair. The silence of their batteries proves the truth of what has been told us, that their powder is exhausted. They have no longer the means of demolishing our walls; and if they remain much longer, the autumnal rains will interrupt their convoys, and fill their camp with famine and disease. The first storm will disperse their fleet, which has no neighboring port of shelter: Africa will then be open to us, to procure reinforcements and supplies."

The words of Hamet El Zegri were hailed as oracular, by his adherents. Many of the peaceful part of the community, however, ventured to remonstrate, and to implore him to accept the proffered mercy. The stern Hamet silenced them with a terrific threat: he declared, that whoever should talk of capitulating, or should hold any communication with the Christians should be put to death. The Gomeres, like true men of the sword, acted upon the menace of their chieftain as upon a written law, and having detected several of the inhabitants in secret correspondence with the enemy, set upon and slew them, and confiscated their effects. This struck such terror into the citizens, that those who had been loudest in their murmurs became suddenly mute, and were remarked as evincing the greatest bustle and alacrity in the defense of the city.

When the messenger returned to the camp, and reported the contemptuous reception of the royal message, King Ferdinand was exceedingly indignant. Finding the cessation of firing, on the queen's arrival, had encouraged a belief among the enemy that there was a scarcity of powder in the camp, he ordered a general discharge from all the batteries. The sudden burst of war from every quarter soon convinced the Moors of their error, and completed the confusion of the citizens, who knew not which most to dread, their assailants or their defenders, the Christians or the Gomeres.

That evening the sovereigns visited the encampment of the marques of Cadiz, which commanded a view over a great part of the city, the camp, and the sea with its flotillas. The tent of the marques was of great magnitude, furnished with hangings of rich brocade and French cloth of the rarest texture. It was in the oriental style; and, as it crowned the height, with the surrounding tents of other cavaliers, all sumptuously furnished, presented a gay and silken contrast to the opposite towers of Gibralfaro. Here a splendid collation was served up to the sovereigns, and the courtly revel that prevailed in this chivalrous encampment, the glitter of pageantry, and the bursts of festive music, made more striking the gloom and silence that reigned over the Moorish castle.

The marques of Cadiz, while it was yet light, conducted his royal visitors to every point that commanded a view of the warlike scene below. He caused the heavy lombards also to be discharged, that the queen and ladies of the court might witness the effect of those tremendous engines. The fair dames were filled with awe and admiration, as the mountain shook beneath their feet with the thunder of the artillery, and they beheld great fragments of the Moorish walls tumbling down the rocks and precipices.

While the good marques was displaying these things to his royal guests, he lifted up his eyes, and to his astonishment beheld his own banner hanging out from the nearest tower of Gibralfaro. The blood mantled in his cheek, for it was a banner he had lost at the time of the memorable massacre of the heights of Malaga.* To make this taunt more evident, several of the Gomeres displayed themselves upon the battlements, arrayed in the helmets and cuirasses of some of the cavaliers slain or captured on that occasion. The marques of Cadiz restrained his indignation, and held his peace; but several of his cavaliers vowed loudly to revenge this cruel bravado, on the ferocious garrison of Gibralfaro.

* Diego de Valera, *Cronica*, MS.

# CHAPTER LVI.

ATTACK OF THE MARQUES OF CADIZ UPON GIBRALFARO.

THE marques of Cadiz was not a cavalier that readily forgave an injury or an insult. On the morning after the royal banquet, his batteries opened a tremendous fire upon Gibralfaro. All day, the encampment was wrapped in wreaths of smoke; nor did the assault cease with the day—but, throughout the night, there was an incessant flashing and thundering of the lombards, and, the following morning, the assault rather increased than slackened in fury. The Moorish bulwarks were no proof against those formidable engines. In a few days, the lofty tower on which the taunting banner had been displayed, was shattered; a smaller tower in its vicinity reduced to ruins, and a great breach made in the intervening walls.

Several of the hot-spirited cavaliers were eager for storming the breach, sword in hand; others, more cool and wary, pointed out the rashness of such an attempt; for the Moors had worked indefatigably in the night; they had digged a deep ditch within the breach, and had fortified it with palisadoes and a high breastwork. All,

398

however, agreed that the camp might safely be advanced near to the ruined walls, and that it ought to be done so, in return for the insolent defiance of the enemy.

The marques of Cadiz felt the temerity of the measure, but was unwilling to dampen the zeal of these high-spirited cavaliers; and having chosen the post of danger in the camp, it did not become him to decline any service, merely because it might appear perilous. He ordered his outposts, therefore, to be advanced within a stone's-throw of the breach, but exhorted the soldiers to maintain the utmost vigilance.

The thunder of the batteries had ceased; the troops, exhausted by two nights' fatigue and watchfulness, and apprehending no danger from the dismantled walls, were half of them asleep; the rest were scattered about in negligent security. On a sudden, upward of two thousand Moors sallied forth from the castle, led on by Ibrahim Zenete, the principal captain under Hamet. They fell with fearful havoc upon the advanced guard, slaying many of them in their sleep, and putting the rest to headlong flight.

The marques was in his tent, about a bow-shot distant, when he heard the tumult of the onset, and beheld his men flying in confusion. He rushed forth, followed by his standard-bearer. "Turn again, cavaliers!" exclaimed he; "I am here, Ponce de Leon! to the foe! to the foe!" The flying troops stopped at hearing his well-known voice, rallied under his banner, and turned upon the enemy. The encampment, by this time, was roused; several cavaliers from the adjoining stations had hastened to the scene of action, with a number of Galicians and soldiers of the Holy Brotherhood. An obstinate and bloody contest ensued; the ruggedness of the place, the rocks, chasms, and declivities, broke it into numerous combats: Christian and Moor fought hand to hand, with swords and daggers; and often, grappling and struggling, rolled together down the precipices.

The banner of the marques was in danger of being taken; he hastened to its rescue, followed by some of his bravest cavaliers. They were surrounded by the enemy, and several of them cut down. Don Diego Ponce de Leon, brother to the marques, was wounded by an arrow; and his son-in-law, Luis Ponce, was likewise wounded: they succeeded, however, in rescuing the banner, and bearing it off in safety. The battle lasted for an hour; the height was covered with killed and wounded, and the blood flowed in streams down the rocks; at length, Ibrahim Zenete, being disabled by the thrust of a lance, the Moors gave way and retreated to the castle.

They now opened a galling fire from their battlements and towers, approaching the breaches so as to discharge their cross-bows and arquebuses into the advanced guard of the encampment. The marques was singled out; the shot fell thick about him, and one passed through his buckler, and struck upon his cuirass, but without doing him any injury. Every one now saw the danger and inutility of approaching the camp thus near to the castle; and those who had counseled it, were now urgent that it should be withdrawn. It was accordingly removed back to its original ground, from which the marques had most reluctantly advanced it. Nothing but his valor and timely aid had prevented this attack on his outpost from ending in a total rout of all that part of the army.

Many cavaliers of distinction fell in this contest; but the loss of none was felt more deeply than that of Ortega del Prado, captain of escaladors. He was one of the bravest men in the service; the same who had devised the first successful blow of the war, the storming of Alhama, where he was the first to plant and mount the scaling-ladders. He had always been high in the favor and confidence of the noble Ponce de Leon, who knew how to appreciate and avail himself of the merits of all able and valiant men.*

* Zurita. Mariana. Abarca.

26

# CHAPTER LVII.

### SIEGE OF MALAGA CONTINUED.—STRATAGEMS OF VARIOUS KINDS.

REAT were the exertions now made, both by the besiegers and the besieged, to carry on this contest with the utmost vigor. Hamet went the rounds of the walls and towers, doubling the guards, and putting everything in the best posture of defense. The garrison was divided into parties of a hundred, to each of which a captain was appointed. Some were to patrol, others to sally forth and skirmish with the enemy, and others to hold themselves armed and in reserve. Six albatozas, or floating batteries, were manned and armed with pieces of artillery, to attack the fleet.

On the other hand, the Castilian sovereigns kept open a communication by sea with various parts of Spain, from which they received provisions of all kinds; they ordered supplies of powder also from Valencia, Barcelona, Sicily, and Portugal. They made great preparations also for storming the city. Towers of wood were constructed, to move on wheels, each capable of holding one hundred men; they were furnished with ladders, to be thrown from their summits to the tops of the walls;

and within those ladders others were encased, to be let down for the descent of the troops into the city. There were gallipagos or tortoises, also, being great wooden shields, covered with hides, to protect the assailants and those who undermined the walls.

Secret mines were commenced in various places; some were intended to reach to the foundations of the walls, which were to be propped up with wood, ready to be set on fire; others were to pass under the walls, and remain ready to be broken open, so as to give entrance to the besiegers. At these mines the army worked day and night; and, during these secret preparations, the ordnance kept up a fire upon the city, to divert the attention of the besieged.

In the meantime, Hamet displayed wonderful vigor and ingenuity in defending the city, and in repairing or fortifying, by deep ditches, the breaches made by the enemy. He noted, also, every place where the camp might be assailed with advantage, and gave the besieging army no repose night or day. While his troops sallied on the land, his floating batteries attacked the besiegers on the sea; so that there was incessant skirmishing. The tents called the Queen's Hospital were crowded with wounded, and the whole army suffered from constant watchfulness and fatigue. To guard against the sudden assaults of the Moors, the trenches were deepened, and palisadoes erected in front of the camp; and in that part facing Gibralfaro, where the rocky heights did not admit of such defenses, a high rampart of earth was thrown up. The cavaliers Garcilasso de la Vega, Juan de Zuñiga, and Diego de Atayde were appointed to go the rounds, and keep vigilant watch that these fortifications were maintained in good order.

In a little while Hamet discovered the mines secretly commenced by the Christians: he immediately ordered counter-mines. The soldiers mutually worked until they met and fought hand to hand, in these subterranean passages. The Christians were driven out of one of their mines; fire was set to the wooden framework, and the mine destroyed. Encouraged by this success, the Moors attempted a general attack upon the camp, the mines, and the besieging fleet. The battle lasted for six hours, on land and water, above and below ground, on bulwark and in trench and mine; the Moors displayed wonderful intrepidity, but were finally repulsed at all points, and obliged to retire into the city, where they were closely invested, without the means of receiving any assistance from abroad.

The horrors of famine were now added to the other miseries of Malaga. Hamet, with the spirit of a man bred up to war, considered everything as subservient to the wants of the soldier, and ordered all the grain in the city to be gathered and garnered up for the sole use of those who fought. Even this was dealt out sparingly, and each soldier received four ounces of bread in the morning, and two in the evening, for his daily allowance.

The wealthy inhabitants, and all those peacefully in-clined, mourned over a resistance which brought de-struction upon their houses, death into their families, and which they saw must end in their ruin and captivity; still none of them dared to speak openly of capitulation, or even to manifest their grief, lest they should awaken the wrath of their fierce defenders. They surrounded their civic champion, Ali Dordux, the great and opulent merchant, who had buckled on shield and cuirass, and taken spear in hand for the defense of his native city, and, with a large body of the braver citizens, had charge of one of the gates and a considerable portion of the walls. Drawing Ali Dordux aside, they poured forth their griefs to him in secret. "Why," said they, "should we suffer our native city to be made a mere bulwark and fighting-place for foreign barbarians and desperate men? They have no families to care for, no property to lose, no love for the soil, and no value for their lives. They fight to gratify a thirst for blood or a desire for revenge, and will fight on until Malaga becomes a ruin and its people slaves. Let us think and act for ourselves, our wives, and our children. Let us make private terms with the Christians before it is too late, and save our-selves from destruction."

The bowels of Ali Dordux yearned towards his fellow-citizens; he bethought him also of the sweet security of peace, and the bloodless yet gratifying triumphs of gain-ful traffic. The idea also of a secret negotiation or bargain with the Castilian sovereigns, for the redemption of his native city, was more conformable to his accustomed habits than this violent appeal to arms; for though he had for a time assumed the warrior, he had not forgotten the merchant. Ali Dordux communed, therefore, with the citizen-soldiers under his command, and they readily conformed to his opinion. Concerting together, they wrote a proposition to the Castilian sovereigns, offering to admit the army into the part of the city intrusted to their care, on receiving assurance of protection for the lives and properties of the inhabitants. This writing they delivered to a trusty emissary to take to the Christian camp, appointing the hour and place of his return, that they might be ready to admit him unperceived.

The Moor made his way in safety to the camp, and was admitted to the presence of the sovereigns. Eager to gain the city without further cost of blood or treasure, they gave a written promise to grant the condition; and the Moor set out joyfully on his return. As he approached the walls where Ali Dordux and his confederates were waiting to receive him, he was descried by a patrolling band of Gomeres, and considered a spy coming from the camp of the besiegers. They issued forth and seized him, in sight of his employers, who gave themselves up for lost. The Gomeres had conducted him nearly to the gate, when he escaped from their grasp and fled. They endeavored to overtake him, but were en-

cumbered with armor; he was lightly clad, and he fled
for his life. One of the Gomeres paused, and, leveling
his cross-bow, let fly a bolt, which pierced the fugitive
between the shoulders; he fell, and was nearly within
their grasp, but rose again, and with a desperate effort
attained the Christian camp. The Gomeres gave over
the pursuit, and the citizens returned thanks to Allah for
their deliverance from this fearful peril. As to the faithful messenger, he died of his wound shortly after reaching the camp, consoled with the idea that he had preserved the secret and the lives of his employers.*

* Pulgar. *Cronica*, p. 8, c. 80.

# CHAPTER LVIII.

### SUFFERINGS OF THE PEOPLE OF MALAGA.

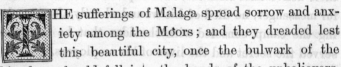THE sufferings of Malaga spread sorrow and anxiety among the Moors; and they dreaded lest this beautiful city, once the bulwark of the kingdom, should fall into the hands of the unbelievers. The old warrior king, Abdallah el Zagal, was still sheltered in Guadix, where he was slowly gathering together his shattered forces. When the people of Guadix heard of the danger and distress of Malaga, they urged to be led to its relief; and the alfaquis admonished El Zagal not to desert so righteous and loyal a city, in its extremity. His own warlike nature made him feel a sympathy for a place that made so gallant a resistance; and he dispatched as powerful a reinforcement as he could spare, under conduct of a chosen captain, with orders to throw themselves into the city.

Intelligence of this reinforcement reached Boabdil el Chico in his royal palace of the Alhambra. Filled with hostility against his uncle, and desirous of proving his loyalty to the Castilian sovereigns, he immediately sent forth a superior force of horse and foot, under an able commander, to intercept the detachment. A sharp conflict ensued; the troops of El Zagal were routed with great loss, and fled back in confusion to Guadix.

Boabdil, not being accustomed to victories, was flushed with this melancholy triumph. He sent tidings of it to the Castilian sovereigns, accompanied with rich silks, boxes of Arabian perfume, a cup of gold, richly wrought, and a female captive of Ubeda, as presents to the queen; and four Arabian steeds, magnificently caparisoned, a sword and dagger richly mounted, and several albornozes and other robes sumptuously embroidered, for the king. He entreated them, at the same time, always to look upon him with favor as their devoted vassal.

Boabdil was fated to be unfortunate, even in his victories. His defeat of the forces of his uncle, destined to the relief of unhappy Malaga, shocked the feelings and cooled the loyalty of many of his best adherents. The mere men of traffic might rejoice in their golden interval of peace; but the chivalrous spirits of Granada spurned a security purchased by such sacrifices of pride and affection. The people at large, having gratified their love of change, began to question whether they had acted generously by their old fighting monarch. "El Zagal," said they, "was fierce and bloody, but then he was faithful to his country; he was an usurper, it is true, but then he maintained the glory of the crown which he usurped. If his sceptre was a rod of iron to his subjects, it was a sword of steel against their enemies. This Boabdil sacrifices religion, friends, country, everything, to a mere shadow of royalty, and is content to hold a rush for a sceptre."

These factious murmurs soon reached the ears of Boabdil, and he apprehended another of his customary reverses. He sent in all haste to the Castilian sovereigns, beseeching military aid to keep him on his throne. Ferdinand graciously complied with a request so much in unison with his policy. A detachment of one thousand cavalry and two thousand infantry was sent, under the command of Don Fernandez Gonsalvo of Cordova, subsequently renowned as the grand captain. With this succor, Boabdil expelled from the city all those who were hostile to him, and in favor of his uncle. He felt secure in these troops, from their being distinct in manners, language, and religion, from his subjects; and compromised with his pride, in thus exhibiting that most unnatural and humiliating of all regal spectacles, a monarch supported on his throne by foreign weapons and by soldiers hostile to his people.

Nor was Boabdil el Chico the only Moorish sovereign that sought protection from Ferdinand and Isabella. A splendid galley, with lateen sails, and several banks of oars, displaying the standard of the crescent, but likewise a white flag in sign of amity, came one day into the harbor. An ambassador landed from it, within the Christian lines. He came from the king of Tremezan, and brought presents similar to those of Boabdil, consisting of Arabian coursers, with bits, stirrups, and other furniture of gold, together with costly Moorish mantles; for the queen, there were sumptuous shawls, robes, and silken stuffs, ornaments of gold, and exquisite oriental perfumes.

The king of Tremezan had been alarmed at the rapid conquests of the Spanish arms, and startled by the descent of several Spanish cruisers on the coast of Africa. He craved to be considered a vassal to the Castilian sovereigns, and that they would extend such favor and security to his ships and subjects as had been shown to other Moors who had submitted to their sway. He requested a painting of their arms, that he and his subjects might recognize and respect their standard, whenever they encountered it. At the same time he implored their clemency toward unhappy Malaga, and that its inhabitants might experience the same favor that had been shown towards the Moors of other captured cities.

The embassy was graciously received by the Christian sovereigns. They granted the protection required; ordering their commanders to respect the flag of Tremezan, unless it should be found rendering assistance to the enemy. They sent also to the Barbary monarch their royal arms, moulded in escutcheons of gold, a hand's-breadth in size.[*]

While thus the chances of assistance from without

* *Cura de los Palacios*, c. 84.   Pulgar, part 3, c. 68.

daily decreased, famine raged in the city. The inhabitants were compelled to eat the flesh of horses, and many died of hunger. What made the sufferings of the citizens the more intolerable was, to behold the sea covered with ships, daily arriving with provisions for the besiegers. Day after day, also, they saw herds of fat cattle and flocks of sheep driven into the camp. Wheat and flour were piled in huge mounds in the centre of the encampments, glaring in the sunshine, and tantalizing the wretched citizens, who, while they and their children were perishing with hunger, beheld prodigal abundance reigning within a bowshot of their walls.

# CHAPTER LIX.

HOW A MOORISH SANTON UNDERTOOK TO DELIVER THE CITY OF MALAGA
FROM THE POWER OF ITS ENEMIES.

THERE lived at this time, in a hamlet in the neighborhood of Guadix, an ancient Moor, of the name of Ibrahim el Guerbi. He was a native of the island of Guerbes, in the kingdom of Tunis, and had for several years led the life of a santon or hermit. The hot sun of Africa had dried his blood, and rendered him of an exalted yet melancholy temperament. He passed most of his time in caves of the mountains, in meditation, prayer, and rigorous abstinence, until his body was wasted and his mind bewildered, and he fancied himself favored with divine revelations, and visited by angels, sent by Mahomet. The Moors, who have a great reverence for all enthusiasts of the kind, believed in his being inspired, listened to all his ravings as veritable prophecies, and denominated him *el santo*, or the saint.

The woes of the kingdom of Granada had long exasperated the gloomy spirit of this man, and he had beheld with indignation this beautiful country wrested from the

413

dominion of the faithful, and becoming a prey to the unbelievers. He had implored the blessings of Allah on the troops which issued forth from Guadix for the relief of Malaga; but when he saw them return, routed and scattered by their own countrymen, he retired to his cell, shut himself up from the world, and was plunged for a time in the blackest melancholy.

On a sudden he made his appearance again in the streets of Guadix, his face haggard, his form emaciated, but his eye beaming with fire. He said that Allah had sent an angel to him in the solitude of his cell, revealing to him a mode of delivering Malaga from its perils, and striking horror and confusion into the camp of the unbelievers. The Moors listened with eager credulity to his words: four hundred of them offered to follow him even to the death, and to obey implicitly his commands. Of this number many were Gomeres, anxious to relieve their countrymen, who formed part of the garrison of Malaga.

They traversed the kingdom by the wild and lonely passes of the mountains, concealing themselves in the day and travelling only in the night, to elude the Christian scouts. At length they arrived at the mountains which tower above Malaga, and, looking down, beheld the city completely invested; a chain of encampments extending round it from shore to shore, and a line of ships blockading it by sea; while the continual thunder of artillery, and the smoke rising in various parts, showed that the siege was pressed with great activity. The hermit scanned the encampments warily, from his lofty height. He saw that the part of the encampment of the marques of Cadiz which was at the foot of the height, and on the margin of the sea, was most assailable, the rocky soil not admitting ditches or palisadoes. Remaining concealed all day, he descended with his followers at night to the sea-coast, and approached silently to the outworks. He had given them their instructions; they were to rush suddenly upon the camp, fight their way through, and throw themselves into the city.

It was just at the gray of the dawning, when objects are obscurely visible, that they made this desperate attempt. Some sprang suddenly upon the sentinels, others rushed into the sea and got round the works, others clambered over the breastworks. There was sharp skirmishing; a great part of the Moors were cut to pieces, but about two hundred succeeded in getting into the gates of Malaga.

The santon took no part in the conflict, nor did he endeavor to enter the city. His plans were of a different nature. Drawing apart from the battle, he threw himself on his knees on a rising ground, and, lifting his hands to Heaven, appeared to be absorbed in prayer. The Christians, as they were searching for fugitives in the clefts of the rocks, found him at his devotions. He stirred not at their approach, but remained fixed as a statue, without changing color or moving a muscle. Filled with surprise, not unmingled with awe, they took him to the marques of Cadiz. He was wrapped in a coarse albornoz, or Moorish mantle; his beard was long and grizzled, and there was something wild and melancholy in his look, that inspired curiosity. On being examined, he gave himself out as a saint to whom Allah had revealed the events that were to take place in that siege. The marques demanded when and how Malaga was to be taken. He replied that he knew full well, but he was forbidden to reveal those important secrets except to the king and queen. The good marques was not more given to superstitious fancies than other commanders of his time, yet there seemed something singular and mysterious about this man; he might have some important intelligence to communicate; so he was persuaded to send him to the king and queen. He was conducted to the royal tent, surrounded by a curious multitude, exclaiming, " *El Moro Santo!* " for the news had spread through the camp, that they had taken a Moorish prophet.

The king, having dined, was taking his siesta, or afternoon's sleep, in his tent; and the queen, though curious to see this singular man, yet, from a natural delicacy and reserve, delayed until the king should be present. He was taken therefore to an adjoining tent, in which were Doña Beatrix de Bobadilla, marchioness of Moya, and Don Alvaro of Portugal, son of the duke of Braganza, with two or three attendants. The Moor, ignorant of the Spanish tongue, had not understood the conversation of the guards, and supposed, from the magnificence of the furniture and the silken hangings, that this was the royal tent. From the respect paid by the attendants to Don Alvaro and the marchioness, he concluded that they were the king and queen.

He now asked for a draught of water; a jar was brought to him, and the guard released his arm to enable him to drink. The marchioness perceived a sudden change in his countenance, and something sinister in the expression of his eye, and shifted her position to a more remote part of the tent. Pretending to raise the water to his lips, the Moor unfolded his albornoz, so as to grasp a scimetar which he wore concealed beneath; then, dashing down the jar, he drew his weapon, and gave Don Alvaro a blow on the head, that struck him to the earth, and nearly deprived him of life. Turning then upon the marchioness, he made a violent blow at her; but in his eagerness and agitation, his scimetar caught in the drapery of the tent; the force of the blow was broken, and the weapon struck harmless upon some golden ornaments of her head-dress.[*]

Ruy Lopez de Toledo, treasurer to the queen, and Juan de Belalcazar, a sturdy friar, who were present, grappled and struggled with the desperado; and immediately the guards, who had conducted him from the marques de Cadiz, fell upon him and cut him to pieces.[†]

The king and queen, brought out of their tents by the noise, were filled with horror when they learned the

[*] Pietro Martyr, *Epist.* 62.      [†] *Cura de los Palacios.*
27

imminent peril from which they had escaped. The mangled body of the Moor was taken by the people to the camp, and thrown into the city from a catapult. The Gomeres gathered up the body with deep reverence, as the remains of a saint; they washed and perfumed it, and buried it with great honor and loud lamentations. In revenge of his death, they slew one of their principal Christian captives, and, having tied his body upon an ass, they drove the animal forth into the camp.

From this time, there was appointed an additional guard around the tents of the king and queen, composed of four hundred cavaliers of rank, of the kingdoms of Castile and Arragon. No person was admitted to the royal presence armed; no Moor was allowed to enter the camp, without a previous knowledge of his character and business; and on no account was any Moor to be introduced into the presence of the sovereigns.

An act of treachery of such ferocious nature, gave rise to a train of gloomy apprehensions. There were many cabins and sheds about the camp, constructed of branches of trees which had become dry and combustible; and fears were entertained that they might be set on fire by the Mudexares or Moorish vassals, who visited the army. Some even dreaded that attempts might be made to poison the wells and fountains. To quiet these dismal alarms, all Mudexares were ordered to leave the camp; and all loose, idle loiterers, who could not give a good account of themselves, were taken into custody.

CHAPTER LX.

HOW HAMET EL ZEGRI WAS HARDENED IN HIS OBSTINACY, BY THE ARTS OF A MOORISH ASTROLOGER.

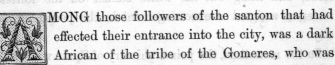

MONG those followers of the santon that had effected their entrance into the city, was a dark African of the tribe of the Gomeres, who was likewise a hermit or dervise, and passed among the Moors for a holy and inspired man. No sooner were the mangled remains of his predecessor buried with the honors of martyrdom, than this dervise elevated himself in his place, and professed to be gifted with the spirit of prophecy. He displayed a white banner, which, he assured the Moors, was sacred; that he had retained it for twenty years for some signal purpose, and that Allah had revealed to him that under that banner the inhabitants of Malaga should sally forth upon the camp of the unbelievers, put it to utter rout, and banquet upon the provisions in which it abounded.* The hungry and credulous Moors were elated at this prediction, and cried out to be led forth at once to the attack; but the

* *Cura de los Palacios,* cap. 84.

419

dervise told them the time was not yet arrived, for every event had its allotted day in the decrees of fate; they must wait patiently, therefore, until the appointed time should be revealed to him by Heaven. Hamet el Zegri listened to the dervise with profound reverence, and his example had great effect in increasing the awe and deference of his followers. He took the holy man up into his stronghold of Gibralfaro, consulted him on all occasions, and hung out his white banner on the loftiest tower, as a signal of encouragement to the people of the city.

In the meantime, the prime chivalry of Spain was gradually assembling before the walls of Malaga. The army which had commenced the siege had been worn out by extreme hardships, having had to construct immense works, to dig trenches and mines, to mount guard by sea and land, to patrol the mountains, and to sustain incessant conflicts. The sovereigns were obliged, therefore, to call upon various distant cities, for reinforcements of horse and foot. Many nobles also assembled their vassals, and repaired, of their own accord, to the royal camp.

Every little while, some stately galley or gallant caravel would stand into the harbor, displaying the well-known banner of some Spanish cavalier, and thundering from its artillery a salutation to the sovereigns and a defiance to the Moors. On the land side also, reinforcements would be seen, winding down from the mountains to the sound of drum and trumpet, and marching into the camp with glistening arms, as yet unsullied by the toils of war.

One morning, the whole sea was whitened by the sails and vexed by the oars of ships and galleys bearing towards the port. One hundred vessels of various kinds and sizes arrived, some armed for warlike service, others deep freighted with provisions. At the same time, the clangor of drum and trumpet bespoke the arrival of a powerful force by land, which came pouring in lengthening columns into the camp. This mighty reinforcement was furnished by the duke of Medina Sidonia, who reigned like a petty monarch over his vast possessions. He came with this princely force, a volunteer to the royal standard, not having been summoned by the sovereigns; and he brought, moreover, a loan of twenty thousand doblas of gold.

When the camp was thus powerfully reinforced, Isabella advised that new offers of an indulgent kind should be made to the inhabitants; for she was anxious to prevent the miseries of a protracted siege, or the effusion of blood that must attend a general attack. A fresh summons was therefore sent for the city to surrender, with a promise of life, liberty, and property in case of immediate compliance; but denouncing all the horrors of war, if the defense were obstinately continued.

Hamet again rejected the offer with scorn. His main fortifications as yet were but little impaired, and were capable of holding out much longer; he trusted to the thousand evils and accidents that beset a besieging army, and to the inclemencies of the approaching season; and it is said that he, as well as his followers, had an infatuated belief in the predictions of the dervise.

The worthy Fray Antonio Agapida does not scruple to affirm that the pretended prophet of the city was an arch nigromancer, or Moorish magician, " of which there be countless many," says he, " in the filthy sect of Mahomet;" and that he was leagued with the prince of the powers of the air, to endeavor to work the confusion and defeat of the Christian army.  The worthy father asserts, also, that Hamet employed him in a high tower of the Gibralfaro, which commanded a wide view over sea and land, where he wrought spells and incantations with astrolabes and other diabolical instruments to defeat the Christian ships and forces, whenever they were engaged with the Moors.

To the potent spells of this sorcerer, he ascribes the perils and losses sustained by a party of cavaliers of the royal household, in a desperate combat to gain two towers in the suburb, near the gate of the city, called la Puerto de Granada.  The Christians, led on by Ruy Lopez de Toledo, the valiant treasurer of the queen, took, and lost, and retook the towers, which were finally set on fire by the Moors, and abandoned to the flames by both parties.  To the same malignant influence he attributes the damage done to the Christian fleet, which was so vigorously assailed by the albatozas, or floating batteries of the Moors, that one ship, belonging to the duke of Medina Sidonia, was sunk, and the rest were obliged to retire.

"Hamet el Zegri," says Fray Antonio Agapida, "stood on the top of the high tower of Gibralfaro, and beheld this injury wrought upon the Christian force; and his proud heart was puffed up. And the Moorish nigromancer stood beside him. And he pointed out to him the Christian host below, encamped on every eminence around the city, and covering its fertile valley, and the many ships floating upon the tranquil sea; and he bade him be strong of heart, for that in a few days all this mighty fleet would be scattered by the winds of Heaven; and that he should sally forth, under the guidance of the sacred banner, and attack this host and utterly defeat it, and make spoil of those sumptuous tents; and Malaga should be triumphantly revenged upon her assailants. So the heart of Hamet was hardened like that of Pharaoh, and he persisted in setting at defiance the Catholic sovereigns and their army of saintly warriors."

# CHAPTER LXI.

SIEGE OF MALAGA CONTINUED.—DESTRUCTION OF A TOWER, BY FRANCISCO
RAMIREZ DE MADRID.

EEING the infatuated obstinacy of the besieged, the Christians now approached their
works to the walls, gaining one position after
another, preparatory to a general assault. Near the barrier of the city was a bridge with four arches, defended
at each end by a strong and lofty tower, by which a part
of the army would have to pass in making an attack.
The commander-in-chief of the artillery, Francisco Ramirez de Madrid, was ordered to take possession of this
bridge. The approach to it was perilous in the extreme,
from the exposed situation of the assailants, and the
number of Moors that garrisoned the towers. Francisco
Ramirez therefore secretly excavated a mine leading beneath the first tower, and placed a piece of ordnance with
its mouth upwards, immediately under the foundation,
with a train of powder to produce an explosion at the
necessary moment.

When this was arranged, he advanced slowly with his
forces in face of the towers, erecting bulwarks at every

step, and gradually gaining ground until he arrived near to the bridge. He then planted several pieces of artillery in his works, and began to batter the tower. The Moors replied bravely from their battlements, but, in the heat of the combat, the piece of ordnance under the foundation was discharged. The earth was rent open, a part of the tower overthrown, and several of the Moors were torn to pieces; the rest took to flight, overwhelmed with terror at this thundering explosion bursting beneath their feet, and at beholding the earth vomiting flames and smoke; for never before had they witnessed such a stratagem in warfare. The Christians rushed forward and took possession of the abandoned post, and immediately commenced an attack upon the other tower at the opposite end of the bridge, to which the Moors had retired. An incessant fire of cross-bows and arquebuses was kept up between the rival towers, volleys of stones were discharged, and no one dared to venture upon the intermediate bridge.

Francisco de Ramirez at length renewed his former mode of approach, making bulwarks step by step, while the Moors stationed at the other end, swept the bridge with their artillery. The combat was long and bloody, —furious on the part of the Moors, patient and persevering on the part of the Christians. By slow degrees, they accomplished their advance across the bridge, drove the enemy before them, and remained masters of this important pass.

For this valiant and skillful achievement, king Ferdinand after the surrender of the city conferred the dignity of knighthood upon Francisco Ramirez, in the tower which he had so gloriously gained.* The worthy padre Fray Antonio Agapida indulges in more than a page of extravagant eulogy, upon this invention of blowing up the foundation of the tower by a piece of ordnance, which, in fact, is said to be the first instance on record of gunpowder being used in a mine.

* Pulgar, pt. 3, c. 91.

## CHAPTER LXII.

### HOW THE PEOPLE OF MALAGA EXPOSTULATED WITH HAMET EL ZEGRI.

WHILE the dervise was deluding the garrison of Malaga with vain hopes, the famine increased to a terrible degree. The Gomeres ranged about the city as though it had been a conquered place, taking by force whatever they found eatable in the houses of the peaceful citizens; and breaking open vaults and cellars, and demolishing walls, wherever they thought provisions might be concealed.

The wretched inhabitants had no longer bread to eat; the horse-flesh also now failed them, and they were fain to devour skins and hides toasted at the fire, and to assuage the hunger of their children with vine-leaves cut up and fried in oil. Many perished of famine, or of the unwholesome food with which they endeavored to relieve it; and many took refuge in the Christian camp, preferring captivity to the horrors which surrounded them.

At length the sufferings of the inhabitants became so great, as to conquer even their fears of Hamet and his Gomeres. They assembled before the house of Ali Dordux, the wealthy merchant, whose stately mansion was at

427

the foot of the Alcazaba, and they urged him to stand forth as their leader, and to intercede with Hamet for a surrender. Ali Dordux was a man of courage, as well as policy; he perceived also that hunger was giving boldness to the citizens, while he trusted it was subduing the fierceness of the soldiery. He armed himself, therefore, cap-a-pie, and undertook this dangerous parley with the alcayde. He associated with him an alfaqui named Abraham Alhariz, and an important inhabitant named Amar ben Amar; and they ascended to the fortress of Gibralfaro, followed by several of the trembling merchants.

They found Hamet el Zegri, not as before, surrounded by ferocious guards and all the implements of war; but in a chamber of one of the lofty towers, at a table of stone, covered with scrolls traced with strange characters and mystic diagrams; while instruments of singular and unknown form lay about the room. Beside Hamet stood the prophetic dervise, who appeared to have been explaining to him the mysterious inscriptions of the scrolls. His presence filled the citizens with awe, for even Ali Dordux considered him a man inspired.

The alfaqui Abraham Alhariz, whose sacred character gave him boldness to speak, now lifted up his voice, and addressed Hamet el Zegri. "We implore thee," said he, solemnly, "in the name of the most powerful God, no longer to persist in a vain resistance, which must end in our destruction, but deliver up the city while clemency is yet to be obtained. Think how many of our warriors have fallen by the sword; do not suffer those who survive to perish by famine. Our wives and children cry to us for bread, and we have none to give them. We see them expire in lingering agony before our eyes, while the enemy mocks our misery by displaying the abundance of his camp. Of what avail is our defense? Are our walls peradventure more strong than the walls of Ronda? Are our warriors more brave than the defenders of Loxa? The walls of Ronda were thrown down, and the warriors of Loxa had to surrender. Do we hope for succor?—whence are we to receive it? The time for hope is gone by. Granada has lost its power; it no longer possesses chivalry, commanders, nor a king. Boabdil sits a vassal in the degraded halls of the Alhambra; El Zagal is a fugitive, shut up within the walls of Guadix. The kingdom is divided against itself,—its strength is gone, its pride fallen, its very existence at an end. In the name of Allah, we conjure thee, who art our captain, be not our direst enemy; but surrender these ruins of our once happy Malaga, and deliver us from these overwhelming horrors."

Such was the supplication forced from the inhabitants by the extremity of their sufferings. Hamet listened to the alfaqui without anger, for he respected the sanctity of his office. His heart, too, was at that moment lifted up with a vain confidence. "Yet a few days of patience," said he, "and all these evils will suddenly have an end. I have been conferring with this holy man, and find that the time of our deliverance is at hand. The decrees of fate are inevitable; it is written in the book of destiny, that we shall sally forth and destroy the camp of the unbelievers, and banquet upon those mountains of grain which are piled up in the midst of it. So Allah hath promised, by the mouth of this his prophet. Allah Achbar! God is great. Let no man oppose the decrees of Heaven!"

The citizens bowed with profound reverence, for no true Moslem pretends to struggle against whatever is written in the book of fate. Ali Dordux, who had come prepared to champion the city and to brave the ire of Hamet, humbled himself before this holy man, and gave faith to his prophecies as the revelations of Allah. So the deputies returned to the citizens, and exhorted them to be of good cheer: "A few days longer," said they, " and our sufferings are to terminate. When the white banner is removed from the tower, then look out for deliverance; for the hour of sallying forth will have arrived." The people retired to their homes, with sorrowful hearts; they tried in vain to quiet the cries of their famishing children; and day by day, and hour by hour, their anxious eyes were turned to the sacred banner, which still continued to wave on the tower of Gibralfaro.

CONQUEST OF GRANADA.

# CHAPTER LXIII.

"THE Moorish nigromancer," observes the worthy Fray Antonio Agapida, "remained shut up in a tower of the Gibralfaro, devising devilish means to work mischief and discomfiture upon the Christians. He was daily consulted by Hamet, who had great faith in those black and magic arts, which he had brought with him from the bosom of heathen Africa."

From the account given of this dervise and his incantations by the worthy father, it would appear that he was an astrologer, and was studying the stars, and endeavoring to calculate the day and hour when a successful attack might be made upon the Christian camp.

Famine had now increased to such a degree as to distress even the garrison of Gibralfaro, although the Gomeres had seized upon all the provisions they could find in the city. Their passions were sharpened by hunger, and they became restless and turbulent, and impatient for action.

Hamet was one day in council with his captains, perplexed by the pressure of events, when the dervise entered among them. "The hour of victory," exclaimed he, "is at hand. Allah has commanded that to-morrow morning ye shall sally forth to the fight. I will bear before you the sacred banner, and deliver your enemies into your hands. Remember, however, that ye are but instruments in the hands of Allah, to take vengeance on the enemies of the faith. Go into battle, therefore, with pure hearts, forgiving each other all past offenses; for those who are charitable towards each other, will be victorious over the foe." The words of the dervise were received with rapture; all Gibralfaro and the Alcazaba resounded immediately with the din of arms; and Hamet sent throughout the towers and fortifications of the city and selected the choicest troops and most distinguished captains for this eventful combat.

In the morning early, the rumor went throughout the city that the sacred banner had disappeared from the tower of Gibralfaro, and all Malaga was roused to witness the sally that was to destroy the unbelievers. Hamet descended from his stronghold, accompanied by his principal captain, Ibrahim Zenete, and followed by his Gomeres. The dervise led the way, displaying the white banner, the sacred pledge of victory. The multitude shouted "Allah Achbar!" and prostrated themselves before the banner as it passed. Even the dreaded Hamet was hailed with praises; for in their hopes of speedy relief through the prowess of his arm, the populace forgot everything but his bravery. Every bosom in Malaga was agitated by hope and fear—the old men, the women and children, and all who went not forth to battle, mounted on tower and battlement and roof, to watch a combat that was to decide their fate.

Before sallying forth from the city, the dervise addressed the troops, reminding them of the holy nature of this enterprise, and warning them not to forfeit the protection of the sacred banner by any unworthy act. They were not to pause to make spoil nor to take prisoners: they were to press forward, fighting valiantly, and granting no quarter. The gate was then thrown open, and the dervise issued forth, followed by the army. They directed their assaults upon the encampments of the master of Santiago and the master of Alcantara, and came upon them so suddenly that they killed and wounded several of the guards. Ibrahim Zenete made his way into one of the tents, where he beheld several Christian striplings just starting from their slumber. The heart of the Moor was suddenly touched with pity for their youth, or perhaps he scorned the weakness of the foe. He smote them with the flat instead of the edge of the sword. "Away, imps," cried he, "away to your mothers." The fanatic dervise reproached him with his clemency. "I did not kill them," replied Zenete, "because I saw no beards!"*

* *Cura de los Palacios*, cap. 84.

28

The alarm was given in the camp, and the Christians rushed from all quarters to defend the gates of the bulwarks. Don Pedro Puerto Carrero, senior of Moguer, and his brother Don Alonzo Pacheco, planted themselves, with their followers, in the gateway of the encampment of the master of Santiago, and bore the whole brunt of battle until they were reinforced. The gate of the encampment of the master of Calatrava was in like manner defended by Lorenzo Saurez de Mendoza. Hamet was furious at being thus checked, where he had expected a miraculous victory. He led his troops repeatedly to the attack, hoping to force the gates before succor should arrive: they fought with vehement ardor, but were as often repulsed; and every time they returned to the assault, they found their enemies doubled in number. The Christians opened a cross-fire of all kinds of missiles, from their bulwarks; the Moors could effect but little damage upon a foe thus protected behind their works, while they themselves were exposed from head to foot. The Christians singled out the most conspicuous cavaliers, the greater part of whom were either slain or wounded. Still the Moors, infatuated by the predictions of the prophet, fought desperately and devotedly, and they were furious to revenge the slaughter of their leaders. They rushed upon certain death, endeavoring madly to scale the bulwarks or force the gates, and fell amidst showers of darts and lances, filling the ditches with their mangled bodies.

Hamet el Zegri raged along the front of the bulwarks, seeking an opening for attack. He gnashed his teeth with fury, as he saw so many of his chosen warriors slain around him. He seemed to have a charmed life; for, though constantly in the hottest of the fight, amidst showers of missiles, he still escaped uninjured. Blindly confiding in the prophecy of victory, he continued to urge on his devoted troops. The dervise, too, ran like a maniac through the ranks, waving his white banner, and inciting the Moors by howlings rather than by shouts. "Fear not! the victory is ours! for so it is written!" cried he. In the midst of his frenzy, a stone from a catapult struck him in the head, and dashed out his bewildered brains.*

When the Moors beheld their prophet slain, and his banner in the dust, they were seized with despair, and fled in confusion to the city. Hamet el Zegri made some effort to rally them, but was himself confounded by the fall of the dervise. He covered the flight of his broken forces, turning repeatedly upon their pursuers, and slowly making his retreat into the city.

The inhabitants of Malaga witnessed from their walls, with trembling anxiety, the whole of this disastrous conflict. At the first onset, when they beheld the guards of the camp put to flight, they exclaimed, "Allah has given us the victory!" and they sent up shouts of triumph.

* Garibay, lib. 18, c. 33.

Their exultation, however, was soon turned into doubt, when they beheld their troops repulsed in repeated attacks. They could see, from time to time, some distinguished warrior laid low, and others brought back bleeding to the city. When at length the sacred banner fell, and the routed troops came flying to the gates, pursued and cut down by the foe, horror and despair seized upon the populace.

As Hamet entered the gates, he heard nothing but loud lamentations; mothers, whose sons had been slain, shrieked curses after him as he passed; some, in the anguish of their hearts, threw down their famishing babes before him, exclaiming, "Trample on them with thy horse's feet; for we have no food to give them, and we cannot endure their cries." All heaped execrations on his head, as the cause of the woes of Malaga.

The warlike part of the citizens, also, and many warriors, who, with their wives and children, had taken refuge in Malaga from the mountain fortresses, now joined in the popular clamor, for their hearts were overcome by the sufferings of their families.

Hamet el Zegri found it impossible to withstand this torrent of lamentations, curses, and reproaches. His military ascendency was at an end; for most of his officers, and the prime warriors of his African band, had fallen in this disastrous sally. Turning his back, therefore, upon the city, and abandoning it to its own councils, he retired with the remnant of his Gomeres to his stronghold in the Gibralfaro.

# CHAPTER LXIV.

### HOW THE CITY OF MALAGA CAPITULATED.

THE people of Malaga, being no longer overawed by Hamet el Zegri and his Gomeres, turned to Ali Dordux, the magnanimous merchant, and put the fate of the city into his hands. He had already gained the alcaydes of the castle of the Genoese and of the citadel into his party, and in the late confusion had gained the sway over those important fortresses. He now associated himself with the alfaqui, Abraham Alhariz, and four of the principal inhabitants, and, forming a provisional junta, they sent heralds to the Christian sovereigns, offering to surrender the city on certain terms, protecting the persons and property of the inhabitants, permitting them to reside as Mudexares or tributary vassals either in Malaga or elsewhere.

When the heralds arrived at the camp, and made known their mission to King Ferdinand, his anger was kindled. " Return to your fellow - citizens," said he, " and tell them that the day of grace is gone by. They have persisted in a fruitless defense until they are driven by necessity to capitulate ; they must surrender unconditionally, and abide the fate of the vanquished. Those who merit death shall suffer death; those who merit captivity shall be made captives."

This stern reply spread consternation among the people of Malaga; but Ali Dordux comforted them, and undertook to go in person, and pray for favorable terms. When the people beheld this great and wealthy merchant, who was so eminent in their city, departing with his associates on this mission, they plucked up heart; for they said, " Surely the Christian king will not turn a deaf ear to such a man as Ali Dordux!"

Ferdinand, however, would not even admit the ambassadors to his presence. "Send them to the devil!" said he, in a great passion, to the commander of Leon; "I'll not see them. Let them get back to their city. They shall all surrender to my mercy, as vanquished enemies." *

To give emphasis to this reply, he ordered a general discharge from all the artillery and batteries; and there was a great shout throughout the camp, and all the lombards and catapults, and other engines of war, thundered furiously upon the city, doing great damage.

Ali Dordux and his companions returned to the city with downcast countenances, and could scarce make the reply of the Christian sovereign be heard, for the roaring of the artillery, the tumbling of the walls, and the cries

* *Cura de los Palacios*, cap. 84.

of women and children. The citizens were greatly astonished and dismayed, when they found the little respect paid to their most eminent man; but the warriors who were in the city exclaimed, "What has this merchant to do with questions between men of battle? Let us not address the enemy as abject suppliants who have no power to injure, but as valiant men, who have weapons in their hands."

So they dispatched another message to the Christian sovereigns, offering to yield up the city and all their effects, on condition of being secured in their personal liberty. Should this be denied, they declared they would hang from the battlements fifteen hundred Christian captives, male and female; that they would put all their old men, their women, and children into the citadel, set fire to the city, and sally forth, sword in hand, to fight until the last gasp. "In this way," said they, "the Spanish sovereigns shall gain a bloody victory, and the fall of Malaga be renowned while the world endures."

To this fierce and swelling message, Ferdinand replied, that if a single Christian captive were injured, not a Moor in Malaga but should be put to the edge of the sword.

A great conflict of counsels now arose in Malaga. The warriors were for following up their menace by some desperate act of vengeance or of self-devotion. Those who had families looked with anguish upon their wives and daughters, and thought it better to die than to live to see them captives. By degrees, however, the transports of passion and despair subsided, the love of life resumed its sway, and they turned once more to Ali Dordux, as the man most prudent in council and able in negotiation. By his advice, fourteen of the principal inhabitants were chosen from the fourteen districts of the city, and sent to the camp, bearing a long letter, couched in terms of the most humble supplication.

Various debates now took place in the Christian camp. Many of the cavaliers were exasperated against Malaga for its long resistance, which had caused the death of many of their relatives and favorite companions. It had long been a stronghold, also, for Moorish depredators, and the mart where most of the warriors captured in the Axarquia had been exposed in triumph and sold to slavery. They represented, moreover, that there were many Moorish cities yet to be besieged; and that an example ought to be made of Malaga, to prevent all obstinate resistance thereafter. They advised, therefore, that all the inhabitants should be put to the sword.*

The humane heart of Isabella revolted at such sanguinary counsels: she insisted that their triumph should not be disgraced by cruelty. Ferdinand, however, was inflexible in refusing to grant any preliminary terms, insisting on an unconditional surrender.

The people of Malaga now abandoned themselves to

* Pulgar.

paroxysms of despair; on one side they saw famine and death, on the other slavery and chains. The mere men of the sword, who had no families to protect, were loud for signalizing their fall by some illustrious action. "Let us sacrifice our Christian captives, and then destroy ourselves," cried some. "Let us put all the women and children to death, set fire to the city, fall on the Christian camp, and die sword in hand," cried others.

Ali Dordux gradually made his voice be heard amidst the general clamor. He addressed himself to the principal inhabitants, and to those who had children. "Let those who live by the sword, die by the sword," cried he; "but let us not follow their desperate counsels. Who knows what sparks of pity may be awakened in the bosoms of the Christian sovereigns, when they behold our unoffending wives and daughters, and our helpless little ones! The Christian queen, they say, is full of mercy!"

At these words, the hearts of the unhappy people of Malaga yearned over their families, and they empowered Ali Dordux to deliver up their city to the mercy of the Castilian sovereigns.

The merchant now went to and fro, and had several communications with Ferdinand and Isabella and interested several principal cavaliers in his cause; and he sent rich presents to the king and queen, of oriental merchandise, and silks and stuffs of gold, and jewels and precious stones, and spices and perfumes, and many other sumptuous things, which he had accumulated in his great tradings with the East; and he gradually found favor in the eyes of the sovereigns.* Finding that there was nothing to be obtained for the city, he now, like a prudent man and able merchant, began to negotiate for himself and his immediate friends. He represented that from the first they had been desirous of yielding up the city, but had been prevented by warlike and high-handed men, who had threatened their lives; he entreated, therefore, that mercy might be extended to them, and that they might not be confounded with the guilty.

The sovereigns had accepted the presents of Ali Dordux—how could they then turn a deaf ear to his petition? So they granted a pardon to him, and to forty families which he named; and it was agreed that they should be protected in their liberties and property, and permitted to reside in Malaga as Mudexares or Moslem vassals, and to follow their customary pursuits.† All this being arranged, Ali Dordux delivered up twenty of the principal inhabitants, to remain as hostages, until the whole city should be placed in the possession of the Christians.

Don Gutierrez de Cardenas, senior commander of Leon, now entered the city, armed cap-a-pie, on horseback, and took possession in the name of the Castilian sovereigns. He was followed by his retainers, and by the captains and cavaliers of the army; and in a little while, the stand-

*on. of Valera.                † Cura de los Palacios,

ards of the cross and of the blessed Santiago, and of the Catholic sovereigns, were elevated on the principal tower of the Alcazaba. When these standards were beheld from the camp, the queen and the princess and the ladies of the court, and all the royal retinue, knelt down and gave thanks and praises to the holy virgin and to Santiago, for this great triumph of the faith ; and the bishops and other clergy who were present, and the choristers of the royal chapel, chanted " *Te Deum Laudamus*," and " *Gloria in Excelsis.*"

# CHAPTER LXV.

O sooner was the city delivered up, than the wretched inhabitants implored permission to purchase bread for themselves and their children, from the heaps of grain which they had so often gazed at wistfully from their walls. Their prayer was granted, and they issued forth with the famished eagerness of starving men. It was piteous to behold the struggles of those unhappy people, as they contended who first should have their necessities relieved.

"Thus," says the pious Fray Antonio Agapida, "thus are the predictions of false prophets sometimes permitted to be verified, but always to the confusion of those who trust in them : for the words of the Moorish nigromancer came to pass, that the people of Malaga should eat of those heaps of bread ; but they ate in humiliation and defeat, and with sorrow and bitterness of heart."

Dark and fierce were the feelings of Hamet el Zegri, as he looked down from the castle of Gibralfaro, and beheld the Christian legions pouring into the city, and the stand-

444

ard of the cross supplanting the crescent on the citadel. "The people of Malaga," said he, "have trusted to a man of trade, and he has trafficked them away; but let us not suffer ourselves to be bound hand and foot, and delivered up as part of his bargain. We have yet strong walls around us, and trusty weapons in our hands. Let us fight until buried beneath the last tumbling tower of Gibralfaro, or, rushing down from among its ruins, carry havoc among the unbelievers, as they throng the streets of Malaga!"

The fierceness of the Gomeres, however, was broken. They could have died in the breach, had their castle been assailed; but the slow advances of famine subdued their strength without rousing their passions, and sapped the force both of soul and body. They were almost unanimous for a surrender.

It was a hard struggle for the proud spirit of Hamet to bow itself to ask for terms. Still he trusted that the valor of his defense would gain him respect in the eyes of a chivalrous foe. "Ali," said he, "has negotiated like a merchant; I will capitulate as a soldier." He sent a herald, therefore, to Ferdinand, offering to yield up his castle, but demanding a separate treaty.* The Castilian sovereign made a laconic and stern reply: "He shall receive no terms but such as have been granted to the community of Malaga."

---

\* *Cura de los Palacios*, cap. 84.

For two days Hamet el Zegri remained brooding in his
castle, after the city was in possession of the Christians ;
at length, the clamors of his followers compelled him to
surrender.   When the remnant of this fierce African garrison descended from their cragged fortress, they were
so worn by watchfulness, famine, and battle, yet carried
such a lurking fury in their eyes, that they looked more
like fiends than men.   They were all condemned to slavery, excepting Ibrahim Zenete.   The instance of clemency which he had shown in refraining to harm the
Spanish striplings, on the last sally from Malaga, won
him favorable terms.   It was cited as a magnanimous act
by the Spanish cavaliers, and all admitted, that though a
Moor in blood, he possessed the Christian heart of a Castilian hidalgo.*

As to Hamet el Zegri, on being asked what moved
him to such hardened obstinacy, he replied, "When I
undertook my command, I pledged myself to fight in
defense of my faith, my city, and my sovereign, until slain
or made prisoner ; and depend upon it, had I had men
to stand by me, I should have died fighting, instead of
thus tamely surrendering myself without a weapon in my
hand."

"Such," says the pious Fray Antonio Agapida, " was
the diabolical hatred and stiff-necked opposition of this
infidel to our holy cause.   But he was justly served by

* *Cura de los Palacios,* cap. 84.

our most Catholic and high-minded sovereign, for his pertinacious defense of the city; for Ferdinand ordered that he should be loaded with chains and thrown into a dungeon." He was subsequently retained in rigorous confinement at Carmona.*

* Pulgar, pt. 3, cap. 93.   Pietro Martyr, lib. 1, cap. 69.   Alcantara, *Hist. Granada*, vol. 4, c. 18.

# CHAPTER LXVI.

HOW THE CASTILIAN SOVEREIGNS TOOK POSSESSION OF THE CITY OF MALAGA, AND HOW KING FERDINAND SIGNALIZED HIMSELF BY HIS SKILL IN BARGAINING WITH THE INHABITANTS FOR THEIR RANSOM.

NE of the first cares of the conquerors, on entering Malaga, was to search for Christian captives. Nearly sixteen hundred men and women were found, and among them were persons of distinction. Some of them had been ten, fifteen, and twenty years in captivity. Many had been servants to the Moors, or laborers on public works, and some had passed their time in chains and dungeons. Preparations were made to celebrate their deliverance as a Christian triumph. A tent was erected not far from the city, and furnished with an altar and all the solemn decorations of a chapel. Here the king and queen waited to receive the Christian captives. They were assembled in the city, and marshaled forth in piteous procession. Many of them had still the chains and shackles on their legs; they were wasted with famine, their hair and beards overgrown and matted, and their faces pale and haggard from long confinement. When they found themselves restored to

448

liberty, and surrounded by their countrymen, some stared wildly about as if in a dream, others gave way to frantic transports, but most of them wept for joy. All present were moved to tears, by so touching a spectacle. When the procession arrived at what is called the Gate of Granada, it was met by a great concourse from the camp, with crosses and pennons, who turned and followed the captives, singing hymns of praise and thanksgiving. When they came in presence of the king and queen, they threw themselves on their knees and would have kissed their feet, as their saviors and deliverers; but the sovereigns prevented such humiliation, and graciously extended to them their hands. They then prostrated themselves before the altar, and all present joined them in giving thanks to God for their liberation from this cruel bondage. By orders of the king and queen, their chains were then taken off, and they were clad in decent raiment, and food was set before them. After they had ate and drunk, and were refreshed and invigorated, they were provided with money and all things necessary for their journey, and sent joyfully to their homes.

While the old chroniclers dwell with becoming enthusiasm on this pure and affecting triumph of humanity, they go on, in a strain of equal eulogy, to describe a spectacle of a far different nature. It so happened, that there were found in the city twelve of those renegado Christians who had deserted to the Moors, and conveyed false intelligence, during the siege: a barbarous species

29

of punishment was inflicted upon them, borrowed, it is said, from the Moors, and peculiar to these wars. They were tied to stakes in a public place, and horsemen exercised their skill in transpiercing them with pointed reeds, hurled at them while careering at full speed, until the miserable victims expired beneath their wounds. Several apostate Moors, also, who, having embraced Christianity, had afterwards relapsed into their early faith, and had taken refuge in Malaga from the vengeance of the Inquisition, were publicly burnt. "These," says an old Jesuit historian, exultingly, "these were the tilts of reeds and the illuminations most pleasing for this victorious festival, and for the Catholic piety of our sovereigns!"*

When the city was cleansed from the impurities and offensive odors which had collected during the siege, the bishops and other clergy who accompanied the court, and the choir of the royal chapel, walked in procession to the principal mosque, which was consecrated, and entitled Santa Maria de la Incarnacion. This done, the king and queen entered the city, accompanied by the grand cardinal of Spain, and the principal nobles and cavaliers of the army, and heard a solemn mass. The church was then elevated into a cathedral, and Malaga was made a bishopric, and many of the neighboring

* "Los renegados fuernon acañavareados : y los conversos quemados ; y estos fueron las cañas, y luminarias mas alegres, por la fiesta de la vitoria para la piedad Catholica de nuestros Reyes."—Abarca, *Anales de Aragon*, tom. 2, Rey xxx., c. 3.

towns were comprehended in its diocese. The queen took up her residence in the Alcazaba, in the apartments of her valiant treasurer, Ruy Lopez, whence she had a view of the whole city; but the king established his quarters in the warrior castle of Gibralfaro.

And now came to be considered the disposition of the Moorish prisoners. All those who were strangers in the city, and had either taken refuge there, or had entered to defend it, were at once considered slaves. They were divided into three lots: one was set apart for the service of God, in redeeming Christian captives from bondage, either in the kingdom of Granada or in Africa; the second lot was divided among those who had aided either in field or cabinet, in the present siege, according to their rank; the third was appropriated to defray, by their sale, the great expenses incurred in the reduction of the place. A hundred of the Gomeres were sent as presents to Pope Innocent VIII., and were led in triumph through the streets of Rome, and afterwards converted to Christianity. Fifty Moorish maidens were sent to the queen Joanna of Naples, sister to king Ferdinand, and thirty to the queen of Portugal. Isabella made presents of others to the ladies of her household, and of the noble families of Spain.

Among the inhabitants of Malaga were four hundred and fifty Moorish Jews, for the most part women, speaking the Arabic language, and dressed in the Moresco fashion. These were ransomed by a wealthy Jew of Castile, farmer-general of the royal revenues derived from the Jews of Spain. He agreed to make up, within a certain time, the sum of twenty thousand doblas, or pistoles of gold; all the money and jewels of the captives being taken in part payment. They were sent to Castile, in two armed galleys. As to Ali Dordux, such favors and honors were heaped upon him by the Spanish sovereigns for his considerate mediation in the surrender, that the disinterestedness of his conduct has often been called in question. He was appointed chief justice and alcayde of the Mudaxares or Moorish subjects, and was presented with twenty houses, one public bakery, and several orchards, vineyards, and tracts of open country. He retired to Antiquera, where he died several years afterwards, leaving his estate and name to his son Mohammed Dordux. The latter embraced the Christian faith, as did his wife, the daughter of a Moorish noble. On being baptized he received the name of Don Fernando de Malaga, his wife that of Isabella, after the queen. They were incorporated with the nobility of Castile, and their descendants still bear the name of Malaga.*

As to the great mass of Moorish inhabitants, they implored that they might not be scattered and sold into captivity, but might be permitted to ransom themselves by an amount paid within a certain time. Upon this,

* *Conversaciones Malagueñas*, 26, as cited by Alcantara in his *History of Granada*, vol. 4, c. 18.

king Ferdinand took the advice of certain of his ablest counselors : they said to him, "If you hold out a prospect of hopeless captivity, the infidels will throw all their gold and jewels into wells and pits, and you will lose the greater part of the spoil; but if you fix a general rate of ransom, and receive their money and jewels in part payment, nothing will be destroyed." The king relished greatly this advice; and it was arranged that all the inhabitants should be ransomed at the general rate of thirty doblas or pistoles in gold for each individual, male or female, large or small; that all their gold, jewels, and other valuables, should be received immediately in part payment of the general amount, and that the residue should be paid within eight months; that if any of the number, actually living, should die in the interim, their ransom should nevertheless be paid. If, however, the whole of the amount were not paid at the expiration of the eight months, they should all be considered and treated as slaves.

The unfortunate Moors were eager to catch at the least hope of future liberty, and consented to these hard conditions. The most rigorous precautions were taken to exact them to the uttermost. The inhabitants were numbered by houses and families, and their names taken down; their most precious effects were made up into parcels, and sealed and inscribed with their names; and they were ordered to repair with them to certain large corrales or inclosures adjoining the Alcazaba, which were surrounded by high walls and overlooked by watch-towers, to which places the cavalgadas of Christian captives had usually been driven, to be confined until the time of sale, like cattle in a market. The Moors were obliged to leave their houses one by one; all their money, necklaces, bracelets, and anklets of gold, pearl, coral, and precious stones, were taken from them at the threshold, and their persons so rigorously searched that they carried off nothing concealed.

Then might be seen old men and helpless women, and tender maidens, some of high birth and gentle condition, passing through the streets, heavily burdened, towards the Alcazaba. As they left their homes, they smote their breasts, and wrung their hands, and raised their weeping eyes to Heaven in anguish; and this is recorded as their plaint: "O Malaga! city so renowned and beautiful! where now is the strength of thy castle, where the grandeur of thy towers? Of what avail have been thy mighty walls, for the protection of thy children! Behold them driven from thy pleasant abodes, doomed to drag out a life of bondage in a foreign land, and to die far from the home of their infancy! What will become of thy old men and matrons, when their gray hairs shall be no longer reverenced? What will become of thy maidens, so delicately reared and tenderly cherished, when reduced to hard and menial servitude? Behold, thy once happy families scattered asunder, never again to be united; sons separated from their fathers, husbands from their wives, and tender children from their mothers: they will bewail each other in foreign lands, but their lamentations will be the scoff of the stranger. O Malaga! city of our birth! who can behold thy desolation, and not shed tears of bitterness!" *

When Malaga was completely secured, a detachment was sent against two fortresses near the sea, called Mixas and Osuna, which had frequently harassed the Christian camp. The inhabitants were threatened with the sword, unless they instantly surrendered. They claimed the same terms that had been granted to Malaga, imagining them to be freedom of person and security of property. Their claim was granted; they were transported to Malaga with all their riches, and, on arriving there, were overwhelmed with consternation at finding themselves captives. "Ferdinand," observes Fray Antonio Agapida, "was a man of his word; they were shut up in the inclosure at the Alcazaba, with the people of Malaga, and shared their fate."

The unhappy captives remained thus crowded in the court-yards of the Alcazaba, like sheep in a fold, until they could be sent by sea and land to Seville. They were then distributed about in city and country, each Christian family having one or more to feed and maintain as servants, until the term fixed for the payment of the residue of the ransom should expire. The captives had

* Pulgar, *Reyes Catolicos,* c. 93.

obtained permission that several of their number should go about among the Moorish towns of the kingdom of Granada, collecting contributions to aid in the purchase of their liberties; but these towns were too much impoverished by the war, and engrossed by their own distresses, ———————————————————— without the residue of the ransom being paid, and all the captives of Malaga, to the number, as some say, of eleven, and others of fifteen thousand, became slaves! "Never," exclaims the worthy Fray Antonio Agapida, in one of his usual bursts of zeal and loyalty, "never has there been recorded a more adroit and sagacious arrangement than this made by the Catholic monarch, by which he not only secured all the property and half of the ransom of these infidels, but finally got possession of their persons into the bargain. This truly may be considered one of the greatest triumphs of the pious and politic Ferdinand, and as raising him above the generality of conquerors, who have merely the valor to gain victories, but lack the prudence and management necessary to turn them to account.*

* The detestable policy of Ferdinand in regard to the Moorish captives of Malaga is recorded at length by the curate of los Palacios (c. 87), a contemporary, a zealous admirer of the king, and one of the most honest of chroniclers; who really thought he was recording a notable instance of sagacious piety.

# CHAPTER LXVII.

## HOW KING FERDINAND PREPARED TO CARRY THE WAR INTO A DIFFERENT PART OF THE TERRITORIES OF THE MOORS.

THE western part of the kingdom of Granada had now been conquered by the Christian arms. The seaport of Malaga was captured; the fierce and warlike inhabitants of the Serrania de Ronda, and the other mountain-holds of the frontier, were all disarmed, and reduced to peaceful and laborious vassalage; their haughty fortresses, which had so long overawed the valleys of Andalusia, now displayed the standard of Castile and Aragon; the watch-towers, which crowned every height, whence the infidels had kept a vulture eye over the Christian territories, were now either dismantled, or garrisoned with Catholic troops. "What signalized and sanctified this great triumph," adds the worthy Fray Antonio Agapida, "were the emblems of ecclesiastical domination which everywhere appeared. In every direction rose stately convents and monasteries, those fortresses of the faith, garrisoned by its spiritual soldiery of monks and friars. The sacred melody of Christian bells was again heard among the mountains, calling to early matins, or sounding the Angeles at the solemn hour of evening." *

While this part of the kingdom was thus reduced by the Christian sword, the central part, round the city of Granada, forming the heart of the Moorish territory, was held in vassalage of the Castilian monarch, by Boabdil surnamed el Chico. That unfortunate prince lost no occasion to propitiate the conquerors of his country by acts of homage, and by professions that must have been foreign to his heart. No sooner had he heard of the capture of Malaga, than he sent congratulations to the Catholic sovereigns, accompanied with presents of horses richly caparisoned for the king, and precious cloth of gold and oriental perfumes for the queen. His congratulations and his presents were received with the utmost graciousness; and the short-sighted prince, lulled by the temporary and politic forbearance of Ferdinand, flattered himself that he was securing the lasting friendship of that monarch.

The policy of Boabdil had its transient and superficial advantages. The portion of Moorish territory under his immediate sway had a respite from the calamities of war: the husbandmen cultivated their luxuriant fields in security, and the vega of Granada once more blossomed like the rose. The merchants again carried on a gainful traf-

---

* The worthy curate of los Palacios intimates in his Chronicle, that this melody, so grateful to the ears of pious Christians, was a source of perpetual torment to the ears of infidels.

fic; the gates of the city were thronged with beasts of burden, bringing the rich products of every clime. Yet, while the people of Granada rejoiced in their teeming fields and crowded marts, they secretly despised the policy which procured them these advantages, and held Boabdil for little better than an apostate and an unbeliever. Muley Abdallah el Zagal was now the hope of the unconquered part of the kingdom; and every Moor, whose spirit was not quite subdued with his fortunes, lauded the valor of the old monarch, and his fidelity to the faith, and wished success to his standard.

El Zagal, though he no longer sat enthroned in the Alhambra, yet reigned over more considerable domains than his nephew. His territories extended from the frontiers of Jaen along the borders of Murcia to the Mediterranean, and reached into the centre of the kingdom. On the northeast he held the cities of Baza and Guadix, situated in the midst of fertile regions. He had the important seaport of Almeria, also, which at one time rivaled Granada itself in wealth and population. Besides these, his territories included a great part of the Alpuxarra mountains, which extend across the kingdom and shoot out branches towards the sea-coast. This mountainous region was a stronghold of wealth and power. Its stern and rocky heights, rising to the clouds, seemed to set invasion at defiance; yet within their rugged embraces were sheltered delightful valleys, of the happiest temperature and richest fertility. The cool

springs and limpid rills which gushed out in all parts of
the mountains, and the abundant streams, which, for a
great part of the year, were supplied by the Sierra Nevada, spread a perpetual verdure over the skirts and
slopes of the hills, and, collecting in silver rivers in the
valleys, wound along among plantations of mulberry
trees, and groves of oranges and citrons, of almonds, figs,
and pomegranates.  Here was produced the finest silk of
Spain, which gave employment to thousands of manufac-
turers.  The sunburnt sides of the hills, also, were covered with vineyards ; the abundant herbage of the mountain ravines, and the rich pasturage of the valleys, fed
vast flocks and herds ; and even the arid and rocky
bosoms of the heights teemed with wealth, from the
mines of various metals with which they were impreg-
nated.  In a word, the Alpuxarra mountains had ever
been the great source of revenue to the monarchs of Granada.  Their inhabitants, also, were hardy and warlike,
and a sudden summons from the Moorish king could at
any time call forth fifty thousand fighting men from their
rocky fastnesses.

Such was the rich but rugged fragment of an empire
which remained under the sway of the old warrior monarch El Zagal.  The mountain barriers by which it was
locked up, had protected it from most of the ravages of
the present war.  El Zagal prepared himself, by strength-
ening every fortress, to battle fiercely for its maintenance.

The Catholic sovereigns saw that fresh troubles and

toils awaited them. The war had to be carried into a new quarter demanding immense expenditures; and new ways and means must be devised to replenish their exhausted coffers. "As this was a holy war, however," says Fray Antonio Agapida, "and peculiarly redounded to the prosperity of the church, the clergy were full of zeal, and contributed vast sums of money and large bodies of troops. A pious fund was also produced, from the first fruits of that glorious institution, the Inquisition."

It so happened, that about this time there were many families of wealth and dignity in the kingdoms of Aragon and Valentia, and the principality of Catalonia, whose forefathers had been Jews, but had been converted to Christianity. Notwithstanding the outward piety of these families, it was surmised, and soon came to be strongly suspected, that many of them had a secret hankering after Judaism; and it was even whispered, that some of them practiced Jewish rites in private.

The Catholic monarch (continues Agapida) had a righteous abhorrence of all kinds of heresy, and a fervent zeal for the faith: he ordered, therefore, a strict investigation of the conduct of these pseudo Christians. Inquisitions were sent into these provinces for the purpose, who proceeded with their accustomed zeal. The consequence was, that many families were convicted of apostacy from the Christian faith, and of the private practice of Judaism. Some, who had grace and policy sufficient to reform in time, were again received into the

Christian fold, after being severely mulcted and condemned to heavy penance ; others were burnt at *auto de fés*, for the edification of the public, and their property was confiscated for the good of the state.

As these Hebrews were of great wealth, and had an hereditary passion for jewelry, there was found abundant store in their possession of gold and silver, of rings and necklaces, and strings of pearl and coral, and precious stones :—treasures easy of transportation, and wonderfully adapted for the emergencies of war. " In this way," concludes the pious Agapida, " these backsliders, by the all-seeing contrivances of Providence, were made to serve the righteous cause which they had so treacherously deserted ; and their apostate wealth was sanctified by being devoted to the service of Heaven and the crown, in this holy crusade against the infidels."

It must be added, however, that these pious financial expedients received some check from the interference of queen Isabella. Her penetrating eyes discovered that many enormities had been committed under color of religious zeal, and many innocent persons accused by false witnesses of apostacy, either through malice or a hope of obtaining their wealth : she caused strict investigation, therefore into the proceedings which had been held ; many of which were reversed, and suborners punished in proportion to their guilt.*

* Pulgar, pt. 3, c. 100.

# CHAPTER LXVIII.

ULEY ABDALLAH EL ZAGAL," says the venerable Jesuit father, Pedro Abarca, "was the most venomous Mahometan in all Morisma:" and the worthy Fray Antonio Agapida most devoutly echoes his opinion. "Certainly," adds the latter, "none ever opposed a more heathenish and diabolical obstinacy to the holy inroads of the cross and sword."

El Zagal felt that it was necessary to do something to quicken his popularity with the people, and that nothing was more effectual than a successful inroad. The Moors loved the stirring call to arms, and a wild foray among the mountains; and delighted more in a hasty spoil, wrested with hard fighting from the Christians, than in all the steady and certain gains secured by peaceful traffic.

There reigned at this time a careless security along the frontier of Jaen. The alcaydes of the Christian fortresses were confident of the friendship of Boabdil el Chico, and they fancied his uncle too distant and too much engrossed by his own perplexities, to think of molesting

463

them. On a sudden, El Zagal issued out of Guadix with a chosen band, passed rapidly through the mountains which extend behind Granada, and fell like a thunderbolt upon the territories in the neighborhood of Alcala la Real. Before the alarm could be spread and the frontier roused, he had made a wide career of destruction through the country, sacking and burning villages, sweeping off flocks and herds, and carrying away captives. The warriors of the frontier assembled; but El Zagal was already far on his return through the mountains, and he reëntered the gates of Guadix in triumph, his army laden with Christian spoil, and conducting an immense cavalgada. Such was one of El Zagal's preparatives for the expected invasion of the Christian king, exciting the warlike spirit of his people, and gaining for himself a transient popularity.

King Ferdinand assembled his army at Murcia, in the spring of 1488. He left that city on the fifth of June, with a flying camp of four thousand horse and fourteen thousand foot. The marques of Cadiz led the van, followed by the adelantado of Murcia. The army entered the Moorish frontier by the sea-coast, spreading terror through the land; wherever it appeared the towns surrendered without a blow, so great was the dread of experiencing the woes which had desolated the opposite frontier. In this way, Vera, Velez el Rubio, Velez el Blanco, and many towns of inferior note, to the number of sixty, yielded at the first summons.

It was not until it approached Almeria, that the army met with resistance. This important city was commanded by the prince Zelim, a relation of El Zagal. He led forth his Moors bravely to the encounter, and skirmished fiercely with the advanced guard in the gardens near the city. King Ferdinand came up with the main body of the army, and called off his troops from the skirmish. He saw that to attack the place with his present force was fruitless. Having reconnoitered the city and its environs, therefore, against a future campaign, he retired with his army and marched towards Baza.

The old warrior El Zagal was himself drawn up in the city of Baza, with a powerful garrison. He felt confidence in the strength of the place, and rejoiced when he heard that the Christian king was approaching. In the valley in front of Baza, there extended a great tract of gardens, like a continued grove, intersected by canals and water-courses. In this he stationed an ambuscade of arquebussiers and cross-bowmen. The van-guard of the Christian army came marching gayly up the valley, with great sound of drum and trumpet, and led on by the marques of Cadiz and the adelantado of Murcia. As they drew near, El Zagal sallied forth with horse and foot, and attacked them for a time with great spirit. Gradually falling back, as if pressed by their superior valor, he drew the exulting Christians among the gardens. Suddenly the Moors in ambuscade burst from their concealment, and opened such a fire in flank and

30

rear, that many of the Christians were slain, and the rest thrown into confusion. King Ferdinand arrived in time to see the disastrous situation of his troops, and gave signal for the van-guard to retire.

El Zagal did not permit the foe to draw off unmolested. Ordering out fresh squadrons, he fell upon the rear of the retreating troops with triumphant shouts, driving them before him with dreadful havoc. The old war-cry of "El Zagal! El Zagal!" was again put up by the Moors, and echoed with transport from the walls of the city. The Christians were in imminent peril of a complete rout, when fortunately the adelantado of Murcia threw himself with a large body of horse and foot between the pursuers and the pursued, covering the retreat of the latter and giving them time to rally. The Moors were now attacked so vigorously in turn, that they gave over the contest, and drew back slowly into the city. Many valiant cavaliers were slain in this skirmish; among the number was Don Philip of Aragon, master of the chivalry of St. George of Montesor; he was illegitimate son of the king's illegitimate brother Don Carlos, and his death was greatly bewailed by Ferdinand. He had formerly been archbishop of Palermo, but had doffed the cassock for the cuirass, and, according to Fray Antonio Agapida, had gained a glorious crown of martyrdom by falling in this holy war.

The warm reception to his advance guard, brought king Ferdinand to a pause: he encamped on the banks of the neighboring river Guadalquiton, and began to consider whether he had acted wisely in undertaking this campaign with his present force. His late successes had probably rendered him over-confident: El Zagal had again schooled him into his characteristic caution. He saw that the old warrior was too formidably ensconced in Baza, to be dislodged by anything except a powerful army and battering artillery; and he feared, that should he persist in his invasion, some disaster might befall his army, either from the enterprise of the foe, or from a pestilence which prevailed in various parts of the country. He retired, therefore, from before Baza, as he had on a former occasion from before Loxa, all the wiser for a wholesome lesson in warfare, but by no means grateful to those who had given it, and with a solemn determination to have his revenge upon his teachers.

He now took measures for the security of the places gained in this campaign; placing in them strong garrisons, well armed and supplied, charging their alcaydes to be vigilant on their posts and to give no rest to the enemy. The whole of the frontier was placed under the command of Luiz Fernandez Puerto Carrero. As it was evident, from the warlike character of El Zagal, that there would be an abundance of active service and hard fighting, many hidalgos and young cavaliers, eager for distinction, remained with Puerto Carrero.

All these dispositions being made, king Ferdinand

closed the dubious campaign of this year, not, as usual, by returning in triumph at the head of his army to some important city of his dominions, but by disbanding the troops, and repairing to pray at the cross of Caravaca.

# CHAPTER LXIX.

HILE the pious king Ferdinand," observes Fray Antonio Agapida, "was humbling himself before the cross, and devoutly praying for the destruction of his enemies, that fierce pagan, El Zagal, depending merely on arm of flesh and sword of steel, pursued his diabolical outrages upon the Christians." No sooner was the invading army disbanded than he sallied forth from his stronghold, and carried fire and sword into all those parts which had submitted to the Spanish yoke. The castle of Nixar, being carelessly guarded, was taken by surprise, and its garrison put to the sword. The old warrior raged with sanguinary fury about the whole frontier, attacking convoys, slaying, wounding, and making prisoners, and coming by surprise upon the Christians wherever they were off their guard.

Carlos de Biedma, alcayde of the fortress of Culla, confiding in the strength of its walls and towers, and in its difficult situation, being built on the summit of a lofty hill, and surrounded by precipices, ventured to absent himself from his post. He was engaged to be married to a fair and noble lady of Baeza, and repaired to that city to celebrate his nuptials, escorted by a brilliant array of the best horsemen of his garrison. Apprised of his absence, the vigilant El Zagal suddenly appeared before Culla with a powerful force, stormed the town sword in hand, fought the Christians from street to street, and drove them, with great slaughter, to the citadel. Here a veteran captain, by the name of Juan de Avalos, a gray-headed warrior, scarred in many a battle, assumed the command, and made an obstinate defense. Neither the multitude of the enemy, nor the vehemence of their attacks, though led on by the terrible El Zagal himself, had power to shake the fortitude of this doughty old soldier.

The Moors undermined the outer walls and one of the towers of the fortress, and made their way into the exterior court. The alcayde manned the tops of his towers, pouring down melted pitch, and showering darts, arrows, stones, and all kinds of missiles upon the assailants. The Moors were driven out of the court; but, being reinforced with fresh troops, returned repeatedly to the assault. For five days the combat was kept up: the Christians were nearly exhausted, but were sustained by the cheerings of their stanch old alcayde, and the fear of death from El Zagal should they surrender. At length the approach of a powerful force under Don Luis Puerto Carrero relieved them from this fearful peril. El Zagal abandoned the assault, but set fire to the town in his rage and disappointment, and retired to his stronghold of Guadix.

The example of El Zagal roused his adherents to action. Two bold Moorish alcaydes, Ali Aliatar and Yzan Aliatar, commanding the fortresses of Alhenden and Salobreña, laid waste the country of the subjects of Boabdil, and the places which had recently submitted to the Christians : they swept off the cattle, carried off captives, and harassed the whole of the newly conquered frontier.

The Moors, also, of Almeria, and Tavernas, and Purchena, made inroads into Murcia, and carried fire and sword into its most fertile regions. On the opposite frontier, also, among the wild valleys and rugged recesses of the Sierra Bermeja, or Red Mountains, many of the Moors who had lately submitted again flew to arms. The marques of Cadiz suppressed by timely vigilance the rebellion of the mountain town of Gausin, situated on a high peak, almost among the clouds ; but others of the Moors fortified themselves in rock-built towers and castles, inhabited solely by warriors ; whence they carried on a continual war of forage and depredation ; sweeping down into the valleys, and carrying off flocks and herds and all kinds of booty to these eagle-nests, to which it was perilous and fruitless to pursue them.

The worthy father, Fray Antonio Agapida, closes his history of this checkered year in quite a different strain from those triumphant periods with which he is accustomed to wind up the victorious campaigns of the sovereigns. "Great and mighty," says this venerable chronicler, "were the floods and tempests which prevailed throughout the kingdoms of Castile and Aragon about this time. It seemed as though the windows of heaven were again opened, and a second deluge overwhelming the face of nature. The clouds burst, as it were, in cataracts upon the earth; torrents rushed down from the mountains, overflowing the valleys; brooks were swelled into raging rivers; houses were undermined; mills were swept away by their own streams; the affrighted shepherds saw their flocks drowned in the midst of the pasture, and were fain to take refuge for their lives in towers and high places. The Guadalquivir for a time became a roaring and tumultuous sea, inundating the immense plain of the Tablada, and filling the fair city of Seville with affright.

"A vast black cloud moved over the land, accompanied by a hurricane and a trembling of the earth. Houses were unroofed, the walls and battlements of fortresses shaken, and lofty towers rocked to their foundations. Ships, riding at anchor, were either stranded or swallowed up; others, under sail, were tossed to and fro upon mountain waves, and cast upon the land, where the whirlwind rent them in pieces and scattered them in fragments in the air. Doleful was the ruin and great the terror where this baleful cloud passed by; and it left a long track of desolation over sea and land. Some of the faint-hearted," adds Antonio Agapida, "looked upon this torment of the elements as a prodigious event, out of the course of nature. In the weakness of their fears, they connected it with those troubles which occurred in various places, considering it a portent of some great calamity, about to be wrought by the violence of the bloody-handed El Zagal and his fierce adherents." *

* See *Cura de los Palacios*, cap. 91. Palencia, *De Bella Granad*. lib. 8.

# CHAPTER LXX.

HE stormy winter had passed away, and the spring of 1489 was advancing; yet the heavy rains had broken up the roads, the mountain brooks were swollen to raging torrents, and the late shallow and peaceful rivers were deep, turbulent, and dangerous. The Christian troops had been summoned to assemble in early spring on the frontiers of Jaen, but were slow in arriving at the appointed place. They were entangled in the miry defiles of the mountains, or fretted impatiently on the banks of impassable floods. It was late in the month of May, before they assembled in sufficient force to attempt the proposed invasion; when, at length a valiant army, of thirteen thousand horse and forty thousand foot, marched merrily over the border. The queen remained at the city of Jaen, with the prince-royal and the princesses her children, accompanied and supported by the venerable cardinal of Spain, and those reverend prelates who assisted in her councils throughout this holy war.

474

The plan of king Ferdinand was to lay siege to the city of Baza, the key of the remaining possessions of the Moor. That important fortress taken, Guadix and Almeria must soon follow, and then the power of El Zagal would be at an end. As the Catholic king advanced, he had first to secure various castles and strongholds in the vicinity of Baza, which might otherwise harass his army. Some of these made obstinate resistance, especially the town of Zujar. The Christians assailed the walls with various machines, to sap them and batter them down. The brave alcayde, Hubec Abdilbar, opposed force to force and engine to engine. He manned his towers with his bravest warriors, who rained down an iron shower upon the enemy; and he linked cauldrons together by strong chains, and cast fire from them, consuming the wooden engines of their assailants, and those who managed them.

The siege was protracted for several days: the bravery of the alcayde could not save his fortress from an overwhelming foe, but it gained him honorable terms. Ferdinand permitted the garrison and the inhabitants to repair with their effects to Baza; and the gallant Hubec marched forth with the remnant of his force, and took the way to that devoted city.

The delays caused to the invading army by these circumstances, had been diligently improved by El Zagal, who felt that he was now making his last stand for empire, and that this campaign would decide, whether he should continue a king, or sink into a vassal. He was but a few leagues from Baza, at the city of Guadix. This last was the most important point of his remaining territories, being a kind of bulwark between them and the hostile city of Granada, the seat of his nephew's power. Though he heard of the tide of war, therefore, collecting and rolling towards the city of Baza, he dared not go in person to its assistance. He dreaded that should he leave Guadix, Boabdil would attack him in rear while the Christian army was battling with him in front. El Zagal trusted in the great strength of Baza, to defy any violent assault, and profited by the delays of the Christian army, to supply it with all possible means of defense. He sent thither all the troops he could spare from his garrison of Guadix, and dispatched missives throughout his territories, calling upon all true Moslems to hasten to Baza, and make a devoted stand in defense of their homes, their liberties, and their religion. The cities of Tavernas and Purchena, and the surrounding heights and valleys, responded to his orders, and sent forth their fighting men to the field. The rocky fastnesses of the Alpuxarras resounded with the din of arms; troops of horse and bodies of foot-soldiers were seen winding down the rugged cliffs and defiles of those marble mountains, and hastening towards Baza. Many brave cavaliers of Granada also, spurning the quiet and security of Christian vassalage, secretly left the city and hastened to join their fighting countrymen. The great dependence of El Zagal, however, was upon the valor and loyalty of his cousin and brother-in-law, Cid Hiaya Alnayar,* who was alcayde of Almeria,—a cavalier experienced in warfare and redoubtable in the field. He wrote to him to leave Almeria, and repair with all speed, at the head of his troops, to Baza. Cid Hiaya departed immediately, with ten thousand of the bravest Moors in the kingdom. These were for the most part hardy mountaineers, tempered to sun and storm, and tried in many a combat. None equaled them for a sally or a skirmish. They were adroit in executing a thousand stratagems, ambuscadoes, and evolutions. Impetuous in their assaults, yet governed in their utmost fury by a word or sign from their commander, at the sound of a trumpet they would check themselves in the midst of their career, wheel off and disperse; and at another sound of a trumpet, they would as suddenly reassemble and return to the attack. They were upon the enemy when least expected, coming like a rushing blast, spreading havoc and consternation, and then passing away in

---

* This name has generally been written Cidi Yahye. The present mode is adopted on the authority of Alcantara in his history of Granada; who appears to have derived it from Arabic manuscripts, existing in the archives of the marques de Corvera, descendant of Cid Hiaya. The latter (Cid Hiaya) was son of Aben Zelim, a deceased prince of Almeria, and was a lineal descendant from the celebrated Aben Hud, surnamed the Just. The wife of Cid Hiaya was sister of the two Moorish generals, Abul Cacim and Reduan Vanegas, and like them the fruit of the union of a Christian knight, Don Pedro Vanegas, with Cetimerien, a Moorish princess.

an instant; so that when one recovered from the shock and looked around, behold nothing was to be seen or heard of this tempest of war, but a cloud of dust and the clatter of retreating hoofs.[*]

When Cid Hiaya led his train of ten thousand valiant warriors into the gates of Baza, the city rang with acclamations, and for a time the inhabitants thought themselves secure. El Zagal, also, felt a glow of confidence, notwithstanding his own absence from the city. "Cid Hiaya," said he, "is my cousin and my brother-in-law; related to me by blood and marriage, he is a second self: happy is that monarch who has his kindred to command his armies."

With all these reinforcements, the garrison of Baza amounted to above twenty thousand men. There were at this time three principal leaders in the city: Mohammed Ibn Hassan, surnamed the Veteran, who was military governor or alcayde, an old Moor of great experience and discretion; the second was Hamet Abu Zali, who was captain of the troops stationed in the place; and the third was Hubec Abdilbar, late alcayde of Zujar, who had repaired hither with the remains of his garrison. Over all these Cid Hiaya exercised a supreme command, in consequence of his being of the blood-royal, and in the especial confidence of Muley Abdallah el Zagal. He was eloquent and ardent in council, and fond

[*] Pulgar, pt. 3, c. 106.

of striking and splendid achievements; but he was a little prone to be carried away by the excitement of the moment, and the warmth of his imagination. The councils of war of these commanders, therefore, were more frequently controlled by the opinions of the old alcayde Mohammed Ibn Hassan, for whose shrewdness, caution, and experience, Cid Hiaya himself felt the greatest deference.

The city of Baza was situated in a great valley, eight leagues in length and three in breadth, called the Hoya, or basin of Baza. It was surrounded by a range of mountains, called the Sierra of Xabalcohol, the streams of which, collecting themselves into two rivers, watered and fertilized the country. The city was built in the plain; one part of it protected by the rocky precipices of the mountain, and by a powerful citadel; the other by massive walls, studded with immense towers. It had suburbs towards the plain, imperfectly fortified by earthen walls. In front of these suburbs extended a tract of orchards and gardens nearly a league in length, so thickly planted as to resemble a continued forest. Here, every citizen who could afford it, had his little plantation, and his garden of fruits and flowers and vegetables, watered by canals and rivulets, and dominated by a small tower for recreation or defense. This wilderness of groves and gardens, intersected in all parts by canals and runs of water, and studded by above a thousand small towers, formed a kind of protection to this side of the city, rendering all approach extremely difficult and perplexed.

While the Christian army had been detained before the frontier posts, the city of Baza had been a scene of hurried and unremitting preparation. All the grain of the surrounding valley, though yet unripe, was hastily reaped and borne into the city, to prevent it from yielding sustenance to the enemy. The country was drained of all its supplies; flocks and herds were driven, bleating and bellowing, into the gates; long trains of beasts of burden, some laden with food, others with lances, darts, and arms of all kinds, kept pouring into the place. Already were munitions collected sufficient for a siege of fifteen months; still the eager and hasty preparation was going on, when the army of Ferdinand came in sight.

On one side might be seen scattered parties of foot and horse spurring to the gates, and muleteers hurrying forward their burdened animals, all anxious to get under shelter before the gathering storm; on the other side, the cloud of war came sweeping down the valley, the roll of drum or clang of trumpet resounding occasionally from its deep bosom, or the bright glance of arms flashing forth, like vivid lightning, from its columns. King Ferdinand pitched his tents in the valley, beyond the green labyrinth of gardens. He sent his heralds to summon the city to surrender, promising the most favorable terms in case of immediate compliance, and avowing in the most solemn terms his resolution never to abandon the siege until he had possession of the place.

Upon receiving this summons, the Moorish commanders held a council of war. The prince Cid Hiaya, indignant at the menaces of the king, was for retorting by a declaration that the garrison never would surrender, but would fight until buried under the ruins of the walls. "Of what avail," said the veteran Mohammed, "is a declaration of the kind, which we may falsify by our deeds? Let us threaten what we know we can perform, and let us endeavor to perform more than we threaten."

In conformity to his advice, therefore, a laconic reply was sent to the Christian monarch, thanking him for his offer of favorable terms, but informing him that they were placed in the city to defend, not to surrender it.

31

# CHAPTER LXXI.

WHEN the reply of the Moorish commanders was brought to King Ferdinand, he prepared to press the siege with the utmost rigor. Finding the camp too far from the city, and that the intervening orchards afforded shelter for the sallies of the Moors, he determined to advance it beyond the gardens, in the space between them and the suburbs, where his batteries would have full play upon the city walls. A detachment was sent in advance, to take possession of the gardens, and keep a check upon the suburbs, opposing any sally, while the encampment should be formed and fortified. The various commanders entered the orchards at different points. The young cavaliers marched fearlessly forward, but the experienced veterans foresaw infinite peril in the mazes of this verdant labyrinth. The master of St. Jago, as he led his troops into the centre of the gardens, exhorted them to keep by one another, and to press forward in defiance of all difficulty or danger; assuring them that God would give them the victory, if they attacked hardily and persisted resolutely.

482

Scarce had they entered the verge of the orchards, when a din of drums and trumpets, mingled with war-cries, was heard from the suburbs, and a legion of Moorish warriors on foot poured forth. They were led on by the prince Cid Hiaya. He saw the imminent danger of the city, should the Christians gain possession of the orchards. "Soldiers," he cried, "we fight for life and liberty, for our families, our country, our religion;* nothing is left for us to depend upon, but the strength of our hands, the courage of our hearts, and the almighty protection of Allah." The Moors answered him with shouts of war, and rushed to the encounter. The two hosts met in the midst of the gardens. A chance-medley combat ensued, with lances, arquebuses, cross-bows, and scimetars; the perplexed nature of the ground, cut up and intersected by canals and streams, the closeness of the trees, the multiplicity of towers and petty edifices, gave greater advantages to the Moors, who were on foot, than to the Christians, who were on horseback. The Moors, too, knew the ground, with all its alleys and passes; and were thus enabled to lurk, to sally forth, attack, and retreat, almost without injury.

The Christian commanders seeing this, ordered many of the horsemen to dismount and fight on foot. The battle then became fierce and deadly, each disregarding his own life, provided he could slay his enemy. It was not

* "Illi (Mauri) pro fortunis, pro libertate, pro laribus patriis, pro vita denique certabant."—Pietro Martyr, *Epist.* 70.

so much a general battle, as a multitude of petty actions;
for every orchard and garden had its distinct contest.
No one could see further than the little scene of fury
and bloodshed around him, nor know how the general
battle fared. In vain the captains exerted their voices,
in vain the trumpets brayed forth signals and commands
—all was confounded and unheard, in the universal din
and uproar. No one kept to his standard, but fought as
his own fury or fear dictated. In some places the Christians had the advantage, in others the Moors; often, a
victorious party, pursuing the vanquished, came upon a
superior and triumphant force of the enemy, and the
fugitives turned back upon them in an overwhelming
wave. Some broken remnants, in their terror and confusion, fled from their own countrymen and sought refuge
among their enemies, not knowing friend from foe, in the
obscurity of the groves. The Moors were more adroit in
these wild skirmishings, from their flexibility, lightness,
and agility, and the rapidity with which they would disperse, rally, and return again to the charge.*

The hardest fighting was about the small garden
towers and pavilions, which served as so many petty
fortresses. Each party by turns gained them, defended
them fiercely, and were driven out; many of the towers
were set on fire, and increased the horrors of the fight by
the wreaths of smoke and flame in which they wrapped

* Mariana, lib. 25, cap. 13.

the groves, and by the shrieks of those who were burning.

Several of the Christian cavaliers, bewildered by the uproar and confusion, and shocked at the carnage which prevailed, would have led their men out of the action; but they were entangled in a labyrinth, and knew not which way to retreat. While in this perplexity, Juan Perea, the standard-bearer of one of the squadrons of the grand cardinal, had his arm carried off by a cannon-ball; the standard was well nigh falling into the hands of the enemy, when Rodrigo de Mendoza, an intrepid youth, natural son of the grand cardinal, rushed to its rescue, through a shower of balls, lances, and arrows, and, bearing it aloft, dashed forward with it into the hottest of the combat, followed by his shouting soldiery.

King Ferdinand, who remained in the skirts of the orchard, was in extreme anxiety. It was impossible to see much of the action, for the multiplicity of trees and towers, and the wreaths of smoke; and those who were driven out defeated, or came out wounded and exhausted, gave different accounts, according to the fate of the partial conflicts in which they had been engaged. Ferdinand exerted himself to the utmost to animate and encourage his troops to this blind encounter, sending reinforcements of horse and foot to those points where the battle was most sanguinary and doubtful.

Among those who were brought forth mortally wounded was Don Juan de Luna, a youth of uncommon merit, greatly prized by the king, beloved by the army, and married to Doña Catalina de Urrea, a young lady of distinguished beauty.* They laid him at the foot of a tree, and endeavored to stanch and bind up his wounds with a scarf which his bride had wrought for him; but his life-blood flowed too profusely; and while a holy friar was yet administering to him the last sacred offices of the church, he expired, almost at the feet of his sovereign.

On the other hand, the veteran alcayde, Mohammed Ibn Hassan, surrounded by a little band of chieftains, kept an anxious eye upon the scene of combat, from the walls of the city. For nearly twelve hours the battle raged without intermission. The thickness of the foliage hid all the particulars from their sight; but they could see the flash of swords and glance of helmets among the trees. Columns of smoke rose in every direction, while the clash of arms, the thundering of ribadoquines and arquebuses, the shouts and cries of the combatants, and the groans and supplications of the wounded, bespoke the deadly conflict waging in the bosom of the groves. They were harassed, too, by the shrieks and lamentations of the Moorish women and children, as their wounded relatives were brought bleeding from the scene of action; and were stunned by a general outcry of woe on the part of the inhabitants, as the body of Reduan Zafargal, a

* Mariana. P. Martyr. Zurita.

renegado Christian, and one of the bravest of their generals, was borne breathless into the city.

At length the din of battle approached nearer to the skirts of the orchard. They beheld their warriors driven out from among the groves by fresh squadrons of the enemy, and, after disputing the ground inch by inch, obliged to retire to a place between the orchards and the suburbs, which was fortified with palisadoes.

The Christians immediately planted opposing palisadoes, and established strong outposts near to this retreat of the Moors, while, at the same time, King Ferdinand ordered that his encampment should be pitched within the hard-won orchards.

Mohammed Ibn Hassan sallied forth to the aid of the prince Cid Hiaya, and made a desperate attempt to dislodge the enemy from this formidable position; but the night had closed, and the darkness rendered it impossible to make any impression. The Moors, however, kept up constant assaults and alarms throughout the night; and the weary Christians, exhausted by the toils and sufferings of the day, were not allowed a moment of repose.*

* Pulgar, pt. 3, cap. 106, 107. *Cura de los Palacios,* cap. 92. Zurita, lib. 20, cap. 81.

## CHAPTER LXXII.

HE morning sun rose upon a piteous scene before the walls of Baza. The Christian outposts, harassed throughout the night, were pale and haggard; while the multitudes of slain which lay before their palisadoes, showed the fierce attacks they had sustained, and the bravery of their defense.

Beyond them lay the groves and gardens of Baza; once favorite resorts for recreation and delight—now, a scene of horror and desolation. The towers and pavilions were smoking ruins; the canals and water-courses were discolored with blood, and choked with the bodies of the slain. Here and there the ground, deep dinted with the tramp of man and steed, and plashed and slippery with gore, showed where had been some fierce and mortal conflict; while the bodies of Moors and Christians, ghastly in death, lay half-concealed among the matted and trampled shrubs, and flowers, and herbage.

Amidst these sanguinary scenes rose the Christian tents, hastily pitched among the gardens in the preceding evening. The experience of the night, however, and the forlorn aspect of everything in the morning, convinced king Ferdinand of the perils and hardships to which his camp must be exposed, in its present situation; and, after a consultation with his principal cavaliers, he resolved to abandon the orchards.

It was a dangerous movement, to extricate his army from so entangled a situation, in the face of so alert and daring an enemy. A bold front was therefore kept up towards the city; additional troops were ordered to the advanced posts, and works begun as if for a settled encampment. Not a tent was struck in the gardens; but in the meantime, the most active and unremitting exertions were made to remove all the baggage and furniture of the camp back to the original station.

All day, the Moors beheld a formidable show of war maintained in front of the gardens; while in the rear, the tops of the Christian tents, and the pennons of the different commanders, were seen rising above the groves. Suddenly, towards evening, the tents sank and disappeared; the outposts broke up their stations and withdrew, and the whole shadow of an encampment was fast vanishing from their eyes.

The Moors saw too late the subtle manœuvre of king Ferdinand. Cid Hiaya again sallied forth with a large force of horse and foot, and pressed furiously upon the Christians. The latter, however, experienced in Moorish attack, retired in close order, sometimes turning upon the enemy and driving them to their barricadoes, and then pursuing their retreat. In this way the army was extricated, without much further loss, from the perilous labyrinths of the gardens.

The camp was now out of danger; but it was also too distant from the city to do mischief, while the Moors could sally forth and return without hindrance. The king called a council of war, to consider in what manner to proceed. The marques of Cadiz was for abandoning the siege for the present, the place being too strong, too well garrisoned and provided, and too extensive, for their limited forces either to carry it by assault, or invest and reduce it by famine; while, in lingering before it, the army would be exposed to the usual maladies and sufferings of besieging armies, and, when the rainy season came on, would be shut up by the swelling of the rivers. He recommended, instead, that the king should throw garrisons of horse and foot into all the towns captured in the neighborhood, and leave them to keep up a predatory war upon Baza, while he should overrun and ravage all the country; so that, in the following year, Almeria and Guadix, having all their subject towns and territories taken from them, might be starved into submission.

Don Gutierre de Cardenas, senior commander of Leon, on the other hand, maintained that to abandon the siege would be construed by the enemy into a sign of weakness and irresolution. It would give new spirits to the partisans of El Zagal, and would gain to his standard many of the wavering subjects of Boabdil, if it did not encourage the fickle populace of Granada to open rebellion. He advised, therefore, that the siege should be prosecuted with vigor.

The pride of Ferdinand pleaded in favor of the last opinion; for it would be doubly humiliating, again to return from a campaign in this part of the Moorish kingdom, without effecting a blow. But when he reflected on all that his army had suffered, and on all that they must suffer should the siege continue,—especially from the difficulty of obtaining a regular supply of provisions for so numerous a host, across a great extent of rugged and mountainous country, — he determined to consult the safety of his people, and to adopt the advice of the marques of Cadiz.

When the soldiery heard that the king was about to raise the siege in mere consideration of their sufferings, they were filled with generous enthusiasm, and entreated, as with one voice, that the siege might never be abandoned until the city surrendered.

Perplexed by conflicting counsels, the king dispatched messengers to the queen at Jaen, requesting her advice. Posts had been stationed between them, in such manner that missives from the camp could reach the queen within ten hours. Isabella sent instantly her reply. She left the policy of raising or continuing the siege to the decision of the king and his captains; but should they determine to persevere, she pledged herself, with the aid of God, to forward them men, money, provisions, and all other supplies, until the city should be taken.

The reply of the queen determined Ferdinand to persevere; and when his determination was made known to the army, it was hailed with as much joy as if it had been tidings of a victory.

## CHAPTER LXXIII.

THE Moorish prince Cid Hiaya had received tidings of the doubts and discussions in the Christian camp, and flattered himself with hopes that the besieging army would soon retire in despair, though the veteran Mohammed shook his head with incredulity. A sudden movement one morning in the Christian camp, seemed to confirm the sanguine hopes of the prince. The tents were struck, the artillery and baggage were conveyed away, and bodies of soldiers began to march along the valley. The momentary gleam of triumph was soon dispelled. The Catholic king had merely divided his host into two camps, the more effectually to distress the city. One, consisting of four thousand horse and eight thousand foot, with all the artillery and battering engines, took post on the side of the city towards the mountain. This was commanded by the marques of Cadiz, with whom were Don Alonzo de Aguilar, Luis Fernandez Puerto Carrero, and many other distinguished cavaliers.

493

The other camp was commanded by the king, having six thousand horse and a great host of foot-soldiers, the hardy mountaineers of Biscay, Guipuscoa, Galicia, and the Asturias. Among the cavaliers who were with the king were the brave count de Tendilla, Don Rodrigo de Mendoza, and Don Alonzo de Cardenas, master of Santiago. The two camps were wide asunder, on opposite sides of the city, and between them lay the thick wilderness of orchards. Both camps were therefore fortified by great trenches, breastworks, and palisadoes. The veteran Mohammed, as he saw these two formidable camps glittering on each side of the city, and noted the well-known pennons of renowned commanders fluttering above them, still comforted his companions : "These camps," said he, "are too far removed from each other, for mutual succor and coöperation ; and the forest of orchards is as a gulf between them." This consolation was but of short continuance. Scarcely were the Christian camps fortified, when the ears of the Moorish garrison were startled by the sound of innumerable axes, and the crash of falling trees. They looked with anxiety from their highest towers, and beheld their favorite groves sinking beneath the blows of the Christian pioneers. The Moors sallied forth with fiery zeal to protect their beloved gardens, and the orchards in which they so much delighted. The Christians, however, were too well supported to be driven from their work. Day after day, the gardens became the scene of incessant and bloody skirmishings; yet still the devastation of the groves went on, for king Ferdinand was too well aware of the necessity of clearing away this screen of woods, not to bend all his forces to the undertaking. It was a work, however, of gigantic toil and patience. The trees were of such magnitude, and so closely set together, and spread over so wide an extent, that notwithstanding four thousand men were employed, they could scarcely clear a strip of land ten paces broad within a day; and such were the interruptions from the incessant assaults of the Moors, that it was full forty days before the orchards were completely leveled.

The devoted city of Baza now lay stripped of its beautiful covering of groves and gardens, at once its ornament, its delight, and its protection. The besiegers went on slowly and surely, with almost incredible labors, to invest and isolate the city. They connected their camps by a deep trench across the plain, a league in length, into which they diverted the waters of the mountain streams. They protected this trench by palisadoes, fortified by fifteen castles, at regular distances. They dug a deep trench, also, two leagues in length, across the mountain in the rear of the city, reaching from camp to camp, and fortified it on each side with walls of earth, and stone, and wood. Thus the Moors were inclosed on all sides by trenches, palisadoes, walls, and castles; so that it was impossible for them to sally beyond this great line of circumvallation—nor could any force enter to their succor. Ferdinand made an attempt likewise, to cut off the supply of water from the city; "for water," observes the worthy Agapida, "is more necessary to these infidels than bread, making use of it in repeated daily ablutions enjoined by their damnable religion, and employing it in baths and in a thousand other idle and extravagant modes, of which we Spaniards and Christians make but little account."

There was a noble fountain of pure water, which gushed out at the foot of the hill Albohacen, just behind the city. The Moors had almost a superstitious fondness for this fountain, and chiefly depended upon it for their supplies. Receiving intimation from some deserters, of the plan of king Ferdinand to get possession of this precious fountain, they sallied forth at night, and threw up such powerful works upon the impending hill, as to set all attempts of the Christian assailants at defiance.

## CHAPTER LXXIV.

#### EXPLOIT OF HERNANDO PEREZ DEL PULGAR AND OTHER CAVALIERS.

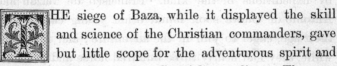HE siege of Baza, while it displayed the skill and science of the Christian commanders, gave but little scope for the adventurous spirit and fiery valor of the young Spanish cavaliers. They repined at the tedious monotony and dull security of their fortified camp, and longed for some soul-stirring exploit of difficulty and danger. Two of the most spirited of these youthful cavaliers were Francisco de Bazan and Antonio de Cueva, the latter of whom was son to the duke of Albuquerque. As they were one day seated on the ramparts of the camp, and venting their impatience at this life of inaction, they were overheard by a veteran adalid, one of those scouts or guides who are acquainted with all parts of the country. "Señors," said he, "if you wish for a service of peril and profit, if you are willing to pluck the fiery old Moor by the beard, I can lead you to where you may put your mettle to the proof. Hard by the city of Guadix, are certain hamlets rich in booty. I can conduct you by a way in which you may come upon them by surprise; and if you are as cool in

the head, as you are hot in the spur, you may bear off your spoils from under the very eyes of old El Zagal."

The idea of thus making booty at the very gates of Guadix, pleased the hot-spirited youths. These predatory excursions were frequent about this time; and the Moors of Padul, Alhenden, and other towns of the Alpuxarras, had recently harassed the Christian territories by expeditions of the kind. Francisco de Bazan and Antonio de Cueva soon found other young cavaliers of their age, eager to join in the adventure; and in a little while, they had nearly three hundred horse and two hundred foot, ready equipped and eager for the foray.

Keeping their destination secret, they sallied out of the camp on the edge of an evening, and, guided by the adalid, made their way by starlight through the most secret roads of the mountains. In this way they pressed on rapidly day and night, until early one morning, before cock-crowing they fell suddenly upon the hamlets, made prisoners of the inhabitants, sacked the houses, ravaged the fields, and sweeping through the meadows, gathered together all the flocks and herds. Without giving themselves time to rest, they set out upon their return, making with all speed for the mountains, before the alarm should be given and the country roused.

Several of the herdsmen, however, had fled to Guadix, and carried tidings of the ravage to El Zagal. The beard of old Muley trembled with rage; he immediately sent out six hundred of his choicest horse and foot, with orders to recover the booty and to bring those insolent marauders captive to Guadix.

The Christian cavaliers were urging their cavalgada of cattle and sheep up a mountain, as fast as their own weariness would permit, when, looking back, they beheld a great cloud of dust, and presently descried the turbaned host hot upon their traces.

They saw that the Moors were superior in number; they were fresh also, both man and steed, whereas both they and their horses were fatigued by two days and two nights of hard marching. Several of the horsemen therefore gathered round the commanders, and proposed that they should relinquish their spoil, and save themselves by flight. The captains, Francisco de Bazan and Antonio de Cueva, spurned at such craven counsel. "What!" cried they, "abandon our prey without striking a blow? Leave our foot-soldiers too in the lurch, to be overwhelmed by the enemy? If any one gives such counsel through fear, he mistakes the course of safety; for there is less danger in presenting a bold front to the foe, than in turning a dastard back; and fewer men are killed in a brave advance, than in a cowardly retreat."

Some of the cavaliers were touched by these words, and declared that they would stand by the foot-soldiers like true companions in arms; the great mass of the party, however, were volunteers, brought together by chance, who received no pay, nor had any common tie to keep them together in time of danger. The pleasure of the expedition being over, each thought but of his own safety, regardless of his companions. As the enemy approached, the tumult of opinions increased, and everything was in confusion. The captains, to put an end to the dispute, ordered the standard-bearer to advance against the Moors, well knowing that no true cavalier would hesitate to follow and defend his banner. The standard-bearer hesitated—the troops were on the point of taking to flight.

Upon this a cavalier of the royal guards rode to the front. It was Hernan Perez del Pulgar, alcayde of the fortress of Salar: the same dauntless ambassador who once bore to the turbulent people of Malaga the king's summons to surrender. Taking off a handkerchief which he wore round his head, after the Andalusian fashion, he tied it to the end of a lance and elevated it in the air. "Cavaliers," cried he, "why do ye take weapons in your hands, if you depend upon your feet for safety? This day will determine who is the brave man, and who the coward. He who is disposed to fight, shall not want a standard: let him follow this handkerchief." So saying, he waved his banner, and spurred bravely against the Moors. His example shamed some, and filled others with generous emulation: all turned with one accord, and following Pulgar, rushed with shouts upon the enemy. The Moors scarcely waited to receive the shock of their encounter. Seized with a panic, they took to flight, and were pursued for a considerable distance, with great slaughter. Three

hundred of their dead strewed the road, and were stripped and despoiled by the conquerors; many were taken
prisoners, and the Christian cavaliers returned in triumph
to the camp, with a long cavalgada of sheep and cattle,
and mules laden with booty, and bearing before them the
singular standard which had conducted them to victory.

King Ferdinand was so pleased with the gallant action
of Hernan Perez del Pulgar that he immediately conferred on him the honor of knighthood; using in the
ceremony the sword of Diego de Aguero, the captain of
the royal guards; the duke of Esculona girded one of his
own gilt spurs upon his heel, and the grand master of
Santiago, the Count de Cabra, and Gonsalvo of Cordova
officiated as witnesses. Furthermore, to perpetuate in
his family the memory of his achievement, the sovereigns
authorized him to emblazon on his escutcheon a golden
lion in an azure field, bearing a lance with a handkerchief at the end of it. Round the border of the escutcheon were depicted the eleven alcaydes vanquished in
the battle.* The foregoing is but one of many hardy
and heroic deeds done by this brave cavalier, in the wars
against the Moors; by which he gained great renown,
and the distinguished appellation of "El de las hazañas,"
or "He of the exploits." †

* Alcantara, *Hist. de Granada*, tom. iv., cap. 18.  Pulgar, *Cron.* pt. iii.
† Hernan or Hernando del Pulgar, the historian, secretary to Queen
Isabella, is confounded with this cavalier, by some writers.  He was also
present at the siege of Baza, and has recounted this transaction in his
chronicle of the Catholic sovereigns, Ferdinand and Isabella.

# CHAPTER LXXV.

CONTINUATION OF THE SIEGE OF BAZA.

HE Moorish king El Zagal mounted a tower, and looked out eagerly to enjoy the sight of the Christian marauders brought captive into the gates of Guadix; but his spirits fell when he beheld his own troops stealing back in the dusk of the evening, in broken and dejected parties.

The fortune of war bore hard against the old monarch; his mind was harassed by disastrous tidings brought each day from Baza, of the sufferings of the inhabitants, and the numbers of the garrison slain in the frequent skirmishes. He dared not go in person to the relief of the place, for his presence was necessary in Guadix, to keep a check upon his nephew in Granada. He sent reinforcements and supplies; but they were intercepted, and either captured or driven back. Still his situation was in some respects preferable to that of his nephew Boabdil. He was battling like a warrior, on the last step of his throne; El Chico remained a kind of pensioned vassal, in the luxurious abode of the Alhambra. The chivalrous part of the inhabitants of Granada could

not but compare the generous stand made by the warriors of Baza for their country and their faith, with their
own time-serving submission to the yoke of an unbeliever. Every account they received of the woes of Baza
wrung their hearts with agony; every account of the exploits of its devoted defenders brought blushes to their
cheeks. Many stole forth secretly with their weapons,
and hastened to join the besieged; and the partisans of
El Zagal wrought upon the patriotism and passions of
the remainder, until another of those conspiracies was
formed, that were continually menacing the unsteady
throne of Granada. It was concerted by the conspirators
to assail the Alhambra on a sudden, slay Boabdil, assemble the troops, and march to Guadix; where, being
reinforced by the garrison of that place, and led on by
the old warrior monarch, they might fall with overwhelming power upon the Christian army before Baza.

Fortunately for Boabdil, he discovered the conspiracy
in time, and the heads of the leaders were struck off, and
placed upon the walls of the Alhambra—an act of severity unusual with this mild and wavering monarch, which
struck terror into the disaffected, and produced a kind
of mute tranquillity throughout the city.

Ferdinand had full information of all the movements
and measures for the relief of Baza, and took precautions
to prevent them. Bodies of horsemen held watch in the
mountain passes, to prevent supplies, and intercept any
generous volunteers from Granada; and watch-towers

were erected, or scouts placed on every commanding height, to give the alarm at the least sign of a hostile turban.

The prince Cid Hiaya and his brave companions in arms were thus gradually walled up, as it were, from the rest of the world. A line of towers, the battlements of which bristled with troops, girded their city; and behind the intervening bulwarks and palisadoes passed and repassed continual squadrons of troops. Week after week and month after month passed away, but Ferdinand waited in vain for the garrison to be either terrified or starved into surrender. Every day they sallied forth with the spirit and alacrity of troops high fed, and flushed with confidence. "The Christian monarch," says the veteran Mohammed Ibn Hassan, "builds his hopes upon our growing faint and desponding—we must manifest unusual cheerfulness and vigor. What would be rashness in other service becomes prudence with us." The prince Cid Hiaya agreed with him in opinion, and sallied forth with his troops upon all kinds of harebrained exploits. They laid ambushes, concerted surprises, and made the most desperate assaults. The great extent of the Christian works rendered them weak in many parts: against these the Moors directed their attacks, suddenly breaking into them, making a hasty ravage, and bearing off their booty in triumph to the city. Sometimes they would sally forth by passes and clefts of the mountain in the rear of the city, which it was difficult to guard, and, hurrying down into the plain, swept off all cattle and sheep that were grazing near the suburbs, and all stragglers from the camp.

These partisan sallies brought on many sharp and bloody encounters, in some of which Don Alonzo de Aguilar and the alcayde de los Donceles distinguished themselves greatly. During one of these hot skirmishes, which happened on the skirts of the mountain, about twilight, a cavalier, named Martin Galindo, beheld a powerful Moor dealing deadly blows about him, and making great havoc among the Christians. Galindo pressed forward and challenged him to single combat. The Moor was not slow in answering the call. Couching their lances, they rushed furiously upon each other. At the first shock the Moor was wounded in the face, and borne out of his saddle. Before Galindo could check his steed, and turn from his career, the Moor sprang upon his feet, recovered his lance, and, rushing upon him, wounded him in the head and the arm. Though Galindo was on horseback and the Moor on foot, yet such was the prowess and address of the latter, that the Christian knight, being disabled in the arm, was in the utmost peril, when his comrades hastened to his assistance. At their approach, the valiant pagan retreated slowly up the rocks, keeping them at bay, until he found himself among his companions.

Several of the young Spanish cavaliers, stung by the triumph of this Moslem knight, would have challenged

others of the Moors to single combat; but King Ferdinand prohibited all vaunting encounters of the kind.
He forbade his troops, also, to provoke skirmishes, well
knowing that the Moors were more dexterous than most
people in this irregular mode of fighting, and were better
acquainted with the ground.

# CHAPTER LXXVI.

HOW TWO FRIARS FROM THE HOLY LAND ARRIVED AT THE CAMP.

WHILE the holy Christian army (says Fray Antonio Agapida) was thus beleaguering this infidel city of Baza, there rode into the camp one day two reverend friars of the order of St. Francis. One was of portly person and authoritative air: he bestrode a goodly steed, well conditioned and well caparisoned; while his companion rode beside him, upon a humble hack, poorly accoutered; and, as he rode, he scarcely raised his eyes from the ground, but maintained a meek and lowly air.

The arrival of two friars in the camp was not a matter of much note, for in these holy wars the church militant continually mingled in the affray, and helmet and cowl were always seen together; but it was soon discovered that these worthy saints-errant were from a far country and on a mission of great import.

They were, in truth, just arrived from the Holy Land, being two of the saintly men who kept vigil over the sepulchre of our blessed Lord at Jerusalem. He of the tall and portly form and commanding presence was Fray

507

Antonio Millan, prior of the Franciscan convent in the Holy City. He had a full and florid countenance, a sonorous, voice and was round, and swelling, and copious in his periods, like one accustomed to harangue, and to be listened to with deference. His companion was small and spare in form, pale of visage, and soft and silken, and almost whispering in speech. "He had a humble and lowly way," says Agapida, "evermore bowing the head, as became one of his calling." Yet he was one of the most active, zealous, and effective brothers of the convent; and, when he raised his small black eye from the earth, there was a keen glance out of the corner which showed that, though harmless as a dove, he was nevertheless as wise as a serpent.

Those holy men had come on a momentous embassy from the grand soldan of Egypt; or, as Agapida terms him in the language of the day, the soldan of Babylon. The league which had been made between that potentate and his arch foe, the Grand Turk Bajazet II., to unite in arms for the salvation of Granada, as has been mentioned in a previous chapter of this chronicle, had come to nought. The infidel princes had again taken up arms against each other, and had relapsed into their ancient hostility. Still the grand soldan, as head of the whole Moslem religion, considered himself bound to preserve the kingdom of Granada from the grasp of unbelievers. He dispatched, therefore, these two holy friars with letters to the Castilian sovereigns, as well as to the

Pope and to the king of Naples, remonstrating against the evil done to the Moors of the kingdom of Granada, who were of his faith and kindred; whereas it was well known that great numbers of Christians were indulged and protected in the full enjoyment of their property, their liberty, and their faith in his dominions. He insisted, therefore, that this war should cease; that the Moors of Granada should be reinstated in the territory of which they had been dispossessed; otherwise he threatened to put to death all the Christians beneath his sway, to demolish their convents and temples, and to destroy the Holy Sepulchre.

This fearful menace had spread consternation among the Christians of Palestine; and when the intrepid Fray Antonio Millan and his lowly companion departed on their mission, they were accompanied far from the gates of Jerusalem by an anxious throng of brethren and disciples, who remained watching them with tearful eyes as long as they were in sight.

These holy ambassadors were received with great distinction by King Ferdinand; for men of their cloth had ever high honor and consideration in his court. He had long and frequent conversations with them about the Holy Land; the state of the Christian church in the dominions of the grand soldan, and of the policy and conduct of that arch infidel towards it. The portly prior of the Franciscan convent was full, and round, and oratorical in his replies; and the king expressed himself much pleased with the eloquence of his periods; but the politic monarch was observed to lend a close and attentive ear to the whispering voice of the lowly companion, "whose discourse," adds Agapida, "though modest and low, was clear and fluent, and full of subtle wisdom." These holy friars had visited Rome in their journeying, where they had delivered the letter of the soldan to the sovereign pontiff. His holiness had written by them to the Castilian sovereigns, requesting to know what reply they had to offer to this demand of the oriental potentate.

The king of Naples also wrote to them on the subject, but in wary terms. He inquired into the cause of this war with the Moors of Granada, and expressed great marvel at its events, as if (says Agapida) both were not notorious throughout all the Christian world. "Nay," adds the worthy friar, with becoming indignation, "he uttered opinions savoring of little better than damnable heresy; for he observed that, although the Moors were of a different sect, they ought not to be maltreated without just cause; and hinted that if the Castilian sovereigns did not suffer any crying injury from the Moors, it would be improper to do anything which might draw great damage upon the Christians; as if, when once the sword of the faith was drawn, it ought ever to be sheathed until this scum of heathendom were utterly destroyed or driven from the land. But this monarch," he continues, "was more kindly disposed towards the infidels than was honest and lawful in a Christian prince, and was at that very time in league with the soldan against their common enemy the Grand Turk."

These pious sentiments of the truly Catholic Agapida are echoed by Padre Mariana, in his history;* but the worthy chronicler, Pedro Abarca, attributes the interference of the king of Naples, not to lack of orthodoxy in religion, but to an excess of worldly policy; he being apprehensive that, should Ferdinand conquer the Moors of Granada, he might have time and means to assert a claim of the house of Aragon to the crown of Naples."

"King Ferdinand," continues the worthy father Pedro Abarca, "was no less master of dissimulation than his cousin of Naples; so he replied to him with the utmost suavity of manner, going into a minute and patient vindication of the war, and taking great apparent pains to inform him of those things which all the world knew, but of which the other pretended to be ignorant." † At the same time he soothed his solicitude about the fate of the Christians in the empire of the grand soldan, assuring him that the great revenue extorted from them in rents and tributes would be a certain protection against the threatened violence.

To the pope he made the usual vindication of the war; that it was for the recovery of ancient territory, usurped by the Moors; for the punishment of wars and violences

* Mariana, lib. 25, cap. 15.
† Abarca, *Anales de Aragon*, Rey xxx., cap. 3.

inflicted upon the Christians; and finally, that it was a holy crusade for the glory and advancement of the church.

"It was a truly edifying sight," says Agapida, "to behold these friars, after they had had their audience of the king, moving about the camp always surrounded by nobles and cavaliers of high and martial renown. These were insatiable in their questions about the Holy Land, and the state of the sepulchre of our Lord, and the sufferings of the devoted brethren who guarded it, and the pious pilgrims who resorted there to pay their vows. The portly prior of the convent would stand with lofty and shining countenance in the midst of these iron warriors, and declaim with resounding eloquence on the history of the sepulchre; but the humbler brother would ever and anon sigh deeply, and in low tones utter some tale of suffering and outrage, at which his steel-clad hearers would grasp the hilts of their swords and mutter between their clenched teeth prayers for another crusade."

The pious friars having finished their mission to the king, and been treated with all due distinction, took their leave, and wended their way to Jaen, to visit the most Catholic of queens. Isabella, whose heart was the seat of piety, received them as sacred men, invested with more than human dignity. During their residence at Jaen, they were continually in the royal presence; the respectable prior of the convent moved and melted the ladies of the court by his florid rhetoric, but his lowly companion was observed to have continual access to the royal ear. That saintly and soft-spoken messenger (says Agapida) received the reward of his humility; for the queen, moved by his frequent representations, made in all modesty and lowliness of spirit, granted a yearly sum in perpetuity, of one thousand ducats in gold, for the support of the monks of the convent of the Holy Sepulchre.*

Moreover, on the departure of these holy ambassadors, the excellent and most Catholic queen delivered to them a veil devoutly embroidered with her own royal hands, to be placed over the Holy Sepulchre;—a precious and inestimable present, which called forth a most eloquent tribute of thanks from the portly prior, but which brought tears into the eyes of his lowly companion.†

* "La Reyna dio a los Frayles mil ducados de renta cado año para el sustento de los religiosos del santo sepulcro, que es la mejor limosna y sustento que hasta nuestros dias ha quedado a estos religiosos de Gerusalem: para donde les dio la Reyna un velo labrado por sus manos, para poner encima de la santa sepultura del Señor."—Garibay, *Compend. Hist.* lib. 18, cap. 36.

† It is proper to mention the result of this mission of the two friars, and which the worthy Agapida has neglected to record. At a subsequent period, the Catholic sovereigns sent the distinguished historian, Pietro Martyr, of Angleria, as ambassador to the grand soldan. That able man made such representations as were perfectly satisfactory to the oriental potentate. He also obtained from him the remission of many exactions and extortions heretofore practiced upon Christian pilgrims visiting the Holy Sepulchre ; which, it is presumed, had been gently but cogently detailed to the monarch by the lowly friar. Pietro Martyr wrote an account of his embassy to the grand soldan—a work greatly esteemed by the learned, and containing much curious information. It is entitled, *De Legatione Babylonica.*

33

companion was observed to have continual access to the

# CHAPTER LXXVII.

HOW QUEEN ISABELLA DEVISED MEANS TO SUPPLY THE ARMY WITH PROVI-
SIONS.

T has been the custom to laud the conduct and
address of King Ferdinand, in this most arduous and protracted war; but the sage Agapida
is more disposed to give credit to the counsels and measures of the queen, who, he observes, though less osten-
sible in action, was in truth the very soul, the vital
principle of this great enterprise. While King Ferdinand was bustling in his camp and making a glittering
display with his gallant chivalry, she, surrounded by her
saintly counselors, in the episcopal palace of Jaen, was
devising ways and means to keep the king and his army
in existence. She had pledged herself to keep up a
supply of men, and money, and provisions, until the city
should be taken. The hardships of the siege caused a
fearful waste of life, but the supply of men was the least
difficult part of her undertaking. So beloved was the
queen by the chivalry of Spain, that on her calling on
them for assistance, not a grandee or cavalier that yet
lingered at home, but either repaired in person or sent

forces to the camp; the ancient and warlike families vied with each other in marshaling forth their vassals; and thus the besieged Moors beheld each day fresh troops arriving before their city, and new ensigns and pennons displayed, emblazoned with arms well known to the veteran warriors.

But the most arduous task was to keep up a regular supply of provisions. It was not the army alone that had to be supported, but also the captured towns and their garrisons; for the whole country around them had been ravaged, and the conquerors were in danger of starving in the midst of the land they had desolated. To transport the daily supplies for such immense numbers, was a gigantic undertaking, in a country where there was neither water conveyance nor roads for carriages. Everything had to be borne by beasts of burden over rugged and broken paths of the mountains, and through dangerous defiles, exposed to the attacks and plunderings of the Moors.

The wary and calculating merchants, accustomed to supply the army, shrank from engaging, at their own risk, in so hazardous an undertaking. The queen, therefore, hired fourteen thousand beasts of burden, and ordered all the wheat and barley to be bought up in Andalusia, and in the domains of the knights of Santiago and Calatrava. She intrusted the administration of these supplies to able and confidential persons. Some were employed to collect the grain; others, to take it to the mills; others, to superintend the grinding and delivery; and others, to convey it to the camp. To every two hundred animals a muleteer was allotted, to take charge of them on the route. Thus, great lines of convoys were in constant movement, traversing to and fro, guarded by large bodies of troops, to defend them from hovering parties of the Moors. Not a single day's intermission was allowed, for the army depended upon the constant arrival of these supplies for daily food. The grain, when brought into the camp, was deposited in an immense granary, and sold to the army at a fixed price, which was never either raised or lowered.

Incredible were the expenses incurred in these supplies; but the queen had ghostly advisers thoroughly versed in the art of getting at the resources of the country. Many worthy prelates opened the deep purses of the church, and furnished loans from the revenues of their diocese and convents; and their pious contributions were eventually rewarded by Providence, a hundred-fold. Merchants and other wealthy individuals, confident of the punctual faith of the queen, advanced large sums on the security of her word; many noble families lent their plate, without waiting to be asked. The queen also sold certain annual rents in inheritance at great sacrifices, assigning the revenues of towns and cities for the payment. Finding all this insufficient to satisfy the enormous expenditure, she sent her gold and plate and all her jewels to the cities of Valentia and Barcelona, where they were pledged for a great amount of money, which was immediately appropriated to keep up the supplies of the army.

Thus, through the wonderful activity, judgment, and enterprise, of this heroic and magnanimous woman, a great host, encamped in the heart of a warlike country, accessible only over mountain roads, was maintained in continual abundance. Nor was it supplied merely with the necessaries and comforts of life. The powerful escorts drew merchants and artificers from all parts, to repair, as if in caravans, to this great military market. In a little while, the camp abounded with tradesmen and artists of all kinds, to administer to the luxury and ostentation of the youthful chivalry. Here might be seen cunning artificers in steel, and accomplished armorers, achieving those rare and sumptuous helmets and cuirasses, richly gilt, inlaid, and embossed, in which the Spanish cavaliers delighted. Saddlers and harness-makers and horse-milliners, also, were there, whose tents glittered with gorgeous housings and caparisons. The merchants spread forth their sumptuous silks, cloths, brocades, fine linen, and tapestry. The tents of the nobility were prodigally decorated with all kinds of the richest stuffs, and dazzled the eye with their magnificence: nor could the grave looks and grave speeches of King Ferdinand prevent his youthful cavaliers from vying with each other in the splendor of their dresses and caparisons, on all occasions of parade and ceremony.

# CHAPTER LXXVIII.

WHILE the Christian camp, thus gay and gorgeous, spread itself out like a holiday pageant before the walls of Baza,—while a long line of beasts of burden laden with provisions and luxuries were seen descending the valley from morning till night, and pouring into the camp a continued stream of abundance, —the unfortunate garrison found their resources rapidly wasting away, and famine already began to pinch the peaceful part of the community.

Cid Hiaya had acted with great spirit and valor, as long as there was any prospect of success; but he began to lose his usual fire and animation, and was observed to pace the walls of Baza with a pensive air, casting many a wistful look towards the Christian camp, and sinking into profound reveries and cogitations. The veteran alcayde, Mohammed Ibn Hassan, noticed these desponding moods, and endeavored to rally the spirits of the prince. "The rainy season is at hand," would he cry; "the floods will soon pour down from the mountains; the rivers will overflow their banks, and inundate the valleys. The

Christian king already begins to waver; he dare not linger, and encounter such a season, in a plain cut up by canals and rivulets. A single wintry storm from our mountains would wash away his canvas city, and sweep off those gay pavilions like wreaths of snow before the blast."

The prince Cid Hiaya took heart at these words, and counted the days as they passed until the stormy season should commence. As he watched the Christian camp, he beheld it one morning in universal commotion: there was an unusual sound of hammers in every part, as if some new engines of war were constructing. At length, to his astonishment, the walls and roofs of houses began to appear above the bulwarks. In a little while, there were above a thousand edifices of wood and plaster erected, covered with tiles taken from the demolished towers of the orchards, and bearing the pennons of various commanders and cavaliers; while the common soldiery constructed huts, of clay and branches of trees, thatched with straw. Thus, to the dismay of the Moors, within four days, the light tents and gay pavilions which had whitened their hills and plains, passed away like summer clouds; and the unsubstantial camp assumed the solid appearance of a city laid out into streets and squares. In the centre rose a large edifice, which overlooked the whole; and the royal standard of Aragon and Castile, proudly floating above it, showed it to be the palace of the king.*

* *Cura de los Palacios*, Pulgar, etc.

Ferdinand had taken the sudden resolution thus to turn his camp into a city, partly to provide against the approaching season, and partly to convince the Moors of his fixed determination to continue the siege. In their haste to erect their dwellings, however, the Spanish cavaliers had not properly considered the nature of the climate. For the greater part of the year, there scarcely falls a drop of rain on the thirsty soil of Andalusia. The ramblas, or dry channels of the torrents, remain deep and arid gashes and clefts in the sides of the mountains; the perennial streams shrink up to mere threads of water, which, tinkling down the bottoms of the deep barrancas or ravines, scarce feed and keep alive the rivers of the valleys. The rivers, almost lost in their wide and naked beds, seem like thirsty rills, winding in serpentine mazes through deserts of sand and stones; and so shallow and tranquil in their course, as to be forded in safety in almost every part. One autumnal tempest, however, changes the whole face of nature: the clouds break in deluges among the vast congregation of mountains; the ramblas are suddenly filled with raging floods; the tinkling rivulets swell to thundering torrents, that come roaring down from the mountains, tumbling great masses of rocks in their career. The late meandering river spreads over its once naked bed, lashes its surges against the banks, and rushes like a wide and foaming inundation through the valley.

Scarcely had the Christians finished their slightly-built edifices, when an autumnal tempest of the kind came scouring from the mountains. The camp was immediately overflowed. Many of the houses, undermined by the floods or beaten by the rain, crumbled away and fell to the earth, burying man and beast beneath their ruins. Several valuable lives were lost, and great numbers of horses and other animals perished. To add to the distress and confusion of the camp, the daily supply of provisions suddenly ceased; for the rain had broken up the roads, and rendered the rivers impassable. A panic seized upon the army, for the cessation of a single day's supply produced a scarcity of bread and provender. Fortunately the rain was but transient; the torrents rushed by, and ceased; the rivers shrank back again to their narrow channels, and the convoys which had been detained upon their banks arrived safely in the camp.

No sooner did Queen Isabella hear of this interruption of her supplies, than, with her usual vigilance and activity, she provided against its recurrence. She dispatched six thousand foot-soldiers, under the command of experienced officers, to repair the roads, and to make causeways and bridges for the distance of seven Spanish leagues. The troops, also, who had been stationed in the mountains by the king to guard the defiles, made two paths, one for the convoys going to the camp, and the other for those returning, that they might not

meet and impede each other. The edifices which had
been demolished by the late floods were rebuilt in a
firmer manner, and precautions were taken to prevent
the camp from future inundations.

# CHAPTER LXXIX.

HEN King Ferdinand beheld the ravage and confusion produced by a single autumnal storm, and bethought him of all the maladies to which a besieging camp is exposed in inclement seasons, he began to feel his compassion kindling for the suffering people of Baza, and an inclination to grant them more favorable terms. He sent, therefore, several messages to the alcayde Mohammed Ibn Hassan, offering liberty of person and security of property for the inhabitants, and large rewards for himself, if he would surrender the city.

The veteran was not to be dazzled by the splendid offers of the monarch; he had received exaggerated accounts of the damage done to the Christian camp by the late storm, and of the sufferings and discontents of the army in consequence of the transient interruption of supplies: he considered the overtures of Ferdinand as proofs of the desperate state of his affairs. "A little more patience, a little more patience," said the shrewd

523

old warrior, "and we shall see this crowd of Christian locusts driven away before the winter storms. When they once turn their backs, it will be our turn to strike; and, with the help of Allah, the blow shall be decisive." He sent a firm though courteous refusal to the Castilian monarch, and in the meantime animated his companions to sally forth with more spirit than ever, to attack the Spanish outposts and those laboring in the trenches. The consequence was a daily occurrence of daring and bloody skirmishes, that cost the lives of many of the bravest and most adventurous cavaliers of either army.

In one of these sallies, nearly three hundred horse and two thousand foot mounted the heights behind the city, to capture the Christians who were employed upon the works. They came by surprise upon a body of guards, esquires of the count de Ureña, killed some, put the rest to flight, and pursued them down the mountain, until they came in sight of a small force under the count de Tendilla and Gonsalvo of Cordova. The Moors came rushing down with such fury that many of the men of the count de Tendilla took to flight. The count braced his buckler, grasped his trusty weapon, and stood his ground with his accustomed prowess. Gonsalvo of Cordova ranged himself by his side, and, marshaling the troops which remained with them, they made a valiant front to the Moors.

The infidels pressed them hard, and were gaining the advantage, when Alonzo de Aguilar, hearing of the danger of his brother Gonsalvo, flew to his assistance, accompanied by the count of Ureña and a body of their troops. A fight ensued, from cliff to cliff and glen to glen. The Moors were fewer in number, but excelled in the dexterity and lightness requisite for scrambling skirmishes. They were at length driven from their vantage-ground, and pursued by Alonzo de Aguilar and his brother Gonsalvo to the very suburbs of the city, leaving many of their bravest men upon the field.

Such was one of innumerable rough encounters daily taking place, in which many brave cavaliers were slain, without apparent benefit to either party. The Moors, notwithstanding repeated defeats and losses, continued to sally forth daily with astonishing spirit and vigor, and the obstinacy of their defense seemed to increase with their sufferings.

The prince Cid Hiaya was ever foremost in these sallies, but grew daily more despairing of success. All the money in the military chest was expended, and there was no longer wherewithal to pay the hired troops. Still the veteran Mohammed undertook to provide for this emergency. Summoning the principal inhabitants, he represented the necessity of some exertion and sacrifice on their part to maintain the defense of the city. "The enemy," said he, "dreads the approach of winter, and our perseverance drives him to despair. A little longer, and he will leave you in quiet enjoyment of your homes and families. But our troops must be paid, to keep them in good heart. Our money is exhausted, and all our supplies are cut off. It is impossible to continue our defense, without your aid."

Upon this the citizens consulted together, and collected all their vessels of gold and silver, and brought them to Mohammed : "Take these," said they, " and coin, or sell, or pledge them, for money wherewith to pay the troops." The women of Baza also were seized with generous emulation : " Shall we deck ourselves with gorgeous apparel," said they, " when our country is desolate, and its defenders in want of bread ? " So they took their collars, and bracelets, and anklets, and other ornaments of gold, and all their jewels, and put them in the hands of the veteran alcayde : " Take these spoils of our vanity," said they, " and let them contribute to the defense of our homes and families. If Baza be delivered, we need no jewels to grace our rejoicing ; and if Baza fall, of what avail are ornaments to the captive ?"

By these contributions was Mohammed enabled to pay the soldiery, and carry on the defense of the city with unabated spirit.

Tidings were speedily conveyed to king Ferdinand, of this generous devotion on the part of the people of Baza, and the hopes which the Moorish commanders gave them that the Christian army would soon abandon the siege in despair. " They shall have a convincing proof of the fallacy of such hopes," said the politic monarch : so he wrote forthwith to Queen Isabella, praying her to come to the camp in state, with all her train and retinue, and publicly to take up her residence there for the winter. By this means the Moors would be convinced of the settled determination of the sovereigns to persist in the siege until the city should surrender, and he trusted they would be brought to speedy capitulation.

come to the camp in state, with all her train and retinue; and publicly to take up her residence there for the win- ter. By this means the Moors would be convinced of the settled determination of the sovereigns to persist in the siege until the city should surrender, and be trusted they would be brought to speedy capitulation.

## CHAPTER LXXX.

HOW QUEEN ISABELLA ARRIVED AT THE CAMP, AND THE CONSEQUENCES OF
HER ARRIVAL.

OHAMMED IBN HASSAN still encouraged his companions with hopes that the royal army would soon relinquish the siege; when they heard, one day, shouts of joy from the Christian camp, and thundering salvos of artillery. Word was brought, at the same time, from the sentinels on the watch-towers, that a Christian army was approaching down the valley. Mohammed and his fellow-commanders ascended one of the highest towers of the walls, and beheld in truth a numerous force, in shining array, descending the hills, and heard the distant clangor of the trumpet and the faint swell of triumphant music.

As the host drew nearer, they descried a stately dame magnificently attired, whom they soon discovered to be the queen. She was riding on a mule, the sumptuous trappings of which were resplendent with gold, and reached to the ground. On her right hand rode her daughter, the princess Isabella, equally splendid in her array; and on her left the venerable grand cardinal of

Spain. A noble train of ladies and cavaliers followed, together with pages and esquires, and a numerous guard of hidalgos of high rank, arrayed in superb armor. When the veteran Mohammed beheld the queen thus arriving in state to take up her residence in the camp, he shook his head mournfully, and, turning to his captains, "Cavaliers," said he, "the fate of Baza is decided."

The Moorish commanders remained gazing with a mingled feeling of grief and admiration at this magnificent pageant, which foreboded the fall of their city. Some of the troops would have sallied forth on one of their desperate skirmishes to attack the royal guard; but the prince Cid Hiaya forbade them; nor would he allow any artillery to be discharged, or any molestation or insult offered; for the character of Isabella was venerated even by the Moors; and most of the commanders possessed that high and chivalrous courtesy which belongs to heroic spirits—for they were among the noblest and bravest of the Moorish cavaliers.

The inhabitants of Baza eagerly sought every eminence that could command a view of the plain; and every battlement, and tower, and mosque, was covered with turbaned heads gazing at the glorious spectacle. They beheld king Ferdinand issue forth in royal state, attended by the marques of Cadiz, the master of Santiago, the duke of Alva, the admiral of Castile, and many other nobles of renown; while the whole chivalry of the camp, sumptuously arrayed, followed in his train, and the pop-

34

ulace rent the air with acclamations at the sight of the patriot queen.

When the sovereigns had met and embraced, the two hosts mingled together and entered the camp in martial pomp; and the eyes of the infidel beholders were dazzled by the flash of armor, the splendor of golden caparisons, the gorgeous display of silks, brocades, and velvets, of tossing plumes and fluttering banners. There was at the same time a triumphant sound of drums and trumpets, clarions and sackbuts, mingled with the sweet melody of the dulcimer, which came swelling in bursts of harmony that seemed to rise up to the heavens.*

On the arrival of the queen (says the historian Hernando del Pulgar, who was present at the time), it was marvelous to behold how all at once the rigor and turbulence of war were softened, and the storm of passion sank into a calm. The sword was sheathed; the crossbow no longer launched its deadly shafts; and the artillery, which had hitherto kept up an incessant uproar, now ceased its thundering. On both sides there was still a vigilant guard kept up; the sentinels bristled the walls of Baza with their lances, and the guards patrolled the Christian camp; but there was no sallying forth to skirmish, nor any wanton violence or carnage.†

* Cura de los Palacios, cap. 92.
† Many particulars of the scenes and occurrences at the siege of Baza are also furnished in the letters of the learned Peter Martyr, who was present, and an admiring eye-witness.

Prince Cid Hiaya saw, by the arrival of the queen, that the Christians were determined to continue the siege, and he knew that the city would have to capitulate. He had been prodigal of the lives of his soldiers, as long as he thought a military good was to be gained by the sacrifice; but he was sparing of their blood in a hopeless cause, and weary of exasperating the enemy by an obstinate yet hopeless defense.

At the request of the prince, a parley was granted, and the master commander of Leon, Don Gutierrez de Cardenas, was appointed to confer with the veteran alcayde Mohammed. They met at an appointed place, within view of both camp and city, attended by cavaliers of either army. Their meeting was highly courteous, for they had learned, from rough encounters in the field, to admire each other's prowess. The commander of Leon, in an earnest speech, pointed out the hopelessness of any further defense, and warned Mohammed of the ills which Malaga had incurred by its obstinacy. "I promise in the name of my sovereigns," said he, " that if you surrender immediately, the inhabitants shall be treated as subjects, and protected in property, liberty, and religion. If you refuse, you, who are now renowned as an able and judicious commander, will be chargeable with the confiscations, captivities, and deaths which may be suffered by the people of Baza."

The commander ceased, and Mohammed returned to the city to consult with his companions. It was evident that all further resistance was hopeless ; but the Moorish commanders felt that a cloud might rest upon their names, should they, of their own discretion, surrender so important a place without its having sustained an assault. Prince Cid Hiaya requested permission, therefore, to send an envoy to Guadix, with a letter to the old monarch El Zagal, treating of the surrender ; the request was granted, a safe conduct assured to the envoy, and Mohammed Ibn Hassan departed upon this momentous mission.

# CHAPTER LXXXI.

### SURRENDER OF BAZA.

HE old warrior king was seated in an inner chamber of the castle of Guadix, much cast down in spirit, and ruminating on his gloomy fortunes, when an envoy from Baza was announced, and the veteran alcayde Mohammed stood before him. El Zagal saw disastrous tidings written in his countenance: "How fares it with Baza?" said he, summoning up his spirits to the question. "Let this inform thee," replied Mohammed; and he delivered into his hands the letter from the prince Cid Hiaya.

The letter spoke of the desperate situation of Baza; the impossibility of holding out longer, without assistance from El Zagal; and the favorable terms held out by the Castilian sovereigns. Had it been written by any other person, El Zagal might have received it with distrust and indignation; but he confided in Cid Hiaya as in a second self, and the words of his letter sank deep in his heart. When he had finished reading it, he sighed deeply, and remained for some time lost in thought, with his head drooping upon his bosom. Recovering himself

533

at length, he called together the alfaquis and the old men of Guadix, and solicited their advice. It was a sign of sore trouble of mind and dejection of heart, when El Zagal sought the advice of others; but his fierce courage was tamed, for he saw the end of his power approaching. The alfaquis and the old men did but increase the distraction of his mind by a variety of counsel, none of which appeared of any avail; for unless Baza were succored, it was impossible that it should hold out; and every attempt to succor it had proved ineffectual.

El Zagal dismissed his council in despair, and summoned the veteran Mohammed before him. "God is great," exclaimed he; "there is but one God, and Mahomet is his prophet! Return to my cousin, Cid Hiaya; tell him it is out of my power to aid him; he must do as seems to him for the best. The people of Baza have performed deeds worthy of immortal fame; I cannot ask them to encounter further ills and perils, in maintaining a hopeless defense."

The reply of El Zagal determined the fate of the city. Cid Hiaya and his fellow-commanders capitulated, and were granted the most favorable terms. The cavaliers and soldiers who had come from other parts to the defense of the place were permitted to depart with their arms, horses, and effects. The inhabitants had their choice, either to depart with their property, or dwell in the suburbs, in the enjoyment of their religion and laws, taking an oath of fealty to the sovereigns, and paying the same tribute they had paid to the Moorish kings. The city and citadel were to be delivered up in six days, within which period the inhabitants were to remove all their effects; and in the meantime they were to place, as hostages, fifteen Moorish youths, sons of the principal inhabitants, in the hands of the commander of Leon. When Cid Hiaya and the alcayde Mohammed came to deliver up the hostages, among whom were the sons of the latter, they paid homage to the king and queen, who received them with the utmost courtesy and kindness, and ordered magnificent presents to be given to them, and likewise to the other Moorish cavaliers, consisting of money, robes, horses, and other things of great value.

The prince Cid Hiaya was so captivated by the grace, the dignity, and generosity of Isabella, and the princely courtesy of Ferdinand, that he vowed never again to draw his sword against such magnanimous sovereigns. The queen, charmed with his gallant bearing and his animated professions of devotion, assured him that, having him on her side, she already considered the war terminated which had desolated the kingdom of Granada.

Mighty and irresistible are the words of praise from the lips of sovereigns. Cid Hiaya was entirely subdued by this fair speech from the illustrious Isabella. His heart burned with a sudden flame of loyalty towards the sovereigns. He begged to be enrolled amongst the most devoted of their subjects; and, in the fervor of his sudden zeal, engaged not merely to dedicate his

sword to their service, but to exert all his influence,
which was great, in persuading his cousin, Muley Abdallah el Zagal, to surrender the cities of Guadix and
Almeria, and to give up all further hostilities. Nay, so
powerful was the effect produced upon his mind by his
conversation with the sovereigns, that it extended even
to his religion; for he became immediately enlightened
as to the heathenish abominations of the vile sect of
Mahomet, and struck with the truths of Christianity, as
illustrated by such powerful monarchs. He consented,
therefore, to be baptized, and to be gathered into the
fold of the church. The pious Agapida indulges in a
triumphant strain of exultation on the sudden and surprising conversion of this princely infidel: he considers
it one of the greatest achievements of the Catholic sovereigns, and, indeed, one of the marvelous occurrences
of this holy war. "But it is given to saints and pious
monarchs," says he, "to work miracles in the cause of
the faith; and such did the most Catholic Ferdinand in
the conversion of the prince Cid Hiaya."

Some of the Arabian writers have sought to lessen the
wonder of this miracle, by alluding to great revenues
granted to the Prince and his heirs by the Castilian
monarchs, together with a territory in Marchena, with
towns, lands, and vassals; but in this (says Agapida) we
only see a wise precaution of king Ferdinand to clinch
and secure the conversion of his proselyte. The policy
of the Catholic monarch was at all times equal to his

piety. Instead, also, of vaunting of this great conversion, and making a public parade of the entry of the prince into the church, King Ferdinand ordered that the baptism should be performed in private, and kept a profound secret. He feared that Cid Hiaya might otherwise be denounced as an apostate, and abhorred and abandoned by the Moors, and thus his influence destroyed in bringing the war to a speedy termination.[*]

The veteran Mohammed Ibn Hassan was likewise won by the magnanimity and munificence of the Castilian sovereigns, and entreated to be received into their service; and his example was followed by many other Moorish cavaliers, whose services were generously accepted and magnificently rewarded.

Thus, after a siege of six months and twenty days, the city of Baza surrendered on the 4th of December, 1489; the festival of the glorious Santa Barbara, who is said, in the Catholic calendar, to preside over thunder and lightning, fire and gunpowder, and all kinds of combustious explosions. The king and queen made their solemn and triumphant entry on the following day; and the public joy was heightened by the sight of upwards of five hundred Christian captives, men, women, and children, delivered from the Moorish dungeons.

The loss of the Christians in this siege amounted to twenty thousand men, of whom seventeen thousand died

---

[*] Conde, tom. 3, cap. 40.

of disease, and not a few of mere cold—a kind of death (says the historian Mariana) peculiarly uncomfortable; but (adds the venerable Jesuit), as these latter were chiefly people of ignoble rank, baggage-carriers and such like, the loss was not of great importance.

The surrender of Baza was followed by that of Almunecar, Tavernas, and most of the fortresses of the Alpuxarra mountains; the inhabitants hoped, by prompt and voluntary submission, to secure equally favorable terms with those granted to the captured city, and the alcaydes to receive similar rewards to those lavished on its commanders; nor were either of them disappointed. The inhabitants were permitted to remain as Mudexares, in the quiet enjoyment of their property and religion; and as to the alcaydes, when they came to the camp to render up their charges, they were received by Ferdinand with distinguished favor, and rewarded with presents of money in proportion to the importance of the places they had commanded. Care was taken by the politic monarch, however, not to wound their pride nor shock their delicacy; so these sums were paid under color of arrears due to them for their services to the former government. Ferdinand had conquered by dint of sword, in the earlier part of the war; but he found gold as potent as steel, in this campaign of Baza.

With several of these mercenary chieftains came one named Ali Aben Fahar, a seasoned warrior, who had held many important commands. He was a Moor of a lofty, stern, and melancholy aspect, and stood silent and apart, while his companions surrendered their several fortresses and retired laden with treasure. When it came to his turn to speak, he addressed the sovereigns with the frankness of a soldier, but with the tone of dejection and despair.

" I am a Moor," said he, " and of Moorish lineage, and am alcayde of the fair towns and castles of Purchena and Paterna. These were intrusted to me to defend; but those who should have stood by me have lost all strength and courage, and seek only for security. These fortresses, therefore, most potent sovereigns, are yours, whenever you will send to take possession of them."

Large sums of gold were immediately ordered by Ferdinand to be delivered to the alcayde, as a recompense for so important a surrender. The Moor, however, put back the gift with a firm and dignified demeanor: " I came not," said he, " to sell what is not mine, but to yield what fortune has made yours; and your majesties may rest assured that, had I been properly seconded, death would have been the price at which I would have sold my fortresses, and not the gold you offer me."

The Castilian monarchs were struck with the lofty and loyal spirit of the Moor, and desired to engage a man of such fidelity in their service; but the proud Moslem could not be induced to serve the enemies of his nation and his faith.

" Is there nothing, then," said Queen Isabella, " that

we can do to gratify thee, and to prove to thee our regard?"  "Yes," replied the Moor; "I have left behind
me, in the towns and valleys which I have surrendered,
many of my unhappy countrymen, with their wives and
children, who cannot tear themselves from their native
abodes.  Give me your royal word that they shall be
protected in the peaceable enjoyment of their religion
and their homes."  "We promise it," said Isabella;
"they shall dwell in peace and security.  But for thyself
—what dost thou ask for thyself?"  "Nothing," replied
Ali, "but permission to pass unmolested, with my horses
and effects, into Africa."

The Castilian monarchs would fain have forced upon
him gold and silver, and superb horses richly caparisoned, not as rewards, but as marks of personal esteem;
but Ali Aben Fahar declined all presents and distinctions, as if he thought it criminal to flourish individually
during a time of public distress; and disdained all prosperity, that seemed to grow out of the ruins of his country.

Having received a royal passport, he gathered together
his horses and servants, his armor and weapons, and all
his warlike effects; bade adieu to his weeping countrymen with a brow stamped with anguish, but without
shedding a tear; and, mounting his Barbary steed, turned
his back upon the delightful valleys of his conquered
country, departing on his lonely way, to seek a soldier's
fortune amidst the burning sands of Africa.*

* Pulgar, pt. 3, cap. 124.  Garibay, lib. 40, cap. 40.  *Cura de los Palacios.*

## CHAPTER LXXXII.

### SUBMISSION OF EL ZAGAL TO THE CASTILIAN SOVEREIGNS.

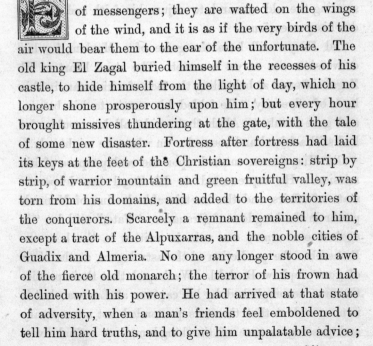

VIL tidings never fail by the way, through lack of messengers; they are wafted on the wings of the wind, and it is as if the very birds of the air would bear them to the ear of the unfortunate. The old king El Zagal buried himself in the recesses of his castle, to hide himself from the light of day, which no longer shone prosperously upon him; but every hour brought missives thundering at the gate, with the tale of some new disaster. Fortress after fortress had laid its keys at the feet of the Christian sovereigns: strip by strip, of warrior mountain and green fruitful valley, was torn from his domains, and added to the territories of the conquerors. Scarcely a remnant remained to him, except a tract of the Alpuxarras, and the noble cities of Guadix and Almeria. No one any longer stood in awe of the fierce old monarch; the terror of his frown had declined with his power. He had arrived at that state of adversity, when a man's friends feel emboldened to tell him hard truths, and to give him unpalatable advice;

541

and when his spirit is bowed down to listen quietly, if not meekly.

El Zagal was seated on his divan, his whole spirit absorbed in rumination on the transitory nature of human glory, when his kinsman and brother-in-law, the prince Cid Hiaya, was announced. That illustrious convert to the true faith and the interests of the conquerors of his country, had hastened to Guadix with all the fervor of a new proselyte, eager to prove his zeal in the service of Heaven and the Castilian sovereigns, by persuading the old monarch to abjure his faith and surrender his possessions.

Cid Hiaya still bore the guise of a Moslem, for his conversion was as yet a secret. The stern heart of El Zagal softened at beholding the face of a kinsman, in this hour of adversity. He folded his cousin to his bosom, and gave thanks to Allah that amidst all his troubles he had still a friend and counselor on whom he might rely.

Cid Hiaya soon entered upon the real purpose of his mission. He represented to El Zagal the desperate state of affairs, and the irretrievable decline of Moorish power in the kingdom of Granada. "Fate," said he, "is against our arms; our ruin is written in the heavens. Remember the prediction of the astrologers, at the birth of your nephew Boabdil. We hoped that their prediction was accomplished by his capture at Lucena; but it is now evident that the stars portended not a temporary and passing reverse of the kingdom, but a final overthrow. The constant succession of disasters which have attended our efforts, show that the sceptre of Granada is doomed to pass into the hands of the Christian monarchs. Such," concluded the prince emphatically, and with a profound and pious reverence, "such is the almighty will of God!"

El Zagal listened to these words in mute attention, without so much as moving a muscle of his face, or winking an eyelid. When the prince had concluded, he remained for a long time silent and pensive; at length, heaving a profound sigh from the very bottom of his heart, "Alahuma subahana hu!" exclaimed he, "the will of God be done! Yes, my cousin, it is but too evident that such is the will of Allah; and what he wills, he fails not to accomplish. Had he not decreed the fall of Granada, this arm and this scimetar would have maintained it."*

"What then remains," said Cid Hiaya, "but to draw the most advantage from the wreck of empire left to you? To persist in a war is to bring complete desolation upon the land, and ruin and death upon its faithful inhabitants. Are you disposed to yield up your remaining towns to your nephew El Chico, that they may augment his power, and derive protection from his alliance with the Christian sovereigns?"

The eye of El Zagal flashed fire at this suggestion.

* Conde, tom. 3, cap. 40.

He grasped the hilt of his scimetar, and gnashed his teeth in fury. "Never," cried he, "will I make terms with that recreant and slave! Sooner would I see the banners of the Christian monarchs floating above my walls, than they should add to the possessions of the vassal Boabdil!"

Cid Hiaya immediately seized upon this idea, and urged El Zagal to make a frank and entire surrender: "Trust," said he, "to the magnanimity of the Castilian sovereigns; they will doubtless grant you high and honorable terms. It is better to yield to them as friends, what they must infallibly and before long wrest from you as enemies; for such, my cousin, is the almighty will of God!"

"Alahuma subahana hu!" repeated El Zagal, "the will of God be done!" So the old monarch bowed his haughty neck, and agreed to surrender his territories to the enemies of his faith, rather than suffer them to augment the Moslem power under the sway of his nephew.

Cid Hiaya now returned to Baza, empowered by El Zagal to treat on his behalf with the Christian sovereigns. The prince felt a species of exultation, as he expatiated on the rich relics of empire which he was authorized to cede. There was a great part of that line of mountains extending from the metropolis to the Mediterranean sea, with their series of beautiful green valleys, like precious emeralds set in a golden chain. Above all, there were

Guadix and Almeria, two of the most inestimable jewels in the crown of Granada.

In return for these possessions, and for the claim of El Zagal to the rest of the kingdom, the sovereigns received him into their friendship and alliance, and gave him in perpetual inheritance the territory of Andarax and the valley of Alhaurin in the Alpuxarras, with the fourth part of the salinas or salt-pits of Malaha. He was to enjoy the title of king of Andarax, with two thousand Mudexares, or conquered Moors, for subjects; and his revenues were to be made up to the sum of four millions of marevedis. All these he was to hold as a vassal of the Castilian crown.

These arrangements being made, Cid Hiaya returned with them to Muley Abdallah; and it was concerted that the ceremony of surrender and homage should take place at the city of Almeria.

On the 17th of December King Ferdinand departed for that city. Cid Hiaya and his principal officers, incorporated with a division commanded by the count de Tendilla, marched in the van-guard. The king was with the centre of the army, and the queen with the rear-guard. In this martial state Ferdinand passed by several of the newly acquired towns, exulting in these trophies of his policy rather than his valor. In traversing the mountainous region, which extends towards the Mediterranean, the army suffered exceedingly from raging vandavales, or southwest gales, accompanied by

35

snow-storms. Several of the soldiers and many horses and beasts of burden, perished with the cold. One of the divisions under the marques of Cadiz, found it impossible to traverse in one day the frozen summits of Filabres, and had to pass the night in those inclement regions. The marques caused two immense fires to be kindled in the vicinity of his encampment to guide and enlighten those lost and wandering among the defiles, and to warm those who were benumbed and almost frozen.

The king halted at Tavernas, to collect his scattered troops and give them time to breathe after the hardships of the mountains. The queen was travelling a day's march in the rear.

On the 21st of December, the king arrived and encamped in the vicinity of Almeria. Understanding that El Zagal was sallying forth to pay him homage, according to appointment, he mounted on horseback and rode forth to receive him, attended by Don Alonzo de Cardenas, master of Santiago, on his right hand, and the marques of Cadiz on his left, and dispatched in the advance Don Gutierrez de Cardenas, commander of Leon, and other cavaliers to meet and form an honorable escort to the Moorish monarch. With this escort went that curious eye-witness, Peter Martyr, from whom we have many of these particulars.

El Zagal was accompanied by twelve cavaliers on horseback, among whom was his cousin, the prince Cid

Hiaya (who had no doubt joined him from the Spanish camp) and the brave Reduan Vanegas. Peter Martyr declares that the appearance of El Zagal touched him with compassion, for though a "lawless barbarian, he was a king, and had given signal proofs of heroism." The historian Palencia gives us a particular description of his appearance. He was, says he, of elevated stature and well proportioned, neither robust nor meagre; the natural fairness of his countenance was increased by an extreme paleness which gave it a melancholy expression. His aspect was grave; his movements were quiet, noble, and dignified. He was modestly attired in a garb of mourning, a sayo, or loose surcoat, of dark cloth, a simple albornoz or Moorish mantle, and a turban of dazzling whiteness.

On being met by the commander, Gutierrez de Cardenas, El Zagal saluted him courteously, as well as the cavaliers who accompanied him, and rode on, conversing with him through the medium of interpreters. Beholding King Ferdinand and his splendid train at a distance, he alighted and advanced towards him on foot. The punctilious Ferdinand supposing this voluntary act of humiliation had been imposed by Don Gutierrez, told that cavalier, with some asperity, that it was an act of great discourtesy to cause a vanquished king to alight before another king who was victorious. At the same time he made him signs to remount his horse and place himself by his side. El Zagal, persisting in his act of homage, offered to kiss the king's hand; but being prevented by that monarch, he kissed his own hand, as the Moorish cavaliers were accustomed to do in presence of their sovereigns; and accompanied the gesture by a few words expressive of obedience and fealty. Ferdinand replied in a gracious and amiable manner; and causing him to remount and place himself on his left hand, they proceeded, followed by the whole train to the royal pavilion, pitched in the most conspicuous part of the camp.

There a banquet was served up to the two kings, according to the rigorous style and etiquette of the Spanish court. They were seated in two chairs of state under the same canopy, El Zagal on the left hand of Ferdinand. The cavaliers and courtiers admitted to the royal pavilion remained standing. The count de Tendilla served the viands to King Ferdinand in golden dishes, and the count Cifuentes gave him to drink out of cups of the same precious metal; Don Alvara Bazan and Garcilasso de la Vega performed the same offices in similar style and with vessels of equal richness, to the Moorish monarch.

The banquet ended, El Zagal took courteous leave of Ferdinand, and sallied from the pavilion attended by the cavaliers who had been present. Each of these now made himself known to the old monarch by his name, title or dignity, and each received an affable gesture in reply. They would all have escorted the old king back to the gates of Almeria, but he insisted on their remaining in the camp, and with difficulty could be persuaded upon to accept the honorable attendance of the marques of Villena, the commander, Don Gutierrez de Cardenas, the count de Cifuentes, and Don Luis Puerto Carrero.

On the following morning (22d December), the troops were all drawn out in splendid array in front of the camp, awaiting the signal of the formal surrender of the city. This was given at midday, when the gates were thrown open and a corps marched in, led by Don Gutierrez de Cardenas, who had been appointed governor. In a little while the gleam of Christian warriors was seen on the walls and bulwarks; the blessed cross was planted in place of the standard of Mahomet, and the banner of the sovereigns floated triumphantly above the Alcazar. At the same time a numerous deputation of alfaquis and the noblest and wealthiest inhabitants of the place sallied forth to pay homage to King Ferdinand.

On the 23d of December, the king himself entered the city with grand military and religious pomp, and repaired to the mosque of the castle, which had been previously purified and sanctified and converted into a Christian temple; here grand mass was performed in solemn celebration of this great triumph of the faith.

These ceremonies were scarcely completed, when joyful notice was given of the approach of the queen Isabella, with the rear-guard of the army. She came accompanied by the princess Isabella, and attended by her ghostly counselor, the cardinal Mendoza, and her confessor, Talavera. The king sallied forth to meet her, accompanied by El Zagal, and it is said the reception of the latter by the queen was characterized by that deference and considerate delicacy which belonged to her magnanimous nature.

The surrender of Almeria was followed by that of Almuñecar, Salobriña, and other fortified places of the coast and the interior, and detachments of Christian troops took quiet possession of the Alpuxarra mountains and their secluded and fertile valleys.*

* *Cura de los Palacios,* cap. 93, 94. Pulgar, *Cron.* pt. 3, cap. 124. Garibay, *Comp. Hist.* lib. 18, cap. 37, &c., &c.

# CHAPTER LXXXIII.

EVENTS AT GRANADA, SUBSEQUENT TO THE SUBMISSION OF EL ZAGAL.

WHO can tell when to rejoice, in this fluctuating world? Every wave of prosperity has its re-acting surge, and we are often overwhelmed by the very billow on which we thought to be wafted into the haven of our hopes. When Yusef Aben Comixa, the vizier of Boabdil, surnamed El Chico, entered the royal saloon of the Alhambra and announced the capitulation of El Zagal, the heart of the youthful monarch leaped for joy. His great wish was accomplished; his uncle was defeated and dethroned, and he reigned without a rival, sole monarch of Granada. At length, he was about to enjoy the fruits of his humiliation and vassalage. He beheld his throne fortified by the friendship and alliance of the Castilian monarchs; there could be no question, therefore, of its stability. "Allah Achbar! God is great!" exclaimed he; "Rejoice with me, O Yusef; the stars have ceased their persecution. Henceforth let no man call me El Zogoybi."

In the first moment of his exultation, Boabdil would have ordered public rejoicings; but the shrewd Yusef

551

shook his head. "The tempest has ceased, from one point of the heavens," said he, "but it may begin to rage from another. A troubled sea is beneath us, and we are surrounded by rocks and quicksands: let my lord the king defer rejoicings, until all has settled into a calm." El Chico, however, could not remain tranquil in this day of exultation: he ordered his steed to be sumptuously caparisoned, and issuing out of the gate of the Alhambra, descended, with glittering retinue, along the avenue of trees and fountains, into the city, to receive the acclamations of the populace. As he entered the great square of the Vivarrambla, he beheld crowds of people in violent agitation; but, as he approached, what was his surprise, to hear groans and murmurs and bursts of execration! The tidings had spread through Granada, that Muley Abdallah El Zagal had been driven to capitulate, and that all his territories had fallen into the hands of the Christians. No one had inquired into the particulars, but all Granada had been thrown into a ferment of grief and indignation. In the heat of the moment, old Muley was extolled to the skies as a patriot prince, who had fought to the last for the salvation of his country—as a mirror of monarchs, scorning to compromise the dignity of his crown by any act of vassalage. Boabdil, on the contrary, had looked on exultingly at the hopeless yet heroic struggle of his uncle; he had rejoiced in the defeat of the faithful, and the triumph of unbelievers; he had aided in the dismemberment and downfall of the empire. When they beheld him riding forth in gorgeous state, on what they considered a day of humiliation for all true Moslems, they could not contain their rage; and amidst the clamors that met his ears, Boabdil more than once heard his name coupled with the epithets of traitor and renegado.

Shocked and discomfited, the youthful monarch returned in confusion to the Alhambra; shut himself up within its innermost courts, and remained a kind of voluntary prisoner until the first burst of popular feeling should subside. He trusted that it would soon pass away; that the people would be too sensible of the sweets of peace, to repine at the price at which it was obtained; at any rate, he trusted to the strong friendship of the Christian sovereigns, to secure him even against the factions of his subjects.

The first missives from the politic Ferdinand showed Boabdil the value of his friendship. The Christian monarch reminded him of a treaty which he had made when captured in the city of Loxa. By this, he had engaged that, in case the Catholic sovereigns should capture the cities of Guadix, Baza, and Almeria, he would surrender Granada into their hands within a limited time, and accept in exchange certain Moorish towns, to be held by him as their vassal. Guadix, Baza, and Almeria, had now fallen; Ferdinand called upon him, therefore, to fulfill his engagement.

If the unfortunate Boabdil had possessed the will, he

had not the power to comply with this demand.   He was shut up in the Alhambra, while a tempest of popular fury raged without.   Granada was thronged by refugees from the captured towns, many of them disbanded soldiers, and others broken-down citizens, rendered fierce and desperate by ruin.   All railed at him, as the real cause of their misfortunes.   How was he to venture forth in such a storm?—above all, how was he to talk to such men of surrender?   In his reply to Ferdinand, he represented the difficulties of his situation, and that, so far from having control over his subjects, his very life was in danger from their turbulence.   He entreated the king, therefore, to rest satisfied for the present with his recent conquests, promising that should he be able to regain full empire over his capital and its inhabitants, it would be but to rule over them as vassal to the Castilian crown.

Ferdinand was not to be satisfied with such a reply. The time was come to bring his game of policy to a close, and to consummate his conquest, by seating himself on the throne of the Alhambra.   Professing to consider Boabdil as a faithless ally, who had broken his plighted word, he discarded him from his friendship, and addressed a second letter, not to him, but to the commanders and council of the city.   He demanded a complete surrender of the place, with all the arms in the possession either of the citizens or of others who had recently taken refuge within its walls.   If the inhabitants should comply with this summons, he promised them the indulgent terms granted to Baza, Guadix, and Almeria; if they should refuse, he threatened them with the fate of Malaga.*

This message produced the greatest commotion in the city. The inhabitants of the Alcaiceria, that busy hive of traffic, and all others who had tasted the sweets of gainful commerce during the late cessation of hostilities, were for securing their golden advantages by timely submission: others, who had wives and children, looked on them with tenderness and solicitude, and dreaded, by resistance, to bring upon them the horrors of slavery.

On the other hand, Granada was crowded with men from all parts, ruined by the war, exasperated by their sufferings, and eager only for revenge; with others, who had been reared amidst hostilities, who had lived by the sword, and whom a return of peace would leave without home or hope. Besides these, there were others no less fiery and warlike in disposition, but animated by a loftier spirit. These were valiant and haughty cavaliers of the old chivalrous lineages, who had inherited a deadly hatred to the Christians from a long line of warrior ancestors, and to whom the idea was worse than death, that Granada, illustrious Granada! for ages the seat of Moorish grandeur and delight, should become the abode of unbelievers.

Among these cavaliers, the most eminent was Muza

* *Cura de los Palacios*, cap. 96.

Abul Gazan. He was of royal lineage, of a proud and generous nature, and a form combining manly strength and beauty. None could excel him in the management of the horse, and dexterous use of all kinds of weapons: his gracefulness and skill in the tourney were the theme of praise among the Moorish dames, and his prowess in the field had made him the terror of the enemy. He had long repined at the timid policy of Boabdil, and endeavored to counteract its enervating effects, and keep alive the martial spirit of Granada. For this reason, he had promoted jousts and tiltings with the reed, and all those other public games which bear the semblance of war. He endeavored also to inculcate into his companions in arms those high chivalrous sentiments which lead to valiant and magnanimous deeds, but which are apt to decline with the independence of a nation. The generous efforts of Muza had been in a great measure successful: he was the idol of the youthful cavaliers; they regarded him as a mirror of chivalry, and endeavored to imitate his lofty and heroic virtues.

When Muza heard the demand of Ferdinand that they should deliver up their arms, his eye flashed fire: "Does the Christian king think that we are old men," said he, "and that staffs will suffice us?—or that we are women, and can be contented with distaffs? Let him know that a Moor is born to the spear and scimetar; to career the steed, bend the bow, and launch the javelin: deprive him of these, and you deprive him of his nature. If the Christian king desires our arms, let him come and win them; but let him win them dearly. For my part, sweeter were a grave beneath the walls of Granada, on the spot I had died to defend, than the richest couch within her palaces, earned by submission to the unbeliever."

The words of Muza were received with enthusiastic shouts, by the warlike part of the populace. Granada once more awoke, as a warrior shaking off a disgraceful lethargy. The commanders and council partook of the public excitement, and dispatched a reply to the Christian sovereigns, declaring that they would suffer death rather than surrender their city.

## CHAPTER LXXXIV.

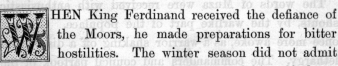WHEN King Ferdinand received the defiance of the Moors, he made preparations for bitter hostilities. The winter season did not admit of an immediate campaign; he contented himself, therefore, with throwing strong garrisons into all his towns and fortresses in the neighborhood of Granada, and gave the command of all the frontier of Jaen to Inigo Lopez de Mendoza, count of Tendilla, who had shown such consummate vigilance and address in maintaining the dangerous post of Alhama. This renowned veteran established his head-quarters in the mountain city of Alcala la Real, within eight leagues of the city of Granada, and commanding the most important passes of that rugged frontier.

In the meantime, Granada resounded with the stir of war. The chivalry of the nation had again control of its councils; and the populace, having once more resumed their weapons, were anxious to wipe out the disgrace of their late passive submission, by signal and daring exploits.

Muza Abul Gazan was the soul of action. He commanded the cavalry, which he had disciplined with uncommon skill; he was surrounded by the noblest youth of Granada, who had caught his own generous and martial fire, and panted for the field; while the common soldiers, devoted to his person, were ready to follow him in the most desperate enterprises. He did not allow their courage to cool for want of action. The gates of Granada once more poured forth legions of light scouring cavalry, which skirred the country up to the very gates of the Christian fortresses, sweeping off flocks and herds. The name of Muza became formidable throughout the frontier; he had many encounters with the enemy in the rough passes of the mountains, in which the superior lightness and dexterity of his cavalry gave him the advantage. The sight of his glistening legion, returning across the vega with long cavalgadas of booty, was hailed by the Moors as a revival of their ancient triumphs; but when they beheld Christian banners borne into their gates as trophies, the exultation of the light-minded populace was beyond all bounds.

The winter passed away; the spring advanced, yet Ferdinand delayed to take the field. He knew the city of Granada was too strong and populous to be taken by assault, and too full of provisions to be speedily reduced by siege. "We must have patience and perseverance," said the politic monarch; "by ravaging the country this year, we shall produce a scarcity the next, and then the city may be invested with effect."

An interval of peace, aided by the quick vegetation of a prolific soil and happy climate, had restored the vega to all its luxuriance and beauty; the green pastures on the borders of the Xenil were covered with flocks and herds; the blooming orchards gave promise of abundant fruit, and the open plain was waving with ripening corn. The time was at hand to put in the sickle and reap the golden harvest, when suddenly a torrent of war came sweeping down from the mountains; and Ferdinand, with an army of five thousand horse and twenty thousand foot, appeared before the walls of Granada. He had left the queen and princess at the fortress of Moclin, and came attended by the duke of Medina Sidonia, the marques of Cadiz, the marques de Villena, the counts of Ureña and Cabra, Don Alonzo de Aguilar, and other renowned cavaliers. On this occasion, he for the first time led his son prince Juan into the field, and bestowed upon him the dignity of knighthood. As if to stimulate him to grand achievements, the ceremony took place on the banks of the grand canal, almost beneath the embattled walls of that warlike city, the object of such daring enterprises, and in the midst of that famous vega, the field of so many chivalrous exploits. Above them shone resplendent the red towers of the Alhambra, rising from amidst delicious groves, with the standard of Mahomet waving defiance to the Christian arms.

The duke of Medina Sidonia, and Roderigo Ponce de Leon, marques of Cadiz, were sponsors; and all the chivalry of the camp was assembled on the occasion. The prince, after he was knighted, bestowed the same honor on several youthful cavaliers of high rank, just entering, like himself, on the career of arms.

Ferdinand did not loiter, in carrying his desolating plans into execution. He detached parties in every direction, to lay waste the country; villages were sacked, burnt, and destroyed, and the lovely vega was once more laid waste with fire and sword. The ravage was carried so close to Granada, that the city was wrapped in the smoke of its gardens and hamlets. The dismal cloud rolled up the hill and hung about the towers of the Alhambra, where the unfortunate Boabdil still remained shut up from the indignation of his subjects. The hapless monarch smote his breast, as he looked down from his mountain palace on the desolation effected by his late ally. He dared not even show himself in arms among the populace, for they cursed him as the cause of the miseries once more brought to their doors.

The Moors, however, did not suffer the Christians to carry on their ravages unmolested as in former years. Muza incited them to incessant sallies. He divided his cavalry into small squadrons, each led by a daring commander. They were taught to hover round the Christian camp, to harass it from various and opposite quarters, cutting off convoys and straggling detachments; to waylay the army in its ravaging expeditions, lurking among rocks and passes of the mountains, or in hollows

36

and thickets of the plain, and practicing a thousand stratagems and surprises.

The Christian army had one day spread itself out rather unguardedly, in its foraging about the vega. As the troops commanded by the marques of Villena approached the skirts of the mountains, they beheld a number of Moorish peasants hastily driving a herd of cattle into a narrow glen. The soldiers, eager for booty, pressed in pursuit of them. Scarcely had they entered the glen, when shouts arose from every side, and they were furiously attacked by an ambuscade of horse and foot. Some of the Christians took to flight; others stood their ground, and fought valiantly. The Moors had the vantage-ground; some showered darts and arrows from the cliffs of the rocks, others fought hand to hand on the plain; while their cavalry carried havoc and confusion into the midst of the Christian forces.

The marques de Villena, with his brother Don Alonzo de Pacheco, at the first onset of the Moors, spurred into the hottest of the fight. They had scarce entered, when Don Alonzo was struck lifeless from his horse, before the eyes of his brother. Estevan Luzon, a gallant captain, fell fighting bravely by the side of the marques, who remained, with his chamberlain Soler and a handful of knights, surrounded by the enemy. Several cavaliers from other parts of the army hastened to their assistance, when King Ferdinand, seeing that the Moors had the vantage-ground, and that the Christians were suffering severely, gave a signal for retreat. The marques obeyed slowly and reluctantly, for his heart was full of grief and rage at the death of his brother. As he was retiring, he beheld his faithful chamberlain Soler defending himself valiantly against six Moors. The marques turned, and rushed to his rescue; he killed two of the enemy with his own hand, and put the rest to flight. One of the Moors, however, in retreating, rose in his stirrups, and hurling his lance at the marques, wounded him in the right arm and crippled him for life.*

Such was one of the many ambuscadoes concerted by Muza; nor did he hesitate at times to present a bold front to the Christian forces, and defy them in the open field. Ferdinand soon perceived, however, that the Moors seldom provoked a battle without having the advantage of the ground; and that though the Christians generally appeared to have the victory, they suffered the greatest loss; for retreating was a part of the Moorish system, by which they would draw their pursuers into confusion, and then turn upon them with a more violent and fatal

* In consequence of this wound, the marques was ever after obliged to write his signature with his left hand, though capable of managing his lance with his right. The queen one day demanded of him, why he had adventured his life for that of a domestic? "Does not your majesty think," replied he, "that I ought to risk one life for him who would have adventured three for me had he possessed them?" The queen was charmed with the magnanimity of the reply, and often quoted the marques as setting an heroic example to the chivalry of the age. Mariana, lib. 25, cap. 15.

attack. He commanded his captains, therefore, to decline all challenges to skirmish, and pursue a secure system of destruction, ravaging the country, and doing all
possible injury to the enemy, with slight risk to themselves.

# CHAPTER LXXXV.

## THE FATE OF THE CASTLE OF ROMA.

BOUT two leagues from Granada, on an eminence commanding an extensive view of the vega, stood the strong Moorish castle of Roma. Hither the neighboring peasantry drove their flocks and herds, and hurried with their most precious effects, on the irruption of a Christian force; and any foraging or skirmishing party from Granada, on being intercepted in their return, threw themselves into Roma, manned its embattled towers, and set the enemy at defiance. The garrison were accustomed to have parties of Moors clattering up to their gates, so hotly pursued that there was barely time to throw open the portal, receive them within, and shut out their pursuers; while the Christian cavaliers had many a time reined up their panting steeds, at the very entrance of the barbacan, and retired, cursing the strong walls of Roma, that robbed them of their prey.

The late ravages of Ferdinand, and the continual skirmishings in the vega, had roused the vigilance of the castle. One morning early, as the sentinels kept watch upon the battlements, they beheld a cloud of dust advancing rapidly from a distance : turbans and Moorish weapons soon caught their eyes : and as the whole approached, they descried a drove of cattle, urged on in great haste, and convoyed by one hundred and fifty Moors, who led with them two Christian captives in chains.

When the cavalgada arrived near the castle, a Moorish cavalier, of noble and commanding mien and splendid attire, rode up to the foot of the tower, and entreated admittance. He stated that they were returning with rich booty from a foray into the lands of the Christians, but that the enemy was on their traces, and they feared to be overtaken before they could reach Granada. The sentinels descended in all haste, and flung open the gates. The long cavalgada defiled into the courts of the castle, which were soon filled with bleating and lowing flocks and herds, with neighing and stamping steeds, and with fierce-looking Moors from the mountains. The cavalier who had asked admission was the chief of the party ; he was somewhat advanced in life, of a lofty and gallant bearing, and had with him a son, a young man of great spirit and fire. Close by them followed the two Christian captives, with looks cast down and disconsolate.

The soldiers of the garrison had roused themselves from their sleep, and were busily occupied attending to the cattle which crowded the courts : while the foraging party distributed themselves about the castle, to seek refreshment or repose. Suddenly a shout arose, that was echoed from courtyard, and hall, and battlement. The garrison, astonished and bewildered, would have rushed to their arms, but found themselves, almost before they could make resistance, completely in the power of an enemy.

The pretended foraging party consisted of Mudexares, or Moors tributary to the Christians; and the commanders were the prince Cid Hiaya, and his son Alnayer. They had hastened from the mountains with this small force, to aid the Catholic sovereigns during the summer's campaign; and had concerted to surprise this important castle, and present it to king Ferdinand, as a gage of their faith, and the first fruits of their devotion.

The politic monarch overwhelmed his new converts and allies with favors and distinctions, in return for this important acquisition; but he took care to dispatch a strong force of veteran and genuine Christian troops, to man the fortress.

As to the Moors who had composed the garrison, Cid Hiaya remembered that they were his countrymen, and could not prevail upon himself to deliver them into Christian bondage. He set them at liberty, and permitted them to repair to Granada; "a proof," says the pious Agapida, "that his conversion was not entirely consummated, but that there were still some lingerings of the infidel in his heart." His lenity was far from procuring him indulgence in the opinions of his countrymen; on the contrary, the inhabitants of Granada, when they learnt from the liberated garrison the stratagem by which Roma had been captured, cursed Cid Hiaya for a traitor; and the garrison joined in the malediction.*

But the indignation of the people of Granada was destined to be roused to tenfold violence. The old warrior Muley Abdallah el Zagal had retired to his little mountain territory, and for a short time endeavored to console himself with his petty title of king of Andarax. He soon grew impatient, however, of the quiet and inaction of his mimic kingdom. His fierce spirit was exasperated by being shut up within such narrow limits, and his hatred rose to downright fury against Boabdil, whom he considered as the cause of his downfall. When tidings were brought him that king Ferdinand was laying waste the vega, he took a sudden resolution. Assembling the whole disposable force of his kingdom, which amounted but to two hundred men, he descended from the Alpuxarras and sought the Christian camp, content to serve as a vassal the enemy of his faith and his nation, so that he might see Granada wrested from the sway of his nephew.

In his blind passion, the old wrathful monarch injured his cause, and strengthened the cause of his adversary. The Moors of Granada had been clamorous in his praise, extolling him as a victim to his patriotism, and had refused to believe all reports of his treaty with the Christians; but when they beheld, from the walls of the city,

* Pulgar, *Cron.* pt. 3, cap. 130. *Cura de los Palacios,* cap. 90.

his banner mingling with the banners of the unbelievers, and arrayed against his late people, and the capital he had commanded, they broke forth into revilings, and heaped curses upon his name.

Their next emotion, of course, was in favor of Boabdil. They gathered under the walls of the Alhambra, and hailed him as their only hope, as the sole dependence of the country. Boabdil could scarcely believe his senses, when he heard his name mingled with praises and greeted with acclamations. Encouraged by this unexpected gleam of popularity, he ventured forth from his retreat, and was received with rapture. All his past errors were attributed to the hardships of his fortune, and the usurpation of his tyrant uncle; and whatever breath the populace could spare from uttering curses on El Zagal, was expended in shouts in honor of El Chico.

# CHAPTER LXXXVI.

### HOW BOABDIL EL CHICO TOOK THE FIELD; AND HIS EXPEDITION AGAINST ALHENDIN.

OR thirty days had the vega been overrun by the Christian forces; and that vast plain, late so luxuriant and beautiful, was one wide scene of desolation. The destroying army, having accomplished its task, passed over the bridge of Pinos and wound up into the mountains, on the way to Cordova, bearing away the spoils of towns and villages, and driving off flocks and herds in long dusty columns. The sound of the last Christian trumpet died away along the side of the mountain of Elvira, and not a hostile squadron was seen glistening on the mournful fields of the vega.

The eyes of Boabdil el Chico were at length opened to the real policy of king Ferdinand, and he saw that he had no longer anything to depend upon but the valor of his arm. No time was to be lost in hastening to counteract the effect of the late Christian ravage, and in opening the channel for distant supplies to Granada.

Scarcely had the retiring squadrons of Ferdinand disappeared among the mountains, when Boabdil buckled on his armor, sallied forth from the Alhambra, and prepared to take the field. When the populace beheld him actually in arms against his late ally, both parties thronged with zeal to his standard. The hardy inhabitants also of the Sierra Nevada, or chain of snow-capped mountains which rise above Granada, descended from their heights, and hastened into the city gates, to proffer their devotion to their youthful king. The great square of the Vivarrambla shone with legions of cavalry, decked with the colors and devices of the most ancient Moorish families, and marshaled forth by the patriot Muza to follow the king to battle.

It was on the 15th of June, that Boabdil once more issued forth from the gates of Granada on martial enterprise. A few leagues from the city, within full view of it, and at the entrance of the Alpuxarra mountains, stood the powerful castle of Alhendin. It was built on an eminence, rising from the midst of a small town, and commanding a great part of the vega and the main road to the rich valleys of the Alpuxarras. The castle was commanded by a valiant Christian cavalier named Mendo de Quexada, and garrisoned by two hundred and fifty men, all seasoned and experienced warriors. It was a continual thorn in the side of Granada: the laborers of the vega were swept off from their fields, by its hardy soldiers; convoys were cut off in the passes of the mountains; and as the garrison commanded a full view of the gates of the city, no band of merchants could venture forth on their needful journeys, without being swooped up by the war-hawks of Alhendin.

It was against this important fortress that Boabdil first led his troops, and for six days and nights it was closely besieged. The alcayde and his veteran garrison defended themselves valiantly, but were exhausted by fatigue and constant watchfulness; for the Moors, being continually relieved by fresh troops from Granada, kept up an unremitted and vigorous attack. Twice the barbacan was forced, and twice the assailants were driven forth headlong with excessive loss. The garrison, however, was diminished in number by the killed and wounded; there were no longer soldiers sufficient to man the walls and gateway; and the brave alcayde was compelled to retire, with his surviving force, to the keep of the castle, in which he continued to make a desperate resistance.

The Moors now approached the foot of the tower, under shelter of wooden screens covered with wet hides, to ward off missiles and combustibles. They went to work vigorously to undermine the tower, placing props of wood under the foundations, to be afterwards set on fire, so as to give the besiegers time to escape before the edifice should fall. Some of the Moors plied their crossbows and arquebuses to defend the workmen, and drive the Christians from the walls: while the latter showered down stones, and darts, and melted pitch, and flaming combustibles, on the miners.

The brave Mendo de Quexada had cast many an anxious eye across the vega, in hopes of seeing some Christian force hastening to his assistance. Not a gleam of spear or helm was to be descried, for no one had dreamt of this sudden irruption of the Moors. The alcayde beheld his bravest men dead or wounded around him, while the remainder were sinking with watchfulness and fatigue. In defiance of all opposition, the Moors had accomplished their mine; the fire was brought before the walls, that was to be applied to the stanchions, in case the garrison persisted in defense. In a little while, the tower would crumble beneath him, and be rent and hurled a ruin to the plain. At the very last moment, the brave alcayde made the signal of surrender. He marched forth with the remnant of his veteran garrison, who were all made prisoners. Boabdil immediately ordered the walls of the fortress to be razed, and fire to be applied to the stanchions, that the place might never again become a stronghold to the Christians, and a scourge to Granada. The alcayde and his fellow-captives were led in dejected convoy across the vega, when they heard a tremendous crash behind them. They turned to look upon their late fortress, but beheld nothing but a heap of tumbling ruins, and a vast column of smoke and dust, where once had stood the lofty tower of Alhendin.

DISTRIBUTION OF THE TOWER OF ALHENDIN. 573

## CHAPTER LXXXVII.

### EXPLOIT OF THE COUNT DE TENDILLA.

OABDIL EL CHICO followed up his success, by capturing the two fortresses of Marchena and Albolodny, belonging to Cid Hiaya; he also sent his alfaquis in every direction, to proclaim a holy war, and to summon all true Moslems of town or castle, mountain or valley, to saddle steed and buckle on armor, and hasten to the standard of the faith. The tidings spread far and wide, that Boabdil el Chico was once more in the field, and was victorious. The Moors of various places, dazzled by this gleam of success, hastened to throw off their sworn allegiance to the Castilian crown, and to elevate the standard of Boabdil; and the youthful monarch flattered himself that the whole kingdom was on the point of returning to its allegiance.

The fiery cavaliers of Granada, eager to renew those forays into the Christian lands, in which they had formerly delighted, concerted an irruption to the north, into the territory of Jaen, to harass the country about Quezada. They had heard of a rich convoy of merchants

574

and wealthy travellers, on the way to the city of Baza; and anticipated a glorious conclusion to their foray in capturing this convoy.

Assembling a number of horsemen, lightly armed and fleetly mounted, and one hundred foot-soldiers, they issued forth by night from Granada, made their way in silence through the defiles of the mountains, crossed the frontier without opposition, and suddenly appeared, as if fallen from the clouds, in the very heart of the Christian country.

The mountainous frontier which separates Granada from Jaen, was at this time under the command of the count de Tendilla, the same veteran who had distinguished himself by his vigilance and sagacity when commanding the fortress of Alhama. He held his headquarters at the city of Alcala la Real, in its impregnable fortress, perched high among the mountains, about six leagues from Granada, and dominating all the frontier. From this cloud-capt hold he kept an eagle eye upon Granada, and had his scouts and spies in all directions, so that a crow could not fly over the border without his knowledge. His fortress was a place of refuge for the Christian captives who escaped by night from the Moorish dungeons of Granada. Often, however, they missed their way in the defiles of the mountains, and, wandering about bewildered, either repaired by mistake to some Moorish town, or were discovered and retaken at daylight by the enemy. To prevent these accidents the count had a tower built at his own expense, on the top of one of the heights near Alcala, which commanded a view of the vega and surrounding country. Here he kept a light blazing throughout the night, as a beacon for all Christian fugitives, to guide them to a place of safety.

The count was aroused one night from his repose, by shouts and cries which came up from the town and approached the castle walls. "To arms! to arms! the Moor is over the border!" was the cry. A Christian soldier, pale and emaciated, who still bore traces of Moorish chains, was brought before the count. He had been taken as guide by the Moorish cavaliers who had sallied from Granada, but had escaped from them among the mountains, and, after much wandering, had found his way to Alcala by the signal-fire.

Notwithstanding the bustle and agitation of the moment, the count de Tendilla listened calmly and attentively, to the account of the fugitive, and questioned him minutely as to the time of departure of the Moors, and the rapidity and direction of their march. He saw that it was too late to prevent their incursion and ravage; but he determined to await them, and give them a warm reception on their return. His soldiers were always on the alert, and ready to take the field at a moment's warning. Choosing one hundred and fifty lances, hardy and valiant men, well disciplined and well seasoned, as indeed were all his troops, he issued forth quietly before break of day, and, descending the defiles of the mountains, stationed his little force in ambush, in a deep barranca, or dry channel of a torrent, near Barzina, but three leagues from Granada, on the road by which the marauders would have to return. In the meantime, he sent out scouts, to post themselves upon different heights, and look out for the approach of the enemy.

All day they remained concealed in the ravine, and for a great part of the following night; not a Moor, however, was to be seen, excepting now and then a peasant returning from his labor, or a solitary muleteer hastening towards Granada. The cavaliers of the count began to grow restless and impatient; fearing that the enemy might have taken some other route, or might have received intelligence of their ambuscade. They urged the count to abandon the enterprise, and return to Alcala. "We are here," said they, "almost at the gates of the Moorish capital, our movements may have been descried, and, before we are aware, Granada may pour forth its legions of swift cavalry, and crush us with an overwhelming force." The count, however, persisted in remaining until his scouts should come in. About two hours before daybreak, there were signal-fires on certain Moorish watch-towers of the mountains. While they were regarding these with anxiety, the scouts came hurrying into the ravine: "The Moors are approaching," said they; "we have reconnoitered them near at hand. They are between one and two hundred strong, but encumbered with many prisoners and much booty." The Christian cava-

37

liers laid their ears to the ground, and heard the distant tramp of horses and the tread of foot-soldiers. They mounted their horses, braced their shields, couched their lances, and drew near to the entrance of the ravine where it opened upon the road.

The Moors had succeeded in waylaying and surprising the Christian convoy, on its way to Baza. They had captured a great number of prisoners, male and female, with great store of gold and jewels, and sumpter mules laden with rich merchandise. With these they had made a forced march over the dangerous parts of the mountains: but now, finding themselves so near to Granada, fancied themselves in perfect security. They loitered along the road, therefore, irregularly and slowly, some singing, others laughing and exulting at having eluded the boasted vigilance of the count de Tendilla; while ever and anon was heard the plaint of some female captive bewailing the jeopardy of her honor, or the heavy sighing of the merchant at beholding his property in the grasp of ruthless spoilers.

The count waited until some of the escort had passed the ravine, then, giving the signal for assault, his cavaliers set up great shouts and cries, and charged into the centre of the foe. The obscurity of the place and the hour added to the terrors of the surprise. The Moors were thrown into confusion; some rallied, fought desperately, and fell covered with wounds. Thirty-six were killed, and fifty-five were made prisoners; the rest, under cover of the darkness, made their escape to the rocks and defiles of the mountains.

The good count unbound the prisoners, gladdening the hearts of the merchants by restoring to them their merchandise. To the female captives also he restored the jewels of which they had been despoiled, excepting such as had been lost beyond recovery. Forty-five saddle horses, of the choice Barbary breed, remained as captured spoils of the Moors, together with costly armor, and booty of various kinds. Having collected everything in haste, and arranged his cavalgada, the count urged his way with all speed for Alcala la Real, lest he should be pursued and overtaken by the Moors of Granada. As he wound up the steep ascent to his mountain city, the inhabitants poured forth to meet him with shouts of joy. His triumph was doubly enhanced by being received at the gates of the city by his wife, the daughter of the marques of Villena, a lady of distinguished merit, whom he had not seen for two years, during which he had been separated from his home by the arduous duties of these iron wars.

We have yet another act to relate of this good count de Tendilla, who was in truth a mirror of knightly virtue. One day, a Christian soldier, just escaped from captivity in Granada, brought word to the count, that an illustrious damsel named Fatima, niece of the alcayde Aben Comixa, was to leave the city on a certain day, escorted by a numerous party of relatives and friends of distinguished rank, on a journey to Almuñecar, there to embark for the African coast, to celebrate her nuptials with the alcayde of Tetuan. This was too brilliant a prize to be neglected. The count accordingly sallied forth with a light company of cavalry, and descending the defiles of the mountains, stationed himself behind the rocky sierra of Elvira, not far from the eventful bridge of Pinos, within a few short miles of Granada. Hence he detached Alonzo de Cardenas Ulloa, with fifty light horsemen, to post himself in ambush, by the road the bridal party had to travel. After a time, the latter came in sight, proving less numerous than had been expected; for the damsel was escorted merely by four armed domestics, and accompanied by a few relatives and two female attendants. The whole party was surrounded and captured almost without resistance, and carried off to the count at the bridge of Pinos. The good count conveyed his beautiful captive to his stronghold at Alcala, where he treated her and her companions with all the delicacy and respect due to their rank and to his own character as a courteous cavalier.

The tidings of the capture of his niece gave poignant affliction to the vizier Aben Comixa. His royal master Boabdil, of whom he was the prime favorite and confidential adviser, sympathized in his distress. With his own hand he wrote a letter to the count, offering in exchange for the fair Fatima one hundred Christian captives, to be chosen from those detained in Granada.

This royal letter was sent by Don Francisco de Zuniga, an Aragonese cavalier, whom Aben Comixa held in captivity, and who was set at liberty for the purpose.

On receiving the letter of Boabdil, the count de Tendilla at once gave freedom to the Moorish maid, making her a magnificent present of jewels, and sending her and her companions under honorable escort to the very gates of Granada.

Boabdil, exceeding his promises, immediately set free twenty captive priests, one hundred and thirty Castilian and Aragonian cavaliers, and a number of peasant women. His favorite and vizier, Aben Comixa, was so rejoiced at the liberation of his niece, and so struck with the chivalrous conduct of her captor, that he maintained from that day a constant and amicable correspondence with the count de Tendilla; and became, in the hands of the latter, one of the most efficacious agents in bringing the war of Granada to a triumphant close.*

* This interesting anecdote of the count de Tendilla, which is a key to the subsequent conduct of the vizier Aben Comixa, and had a singular influence on the fortunes of Boabdil and his kingdom, is originally given in a manuscript history of the counts of Tendilla, written about the middle of the sixteenth century, by Gabriel Rodriguez de Ardila, a Granadine clergyman. It has been brought to light recently by the researches of Alcantara for his *History of Granada* (vol. 4, cap. 18).

# CHAPTER LXXXVIII.

ING BOABDIL found that his diminished territory was too closely dominated by Christian
fortresses like Alcala la Real, and too strictly
watched by vigilant alcaydes like the count of Tendilla,
to be able to maintain itself by internal resources. His
foraging expeditions were liable to be intercepted and
defeated, while the ravage of the vega had swept off
everything on which the city depended for future sustenance. He felt the want of a seaport, through which,
as formerly, he might keep open a communication with
Africa and obtain reinforcements and supplies from beyond the sea. All the ports and harbors were in the
hands of the Christians, and Granada and its remnant of
dependent territory were completely landlocked.

In this emergency, the attention of Boabdil was called
by circumstances to the seaport of Salobreña. This redoubtable town has already been mentioned in this chronicle, as a place deemed impregnable by the Moors; insomuch, that their kings were accustomed, in time of peril,

582

to keep their treasures in its citadel. It was situated on a high rocky hill, dividing one of those rich little vegas or plains which lie open to the Mediterranean, but run like deep green bays into the stern bosoms of the mountains. The vega was covered with beautiful vegetation, with rice and cotton, with groves of oranges, citrons, figs, and mulberries, and with gardens inclosed by hedges of reeds, of aloes and the Indian fig. Running streams of cool water from the springs and snows of the Sierra Nevada kept this delightful valley continually fresh and verdant; while it was almost locked up by mountain barriers, and lofty promontories stretching far into the sea.

Through the centre of this rich vega, the rock of Salobreña reared its rugged back, nearly dividing the plain, and advancing to the margin of the sea, with just a strip of sandy beach at its foot, laved by the blue waves of the Mediterranean.

The town covered the ridge and sides of the rocky hill, and was fortified by strong walls and towers; while on the highest and most precipitate part stood the citadel, a huge castle that seemed to form a part of the living rock; the massive ruins of which, at the present day, attract the gaze of the traveller, as he winds his way far below, along the road through the vega.

This important fortress had been intrusted to the command of Don Francisco Ramirez de Madrid, captain-general of the artillery, and the most scientific of all the Spanish leaders. That experienced veteran, how-

ever, was with the king at Cordova, having left a valiant
cavalier as alcayde of the place.

Boabdil had full information of the state of the garrison and the absence of its commander. Putting himself
at the head of a powerful force, therefore, he departed
from Granada, and made a rapid march through the
mountains; hoping to seize upon Salobreña before king
Ferdinand could come to its assistance.

The inhabitants of Salobreña were Mudexares, or
Moors who had sworn allegiance to the Christians.
Still, when they heard the sound of the Moorish drums
and trumpets, and beheld the squadrons of their countrymen advancing across the vega, their hearts yearned
towards the standard of their nation and their faith. A
tumult arose in the place ; the populace shouted the
name of Boabdil el Chico, and, throwing open the gates,
admitted him within the walls.

The Christian garrison was too few in number to contend for the possession of the town : they retreated to
the citadel, and shut themselves within its massive walls,
which were considered impregnable. Here they maintained a desperate defense, hoping to hold out until succor should arrive from the neighboring fortresses.

The tidings that Salobreña was invested by the Moorish king, spread along the sea-coast, and filled the Christians with alarm. Don Francisco Enriquez, uncle of the
king, commanded the city of Velez Malaga, about twelve
leagues distant, but separated by ranges of those vast

rocky mountains which are piled along the Mediterranean, and tower in steep promontories and precipices above its waves.

Don Francisco summoned the alcaydes of his district to hasten with him to the relief of this important fortress. A number of cavaliers and their retainers answered to his call, among whom was Hernan Perez del Pulgar, surnamed "El de las Hazanas" (he of the exploits)—the same who had signalized himself in a foray, by elevating a handkerchief on a lance for a banner, and leading on his disheartened comrades to victory. As soon as Don Francisco beheld a little band collected round him, he set out with all speed for Salobreña. The march was rugged and severe, climbing and descending immense mountains, and sometimes winding along the edge of giddy precipices, with the surges of the sea raging far below. When Don Francisco arrived with his followers at the lofty promontory that stretches along one side of the little vega of Salobreña, he looked down with sorrow and anxiety upon a Moorish army of great force, encamped at the foot of the fortress, while Moorish banners, on various parts of the walls, proved that the town was already in possession of the infidels. A solitary Christian standard alone floated on the top of the castle-keep, showing that the brave garrison were hemmed up in their rock-built citadel. They were in fact reduced to great extremity, through want of water and provisions.

Don Francisco found it impossible, with his small force, to make any impression on the camp of the Moors, or to get to the relief of the castle. He stationed his little band upon a rocky height near the sea, where they were safe from the assaults of the enemy. The sight of his friendly banner waving in their neighborhood cheered the heart of the garrison, and gave them assurance of speedy succor from the king; while the hostile menaces of Don Franciso, served to check the attacks of the Moors upon the citadel.

In the meantime, Hernan Perez del Pulgar, who always burned to distinguish himself by bold and striking exploits, had discovered in the course of his prowlings, a postern gate of the castle opening upon the steep part of the rocky hill looking towards the mountains. The thought occurred to him, that by a bold dash at a favorable moment, this postern might be attained, and succor thrown into the castle. He pointed the place out to his comrades. "Who will follow my banner," said he, "and make a dash for yonder postern?" A bold proposition in time of warfare never wants for bold spirits to accept it. Seventy resolute men stepped forward to second him. Pulgar chose the early daybreak for his enterprise, when the Moors, just aroused from sleep, were changing guard, and making the various arrangements of the morning. Favored by these movements, and the drowsiness of the hour, Pulgar approached the Moorish line silently and steadily, most of his followers armed with cross-bows and espingardas, or muskets. Then suddenly making an onset, they broke through a weak part of the camp, before the alarm had spread through the army, and succeeded in fighting their way up to the gate, which was eagerly thrown open to receive them.

The garrison, roused to new spirit by this unlooked-for reinforcement, was enabled to make a more vigorous resistance. The Moors, however, who knew there was a great scarcity of water in the castle, exulted in the idea that this additional number of warriors would soon exhaust the cisterns, and compel a surrender. Pulgar, hearing of this hope, caused a bucket of water to be lowered from the battlements, and threw a silver cup in bravado to the Moors.

The garrison, in truth, suffered intensely from thirst, while, to tantalize them in their sufferings, they beheld limpid streams winding in abundance through the green plain below them. They began to fear that all succor would arrive too late, when one day they beheld a little squadron of vessels far at sea, but standing towards the shore. There was some doubt at first whether it might not be a hostile armament from Africa; but as it approached they descried, to their great joy, the banner of Castile.

It was a reinforcement, brought in all haste by the governor of the fortress, Don Francisco Ramirez. The squadron anchored at a steep rocky island, which rises

from the very margin of the smooth sandy beach, directly in front of the rock of Salobreña, and stretches out
into the sea. On this island Ramirez landed his men,
and was as strongly posted as if in a fortress. His force
was too scanty to attempt a battle, but he assisted to
harass and distract the besiegers. Whenever king Boabdil made an attack upon the fortress, his camp was
assailed on one side by the troops of Ramirez, who
landed from their island, and on another by those of
Francisco Enriquez, who swept down from their rock;
while Hernan del Pulgar kept up a brave defense, from
every tower and battlement of the castle.

The attention of the Moorish king was diverted, also,
for a time, by an ineffectual attempt to relieve the little
port of Adra, which had recently declared in his favor,
but which had been recaptured for the Christians by Cid
Hiaya and his son Alnayar. Thus the unlucky Boabdil,
bewildered on every hand, lost all the advantage that he
had gained by his rapid march from Granada. While he
was yet besieging the obstinate citadel, tidings were
brought him that King Ferdinand was in full march,
with a powerful host, to its assistance. There was no
time for further delay: he made a furious attack with all
his forces upon the castle, but was again repulsed by
Pulgar and his coadjutors; when, abandoning the siege,
in despair, he retreated with his army, lest King Ferdinand should get between him and his capital. On his
way back to Granada, however, he in some sort consoled

himself for his late disappointment, by overrunning a part of the territories and possessions lately assigned to his uncle El Zagal, and to Cid Hiaya. He defeated their alcaydes, destroyed several of their fortresses, burnt their villages, and, leaving the country behind him reeking and smoking with his vengeance, returned with considerable booty, to repose himself within the walls of the Alhambra.*

* Pulgar, *Cron.* pt. 3, cap. 131. *Cura de los Palacios*, cap. 97.

# CHAPTER LXXXIX.

SCARCELY had Boabdil ensconced himself in
his capital, when King Ferdinand, at the head
of seven thousand horse and twenty thousand
foot, again appeared in the vega. He had set out in all
haste from Cordova, to the relief of Salobreña; but,
hearing on his march that the siege was raised, he
turned to make a second ravage round the walls of devoted Granada. His present forage lasted fifteen days,
in the course of which almost everything that had escaped his former desolating visit was destroyed, and
scarce a green thing or a living animal was left on the
face of the land. The Moors sallied frequently, and
fought desperately, in defense of their fields: but the
work of destruction was accomplished—and Granada,
once the queen of gardens, was left surrounded by a
desert.

Ferdinand next hastened to crush a conspiracy in the
cities of Guadix, Baza, and Almeria. These recently
conquered places had entered into secret correspondence

590

with Boabdil, inviting him to march to their gates, promising to rise upon the Christian garrisons, seize upon the citadels, and surrender them into his power. The marques of Villena had received notice of the conspiracy, and suddenly thrown himself, with a large force, into Guadix. Under pretense of a review of the inhabitants, he made them sally forth into the fields before the city. When the whole Moorish population capable of bearing arms was thus without the walls, he ordered the gates to be closed. He then permitted them to enter, two by two and three by three, and take forth their wives, children, and effects. The houseless Moors were fain to make themselves temporary hovels, in the gardens and orchards about the city; they were clamorous in their complaints at being thus excluded from their homes, but were told they must wait with patience until the charges against them could be investigated, and the pleasure of the king be known.*

When Ferdinand arrived at Guadix, he found the unhappy Moors in their cabins among the orchards. They complained bitterly of the deception practiced upon them, and implored permission to return into the city, and live peaceably in their dwellings, as had been promised them in their articles of capitulation.

King Ferdinand listened graciously to their complaints. "My friends," said he in reply, "I have been

* Zurita, cap. 85. *Cura de los Palacios*, cap. 97.

informed that there has been a conspiracy among you to
kill my alcayde and garrison, and to take part with my
enemy, the king of Granada. I shall make a thorough
investigation of this conspiracy. Those among you who
shall be proved innocent shall be restored to their dwellings, but the guilty shall incur the penalty of their offenses. As I wish, however, to proceed with mercy as
well as justice, I now give you your choice, either to depart at once without further question, going wherever
you please, and taking with you your families and effects,
under an assurance of safety; or to deliver up those who
are guilty, not one of whom, I give you my royal word,
shall escape punishment."

When the people of Guadix heard these words, they
communed among themselves; and as most of them (says
the worthy Agapida) were either culpable or feared to be
considered so, they accepted the alternative, and departed
sorrowfully, they and their wives and their little ones.
"Thus," in the words of that excellent and contemporary
historian, Andres Bernaldez, commonly called the curate
of Los Palacios,—"thus did the king deliver Guadix from
the hands of the enemies of our holy faith, after seven
hundred and seventy years that it had been in their possession, ever since the time of Roderick the Goth; and
this was one of the mysteries of our Lord, who would not
consent that the city should remain longer in the power
of the Moors"—a pious and sage remark, which is quoted
with peculiar approbation by the worthy Agapida.

King Ferdinand offered similar alternatives to the Moors of Baza, Almeria, and other cities accused of participation in this conspiracy; who generally preferred to abandon their homes, rather than incur the risk of an investigation. Most of them relinquished Spain, as a country where they could no longer live in security and independence, and departed with their families for Africa; such as remained were suffered to live in villages and hamlets, and other unwalled places.*

While Ferdinand was thus occupied at Guadix, dispensing justice and mercy, and receiving cities in exchange, the old monarch Muley Abdallah, surnamed El Zagal, appeared before him. He was haggard with care, and almost crazed with passion. He had found his little territory of Andarax, and his two thousand subjects, as difficult to govern as had been the distracted kingdom of Granada. The charm, which had bound the Moors to him, was broken when he appeared in arms under the banner of Ferdinand. He had returned from his inglorious campaign with his petty army of two hundred men, followed by the execrations of the people of Granada, and the secret repining of those he had led into the field. No sooner had his subjects heard of the successes of Boabdil el Chico, than they had seized their arms, assembled tumultuously, declared for the young monarch, and threatened the life of El Zagal.†

* Garibay, lib. 13, cap. 39.  Pulgar, pt. 3, cap. 132.
† *Cura de los Palacios*, cap. 97.

The unfortunate old king had with difficulty evaded their fury; and this last lesson seemed entirely to have cured him of his passion for sovereignty. He now entreated Ferdinand to purchase the towns and castles, and other possessions which had been granted to him; offering them at a low rate, and begging safe passage for himself and his followers to Africa. King Ferdinand graciously complied with his wishes. He purchased of him three-and-twenty towns and villages in the valleys of Andarax and Alhaurin, for which he gave him five millions of maravedis. El Zagal relinquished his right to one half of the salinas or salt-pits of Maleha, in favor of his brother-in-law, Cid Hiaya. Having thus disposed of his petty empire and possessions, he packed up all his treasure, of which he had a great amount, and, followed by many Moorish families, passed over to Africa.*

And here let us cast an eye beyond the present period of our chronicle, and trace the remaining career of El Zagal. His short and turbulent reign, and disastrous end, would afford a wholesome lesson to unprincipled ambition, were not all ambition of the kind fated to be blind to precept and example. When he arrived in Africa, instead of meeting with kindness and sympathy, he was seized and thrown into prison by the caliph of Fez, Benimerin, as though he had been his vassal. He was accused of being the cause of the dissensions and

* Conde, pt. 4, cap. 41.

downfall of the kingdom of Granada; and the accusation being proved to the satisfaction of the king of Fez, he condemned the unhappy El Zagal to perpetual darkness. A basin of glowing copper was passed before his eyes, which effectually destroyed his sight. His wealth, which had probably been the secret cause of these cruel measures, was confiscated and seized upon by his oppressor; and El Zagal was thrust forth, blind, helpless, and destitute, upon the world. In this wretched condition, the late Moorish monarch groped his way through the regions of Tingitania, until he reached the city of Velez de la Gomera. The emir of Velez had formerly been his ally, and felt some movement of compassion at his present altered and abject state. He gave him food and raiment, and suffered him to remain unmolested in his dominions. Death, which so often hurries off the prosperous and happy from the midst of untasted pleasures, spares on the other hand, the miserable, to drain the last drop of his cup of bitterness. El Zagal dragged out a wretched existence of many years, in the city of Velez. He wandered about blind and disconsolate, an object of mingled scorn and pity, and bearing above his raiment a parchment on which was written in Arabic, "This is the unfortunate king of Andalusia." *

* Marmol, *de Rebelione Maur.* lib. 1, cap. 16. Padraza, *Hist. Granad.* pt. 3, cap. 4. Suarez, *Hist. Coisp. de Guadix y Baza*, cap. 10.

## CHAPTER XC.

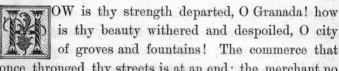

OW is thy strength departed, O Granada! how is thy beauty withered and despoiled, O city of groves and fountains! The commerce that once thronged thy streets is at an end; the merchant no longer hastens to thy gates, with the luxuries of foreign lands. The cities which once paid thee tribute are wrested from thy sway; the chivalry which filled thy Vivarrambla with sumptuous pageantry, have fallen in many battles. The Alhambra still rears its ruddy towers from the midst of groves, but melancholy reigns in its marble halls; and the monarch looks down from his lofty balconies upon a naked waste, where once extended the blooming glories of the vega!

Such is the lament of the Moorish writers, over the lamentable state of Granada, now a mere phantom of former greatness. The two ravages of the vega, following so closely upon each other, had swept off all the produce of the year; and the husbandman had no longer the heart to till the field, seeing the ripening harvest only brought the spoiler to his door.

596

During the winter season, Ferdinand made diligent preparations for the campaign, that was to decide the fate of Granada. As this war was waged purely for the promotion of the Christian faith, he thought it meet that its enemies should bear the expenses. He levied, therefore, a general contribution upon the Jews throughout his kingdom, by synagogues and districts: and obliged them to render in the proceeds, at the city of Seville.*

On the 11th of April, Ferdinand and Isabella departed for the Moorish frontier, with the solemn determination to lay close siege to Granada, and never quit its walls until they had planted the standard of the faith on the towers of the Alhambra. Many of the nobles of the kingdom, particularly those from parts remote from the scene of action, wearied by the toils of war, and foreseeing that this would be a tedious siege, requiring patience and vigilance rather than hardy deeds of arms, contented themselves with sending their vassals, while they staid at home, to attend to their domains. Many cities furnished soldiers at their cost, and the king took the field with an army of forty thousand infantry and ten thousand horse. The principal captains who followed him in this campaign, were Roderigo Ponce de Leon, the marques of Cadiz, the master of Santiago, the marques of Villena, the counts of Tendilla, Cifuentes, Cabra, and Urena, and Don Alonzo de Aguilar.

* Garibay, lib. 18, c. 39.

Queen Isabella, accompanied by her son, the Prince Juan, and the princesses Juana, Maria, and Cathalina, her daughters, proceeded to Alcala la Real, the mountain fortress and stronghold of the count de Tendilla. Here she remained, to forward supplies to the army, and to be ready to repair to the camp, whenever her presence might be required.

The army of Ferdinand poured into the vega, by various defiles of the mountains; and, on the 23d of April, the royal tent was pitched at a village called Los Ojos de Huescar, about a league and a half from Granada. At the approach of this formidable force, the harassed inhabitants turned pale, and even many of the warriors trembled; for they felt that the last desperate struggle was at hand.

Boabdil el Chico assembled his council in the Alhambra, from the windows of which they could behold the Christian squadrons glistening through clouds of dust, as they poured along the vega. The utmost confusion and consternation reigned in the council. Many of the members, terrified with the horrors impending over their families, advised Boabdil to throw himself upon the generosity of the Christian monarch : even several of the bravest suggested the possibility of obtaining honorable terms.

The wazir of the city, Abul Casim Abdel Melic, was called upon to report the state of the public means for sustenance and defense. There were sufficient provisions, he said, for a few months' supply, independent of what might exist in the possession of merchants and other rich inhabitants. "But of what avail," said he, "is a supply for a few months, against the sieges of the Castilian monarch, which are interminable?"

He produced, also, the lists of men capable of bearing arms. "The number," said he, "is great; but what can be expected from mere citizen-soldiers? They vaunt and menace, in time of safety; none are so arrogant, when the enemy is at a distance—but when the din of war thunders at the gates, they hide themselves in terror."

When Muza heard these words, he rose with generous warmth: "What reason have we," said he, "to despair? The blood of those illustrious Moors, the conquerors of Spain, still flows in our veins. Let us be true to ourselves, and fortune will again be with us. We have a veteran force, both horse and foot, the flower of our chivalry, seasoned in war and scarred in a thousand battles. As to the multitude of our citizens, spoken of so slightly, why should we doubt their valor? There are twenty thousand young men, in the fire of youth, whom I will engage, that in the defense of their homes they will rival the most valiant veterans. Do we want provisions? Our horses are fleet, and our horsemen daring in the foray. Let them scour and scourge the country of those apostate Moslems who have surrendered to the Christians. Let them make inroads into the lands of our enemies. We shall soon see them returning with cavalgadas to our gates; and, to a soldier, there is no morsel so sweet as that wrested with hard fighting from the foe."

Boabdil, though he wanted firm and durable courage, was readily excited to sudden emotions of bravery. He caught a glow of resolution from the noble ardor of Muza. "Do what is needful," said he to his commanders; "into your hands I confide the common safety. You are the protectors of the kingdom, and with the aid of Allah, will revenge the insults of our religion, the deaths of our friends and relations, and the sorrows and sufferings heaped upon our land."*

To every one was now assigned his separate duty. The wazir had charge of the arms and provisions, and the enrolling of the people. Muza was to command the cavalry, to defend the gates, and to take the lead in all sallies and skirmishings. Naim Reduan, and Muhamed Aben Zayde were his adjutants. Abdel Kerim Zegri, and the other captains, were to guard the walls; and the alcaydes of the Alcazaba, and of the Red Towers, had command of the fortresses.

Nothing now was heard but the din of arms, and the bustle of preparation. The Moorish spirit, quick to catch fire, was immediately in a flame; and the populace, in the excitement of the moment, set at naught the power of the Christians. Muza was in all parts of the city, infusing his own generous zeal into the bosoms of

* Conde.

the soldiery. The young cavaliers rallied round him as their model; the veteran warriors regarded him with a soldier's admiration; the vulgar throng followed him with shouts, and the helpless part of the inhabitants, the old men and the women, hailed him with blessings as their protector.

On the first appearance of the Christian army, the principal gates of the city had been closed, and secured with bars and bolts and heavy chains: Muza now ordered them to be thrown open; "To me and my cavaliers," said he, "is intrusted the defense of the gates; our bodies shall be their barriers." He stationed at each gate a strong guard, chosen from his bravest men. His horsemen were always completely armed, and ready to mount at a moment's warning; their steeds stood saddled and caparisoned in the stables, with lance and buckler beside them. On the least approach of the enemy, a squadron of horse gathered within the gate, ready to launch forth like the bolt from the thunder-cloud. Muza made no empty bravado nor haughty threat; he was more terrible in deeds than in words, and executed daring exploits, beyond even the vaunt of the vainglorious. Such was the present champion of the Moors. Had they possessed many such warriors, or had Muza risen to power at an earlier period of the war, the fate of Granada might have been deferred, and the Moor for a long time have maintained his throne within the walls of the Alhambra.

# CHAPTER XCI.

HOW KING FERDINAND CONDUCTED THE SIEGE CAUTIOUSLY ; AND HOW QUEEN
ISABELLA ARRIVED AT THE CAMP.

HOUGH Granada was shorn of its glories, and
nearly cut off from all external aid, still its
mighty castles and massive bulwarks seemed
to set all attack at defiance. Being the last retreat of
Moorish power, it had assembled within its walls the
remnants of the armies which had contended, step by
step, with the invaders, in their gradual conquest of the
land. All that remained of high-born and high-bred
chivalry, was here; all that was loyal and patriotic was
roused to activity by the common danger; and Granada,
so long lulled into inaction by vain hopes of security,
now assumed a formidable aspect in the hour of its
despair.

Ferdinand saw that any attempt to subdue the city by
main force would be perilous and bloody. Cautious in
his policy, and fond of conquests gained by art rather
than valor, he resorted to the plan so successful with
Baza, and determined to reduce the place by famine.
For this purpose, his armies penetrated into the very

602

heart of the Alpuxarras, and ravaged the valleys, and sacked and burnt the towns, upon which the city depended for its supplies. Scouting parties, also, ranged the mountains behind Granada, and captured every casual convoy of provisions. The Moors became more daring, as their situation became more hopeless. Never had Ferdinand experienced such vigorous sallies and assaults. Muza, at the head of his cavalry, harassed the borders of the camp, and even penetrated into the interior, making sudden spoil and ravage, and leaving his course to be traced by the slain and wounded. To protect his camp from these assaults, Ferdinand fortified it with deep trenches and strong bulwarks. It was of a quadrangular form, divided into streets like a city, the troops being quartered in tents, and in booths constructed of bushes and branches of trees. When it was completed, Queen Isabella came in state, with all her court, and the prince and princesses, to be present at the siege. This was intended, as on former occasions, to reduce the besieged to despair, by showing the determination of the sovereigns to reside in the camp until the city should surrender. Immediately after her arrival, the queen rode forth, to survey the camp and its environs : wherever she went, she was attended by a splendid retinue ; and all the commanders vied with each other, in the pomp and ceremony with which they received her. Nothing was heard, from morning until night, but shouts and acclamations, and bursts of martial music; so that it appeared to the Moors as if a continual festival and triumph reigned in the Christian camp.

The arrival of the queen, however, and the menaced obstinacy of the siege, had no effect in damping the fire of the Moorish chivalry. Muza inspired the youthful warriors with the most devoted heroism: "We have nothing left to fight for," said he, "but the ground we stand on; when this is lost, we cease to have a country and a name."

Finding the Christian king forbore to make an attack, Muza incited his cavaliers to challenge the youthful chivalry of the Christian army to single combat, or partial skirmishes. Scarce a day passed without gallant conflicts of the kind, in sight of the city and the camp. The combatants rivaled each other in the splendor of their armor and array, as well as in the prowess of their deeds. Their contests were more like the stately ceremonials of tilts and tournaments, than the rude conflicts of the field. Ferdinand soon perceived that they animated the fiery Moors with fresh zeal and courage, while they cost the lives of many of his bravest cavaliers: he again, therefore, forbade the acceptance of any individual challenges, and ordered that all partial encounters should be avoided. The cool and stern policy of the Catholic sovereign bore hard upon the generous spirits of either army, but roused the indignation of the Moors, when they found that they were to be subdued in this inglorious manner:

" Of what avail," said they, " are chivalry and heroic valor? the crafty monarch of the Christians has no magnanimity in warfare; he seeks to subdue us through the weakness of our bodies, but shuns to encounter the courage of our souls."

# CHAPTER XCII.

### OF THE INSOLENT DEFIANCE OF TARFE THE MOOR, AND THE DARING EXPLOIT OF HERNAN PEREZ DEL PULGAR.

WHEN the Moorish knights beheld that all courteous challenges were unavailing, they sought various means to provoke the Christian warriors to the field. Sometimes a body of them, fleetly mounted, would gallop up to the skirts of the camp, and try who should hurl his lance farthest within the barriers, having his name inscribed upon it, or a label affixed, containing some taunting defiance. These bravadoes caused great irritation; still the Spanish warriors were restrained by the prohibition of the king.

Among the Moorish cavaliers was one named Tarfe, renowned for strength and daring spirit; but whose courage partook of fierce audacity, rather than chivalric heroism. In one of these sallies, when skirting the Christian camp, this arrogant Moor outstripped his companions, overleaped the barriers, and, galloping close to the royal quarters, launched his lance so far within, that it remained quivering in the earth close by the pavilions of the sovereigns. The royal guards rushed forth in pursuit, but the Moorish horsemen were already beyond the camp, and scouring in a cloud of dust for the city. Upon wresting the lance from the earth, a label was found upon it, importing that it was intended for the queen.

Nothing could equal the indignation of the Christian warriors at the insolence of the bravado, and the discourteous insult offered to the queen. Hernan Perez del Pulgar, surnamed "he of the exploits," was present, and resolved not to be outbraved by this daring infidel: "Who will stand by me," said he, "in an enterprise of desperate peril?" The Christian cavaliers well knew the hare-brained valor of Hernan, yet not one hesitated to step forward. He chose fifteen companions, all of powerful arm and dauntless heart.

His project was to penetrate Granada in the dead of the night, by a secret pass, made known to him by a Moorish renegade of the city, whom he had christened Pedro Pulgar, and who was to act as guide. They were to set fire to the Alcaiceria and other principal edifices, and then effect their retreat as best they might. At the hour appointed, the adventurous troop set forth provided with combustibles. The renegade led them silently to a drain or channel of the river Darro, up which they proceeded cautiously, single file, until they halted under a bridge near the royal gate. Here dismounting, Pulgar stationed six of his companions to remain silent and motionless and keep guard, while followed by the rest, and still guided by the renegade, he continued up the drain or channel of the Darro, which passes under a part of the city, and was thus enabled to make his way undiscovered into the streets. All was dark and silent. At the command of Pulgar, the renegade led him to the principal mosque. Here the cavalier, pious as brave, threw himself on his knees, and drawing forth a parchment scroll on which was inscribed in large letters AVE MARIA, nailed it to the door of the mosque, thus converting the heathen edifice into a Christian chapel, and dedicating it to the blessed Virgin. This done, he hastened to the Alcaiceria to set it in a blaze. The combustibles were all placed, but Tristan de Montemayor, who had charge of the firebrand, had carelessly left it at the door of the mosque. It was too late to return there. Pulgar was endeavoring to strike fire with flint and steel into the raveled end of a cord, when he was startled by the approach of the Moorish guard going the rounds. His hand was on his sword in an instant. Seconded by his brave companions, he assailed the astonished Moors and put them to flight. In a little while the whole city resounded with alarms, soldiers were hurrying through the streets in every direction; but Pulgar, guided by the renegade, made good his retreat by the channel of the Darro, to his companions at the bridge, and all mounting their horses, spurred back to the camp. The Moors were at a loss to imagine the meaning of this wild and apparently fruitless assault; but great was their exas-

peration, on the following day, when the trophy of hardihood and prowess, the "AVE · MARIA," was discovered
thus elevated in bravado in the very centre of the city.
The mosque thus boldly sanctified by Hernan del Pulgar
was actually consecrated into a cathedral, after the capture of Granada.*

* The account here given of the exploit of Hernan del Pulgar, differs
from that given in the first edition, and is conformable to the record of
the fact in a manuscript called "*The House of Salar*," existing in the
library of Salazar, and cited by Alcantara in his *History of Granada*.

In commemoration of this daring feat of Pulgar, the Emperor Charles
V., in after years, conferred on that cavalier, and on his descendants, the
marquesies of Salar, the privilege of sitting in the choir during high mass,
and assigned as the place of sepulture of Pulgar himself, the identical
spot where he kneeled to affix the sacred scroll; and his tomb is still held
in great veneration. This Hernan Perez del Pulgar was a man of letters,
as well as arms, and inscribed to Charles V. a summary of the achievements of Gonsalvo of Cordova, surnamed the Great Captain, who had
been one of his comrades in arms. He is often confounded with Hernando del Pulgar, historian and secretary to Queen Isabella.—See note to
Pulgar's *Chron. of the Catholic Sovereigns*, part 3, c. iii. edit. Valencia,
1780.

39

# CHAPTER XCIII.

HOW QUEEN ISABELLA TOOK A VIEW OF THE CITY OF GRANADA—AND HOW
HER CURIOSITY COST THE LIVES OF MANY CHRISTIANS AND MOORS.

HE royal encampment lay so distant from Gra_
nada, that the general aspect of the city only
could be seen, as it rose gracefully from the
vega, covering the sides of the hills with palaces and
towers. Queen Isabella had expressed an earnest desire
to behold, nearer at hand, a city whose beauty was so
renowned throughout the world; and the marques of
Cadiz, with his accustomed courtesy, prepared a great
military escort and guard, to protect her and the ladies
of the court, while they enjoyed this perilous gratification.

On the morning of June the 18th, a magnificent and
powerful train issued from the Christian camp. The
advanced guard was composed of legions of cavalry,
heavily armed, looking like moving masses of polished
steel. Then came the king and queen, with the prince
and princesses, and the ladies of the court, surrounded
by the royal body-guard, sumptuously arrayed, composed
of the sons of the most illustrious houses of Spain; after

these was the rear-guard, a powerful force of horse and foot; for the flower of the army sallied forth that day. The Moors gazed with fearful admiration at this glorious pageant, wherein the pomp of the court was mingled with the terrors of the camp. It moved along in radiant line, across the vega, to the melodious thunders of martial music; while banner and plume, and silken scarf, and rich brocade, gave a gay and gorgeous relief to the grim visage of iron war, that lurked beneath.

The army moved towards the hamlet of Zubia, built on the skirts of the mountain to the left of Granada, and commanding a view of the Alhambra, and the most beautiful quarter of the city. As they approached the hamlet, the marques of Villena, the Count Ureña, and Don Alonzo de Aguilar filed off with their battalions, and were soon seen glittering along the side of the mountain above the village. In the meantime the marques of Cadiz, the count de Tendilla, the count de Cabra, and Don Alonzo Fernandez, senior of Alcaudrete and Montemayor, drew up their forces in battle array on the plain below the hamlet, presenting a living barrier of loyal chivalry between the sovereigns and the city.

Thus securely guarded, the royal party alighted, and, entering one of the houses of the hamlet, which had been prepared for their reception, enjoyed a full view of the city from its terraced roof. The ladies of the court gazed with delight at the red towers of the Alhambra, rising from amid shady groves, anticipating the time when the Catholic sovereigns should be enthroned within its walls, and its courts shine with the splendor of Spanish chivalry. "The reverend prelates and holy friars, who always surrounded the queen, looked with serene satisfaction," says Fray Antonio Agapida, "at this modern Babylon, enjoying the triumph that awaited them, when those mosques and minarets should be converted into churches, and goodly priests and bishops should succeed to the infidel alfaquis."

When the Moors beheld the Christians thus drawn forth in full array in the plain, they supposed it was to offer battle, and hesitated not to accept it. In a little while the queen beheld a body of Moorish cavalry pouring into the vega, the riders managing their fleet and fiery steeds with admirable address. They were richly armed, and clothed in the most brilliant colors, and the caparisons of their steeds flamed with gold and embroidery. This was the favorite squadron of Muza, composed of the flower of the youthful cavaliers of Granada. Others succeeded, some heavily armed, others *à la gineta*, with lance and buckler; and lastly came the legions of foot-soldiers, with arquebus and cross-bow, and spear and scimetar.

When the queen saw this army issuing from the city, she sent to the marques of Cadiz, and forbade any attack upon the enemy, or the acceptance of any challenge to a skirmish; for she was loth that her curiosity should cost the life of a single human being.

The marques promised to obey, though sorely against his will; and it grieved the spirit of the Spanish cavaliers to be obliged to remain with sheathed swords while bearded by the foe. The Moors could not comprehend the meaning of this inaction of the Christians, after having apparently invited a battle. They sallied several times from their ranks, and approached near enough to discharge their arrows; but the Christians were immovable. Many of the Moorish horsemen galloped close to the Christian ranks, brandishing their lances and scimetars, and defying various cavaliers to single combat; but Ferdinand had rigorously prohibited all duels of this kind, and they dared not transgress his orders under his very eye.

Here, however, the worthy Fray Antonio Agapida, in his enthusiasm for the triumphs of the faith, records the following incident, which we fear is not sustained by any grave chronicler of the times, but rests merely on tradition, or the authority of certain poets and dramatic writers, who have perpetuated the tradition in their works. While this grim and reluctant tranquillity prevailed along the Christian line, says Agapida, there rose a mingled shout and sound of laughter near the gate of the city. A Moorish horseman, armed at all points, issued forth, followed by a rabble, who drew back as he approached the scene of danger. The Moor was more robust and brawny than was common with his countrymen. His visor was closed; he bore a huge buckler and a ponderous lance; his scimetar was of a Damascus blade, and his richly ornamented dagger was wrought by an artificer of Fez. He was known by his device to be Tarfe, the most insolent, yet valiant, of the Moslem warriors—the same who had hurled into the royal camp his lance, inscribed to the queen. As he rode slowly along in front of the army, his very steed, prancing with fiery eye and distended nostril, seemed to breathe defiance to the Christians.

But what were the feelings of the Spanish cavaliers, when they beheld, tied to the tail of his steed, and dragged in the dust, the very inscription, "AVE MARIA," which Hernan Perez del Pulgar had affixed to the door of the mosque! A burst of horror and indignation broke forth from the army. Hernan was not at hand, to maintain his previous achievement; but one of his young companions in arms, Garcilasso de la Vega by name, putting spurs to his horse, galloped to the hamlet of Zubia, threw himself on his knees before the king, and besought permission to accept the defiance of this insolent infidel, and to revenge the insult offered to our blessed Lady. The request was too pious to be refused: Garcilasso remounted his steed; closed his helmet, graced by four sable plumes, grasped his buckler of Flemish workmanship, and his lance of matchless temper, and defied the haughty Moor in the midst of his career. A combat took place, in view of the two armies and of the Castilian court. The Moor was powerful in wielding his weapons, and dexterous in managing his steed. He was of larger frame than Garcilasso, and more completely armed; and the Christians trembled for their champion. The shock of their encounter was dreadful; their lances were shivered, and sent up splinters in the air. Garcilasso was thrown back in his saddle—his horse made a wide career before he could recover, gather up the reins, and return to the conflict. They now encountered each other with swords. The Moor circled round his opponent, as a hawk circles whereabout to make a swoop; his steed obeyed his rider with matchless quickness; at every attack of the infidel, it seemed as if the Christian knight must sink beneath his flashing scimetar. But if Garcilasso was inferior to him in power, he was superior in agility; many of his blows he parried; others he received upon his Flemish shield, which was proof against the Damascus blade. The blood streamed from numerous wounds received by either warrior. The Moor, seeing his antagonist exhausted, availed himself of his superior force, and, grappling, endeavored to wrest him from his saddle. They both fell to earth; the Moor placed his knee upon the breast of his victim, and, brandishing his dagger, aimed a blow at his throat. A cry of despair was uttered by the Christian warriors, when suddenly they beheld the Moor rolling lifeless in the dust. Garcilasso had shortened his sword, and, as his adversary raised his arm to strike, had pierced him to the heart.

"It was a singular and miraculous victory," says Fray Antonio Agapida; "but the Christian knight was armed by the sacred nature of his cause, and the holy Virgin gave him strength, like another David, to slay this gigantic champion of the Gentiles."

The laws of chivalry were observed throughout the combat—no one interfered on either side. Garcilasso now despoiled his adversary; then, rescuing the holy inscription of "AVE MARIA" from its degrading situation, he elevated it on the point of his sword, and bore it off as a signal of triumph, amidst the rapturous shouts of the Christian army.*

The sun had now reached the meridian; and the hot blood of the Moors was inflamed by its rays, and by the sight of the defeat of their champion. Muza ordered two pieces of ordnance to open a fire upon the Christians. A confusion was produced in one part of their ranks: Muza called to the chiefs of the army, "Let us waste no more time in empty challenges—let us charge upon the enemy: he who assaults has always an advantage in the combat." So saying, he rushed forward, followed by a large body of horse and foot, and charged so furiously upon the advance guard of the Christians, that he drove it in upon the battalion of the marques of Cadiz.

The gallant marques now considered himself absolved

---

* The above incident has been commemorated in old Spanish ballads, and made the subject of a scene in an old Spanish drama, ascribed by some to Lope de Vega.

from all further obedience to the queen's commands. He gave the signal to attack. "Santiago!" was shouted along the line; and he pressed forward to the encounter, with his battalion of twelve hundred lances. The other cavaliers followed his example, and the battle instantly became general.

When the king and queen beheld the armies thus rushing to the combat, they threw themselves on their knees, and implored the holy Virgin to protect her faithful warriors. The prince and princess, the ladies of the court, and the prelates and friars who were present, did the same; and the effect of the prayers of these illustrious and saintly persons, was immediately apparent. The fierceness with which the Moors had rushed to the attack was suddenly cooled; they were bold and adroit for a skirmish, but unequal to the veteran Spaniards in the open field. A panic seized upon the foot-soldiers— they turned, and took to flight. Muza and his cavaliers in vain endeavored to rally them. Some took refuge in the mountains; but the greater part fled to the city, in such confusion that they overturned and trampled upon each other. The Christians pursued them to the very gates. Upwards of two thousand were either killed, wounded, or taken prisoners; and the two pieces of ordnance were brought off as trophies of the victory. Not a Christian lance but was bathed that day in the blood of an infidel.*

* *Cura de los Palacios*, cap. 101.   Zurita, lib. 20, cap. 88.

Such was the brief but bloody action, which was known among the Christian warriors by the name of "the queen's skirmish;" for when the marques of Cadiz waited upon her majesty to apologize for breaking her commands, he attributed the victory entirely to her presence. The queen, however, insisted that it was all owing to her troops being led on by so valiant a commander. Her majesty had not yet recovered from her agitation at beholding so terrible a scene of bloodshed, though certain veterans present pronounced it as gay and gentle a skirmish as they had ever witnessed.

The gayety of this gentle pass at arms, however, was somewhat marred by a rough reverse in the evening. Certain of the Christian cavaliers, among whom were the count de Ureña, Don Alonzo Aguilar, his brother Gonsalvo of Cordova, Diego Castrillo, commander of Calatrava, and others to the number of fifty, remained in ambush near Armilla, expecting the Moors would sally forth at night to visit the scene of battle and to bury their dead. They were discovered by a Moor, who had climbed an elm-tree to reconnoiter, and hastened into the city to give notice of their ambush. Scarce had night fallen when the cavaliers found themselves surrounded by a host which in the darkness seemed innumerable. The Moors attacked them with sanguinary fury, to revenge the disgrace of the morning. The cavaliers fought to every disadvantage, overwhelmed by numbers, ignorant of the ground, perplexed by thickets and by the water-courses of the gardens, the sluices of which were all thrown open. Even retreat was difficult. The count de Ureña was surrounded and in imminent peril, from which he was saved by two of his faithful followers at the sacrifice of their lives. Several cavaliers lost their horses, and were themselves put to death in the water-courses. Gonsalvo of Cordova came near having his own illustrious career cut short in this obscure skirmish. He had fallen into a water-course, whence he extricated himself, covered with mud, and so encumbered with his armor, that he could not retreat. Inigo de Mendoza, a relative of his brother Alonzo, seeing his peril, offered him his horse: "Take it, Señor," said he, "for you cannot save yourself on foot, and I can: but should I fall, take care of my wife and daughters."

Gonsalvo accepted the devoted offer, mounted the horse, and had made but few paces, when a lamentable cry caused him to turn his head, and he beheld the faithful Mendoza transfixed by Moorish lances. The four principal cavaliers already named, with several of their followers, effected their retreat and reached the camp in safety; but this nocturnal reverse obscured the morning's triumph. Gonsalvo remembered the last words of the devoted Mendoza, and bestowed a pension on his widow and marriage portions on his daughters.*

* The account of this nocturnal affair, is from Peter Martyr, lib. 4, *Epist.* 90, and Pulgar, *Hazanas del Gran. Capitan*, page 188, as cited by Alcantara, *Hist. Granada*, tom. 4, cap. 18.

To commemorate the victory of which she had been an eye-witness, Queen Isabella afterwards erected a monastery in the village of Zubia, dedicated to St. Francisco, which still exists, and in its garden is a laurel planted by her hands.*

* The house whence the king and queen contemplated the battle, is likewise to be seen at the present day. It is the first street to the right on entering the village from the vega; and the royal arms are painted on the ceilings. It is inhabited by a worthy farmer, Francisco Garcia, who in showing the house to the writer, refused all compensation, with true Spanish pride; offering, on the contrary, the hospitalities of his mansion. His children are versed in the old Spanish ballads, about the exploits of Hernan Perez del Pulgar and Garcilasso de la Vega.

# CHAPTER XCIV.

## THE LAST RAVAGE BEFORE GRANADA.

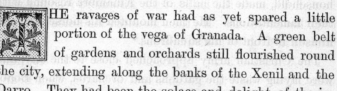HE ravages of war had as yet spared a little portion of the vega of Granada. A green belt of gardens and orchards still flourished round the city, extending along the banks of the Xenil and the Darro. They had been the solace and delight of the inhabitants in their happier days, and contributed to their sustenance in this time of scarcity. Ferdinand determined to make a final and exterminating ravage to the very walls of the city, so that there should not remain a single green thing for the sustenance of man or beast. The eighth of July was the day appointed for this act of desolation. Boabdil was informed by his spies of the intention of the Christian king, and prepared to make a desperate defense. Hernando de Baeza, a Christian, who resided with the royal family in the Alhambra as interpreter, gives in a manuscript memoir an account of the parting of Boabdil from his family as he went forth to battle. At an early hour of the appointed day, the eighth of July, he bathed and perfumed himself as the Moors of high rank were accustomed to do when they went forth

to peril their lives. Arrayed in complete armor he took leave of his mother, his wife, and his sister, in the antechamber of the tower of Comares. Ayxa la Horra, with her usual dignity, bestowed on him her benediction, and gave him her hand to kiss. It was a harder parting with his son and his daughter, who hung round him with sobs and tears; the dueñas and doncellas too, of the royal household, made the halls of the Alhambra resound with their lamentations. He then mounted his horse and put himself in front of his squadrons.*

The Christian army approached close to the city, and were laying waste the gardens and orchards, when Boabdil sallied forth, surrounded by all that was left of the flower and chivalry of Granada. There is one place where even the coward becomes brave—that sacred spot called home. What then must have been the valor of the Moors, a people always of chivalrous spirit, when the war was thus brought to their thresholds! They fought among the scenes of their loves and pleasures, the scenes of their infancy, and the haunts of their domestic life. They fought under the eyes of their wives and children, their old men and their maidens, of all that was helpless and all that was dear to them; for all Granada, crowded on tower and battlement, watched with trembling heart the fate of this eventful day.

* Hernando de Baeza, as cited by Alcantara, *Hist. Granada*, tom. 4, cap. 18.

There was not so much one battle, as a variety of battles; every garden and orchard became a scene of deadly contest; every inch of ground was disputed, with an agony of grief and valor, by the Moors; every inch of ground that the Christians advanced, they valiantly maintained; but never did they advance with severer fighting, or greater loss of blood.

The cavalry of Muza was in every part of the field; wherever it came, it gave fresh ardor to the fight. The Moorish soldier, fainting with heat, fatigue, and wounds, was roused to new life at the approach of Muza; and even he who lay gasping in the agonies of death, turned his face towards him, and faintly uttered cheers and blessings as he passed.

The Christians had by this time gained possession of various towers near the city, whence they had been annoyed by cross-bows and arquebuses. The Moors, scattered in various actions, were severely pressed. Boabdil, at the head of the cavaliers of his guard, mingling in the fight in various parts of the field, endeavored to inspirit the foot-soldiers to the combat. But the Moorish infantry was never to be depended upon. In the heat of the action, a panic seized upon them; they fled, leaving their sovereign exposed with his handful of cavaliers to an overwhelming force. Boabdil was on the point of falling into the hands of the Christians, when, wheeling round, he and his followers threw the reins on the necks of their steeds, and took refuge by dint of hoof within the walls of the city.*

Muza endeavored to retrieve the fortune of the field. He threw himself before the retreating infantry, calling upon them to turn and fight for their homes, their families, for everything sacred and dear to them. All in vain: totally broken and dismayed, they fled tumultuously for the gates. Muza would fain have kept the field with his cavalry; but this devoted band, having stood the brunt of war throughout this desperate campaign, was fearfully reduced in numbers, and many of the survivors were crippled and enfeebled by their wounds. Slowly and reluctantly, therefore, he retreated to the city, his bosom swelling with indignation and despair. Entering the gates, he ordered them to be closed, and secured with bolts and bars: for he refused to place any further confidence in the archers and arquebusiers stationed to defend them, and vowed never more to sally with foot-soldiers to the field.

In the meantime the artillery thundered from the walls, and checked all further advance of the Christians. King Ferdinand, therefore, called off his troops, and returned in triumph to the ruins of his camp, leaving the beautiful city of Granada wrapped in the smoke of her fields and gardens, and surrounded by the bodies of her slaughtered children.

* Zurita, lib. 20, cap. 88.

Such was the last sally of the Moors, in defense of their favorite city. The French ambassador, who witnessed it, was filled with wonder, at the prowess, the dexterity, and daring of the Moslems.

In truth, this whole war was an instance, memorable in history, of the most persevering resolution. For nearly ten years had the war endured—an almost uninterrupted series of disasters to the Moorish arms. Their towns had been taken, one after another, and their brethren slain or led into captivity. Yet they disputed every city and town, and fortress and castle, nay every rock itself, as if they had been inspirited by victories. Wherever they could plant foot to fight, or find wall or cliff whence to launch an arrow, they disputed their beloved country ; and now, when their capital was cut off from all relief, and a whole nation thundered at its gates, they still maintained defense, as if they hoped some miracle to interpose in their behalf. Their obstinate resistance (says an ancient chronicler) shows the grief with which they yielded up the vega, which was to them a paradise and heaven. Exerting all the strength of their arms, they embraced, as it were, that most beloved soil, from which neither wounds, nor defeats, nor death itself, could part them. They stood firm, battling for it with the united force of love and grief, never drawing back the foot while they had hands to fight, or fortune to befriend them.*

* Abarca, *Reyes de Aragon*, R. 30. cap. 3.

## CHAPTER XCV.

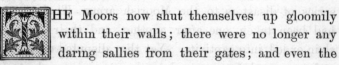

HE Moors now shut themselves up gloomily within their walls; there were no longer any daring sallies from their gates; and even the martial clangor of the drum and trumpet, which had continually resounded within that warrior city, was now seldom heard from its battlements. In the midst of this deep despondency, a signal disaster in the Christian camp, for a moment lit up a ray of hope in the bosom of the Moors.

The setting sun of a hot summer's day, on the 10th of July, shone splendidly upon the Christian camp, which was in a bustle of preparation for the next day's service, when an attack was meditated on the city. The camp made a glorious appearance. The various tents of the royal family and the attendant nobles were adorned with rich hangings, and sumptuous devices, and costly furniture; forming as it were, a little city of silk and brocade, where the pinnacles of pavilions of various gay colors, surmounted with waving standards and fluttering pennons, might vie with the domes and minarets of the capital they were besieging.

In the midst of this little gaudy metropolis, the lofty

tent of the queen domineered over the rest like a stately palace. The marques of Cadiz had courteously surrendered his own tent to the queen. It was the most complete and sumptuous in Christendom, and had been carried about with him throughout the war. In the centre rose a stately alfaneque or pavilion, in oriental taste, the rich hangings being supported by columns of lances, and ornamented with martial devices. This central pavilion, or silken tower, was surrounded by other compartments, some of painted linen lined with silk, and all separated from each other by curtains. It was one of those camp palaces which are raised and demolished in an instant, like the city of canvas which surrounds them.

As the evening advanced, the bustle in the camp subsided. Every one sought repose, preparatory to the next day's trial. The king retired early, that he might be up with the crowing of the cock, to head the destroying army in person. All stir of military preparation was hushed in the royal quarters; the very sound of minstrelsy was mute, and not the tinkling of a guitar was to be heard from the tents of the fair ladies of the court.

The queen had retired to the innermost part of her pavilion, where she was performing her orisons before a private altar; perhaps the peril to which the king might be exposed in the next day's foray, inspired her with more than usual devotion. While thus at her prayers, she was suddenly aroused by a glare of light, and wreaths of suffocating smoke. In an instant, the whole tent was in a blaze; there was a high gusty wind, which whirled the light flames from tent to tent, and wrapped the whole in one conflagration.

Isabella had barely time to save herself by instant flight. Her first thought, on being extricated from her tent, was for the safety of the king. She rushed to his tent, but the vigilant Ferdinand was already at the entrance of it. Starting from bed on the first alarm, and fancying it an assault of the enemy, he had seized his sword and buckler, and sallied forth undressed, with his cuirass upon his arm.

The late gorgeous camp was now a scene of wild confusion. The flames kept spreading from one pavilion to another, glaring upon the rich armor, and golden and silver vessels, which seemed melting in the fervent heat. Many of the soldiers had erected booths and bowers of branches, which, being dry, crackled and blazed, and added to the rapid conflagration. The ladies of the court fled, shrieking and half-dressed, from their tents. There was an alarm of drum and trumpet, and a distracted hurry about the camp of men half armed. The prince Juan had been snatched out of bed by an attendant, and conveyed to the quarters of the count de Cabra, which were at the entrance of the camp. The loyal count immediately summoned his people, and those of his cousin Don Alonzo de Montemayor, and formed a guard round the tent in which the prince was sheltered.

The idea that this was a stratagem of the Moors, soon

subsided; but it was feared they might take advantage of it, to assault the camp. The marques of Cadiz, therefore, sallied forth with three thousand horse, to check any advance from the city. As they passed along, the whole camp was a scene of hurry and consternation— some hastening to their posts, at the call of drum and trumpet; some attempting to save rich effects and glittering armor from the tents, others dragging along terrified and restive horses.

When they emerged from the camp, they found the whole firmament illuminated. The flames whirled up in long light spires, and the air was filled with sparks and cinders. A bright glare was thrown upon the city, revealing every battlement and tower. Turbaned heads were seen gazing from every roof, and armor gleamed along the walls; yet not a single warrior sallied from the gates: the Moors suspected some stratagem on the part of the Christians, and kept quietly within their walls. By degrees, the flames expired; the city faded from sight; all again became dark and quiet, and the marques of Cadiz returned with his cavalry to the camp.

When the day dawned on the Christian camp, nothing remained of that beautiful assemblage of stately pavilions, but heaps of smouldering rubbish, with helms and corselets and other furniture of war, and masses of melted gold and silver glittering among the ashes. The wardrobe of the queen was entirely destroyed, and there was an immense loss in plate, jewels, costly stuffs, and sumptuous armor of the luxurious nobles. The fire at first had been attributed to treachery, but on investigation it proved to be entirely accidental. The queen, on retiring to her prayers, had ordered her lady in attendance to remove a light burning near her couch, lest it should prevent her sleeping. Through heedlessness, the taper was placed in another part of the tent, near the hangings, which being blown against it by a gust of wind, immediately took fire.

The wary Ferdinand knew the sanguine temperament of the Moors, and hastened to prevent their deriving confidence from the night's disaster. At break of day, the drums and trumpets sounded to arms, and the Christian army issued forth from among the smoking ruins of their camp, in shining squadrons, with flaunting banners and bursts of martial melody, as though the preceding night had been a time of high festivity, instead of terror.

The Moors had beheld the conflagration with wonder and perplexity. When the day broke, and they looked towards the Christian camp, they saw nothing but a dark, smoking mass. Their scouts came in with the joyful intelligence that the whole camp was a scene of ruin. In the exultation of the moment, they flattered themselves with hopes that the catastrophe would discourage the besiegers; that as in former years, their invasion would end with the summer and they would withdraw before the autumnal rains.

The measures of Ferdinand and Isabella soon crushed

these hopes. They gave orders to build a regular city upon the site of their camp, to convince the Moors that the siege was to endure until the surrender of Granada. Nine of the principal cities of Spain were charged with this stupendous undertaking, and they emulated each other, with a zeal worthy of the cause. " It verily seems," says Fray Antonio Agapida, " as though some miracle operated to aid this pious work, so rapidly did arise a formidable city, with solid edifices, and powerful walls, and mighty towers, where lately had been seen nothing but tents and light pavilions." The city was traversed by two principal streets in form of a cross, terminating in four gates facing the four winds; and in the centre was a vast square, where the whole army might be assembled. To this city it was proposed to give the name of Isabella, so dear to the army and the nation; " but that pious princess," adds Antonio Agapida, " calling to mind the holy cause in which it was erected, gave it the name of Santa Fé (or the City of the Holy Faith); and it remains to this day, a monument of the piety and glory of the Catholic sovereigns."

Hither the merchants soon resorted, from all points. Long trains of mules were seen every day entering and departing from its gates; the streets were crowded with magazines, filled with all kinds of costly and luxurious merchandise; a scene of bustling commerce and prosperity took place, while unhappy Granada remained shut up and desolate.

# CHAPTER XCVI.

FAMINE AND DISCORD IN THE CITY.

HE besieged city now began to suffer the distress of famine. Its supplies were all cut off; a cavalgada of flocks and herds, and mules laden with money, coming to the relief of the city from the mountains of the Alpuxarras, was taken by the marques of Cadiz, and led in triumph to the camp, in sight of the suffering Moors. Autumn arrived; but the harvests had been swept from the face of the country; a rigorous winter was approaching, and the city was almost destitute of provisions. The people sank into deep despondency. They called to mind all that had been predicted by astrologers at the birth of their ill-starred sovereign, and all that had been foretold of the fate of Granada at the time of the capture of Zahara.

Boabdil was alarmed by the gathering dangers from without, and by the clamors of his starving people. He summoned a council, composed of the principal officers of the army, the alcaydes of the fortresses, the xequis or sages of the city, and the alfaquis or doctors of the faith. They assembled in the great hall of audience of the Al-

632

hambra, and despair was painted in their countenances. Boabdil demanded of them, what was to be done in the present extremity; and their answer was, "Surrender." The venerable Abul Cazim, governor of the city, represented its unhappy state: "Our granaries are nearly exhausted, and no further supplies are to be expected. The provender for the war-horses is required as sustenance for the soldiery; the very horses themselves are killed for food; of seven thousand steeds which once could be sent into the field, three hundred only remain. Our city contains two hundred thousand inhabitants, old and young, with each a mouth that calls piteously for bread."

The xequis and principal citizens declared that the people could no longer sustain the labors and sufferings of a defense: "And of what avail is our defense," said they, "when the enemy is determined to persist in the siege?—what alternative remains, but to surrender or to die?"

The heart of Boabdil was touched by this appeal, and he maintained a gloomy silence. He had cherished some faint hope of relief from the soldan of Egypt or the Barbary powers; but it was now at an end; even if such assistance were to be sent, he had no longer a seaport where it might debark. The counselors saw that the resolution of the king was shaken, and they united their voices in urging him to capitulate.

Muza alone rose in opposition: "It is yet too early,"

said he, "to talk of a surrender. Our means are not exhausted; we have yet one source of strength remaining, terrible in its effects, and which often has achieved the most signal victories—it is our despair. Let us rouse the mass of the people; let us put weapons in their hands; let us fight the enemy to the very utmost, until we rush upon the points of their lances. I am ready to lead the way into the thickest of their squadrons; and much rather would I be numbered among those who fell in the defense of Granada, than of those who survived to capitulate for her surrender!"

The words of Muza were without effect, for they were addressed to broken-spirited and heartless men, or men, perhaps, to whom sad experience had taught discretion. They were arrived at that state of public depression, when heroes and heroism are no longer regarded, and when old men and their counsels rise into importance. Boabdil el Chico yielded to the general voice; it was determined to capitulate with the Christian sovereigns; and the venerable Abul Cazim was sent forth to the camp, empowered to treat for terms.

# CHAPTER XCVII.

## CAPITULATION OF GRANADA.

HE old governor Abul Cazim was received with great courtesy by Ferdinand and Isabella, who being informed of the purport of his embassy, granted the besieged a truce of sixty days from the 5th of October, and appointed Gonsalvo of Cordova, and Fernando de Zafra, the secretary of the king, to treat about the terms of surrender with such commissioners as might be named by Boabdil. The latter on his part named Abul Cazim, Aben Comixa the vizier, and the grand cadi. As a pledge of good faith, Boabdil gave his son in hostage, who was taken to Moclin, where he was treated with the greatest respect and attention by the good count de Tendilla, as general of the frontier.

The commissioners on both parts held repeated conferences in secret in the dead of the night, at the village of Churriana—those who first arrived at the place of meeting giving notice to the others by signal-fires, or by means of spies. After many debates and much difficulty, the capitulation was signed on the 25th of November. According to this, the city was to be delivered up.

with all its gates, towers, and fortresses, within sixty days.

All Christian captives should be liberated, without ransom.

Boabdil and his principal cavaliers should perform the act of homage, and take an oath of fealty to the Castilian crown.

The Moors of Granada should become subjects of the Spanish sovereigns, retaining their possessions, their arms and horses, and yielding up nothing but their artillery. They should be protected in the exercise of their religion, and governed by their own laws, administered by cadis of their own faith, under governors appointed by the sovereigns. They should be exempted from tribute for three years, after which term they should pay the same that they had been accustomed to render to their native monarchs.

Those who chose to depart for Africa within three years, should be provided with a passage for themselves and their effects, free of charge, from whatever port they should prefer.

For the fulfillment of these articles, five hundred hostages from the principal families were required, previous to the surrender, who should be treated with great respect and distinction by the Christians, and subsequently restored. The son of the king of Granada, and all other hostages in possession of the Castilian sovereigns, were to be restored at the same time.

Such are the main articles affecting the public weal, which were agreed upon after much discussion by the mixed commission. There were other articles, however, secretly arranged, which concerned the royal family. These secured to Boabdil, to his wife Morayma, his mother Ayxa, his brothers, and to Zoraya, the widow of Muley Abul Hassan, all the landed possessions, houses, mills, baths, and other hereditaments which formed the royal patrimony, with the power of selling them personally or by agent, at any and all times. To Boabdil was secured, moreover, his wealthy estates, both in and out of Granada, and to him and his decendants in perpetuity, the lordships of various towns and lands and fertile valleys in the Alpuxarras, forming a petty sovereignty. In addition to all which it was stipulated, that, on the day of surrender, he should receive thirty thousand castellanos of gold.*

The conditions of the surrender being finally agreed upon by the commissioners, Abul Cazim proceeded to the royal camp at Sante Fé, where they were signed by Ferdinand and Isabella; he then returned to Granada, accompanied by Fernando de Zafra, the royal secretary, to have the same ratified also by the Moorish king. Boabdil assembled his council, and with a dejected countenance laid before it the articles of capitulation as the best that could be obtained from the besieging foe.

* Alcantara, tom. 4, cap. 18.

When the members of the council found the awful moment arrived when they were to sign and seal the perdition of their empire, and blot themselves out as a nation, all firmness deserted them, and many gave way to tears. Muza alone retained an unaltered mien: "Leave, seniors," cried he, "this idle lamentation to helpless women and children: we are men—we have hearts, not to shed tender tears, but drops of blood. I see the spirit of the people so cast down, that it is impossible to save the kingdom. Yet there still remains an alternative for noble minds—a glorious death! Let us die defending our liberty, and avenging the woes of Granada. Our mother earth will receive her children into her bosom, safe from the chains and oppressions of the conqueror; or, should any fail a sepulchre to hide his remains, he will not want a sky to cover him. Allah forbid it should be said the nobles of Granada feared to die in her defense!"

Muza ceased to speak, and a dead silence reigned in the assembly. Boabdil looked anxiously round, and scanned every face; but he read in all the anxiety of care-worn men, in whose hearts enthusiasm was dead, and who had grown callous to every chivalrous appeal. "Allah Achbar!" exclaimed he; "there is no God but God, and Mahomet is his prophet! We have no longer forces in the city and the kingdom to resist our powerful enemies. It is in vain to struggle against the will of Heaven. Too surely was it written in the book of fate, that I should be unfortunate, and the kingdom expire under my rule."

"Allah Achbar!" echoed the viziers and alfaquis; "the will of God be done!" So they all agreed with the king, that these evils were preordained; that it was hopeless to contend with them; and that the terms offered by the Castilian monarchs were as favorable as could be expected.

When Muza heard them assent to the treaty of surrender, he rose in violent indignation: "Do not deceive yourselves," cried he, "nor think the Christians will be faithful to their promises, or their king as magnanimous in conquest as he has been victorious in war. Death is the least we have to fear. It is the plundering and sacking of our city, the profanation of our mosques, the ruin of our homes, the violation of our wives and daughters, cruel oppression, bigoted intolerance, whips and chains, the dungeon, the fagot, and the stake—such are the miseries and indignities we shall see and suffer; at least, those groveling souls will see and suffer them, who now shrink from an honorable death. For my part, by Allah, I will never witness them!"

With these words he left the council-chamber, and passed gloomily through the Court of Lions, and the outer halls of the Alhambra, without deigning to speak to the obsequious courtiers who attended in them. He repaired to his dwelling, armed himself at all points, mounted his favorite war-horse, and, issuing from the city by the gate of Elvira, was never seen or heard of more.*

* Conde, pt. 4.

## CHAPTER XCVIII.

### COMMOTIONS IN GRANADA.

HE capitulation for the surrender of Granada was signed on the 25th of November, 1491, and produced a sudden cessation of those hostilities which had raged for so many years. Christian and Moor might now be seen mingling courteously on the banks of the Xenil and the Darro, where to have met a few days previous would have produced a scene of sanguinary contest. Still, as the Moors might be suddenly roused to defense, if, within the allotted term of sixty days, succors should arrive from abroad; and as they were at all times a rash, inflammable people, the wary Ferdinand maintained a vigilant watch upon the city, and permitted no supplies of any kind to enter. His garrisons in the seaports, and his cruisers in the Straits of Gibraltar, were ordered likewise to guard against any relief from the grand soldan of Egypt or the princes of Barbary. There was no need of such precautions. Those powers were either too much engrossed by their own wars, or too much daunted by the success of the Spanish arms, to interfere in a desperate cause; and the unfortunate Moors of Granada were abandoned to their fate.

The month of December had nearly passed away; the famine became extreme, and there was no hope of any favorable event within the term specified in the capitulation. Boabdil saw, that to hold out to the end of the allotted time would but be to protract the miseries of his people. With the consent of his council, he determined to surrender the city on the sixth of January. He accordingly sent his grand vizier, Yusef Aben Comixa, to King Ferdinand, to make known his intention; bearing him, at the same time, a present of a magnificent scimetar, and two Arabian steeds superbly caparisoned.

The unfortunate Boabdil was doomed to meet with trouble, to the end of his career. The very next day, the santon or dervise, Hamet Aben Zarrax, the same who had uttered prophecies and excited commotion on former occasions, suddenly made his appearance. Whence he came no one knew; it was rumored that he had been in the mountains of the Alpuxarras, and on the coast of Barbary, endeavoring to rouse the Moslems to the relief of Granada. He was reduced to a skeleton; his eyes glowed like coals in their sockets, and his speech was little better than frantic raving. He harangued the populace, in the streets and squares; inveighed against the capitulation, denounced the king and nobles as Moslems only in name, and called upon the people to sally

41

forth against the unbelievers, for that Allah had decreed them a signal victory.

Upwards of twenty thousand of the populace seized their arms, and paraded the streets with shouts and outcries. The shops and houses were shut up; the king himself did not dare to venture forth, but remained a kind of prisoner in the Alhambra.

The turbulent multitude continued roaming and shouting and howling about the city, during the day and a part of the night. Hunger, and a wintry tempest, tamed their frenzy; and when morning came, the enthusiast who had led them on had disappeared. Whether he had been disposed of by the emissaries of the king, or by the leading men of the city, is not known: his disappearance remains a mystery.*

Boabdil now issued forth from the Alhambra, attended by his principal nobles, and harangued the populace. He set forth the necessity of complying with the capitulation, from the famine that reigned in the city, the futility of defense, and from the hostages having already been delivered into the hands of the besiegers.

In the dejection of his spirits, the unfortunate Boabdil attributed to himself the miseries of the country. "It was my crime in ascending the throne in rebellion against my father," said he mournfully, "which has brought these woes upon the kingdom; but Allah has

* Mariana.

grievously visited my sins upon my head. For your sake, my people, I have now made this treaty, to protect you from the sword, your little ones from famine, your wives and daughters from outrage ; and to secure you in the enjoyment of your properties, your liberties, your laws, and your religion, under a sovereign of happier destinies than the ill-starred Boabdil."

The versatile population were touched by the humility of their sovereign—they agreed to adhere to the capitulation, and there was even a faint shout of "Long live Boabdil the Unfortunate !" and they all returned to their homes in perfect tranquillity.

Boabdil immediately sent missives to King Ferdinand, apprising him of these events, and of his fears lest further delay should produce new tumults. The vizier Yusef Aben Comixa was again the agent between the monarchs. He was received with unusual courtesy and attention by Ferdinand and Isabella, and it was arranged between them that the surrender should take place on the second day of January instead of the sixth. A new difficulty now arose in regard to the ceremonial of surrender. The haughty Ayxa la Horra, whose pride rose with the decline of her fortunes, declared that, as sultana mother, she would never consent that her son should stoop to the humiliation of kissing the hand of his conquerors, and, unless this part of the ceremonial were modified, she would find means to resist a surrender accompanied by such indignities.

Aben Comixa was sorely troubled by this opposition. He knew the high spirit of the indomitable Ayxa, and her influence over her less heroic son, and wrote an urgent letter on the subject to his friend, the count de Tendilla. The latter imparted the circumstance to the Christian sovereigns; a council was called on the matter. Spanish pride and etiquette were obliged to bend in some degree to the haughty spirit of a woman. It was agreed that Boabdil should sally forth on horseback, that on approaching the Spanish sovereigns he should make a slight movement as if about to draw his foot from the stirrup and dismount, but would be prevented from doing so by Ferdinand, who should treat him with a respect due to his dignity and elevated birth. The count de Tendilla dispatched a messenger with this arrangement; and the haughty scruples of Ayxa la Horra were satisfied.*

* Salazar de Mendoza. *Chron. del Gran. Cardinal*, lib. 1, cap. 69, p. 1. Mondajar, *His.* MS. as cited by Alcantara, tom. 4, cap. 18.

CONQUEST OF GRANADA.

## CHAPTER XCIX.

THE night preceding the surrender was a night of doleful lamentings, within the walls of the Alhambra; for the household of Boabdil were preparing to take a last farewell of that delightful abode. All the royal treasures and most precious effects were hastily packed upon mules; the beautiful apartments were despoiled, with tears and wailings, by their own inhabitants. Before the dawn of day, a mournful cavalcade moved obscurely out of a postern-gate of the Alhambra, and departed through one of the most retired quarters of the city. It was composed of the family of the unfortunate Boabdil, which he sent off thus privately, that they might not be exposed to the eyes of scoffers, or the exultation of the enemy. The mother of Boabdil, the sultana Ayxa la Horra, rode on in silence, with dejected yet dignified demeanor; but his wife Morayma, and all the females of his household, gave way to loud lamentations, as they looked back upon their favorite abode, now a mass of gloomy towers behind them. They were attended by the ancient domestics of the household,

645

and by a small guard of veteran Moors, loyally attached to the fallen monarch, and who would have sold their lives dearly in defense of his family. The city was yet buried in sleep, as they passed through its silent streets. The guards at the gate shed tears, as they opened it for their departure. They paused not, but proceeded along the banks of the Xenil on the road that leads to the Alpuxarras, until they arrived at a hamlet at some distance from the city, where they halted, and waited until they should be joined by King Boabdil.

The night which had passed so gloomily in the sumptuous halls of the Alhambra, had been one of joyful anticipation in the Christian camp. In the evening proclamation had been made that Granada was to be surrendered on the following day, and the troops were all ordered to assemble at an early hour under their several banners. The cavaliers, pages, and esquires were all charged to array themselves in their richest and most splendid style, for the occasion; and even the royal family determined to lay by the mourning they had recently assumed for the sudden death of the prince of Portugal, the husband of the princess Isabella. In a clause of the capitulation it had been stipulated that the troops destined to take possession, should not traverse the city, but should ascend to the Alhambra by a road opened for the purpose outside of the walls. This was to spare the feelings of the afflicted inhabitants, and to prevent any angry collision between them and their conquerors. So rigorous was Ferdinand in enforcing this precaution, that the soldiers were prohibited under pain of death from leaving the ranks to enter into the city.

The rising sun had scarce shed his rosy beams upon the snowy summits of the Sierra Nevada, when three signal guns boomed heavily from the lofty fortress of the Alhambra. It was the concerted sign that all was ready for the surrender. The Christian army forthwith poured out of the city, or rather camp of Santa Fé, and advanced across the vega. The king and queen, with the prince and princess, the dignitaries and ladies of the court, took the lead, accompanied by the different orders of monks and friars, and surrounded by the royal guards splendidly arrayed. The procession moved slowly forward, and paused at the village of Armilla, at the distance of half a league from the city.

In the meantime, the grand cardinal of Spain, Don Pedro Gonzalez de Mendoza, escorted by three thousand foot and a troop of cavalry, and accompanied by the commander Don Gutierrez de Cardenas, and a number of prelates and hidalgos, crossed the Xenil and proceeded in the advance, to ascend to the Alhambra and take possession of that royal palace and fortress. The road which had been opened for the purpose led by the Puerta de los Molinos, or Gate of Mills, up a defile to the esplanade on the summit of the Hill of Martyrs. At the approach of this detachment, the Moorish king sallied forth from a postern gate of the Alhambra, having left his vizier Yusef Aben Comixa to deliver up the palace. The gate by which he sallied passed through a lofty tower of the outer wall, called the Tower of the Seven Floors (de los siete suelos). He was accompanied by fifty cavaliers, and approached the grand cardinal on foot. The latter immediately alighted, and advanced to meet him with the utmost respect. They stepped aside a few paces, and held a brief conversation in an undertone, when Boabdil, raising his voice, exclaimed, "Go, Señor, and take possession of those fortresses in the name of the powerful sovereigns, to whom God has been pleased to deliver them in reward of their great merits, and in punishment of the sins of the Moors." The grand cardinal sought to console him in his reverses, and offered him the use of his own tent during any time he might sojourn in the camp. Boabdil thanked him for the courteous offer, adding some words of melancholy import, and then taking leave of him gracefully, passed mournfully on to meet the Catholic sovereigns, descending to the vega by the same road by which the cardinal had come. The latter, with the prelates and cavaliers who attended him, entered the Alhambra, the gates of which were thrown wide open by the alcayde Aben Comixa. At the same time the Moorish guards yielded up their arms, and the towers and battlements were taken possession of by the Christian troops.

While these transactions were passing in the Alhambra and its vicinity, the sovereigns remained with their retinue and guards near the village of Armilla, their eyes fixed on the towers of the royal fortress, watching for the appointed signal of possession. The time that had elapsed since the departure of the detachment seemed to them more than necessary for the purpose, and the anxious mind of Ferdinand began to entertain doubts of some commotion in the city. At length they saw the silver cross, the great standard of this crusade, elevated on the Torre de la Vela, or Great Watch-Tower, and sparkling in the sunbeams. This was done by Hernando de Talavera, bishop of Avila. Beside it was planted the pennon of the glorious apostle St. James, and a great shout of "Santiago! Santiago!" rose throughout the army. Lastly was reared the royal standard by the king of arms, with the shout of "Castile! Castile! For King Ferdinand and Queen Isabella!" The words were echoed by the whole army, with acclamations that resounded across the vega. At sight of these signals of possession, the sovereigns sank upon their knees, giving thanks to God for this great triumph; the whole assembled host followed their example, and the choristers of the royal chapel broke forth into the solemn anthem of "*Te Deum laudamus.*"

The king now advanced with a splendid escort of cavalry and the sound of trumpets, until he came to a small mosque near the banks of the Xenil, and not far from the foot of the Hill of Martyrs, which edifice remains to the present day consecrated as the hermitage of St. Sebastian. Here he beheld the unfortunate king of Granada approaching on horseback, at the head of his slender retinue. Boabdil as he drew near made a movement to dismount, but, as had previously been concerted, Ferdinand prevented him. He then offered to kiss the king's hand, which, according to arrangement, was likewise declined, whereupon he leaned forward and kissed the king's right arm; at the same time he delivered the keys of the city with an air of mingled melancholy and resignation: "These keys," said he, "are the last relics of the Arabian empire in Spain: thine, O king, are our trophies, our kingdom, and our person. Such is the will of God! Receive them with the clemency thou hast promised, and which we look for at thy hands."*

King Ferdinand restrained his exultation into an air of serene magnanimity. "Doubt not our promises," replied he, "nor that thou shalt regain from our friendship the prosperity of which the fortune of war has deprived thee."

Being informed that Don Inigo Lopez de Mendoza, the good count of Tendilla, was to be governor of the city, Boabdil drew from his finger a gold ring set with a precious stone, and presented it to the count. "With this ring," said he, "Granada has been governed; take

*Abarca, *Anales de Aragon*, Reg 30, cap. 3.

it and govern with it, and God make you more fortunate than I." *

He then proceeded to the village of Armilla, where the queen Isabella remained with her escort and attendants. The queen, like her husband, declined all acts of homage, and received him with her accustomed grace and benignity. She at the same time delivered to him his son, who had been held as a hostage for the fulfillment of the capitulation. Boabdil pressed his child to his bosom with tender emotion, and they seemed mutually endeared to each other by their misfortunes.†

Having rejoined his family, the unfortunate Boabdil continued on towards the Alpuxarras, that he might not behold the entrance of the Christians into his capital. His devoted band of cavaliers followed him in gloomy silence; but heavy sighs burst from their bosoms, as shouts of joy and strains of triumphant music were borne on the breeze from the victorious army.

Having rejoined his family, Boabdil set forward with a heavy heart for his allotted residence in the Valley of Purchena. At two leagues' distance, the cavalcade, winding into the skirts of the Alpuxarras, ascended an eminence, commanding the last view of Granada. As they

* This ring remained in the possession of the descendants of the count until the death of the marques Don Inigo, the last male heir, who died in Malaga without children, in 1656. The ring was then lost through inadvertence and ignorance of its value, Doña Maria, the sister of the marques, being absent in Madrid. Alcantara, lib. 4, cap. 18.

† Zurita, *Anales de Aragon*, lib. 20, cap. 92.

arrived at this spot, the Moors paused involuntarily, to take a farewell gaze at their beloved city, which a few steps more would shut from their sight forever. Never had it appeared so lovely in their eyes. The sunshine, so bright in that transparent climate, lit up each tower and minaret, and rested gloriously upon the crowning battlements of the Alhambra; while the vega spread its enameled bosom of verdure below, glistening with the silver windings of the Xenil. The Moorish cavaliers gazed with a silent agony of tenderness and grief upon that delicious abode, the scene of their loves and pleasures. While they yet looked, a light cloud of smoke burst forth from the citadel, and presently a peal of artillery, faintly heard, told that the city was taken possession of, and the throne of the Moslem kings was lost forever. The heart of Boabdil, softened by misfortunes and overcharged with grief, could no longer contain itself: "Allah Achbar! God is great!" said he; but the words of resignation died upon his lips, and he burst into tears.

His mother, the intrepid Ayxa, was indignant at his weakness: "You do well," said she, "to weep like a woman for what you failed to defend like a man!"

The vizier Aben Comixa endeavored to console his royal master. "Consider, Señor," said he, "that the most signal misfortunes often render men as renowned as the most prosperous achievements, provided they sustain them with magnanimity."

The unhappy monarch, however, was not to be consoled; his tears continued to flow. "Allah Achbar!" exclaimed he, "when did misfortunes ever equal mine?"

From this circumstance, the hill, which is not far from Padul, took the name of Feg Allah Achbar, but the point of view commanding the last prospect of Granada is known among Spaniards by the name of *El ultimo suspiro del Moro*, or, "The last sigh of the Moor."

## CHAPTER C.

HOW THE CASTILIAN SOVEREIGNS TOOK POSSESSION OF GRANADA.

UEEN ISABELLA having joined the king, the royal pair, followed by a triumphant host, passed up the road by the Hill of Martyrs, and thence to the main entrance of the Alhambra. The grand cardinal awaited them under the lofty arch of the great Gate of Justice, accompanied by Don Gutierrez de Cardenas and Aben Comixa. Here King Ferdinand gave the keys which had been delivered up to him into the hands of the queen; they were passed successively into the hands of the prince Juan, the grand cardinal, and finally into those of the count de Tendilla, in whose custody they remained, that brave cavalier having been named alcayde of the Alhambra, and captain-general of Granada.

The sovereigns did not remain long in the Alhambra on this first visit, but leaving a strong garrison there under the count de Tendilla, to maintain tranquillity in the palace and the subjacent city, returned to the camp at Santa Fé.

We must not omit to mention a circumstance attending the surrender of the city, which spoke eloquently to the hearts of the victors. As the royal army had advanced in all the pomp of courtly and chivalrous array, a procession of a different kind came forth to meet it. This was composed of more than five hundred Christian captives, many of whom had languished for years in Moorish dungeons. Pale and emaciated, they came clanking their chains in triumph, and shedding tears of joy. They were received with tenderness by the sovereigns. The king hailed them as good Spaniards, as men loyal and brave, as martyrs to the holy cause; the queen distributed liberal relief among them with her own hands, and they passed on before the squadrons of the army, singing hymns of jubilee.*

The sovereigns forbore to enter the city until it should be fully occupied by their troops, and public tranquillity insured. All this was done under the vigilant superintendence of the count de Tendilla, assisted by the marques of Villena; and the glistening of Christian helms and lances along the walls and bulwarks, and the standards of the faith and of the realm flaunting from the towers, told that the subjugation of the city was complete. The proselyte prince, Cid Hiaya, now known by the Christian appellation of Don Pedro de Granada Vanegas,† was appointed chief alguazil of the city, and had

* Abarca, lib. sup. Zurita, etc.

† Cid Hiaya was made cavalier of the order of Santiago. He and his son intermarried with the Spanish nobility, and the marqueses of Compo-

charge of the Moorish inhabitants; and his son, lately the prince Alnayer, now Alonzo de Granada Vanegas, was appointed admiral of the fleets.

It was on the sixth of January, the day of kings and festival of the Epiphany, that the sovereigns made their triumphal entry with grand military parade. First advanced, we are told, a splendid escort of cavaliers in burnished armor, and superbly mounted. Then followed the prince Juan, glittering with jewels and diamonds; on each side of him, mounted on mules, rode the grand cardinal, clothed in purple, Fray Hernando de Talavera, bishop of Arla, and the archbishop elect of Granada. To these succeeded the queen and her ladies, and the king, managing in galliard style, say the Spanish chronicles, a proud and mettlesome steed (*un caballo arrogante*). Then followed the army in shining columns, with flaunting banners and the inspiring clamor of military music. The king and queen (says the worthy Fray Antonio Agapida) looked, on this occasion, as more than mortal: the venerable ecclesiastics, to whose advice and zeal this glorious conquest ought in a great measure to be attributed, moved along with hearts swelling with holy exultation, but with chastened and downcast looks of edifying humility; while the hardy warriors, in tossing plumes and shining steel, seemed elevated with a stern joy at finding

tejar are among their descendants. Their portraits, and the portraits of their grandsons, are to be seen in one of the rooms of the Generalife at Granada.

themselves in possession of this object of so many toils
and perils. As the streets resounded with the tramp
of steeds and swelling peals of music, the Moors buried
themselves in the deepest recesses of their dwellings.
There they bewailed in secret the fallen glory of their
race, but suppressed their groans, lest they should be
heard by their enemies, and increase their triumph.

The royal procession advanced to the principal mosque,
which had been consecrated as a cathedral. Here the
sovereigns offered up prayers and thanksgivings, and the
choir of the royal chapel chanted a triumphant anthem,
in which they were joined by all the courtiers and cavaliers. Nothing (says Fray Antonio Agapida) could exceed the thankfulness to God of the pious King Ferdinand, for having enabled him to eradicate from Spain the
empire and name of that accursed heathen race, and for
the elevation of the cross in that city wherein the impious doctrines of Mahomet had so long been cherished.
In the fervor of his spirit, he supplicated from Heaven a
continuance of its grace, and that this glorious triumph
might be perpetuated.\* The prayer of the pious monarch was responded by the people, and even his enemies
were for once convinced of his sincerity.

When the religious ceremonies were concluded, the
court ascended to the stately palace of the Alhambra,
and entered by the great Gate of Justice. The halls

---

\* The words of Fray Antonio Agapida are little more than an echo of
those of the worthy Jesuit father Mariana (lib. 25, cap. 18).

42

lately occupied by turbaned infidels now rustled with
stately dames and Christian courtiers, who wandered
with eager curiosity over this far-famed palace, admiring
its verdant courts and gushing fountains, its halls decorated with elegant arabesques and storied with inscriptions, and the splendor of its gilded and brilliantly
painted ceilings.

It had been a last request of the unfortunate Boabdil,
and one which showed how deeply he felt the transition
of his fate, that no person might be permitted to enter or
depart by the gate of the Alhambra, through which he
had sallied forth to surrender his capital. His request
was granted; the portal was closed up, and remains so to
the present day—a mute memorial of that event.*

The Spanish sovereigns fixed their throne in the pres-

---

* Garibay, *Compend. Hist.* lib. 40, cap. 42. The existence of this gateway, and the story connected with it, are perhaps known to few; but were
identified, in the researches made to verify this history. The gateway is
at the bottom of a tower, at some distance from the main body of the Alhambra. The tower has been rent and ruined by gunpowder, at the time
when the fortress was evacuated by the French. Great masses lie around
half covered by vines and fig-trees. A poor man, by the name of Matteo
Ximenes, who lives in one of the halls among the ruins of the Alhambra,
where his family has resided for many generations, pointed out to the
author the gateway, still closed up with stones. He remembered to have
heard his father and grandfather say, that it had always been stopped up,
and that out of it King Boabdil had gone when he surrendered Granada.
The route of the unfortunate king may be traced thence across the garden of the convent of Los Martyros, and down a ravine beyond, through
a street of Gypsy caves and hovels, by the gate of Los Molinos, and so on
to the Hermitage of St. Sebastian. None but an antiquarian, however,
will be able to trace it, unless aided by the humble historian of the place,
Matteo Ximenes.

ence-chamber of the palace, so long the seat of Moorish royalty. Hither the principal inhabitants of Granada repaired, to pay them homage and kiss their hands in token of vassalage; and their example was followed by deputies from all the towns and fortresses of the Alpuxarras, which had not hitherto submitted.

Thus terminated the war of Granada, after ten years of incessant fighting; equaling (says Fray Antonio Agapida) the far-famed siege of Troy in duration, and ending, like that, in the capture of the city. Thus ended also the dominion of the Moors in Spain, having endured seven hundred and seventy-eight years, from the memorable defeat of Roderick, the last of the Goths, on the banks of the Guadalete. The authentic Agapida is uncommonly particular in fixing the epoch of this event. This great triumph of our holy Catholic faith, according to his computation, took place in the beginning of January, in the year of our Lord 1492, being 3,655 years from the population of Spain by the patriarch Tubal; 3,797 from the general deluge; 5,453 from the creation of the world, according to Hebrew calculation; and in the month Rabic, in the eight hundred and ninety-seventh year of the Hegira, or flight of Mahomet; whom may God confound! saith the pious Agapida!

ence-chamber of the palace, so long the seat of Moorish royalty. Hither the principal inhabitants of Granada repaired, to pay them homage and kiss their hands in token of vassalage; and their example was followed by deputies from all the towns and fortresses of the Alpuxarras, which had not hitherto submitted.

Thus terminated the war of Granada, after ten years of incessant fighting; equaling (says Fray Antonio Agapida) the far-famed siege of Troy in duration, and ending, like that, in the capture of the city. Thus ended also the dominion of the Moors in Spain, having endured seven hundred and seventy-eight years, from the memorable defeat of Roderick, the last of the Goths, on the banks of the Guadalete. The authentic Agapida is uncommonly particular in fixing the epoch of this event. This great triumph of our holy Catholic faith, according to his computation, took place in the beginning of January, in the year of our Lord 1492, being 3,655 years from the population of Spain by the patriarch Tubal; 3,797 from the general deluge; 5,453 from the creation of the world, according to Hebrew calculation; and in the month Rabic, in the eight hundred and ninety-seventh year of the Hegira, or flight of Mahomet; whom may God confound! saith the pious Agapida!

# APPENDIX.

THE Chronicle of the Conquest of Granada is finished, but the reader may be desirous of knowing the subsequent fortunes of some of the principal personages.

The unfortunate Boabdil retired with his mother, his wife, his son, his sister, his vizier, and bosom counselor Aben Comixa, and many other relatives and friends, to the Valley of Purchena, where a small, but fertile territory had been allotted him, comprising several towns of the Alpuxarras, with all their rights and revenues. Here, surrounded by obedient vassals, devoted friends, and a loving family, and possessed of wealth sufficient to enable him to indulge in his habitual luxury and magnificence, he for a time led a tranquil life, and may have looked back upon his regal career as a troubled dream, from which he had happily awaked. Still he appears to have pleased himself with a shadow of royalty, making occasionally, progresses about his little domains, visiting the different towns, receiving the homage of the inhabitants, and bestowing largesses with a princely hand. His great delight, however, was in sylvan sports and exercises, with horses, hawks, and hounds, being passionately fond of hunting and falconry, so as to pass weeks together in sporting campaigns among the mountains. The jealous suspicions of Ferdinand followed him into his retreat. No exertions were spared by the politically pious monarch, to induce him to embrace the Christian religion, as a means of severing him in feelings and

661

sympathies from his late subjects ; but he remained true to the faith of his fathers ; and it must have added not a little to his humiliation to live a vassal under Christian sovereigns.

His obstinacy, in this respect, aggravated the distrust of Ferdinand, who, looking back upon the past inconstancy of the Moors, could not feel perfectly secure in his newly conquered territories, while there was one within their bounds who might revive pretensions to the throne, and rear the standard of an opposite faith in their behalf. He caused, therefore, a vigilant watch to be kept upon the dethroned monarch in his retirement, and beset him with spies, who were to report all his words and actions. The reader will probably be surprised to learn, that the foremost of these spies was Aben Comixa! Ever since the capture and release of the niece of the vizier by the count de Tendilla, Aben Comixa had kept up a friendly correspondence with that nobleman, and through this channel had gradually been brought over to the views of Ferdinand. Documents which have gradually come to light, leave little doubt that the vizier had been corrupted by the bribes and promises of the Spanish king, and had greatly promoted his views in the capitulation of Granada. It is certain that he subsequently received great estates from the Christian sovereigns. While residing in confidential friendship with Boabdil in his retirement, Aben Comixa communicated secretly with Hernando de Zafra, the secretary of Ferdinand, who resided at Granada, giving him information of all Boabdil's movements ; which the secretary reported by letter to the king. Some of the letters of the secretary still exist in the archives of Samancas, and have been recently published in the collection of unedited documents.*

The jealous doubts of Ferdinand were quickened by the letters of his spies. He saw in the hunting campaigns and royal progresses of the ex-king a mode of keeping up a military spirit, and a concerted intelligence among the Moors of the Alpuxarras, that might prepare them

---

* El rey Muley Babdali (Boabdil) y sus criados andan continuamente á caza con glagos y azores, y allá esta agora en al campo de Dalias y en Verja, aunque su casa tiene en Andarax, y dican que estará allá por todo este mes.— *Carta Secreta de Hernando de Zafra.* Decembre, 1492.

for future rebellion. By degrees, the very residence of Boabdil within the kingdom became incompatible with Ferdinand's ideas of security. He gave his agents, therefore, secret instructions to work upon the mind of the deposed monarch, and induce him, like El Zagal, to relinquish his Spanish estates for valuable considerations, and retire to Africa. Boabdil, however, was not to be persuaded; to the urgent suggestions of these perfidious counselors, he replied, that he had given up a kingdom to live in peace ; and had no idea of going to a foreign land to encounter new troubles, and to be under the control of al-arabes.[*]

Ferdinand persisted in his endeavors, and found means more effectual of operating on the mind of Boabdil and gradually disposing him to enter into negotiations. It would appear that Aben Comixa was secretly active in this matter, in the interests of the Spanish monarch, and was with him at Barcelona, as the vizier and agent of Boabdil. The latter, however, finding that his residence in the Alpuxarras was a cause of suspicion and uneasiness to Ferdinand, determined to go himself to Barcelona, have a conference with the sovereigns, and conduct all his negotiations with them in person. Zafra, the secretary of Ferdinand, who was ever on the alert, wrote a letter from Granada, apprising the king of Boabdil's intention, and that he was making preparations for the journey. He received a letter in reply, charging him by subtle management to prevent, or at least delay, the coming of Boabdil to court.[†] The crafty monarch trusted to effect through Aben Comixa as vizier and agent of Boabdil, an arrangement which it might be impossible to obtain from Boabdil himself. The politic plan was carried into effect. Boabdil was detained at Andarax by the management of Zafra. In the meantime, a scandalous bargain was made on the 17th March, 1493, between Ferdinand and Aben Comixa, in which the latter, as vizier and agent of Boabdil, though without any license or authority from him, made a sale of his territory, and the patrimonial property of the princesses, for eighty thousand ducats of gold, and engaged that he should

[*] Letter of Hernando de Zafra to the sovereigns, Dec. 9, 1493.
[†] Letter of the sovereigns to Hernando de Zafra, from Barcelona, Feb. 1493.

depart for Africa, taking care, at the same time, to make conditions highly advantageous for himself.*

This bargain being hastily concluded, Yusef Aben Comixa loaded the treasure upon mules, and departed for the Alpuxarras. Here, spreading the money before Boabdil: "Senior," said he, "I have observed that as long as you live here, you are exposed to constant peril. The Moors are rash and irritable; they may make some sudden insurrection, elevate your standard as a pretext, and thus overwhelm you and your friends with utter ruin. I have observed, also, that you pine away with grief, being continually reminded in this country that you were once its sovereign, but never more must hope to reign. I have put an end to these evils. Your territory is sold—behold the price of it. With this gold you may buy far greater possessions in Africa, where you may live in honor and security."

When Boabdil heard these words, he burst into a sudden transport of rage, and drawing his scimetar, would have sacrificed the officious Yusef on the spot, had not the attendants interfered, and hurried the vizier from his presence.†

The rage of Boabdil gradually subsided; he saw that he had been duped and betrayed; but he knew the spirit of Ferdinand too well to hope that he would retract the bargain, however illegitimately effected. He contented himself, therefore, with obtaining certain advantageous modifications, and then prepared to bid a final adieu to his late kingdom and his native land.

It took some months to make the necessary arrangements; or rather his departure was delayed by a severe domestic affliction. Morayma, his gentle and affectionate wife, worn out by agitations and alarms, was gradually sinking into the grave, a prey to devouring melancholy. Her death took place toward the end of August. Hernando de Zafra apprised king Ferdinand of the event as one propitious to his purposes: removing an obstacle to the embarkation, which was now fixed for the

---

* Alcantara, *Hist. Granad.* iv. c. 18.
† Marmol. *Rebel.* lib. 1, c. 22.

month of September. Zafra was instructed to accompany the exiles until he saw them landed on the African coast.

The embarkation, however, did not take place until some time in the month of October. A caracca had been prepared at the port of Adra for Boabdil and his immediate family and friends. Another caracca and two galliots received a number of faithful adherents, amounting, it is said, to 1,130, who followed their prince into exile.

A crowd of his former subjects witnessed his embarkation. As the sails were unfurled and swelled to the breeze, and the vessel bearing Boabdil parted from the land, the spectators would fain have given him a farewell cheering ; but the humbled state of their once proud sovereign forced itself upon their minds, and the ominous surname of his youth rose involuntarily to their tongues : "Farewell, Boabdil! Allah preserve thee, *El Zogoybi!*" burst spontaneously from the lips. The unlucky appellation sank into the heart of the expatriated monarch, and tears dimmed his eyes as the snowy summits of the mountains of Granada gradually faded from his view.

He was received with welcome at the court of his relative Muley Ahmed, caliph of Fez, the same who had treated El Zagal with such cruelty in his exile. For thirty-four years he resided in this court, treated with great consideration, and built a palace or alcazar, at Fez, in which, it is said, he endeavored to emulate the beauties and delights of the Alhambra.

The last we find recorded of him is in the year 1536, when he followed the caliph to the field to repel the invasion of two brothers of the famous line of the Xerifes, who, at the head of Berber troops, had taken the city of Morocco and threatened Fez. The armies came in sight of each other on the banks of the Gaudal Hawit, or river of slaves, at the ford of Balcuba. The river was deep, the banks were high and broken; and the ford could only be passed in single file; for three days the armies remained firing at each other across the stream, neither venturing to attempt the dangerous ford. At length the caliph divided his army into three battalions, the command of the first he gave to his brother-in-law, and to Ali Atar, son of the old alcayde of Loxa; another division he commanded himself, and the third, composed of his best marksmen, he put under the command of his son the prince of Fez, and Boabdil, now a gray-haired veteran. The last mentioned column took the lead, dashed boldly across the ford, scrambled up the opposite bank, and attempted to keep the enemy employed until the other battalions should have time to cross. The rebel army, however, attacked them with such fury, that the son of the king of Fez and several of the bravest alcaydes were slain upon the spot ; multitudes were driven back into the river, which was already crowded with passing troops. A dreadful confusion took place ; the horse trampled upon the foot; the enemy pressed on them with fearful slaughter; those who escaped the sword perished by the stream; the river was choked by the dead bodies of men and horses, and by the scattered baggage of the army. In this scene of horrible carnage fell Boabdil, truly called El Zogoybi, or the Unlucky—an instance, says the ancient chronicler, of the scornful caprice of fortune, dying in defense of the kingdom of another, after wanting spirit to die in defense of his own.[*]

The aspersion of the chronicler is more caustic than correct. Boabdil never showed a want of courage in the defense of Granada ; but he wanted firmness and decision; he was beset from the first by perplexities, and ultimately, by the artifices of Ferdinand and the treachery of those in whom he most confided.[†]

#### ZORAYA, THE STAR OF THE MORNING.

Notwithstanding the deadly rivalryship of this youthful sultana, with Ayxa la Horra, the virtuous mother of Boabdil, and the disasters to which her ambitious intrigues gave rise, the placable spirit of Boabdil bore her no lasting enmity. After the death of his father, he treated her with respect and kindness, and evinced a brotherly feeling towards her sons Cad and Nazar. In the capitulations for the surrender of Granada

---

[*] Marmol. *Descrip. de Africa*, pt. 1, lib. 2, c. 40. Idem., *Hist. Reb. de los Moros*, lib. 1, c. 21.

[†] In revising this account of the ultimate fortunes of Boabdil, the author has availed himself of facts recently brought out in Alcantara's history of Granada ; which throw strong lights on certain parts of the subject hitherto covered with obscurity.

he took care of her interests, and the possessions which he obtained for her were in his neighborhood, in the valleys of the Alpuxarras. Zoraya, however, under the influence of Queen Isabella, returned to the Christian faith, the religion of her infancy, and resumed her Spanish name of Isabella. Her two sons Cad and Nazar were baptized under the names of Don Fernando and Don Juan de Granada, and were permitted to take the titles of Infantas or princes. They intermarried with noble Spanish families, and the dukes of Granada, resident in Valladolid, are descendants of Don Juan (once Nazar), and preserve to the present day the blazon of their royal ancestor Muley Abul Hassan, and his motto, Le Galib ile Alá, God alone is conqueror.

## FATE OF ABEN COMIXA.

An ancient chronicle which has long remained in manuscript, but has been published of late years in the collection of Spanish historical documents,* informs us of the subsequent fortunes of the perfidious Aben Comixa. Discarded and despised by Boabdil for his treachery, he repaired to the Spanish court, and obtained favor in the eyes of the devout queen Isabella by embracing the Christian religion, being baptized under her auspices, with the name of Don Juan de Granada. He even carried his zeal for his newly adopted creed so far as to become a Franciscan friar. By degrees his affected piety grew cool, and the friar's garb became irksome. Taking occasion of the sailing of some Venetian galleys from Almeria, he threw off his religious habit, embarked on board of one of them and crossed to Africa, where he landed in the dress of a Spanish cavalier.

In a private interview with Abderraman, the Moorish king of Bujia, he related his whole history, and declared that he had always been and still was at heart a true Mahometan. Such skill had he in inspiring confidence that the Moorish king took him into favor and appointed him governor of Algiers. While enjoying his new dignity, a Spanish squadron of four galleys under the celebrated count Pedro de Navarro, anchored in the harbor, in 1509. Aben Comixa paid the squadron a visit of ceremony

* Padilla, *Cronica de Felipe el Hermosa*, cap. 18 y 19, as cited by Alcantara.

in his capacity of governor ; gave the count repeated fetes, and in secret conversations with him laid open all the affairs of the king of Bujia, and offered if the count should return with sufficient force, to deliver the city into his hands and aid him in conquering the whole territory. The count hastened back to Spain and made known the proposed treachery to the Cardinal Ximenes, then prime minister of Spain. In the following month of January he was sent with thirty vessels and four thousand soldiers to achieve the enterprise. The expedition of Navarro was successful. He made himself master of Bujia, and seized in triumph on the royal palace, but he found there the base Aben Comixa weltering in his blood and expiring under numerous wounds. His treachery had been discovered, and the vengeance of the king of Bujia had closed his perfidious career.

### DEATH OF THE MARQUES OF CADIZ.

The renowned Roderigo Ponce de Leon, Marques, Duke of Cadiz, was unquestionably the most distinguished among the cavaliers of Spain, for his zeal, enterprise, and heroism, in the great crusade of Granada. He began the war by the capture of Alhama: he was engaged in almost every inroad and siege of importance, during its continuance; and was present at the surrender of the capital, the closing scene of the conquest. The renown thus acquired was sealed by his death, which happened in the forty-eighth year of his age, almost immediately at the close of his triumphs, and before a leaf of his laurels had time to wither. He died at his palace in the city of Seville, on the 27th day of August, 1492, but a few months after the surrender of Granada, and of an illness caused by exposures and fatigues undergone in this memorable war. That honest chronicler, Andres Bernaldes, the curate of los Palacios, who was a contemporary of the marques, draws his portrait from actual knowledge and observation. He was universally cited (says he) as the most perfect model of chivalrous virtue of the age. He was temperate, chaste, and rigidly devout ; a benignant commander, a valiant defender of his vassals, a great lover of justice, and an enemy to all flatterers, liars, robbers, traitors, and poltroons.

His ambition was of a lofty kind—he sought to distinguish himself and his family, by heroic and resounding deeds ; and to increase the patrimony of his ancestors, by the acquisition of castles, domains, vassals, and other princely possessions. His recreations were all of a warlike nature; he delighted in geometry as applied to fortifications, and spent much time and treasure in erecting and repairing fortresses. He relished music, but of a military kind—the sound of clarions and sackbuts, of drums and trumpets. Like a true cavalier, he was a protector of the sex on all occasions, and an injured woman never applied to him in vain for redress. His prowess was so well known, and his courtesy to the fair, that the ladies of the court, when they accompanied the queen to the wars, rejoiced to find themselves under his protection; for wherever his banner was displayed, the Moors dreaded to adventure. He was a faithful and devoted friend, but a formidable enemy; for he was slow to forgive, and his vengeance was persevering and terrible.

The death of this good and well-beloved cavalier spread grief and lamentation throughout all ranks. His relations, dependants, and companions in arms, put on mourning for his loss ; and so numerous were they, that half of Seville was clad in black. None, however, deplored his death more deeply and sincerely than his friend and chosen companion, Don Alonzo de Aguilar.

The funeral ceremonies were of the most solemn and sumptuous kind. The body of the marques was arrayed in a costly shirt, a doublet of brocade, a sayo or long robe of black velvet, a marlota or Moorish tunic of brocade reaching to the feet, and scarlet stockings. His sword, superbly gilt, was girded to his side, as he used to wear it when in the field. Thus magnificently attired, the body was inclosed in a coffin, which was covered with black velvet, and decorated with a cross of white damask. It was then placed on a sumptuous bier, in the centre of the great hall of the palace. Here the duchess made great lamentation over the body of her lord, in which she was joined by her train of damsels and attendants, as well as by the pages and esquires, and innumerable vassals.

In the close of the evening, just before the Ave Maria, the funeral train issued from the palace. Ten banners were borne around the bier, the particular trophies of the marques, won from the Moors by his valor in individual enterprises, before king Ferdinand had commenced the war of Granada. The procession was swelled by an immense train of bishops, priests, and friars of different orders, together with the civil and military authorities, and all the chivalry of Seville, headed by the count of Cifuentes, at that time intendente or commander of the city. It moved slowly and solemnly through the streets, stopping occasionally, and chanting litanies and responses. Two hundred and forty waxen tapers shed a light like the day about the bier. The balconies and windows were crowded with ladies, who shed tears as the funeral train passed by ; while the women of the lower classes were loud in their lamentations, as if bewailing the loss of a father or a brother. On approaching the convent of St. Augustine, the monks came forth with the cross and tapers, and eight censers, and conducted the body into the church, where it lay in state until all the vigils were performed, by the different orders; after which it was deposited in the family tomb of the Ponces in the same church, and the ten banners were suspended over the sepulchre.*

The tomb of the valiant Roderigo Ponce de Leon, with his banners mouldering above it, remained for ages an object of veneration with all who had read or heard of his virtues and achievements. In the year 1810, however, the chapel was sacked by the French, its altars were overturned, and the sepulchres of the family of the Ponces shattered to pieces. The present duchess of Benevente, the worthy descendant of this illustrious and heroic line, has since piously collected the ashes of her ancestors, restored the altar, and repaired the chapel. The sepulchres, however, were utterly destroyed ; an inscription in gold letters, on the wall of the chapel, to the right of the altar, is all that denotes the place of sepulture of the brave Ponce de Leon.

* *Cura de los Palacios*, c. 104.

## THE LEGEND OF THE DEATH OF DON ALONZO DE AGUILAR.

To such as feel an interest in the fortune of the valiant Don Alonzo de Aguilar, the chosen friend and companion in arms of Ponce de Leon, marques of Cadiz, and one of the most distinguished heroes of the war of Granada, a few particulars of his remarkable fate will not be unacceptable.

For several years after the conquest of Granada, the country remained feverish and unquiet. The zealous efforts of the Catholic clergy to effect the conversion of the infidels, and the coercion used for that purpose by government, exasperated the stubborn Moors of the mountains. Several missionaries were maltreated; and in the town of Dayrin, two of them were seized, and exhorted, with many menaces, to embrace the Moslem faith; on their resolutely refusing, they were killed with staves and stones, by the Moorish women and children, and their bodies burnt to ashes.*

Upon this event a body of Christian cavaliers assembled in Andalusia to the number of eight hundred, and, without waiting for orders from the king, revenged the death of these martyrs, by plundering and laying waste the Moorish towns and villages. The Moors fled to the mountains, and their cause was espoused by many of their nation, who inhabited those rugged regions. The storm of rebellion began to gather, and mutter its thunders in the Alpuxarras. They were echoed from the Serrania of Ronda, ever ready for rebellion; but the strongest hold of the insurgents was in the Sierra Vermeja, or chain of Red Mountains, which lie near the sea, the savage rocks and precipices of which may be seen from Gibraltar.

When king Ferdinand heard of these tumults, he issued a proclamation ordering all the Moors of the insurgent regions to leave them within ten days, and repair to Castile; giving secret instructions, however, that those who should voluntarily embrace the Christian faith might be permitted

* *Cura de los Palacios*, c. 165.

to remain. At the same time, he ordered Don Alonzo de Aguilar, and the counts of Ureña and Cifuentes, to march against the rebels.

Don Alonzo de Aguilar was at Cordova when he received the commands of the king. "What force is allotted us for this expedition?" said he. On being told, he perceived that the number of troops was far from adequate. "When a man is dead," said he, "we send four men into his house to bring forth the body. We are now sent to chastise these Moors, who are alive, vigorous, in open rebellion, and ensconced in their castles; yet they do not give us man to man." These words of the brave Alonzo de Aguilar were afterwards frequently repeated; but though he saw the desperate nature of the enterprise, he did not hesitate to undertake it.

Don Alonzo was at that time in the fifty-first year of his age: a warrior, in whom the fire of youth was yet unquenched, though tempered by experience. The greater part of his life had been passed in camp and field, until danger was as his habitual element. His muscular frame had acquired the firmness of iron, without the rigidity of age. His armor and weapons seemed to have become a part of his nature, and he sat like a man of steel on his powerful war-horse.

He took with him, on this expedition, his son Don Pedro de Cordova, a youth of bold and generous spirit, in the freshness of his days, and armed and arrayed with the bravery of a young Spanish cavalier. When the populace of Cordova beheld the veteran father, the warrior of a thousand battles, leading forth his son to the field, they bethought themselves of the family appellation: "Behold," cried they, "the eagle teaching his young to fly! Long live the valiant line of Aguilar!" *

The prowess of Don Alonzo, and of his companions in arms, was renowned throughout the Moorish towns. At their approach, therefore, numbers of the Moors submitted, and hastened to Ronda to embrace Christianity. Among the mountaineers, however, were many of the Gandules, a tribe from Africa, too proud of spirit to bend their necks to the yoke. At their head was a Moor named El Feri of Ben Estepar, renowned for strength and courage. At his instigation, his followers

* *Aguilar*—the Spanish for eagle.

gathered together their families and most precious effects, placed them on mules, and driving before them their flocks and herds, abandoned their valleys, and retired up the craggy passes of the Sierra Vermeja. On the summit was a fertile plain, surrounded by rocks and precipices, which formed a natural fortress. Here El Feri placed all the women and children, and all the property. By his orders, his followers piled great stones on the rocks and cliffs which commanded the defiles and the steep sides of the mountain, and prepared to defend every pass that led to his place of refuge.

The Christian commanders arrived, and pitched their camp before the town of Monarda, a strong place, curiously fortified, and situated at the foot of the highest part of the Sierra Vermeja. Here they remained for several days, unable to compel a surrender. They were separated from the skirt of the mountain by a deep barranca or ravine, at the bottom of which flowed a small stream. The Moors, commanded by El Feri, drew down from their mountain height, and remained on the opposite side of the brook, to defend a pass which led up to their stronghold.

One afternoon, a number of Christian soldiers, in mere bravado, seized a banner, crossed the brook, and, scrambling up the opposite bank, attacked the Moors. They were followed by numbers of their companions, some in aid, some in emulation, but most in hope of booty. A sharp action ensued on the mountain side. The Moors were greatly superior in number, and had the vantage-ground. When the counts of Ureña and Cifuentes beheld this skirmish, they asked Don Alonzo de Aguilar his opinion: "My opinion," said he, "was given at Cordova, and remains the same: this is a desperate enterprise: however, the Moors are at hand, and if they suspect weakness in us, it will increase their courage and our peril. Forward then to the attack, and I trust in God we shall gain a victory." So saying, he led his troops into the battle.*

On the skirts of the mountain were several level places, like terraces; here the Christians pressed valiantly upon the Moors, and had the advantage; but the latter retreated to the steep and craggy heights, whence

* Bleda, lib. 5, c. 26.

they hurled darts and rocks upon their assailants. They defended their passes and defiles with valor, but were driven from height to height, until they reached the plain on the summit of the mountain, where their wives and children were sheltered. Here they would have made a stand : but Alonzo de Aguilar, with his son Don Pedro, charged upon them at the head of three hundred men, and put them to flight with great carnage. While they were pursuing the flying enemy, the rest of the army, thinking the victory achieved, dispersed themselves over the little plain in search of plunder. They pursued the shrieking females, tearing off their necklaces, bracelets, and anklets of gold ; and they found so much treasure of various kinds collected in this spot, that they threw by their armor and weapons, to load themselves with booty.

Evening was closing. The Christians, intent upon spoil, had ceased to pursue the Moors, and the latter were arrested in their flight by the cries of their wives and children. Their leader, El Feri, threw himself before them : "Friends, soldiers," cried he, "whither do you fly ? Whither can you seek refuge, where the enemy cannot follow you ? Your wives, your children, are behind you—turn and defend them ; you have no chance for safety, but from the weapons in your hands."

The Moors turned at his words. They beheld the Christians scattered about the plain, many of them without armor, and all encumbered with spoil. "Now is the time !" shouted El Feri ; "charge upon them while laden with your plunder. I will open a path for you !" He rushed to the attack, followed by his Moors, with shouts and cries that echoed through the mountains. The scattered Christians were seized with panic, and throwing down their booty, began to fly in all directions. Don Alonzo de Aguilar advanced his banner, and endeavored to rally them. Finding his horse of no avail in these rocky heights, he dismounted, and caused his men to do the same ; he had a small band of tried followers, with which he opposed a bold front to the Moors, calling on the scattered troops to rally in the rear.

Night had completely closed. It prevented the Moors from seeing the smallness of the force with which they were contending ; and Don

Alonzo and his cavaliers dealt their blows so vigorously, that, aided by the darkness, they seemed multiplied to ten times their number. Unfortunately, a small cask of gunpowder blew up, near to the scene of action. It shed a momentary but brilliant light over all the plain, and on every rock and cliff. The Moors beheld, with surprise, that they were opposed by a mere handful of men, and that the greater part of the Christians were flying from the field. They put up loud shouts of triumph. While some continued the conflict with redoubled ardor, others pursued the fugitives, hurling after them stones and darts, and discharging showers of arrows. Many of the Christians, in their terror and their ignorance of the mountains, rushed headlong from the brinks of precipices, and were dashed in pieces.

Don Alonzo still maintained his ground; but, while some of the Moors assailed him in front, others galled him with all kinds of missiles from the impending cliffs. Some of the cavaliers, seeing the hopeless nature of the conflict, proposed to abandon the height and retreat down the mountain : "No," said Don Alonzo, proudly, "never did the banner of the house of Aguilar retreat one foot in the field of battle." He had scarcely uttered these words, when his son Pedro was stretched at his feet. A stone hurled from a cliff had struck out two of his teeth, and a lance passed quivering through his thigh. The youth attempted to rise, and, with one knee on the ground, to fight by the side of his father. Don Alonzo, finding him wounded, urged him to quit the field. "Fly, my son!" said he; "let us not put everything at venture upon one hazard. Conduct thyself as a good Christian, and live to comfort and honor thy mother."

Don Pedro still refused to leave his side. Whereupon Don Alonzo ordered several of his followers to bear him off by force. His friend Don Francisco Alvarez of Cordova, taking him in his arms, conveyed him to the quarters of the count of Ureña, who had halted on the height, at some distance from the scene of battle, for the purpose of rallying and succoring the fugitives. Almost at the same moment, the count beheld his own son, Don Pedro Giron, brought in grievously wounded.

In the meantime, Don Alonzo, with two hundred cavaliers, maintained the unequal contest. Surrounded by foes, they fell, one after another, like so many stags encircled by the hunters. Don Alonzo was the last survivor, without horse, and almost without armor—his corselet unlaced, and his bosom gashed with wounds. Still he kept a brave front to the enemy, and, retiring between two rocks, defended himself with such valor, that the slain lay in a heap before him.

He was assailed in this retreat, by a Moor of surpassing strength and fierceness. The contest was for some time doubtful; but Don Alonzo received a wound in the head, and another in the breast, which made him stagger. Closing and grappling with his foe, they had a desperate struggle, until the Christian cavalier, exhausted by his wounds, fell upon his back. He still retained his grasp upon his enemy: "Think not," cried he, "thou hast an easy prize ; know that I am Don Alonzo, he of Aguilar!" "If thou art Don Alonzo," replied the Moor, "know that I am El Feri of Ben Estepar." They continued their deadly struggle, and both drew their daggers; but Don Alonzo was exhausted by seven ghastly wounds ; while he was yet struggling, his heroic soul departed from his body, and he expired in the grasp of the Moor.

Thus fell Alonzo de Aguilar, the mirror of Andalusian chivalry—one of the most powerful grandees of Spain, for person, blood, estate, and office. For forty years he had made successful war upon the Moors—in childhood by his household and retainers, in manhood by the prowess of his arm, and in the wisdom and valor of his spirit. His pennon had always been foremost in danger; he had been general of armies, viceroy of Andalusia, and the author of glorious enterprises, in which kings were vanquished, and mighty alcaydes and warriors laid low. He had slain many Moslem chiefs with his own arm, and among others the renowned Ali Atar of Loxa, fighting foot to foot, on the banks of the Xenil. His judgment, discretion, magnanimity, and justice, vied with his prowess. He was the fifth lord of his warlike house, that fell in battle with the Moors.

"His soul," observes the worthy padre Abarca, "it is believed, ascended to heaven, to receive the reward of so Christian a captain ; for that very day, he had armed himself with the sacraments of confession and communion." *

The Moors, elated with their success, pursued the fugitive Christians down the defiles and sides of the mountains. It was with the utmost difficulty that the count de Ureña could bring off a remnant of his forces from that disastrous height. Fortunately, on the lower slope of the mountain, they found the rear-guard of the army, led by the count de Cifuentes, who had crossed the brook and the ravine to come to their assistance. As the fugitives came flying in headlong terror down the mountain, it was with difficulty the count kept his own troops from giving way in panic, and retreating in confusion across the brook. He succeeded, however, in maintaining order, in rallying the fugitives, and checking the fury of the Moors : then, taking his station on a rocky eminence, he maintained his post until morning; sometimes sustaining violent attacks, at other times rushing forth and making assaults upon the enemy. When morning dawned, the Moors ceased to combat, and drew up to the summit of the mountain.

It was then that the Christians had time to breathe, and to ascertain the sad loss they had sustained. Among the many valiant cavaliers who had fallen, was Don Francisco Ramirez of Madrid, who had been captain-general of artillery throughout the war of Granada, and contributed greatly by his valor and ingenuity to that renowned conquest. But all other griefs and cares were forgotten, in anxiety for the fate of Don Alonzo de Aguilar. His son, Don Pedro de Cordova, had been brought off with great difficulty from the battle, and afterwards lived to be marques of Priego ; but of Don Alonzo nothing was known, except that he was left with a handful of cavaliers, fighting valiantly against an overwhelming force.

As the rising sun lighted up the red cliffs of the mountains, the soldiers watched with anxious eyes, if perchance his pennon might be descried, fluttering from any precipice or defile; but nothing of the kind was

* Abarca, *Anales de Aragon*, Rey xxx. cap. ii.

to be seen. The trumpet-call was repeatedly sounded, but empty echoes alone replied. A silence reigned about the mountain summit, which showed that the deadly strife was over. Now and then a wounded warrior came dragging his feeble steps from among the clefts and rocks; but, on being questioned, he shook his head mournfully, and could tell nothing of the fate of his commander.

The tidings of this disastrous defeat, and of the perilous situation of the survivors, reached King Ferdinand at Granada; he immediately marched, at the head of all the chivalry of his court, to the mountains of Ronda. His presence, with a powerful force, soon put an end to the rebellion. A part of the Moors were suffered to ransom themselves, and embark for Africa; others were made to embrace Christianity; and those of the town where the Christian missionaries had been massacred, were sold as slaves. From the conquered Moors, the mournful but heroic end of Alonzo de Aguilar was ascertained.

On the morning after the battle, when the Moors came to strip and bury the dead, the body of Don Alonzo was found, among those of more than two hundred of his followers, many of them alcaydes and cavaliers of distinction. Though the person of Don Alonzo was well known to the Moors, being so distinguished among them both in peace and war, yet it was so covered and disfigured with wounds, that it could with difficulty be recognized. They preserved it with great care, and, on making their submission, delivered it up to King Ferdinand. It was conveyed with great state to Cordova, amidst the tears and lamentations of all Andalusia. When the funeral train entered Cordova, and the inhabitants saw the coffin containing the remains of their favorite hero, and the warhorse, led in mournful trappings, on which they had so lately seen him sally forth from their gates, there was a general burst of grief throughout the city. The body was interred, with great pomp and solemnity, in the church of St. Hypolito.

Many years afterwards, his granddaughter, Doña Catalina of Aguilar and Cordova, marchioness of Priego, caused his tomb to be altered. On examining the body, the head of a lance was found among the bones, received without doubt among the wounds of his last mortal combat. The name of this accomplished and Christian cavalier has ever remained a popular theme of the chronicler and poet, and is endeared to the public memory by many of the historical ballads and songs of his country. For a long time the people of Cordova were indignant at the brave count de Ureña, who they thought had abandoned Don Alonzo in his extremity; but the Castilian monarch acquitted him of all charge of the kind, and continued him in honor and office. It was proved that neither he nor his people could succor Don Alonzo, or even know of his peril, from the darkness of the night. There is a mournful little Spanish ballad or romance, which breathes the public grief on this occasion; and the populace, on the return of the count de Ureña to Cordova, assailed him with one of its plaintive and reproachful verses :—

> Count Ureña! count Ureña!
> Tell us, where is Don Alonzo!
>
> (Dezid Conde de Ureña!
> Don Alonzo, donde queda?) *

> * Bleda, lib. 5, cap. 26.

## THE END.

# MAHOMET

### AND

# HIS SUCCESSORS

BY

## WASHINGTON IRVING

---

*AUTHOR'S REVISED EDITION*

PREFACE.

# PREFACE.

SOME apology may seem necessary for present-ing a life of Mahomet at the present day, when no new fact can be added to those already known concerning him. Many years since, during a residence in Madrid, the author projected a series of writings illustrative of the domination of the Arabs in Spain. These were to be introduced by a sketch of the life of the founder of the Islam faith, and the first mover of Arabian conquest. Most of the particulars for this were drawn from Spanish sources, and from Gagnier's translation of the Arabian historian Abulfeda, a copy of which the author found in the Jesuits' Library of the Convent of St. Isidro, at Madrid.

Not having followed out in its extent the literary plan devised, the manuscript life lay neglected among the author's papers until the year 1831, when he revised and enlarged it for the Family Library of Mr. John Murray. Circumstances prevented its publication at the time, and it again was thrown aside for years.

During his last residence in Spain, the author beguiled

7

the tediousness of a lingering indisposition, by again revising the manuscript, profiting in so doing by recent
lights thrown on the subject by different writers, and
particularly by Dr. Gustav Weil, the very intelligent and
learned librarian of the University of Heidelberg, to
whose industrious researches and able disquisitions, he
acknowledges himself greatly indebted.*

Such is the origin of the work now given to the public;
on which the author lays no claim to novelty of fact, nor
profundity of research. It still bears the type of a work
intended for a Family Library; in constructing which
the whole aim of the writer has been to digest into an
easy, perspicuous and flowing narrative, the admitted
facts concerning Mahomet, together with such legends
and traditions as have been wrought into the whole
system of oriental literature; and at the same time to
give such a summary of his faith as might be sufficient
for the general reader. Under such circumstances, he
has not thought it worth while to encumber his pages
with a scaffolding of references and citations, nor depart
from the old English nomenclature of oriental names.

W. I.

SUNNYSIDE, 1849.

---

* *Mohammed der Prophet, sein Leben und seine Lehere.* Stuttgart, 1843.

# CONTENTS.

9

## CHAPTER VII.

## CHAPTER VIII.

## CHAPTER IX.

## CHAPTER X.

## CHAPTER XI.

16 *CONTENTS.*

## CHAPTER XXXIX.

PAGE

# MAHOMET AND HIS SUCCESSORS.

## CHAPTER I.

PRELIMINARY NOTICE OF ARABIA AND THE ARABS.

URING a long succession of ages, extending from the earliest period of recorded history down to the seventh century of the Christian era, that great chersonese or peninsula formed by the Red Sea, the Euphrates, the Gulf of Persia, and the Indian Ocean, and known by the name of Arabia, remained unchanged and almost unaffected by the events which convulsed the rest of Asia, and shook Europe and Africa to their centre. While kingdoms and empires rose and fell; while ancient dynasties passed away; while the boundaries and names of countries were changed, and their inhabitants were exterminated or carried into captivity, Arabia, though its frontier provinces experienced some vicissitudes, preserved in the depths of its deserts its primitive character and independence, nor had its nomadic tribes ever bent their haughty necks to servitude.

The Arabs carry back the traditions of their country to the highest antiquity. It was peopled, they say, soon after the deluge, by the progeny of Shem the son of Noah, who gradually formed themselves into several tribes, the most noted of which are the Adites and Thamudites. All these primitive tribes are said to have been either swept from the earth in punishment of their iniquities, or obliterated in subsequent modifications of the races, so that little remains concerning them but shadowy traditions and a few passages in the Koran. They are occasionally mentioned in oriental history as the " old primitive Arabians,"—the " lost tribes."

The primitive population of the peninsula is ascribed, by the same authorities, to Kahtan or Joctan, a descendant in the fourth generation from Shem. His posterity spread over the southern part of the peninsula and along the Red Sea. Yarab, one of his sons, founded the kingdom of Yemen, where the territory of Araba was called after him; whence the Arabs derive the names of themselves and their country. Jurham, another son, founded the kingdom of Hedjaz, over which his descendants bore sway for many generations. Among these people Hagar and her son Ishmael were kindly received, when exiled from their home by the patriarch Abraham. In the process of time Ishmael married the daughter of Modâd, a reigning prince of the line of Jurham; and thus a stranger and a Hebrew became grafted on the original Arabian stock. It proved a vigorous graft. Ishmael's wife bore him twelve sons, who acquired dominion over the country, and whose prolific race, divided into twelve tribes, expelled or overran and obliterated the primitive stock of Joctan.

Such is the account given by the peninsular Arabs of their origin ;* and Christian writers cite it as containing the fulfillment of the covenant of God with Abraham, as recorded in Holy Writ. "And Abraham said unto God, O that Ishmael might live before thee. And God said, As for Ishmael, I have heard thee. Behold, I have blessed him, and will make him fruitful, and will multiply him exceedingly : *twelve princes* shall he beget, and I will make him a great nation." (Genesis xvii. 18, 20.)

These twelve princes with their tribes are further spoken of in the Scriptures (Genesis xxv. 18) as occupying the country "from Havilah unto Shur, that is before Egypt, as thou goest towards Assyria;" a region identified by sacred geographers with part of Arabia. The description of them agrees with that of the Arabs of the present day. Some are mentioned as holding towns and castles, others as dwelling in tents, or having villages in

* Besides the Arabs of the peninsula, who were all of the Shemitic race, there were others called Cushites, being descended from Cush the son of Ham. They inhabited the banks of the Euphrates and the Persian Gulf. The name of Cush is often given in Scripture to the Arabs generally as well as to their country. It must be the Arabs of this race who at present roam the deserted regions of ancient Assyria, and have been employed recently in disinterring the long-buried ruins of Nineveh. They are sometimes distinguished as the Syro-Arabians. The present work relates only to the Arabs of the peninsula, or Arabia Proper.

the wilderness.  Nebaioth and Kedar, the two first-born
of Ishmael, are most noted among the princes for their
wealth in flocks and herds, and for the fine wool of their
sheep.  From Nebaioth came the Nebaithai who inhabited Stony Arabia; while the name of Kedar is occasionally given in Holy Writ to designate the whole Arabian
nation.  "Woe is me," says the Psalmist, "that I sojourn in Mesech, that I dwell in the tents of Kedar."
Both appear to have been the progenitors of the wandering or pastoral Arabs; the free rovers of the desert.
"The wealthy nation," says the prophet Jeremiah, "that
dwelleth without care; which have neither gates nor
bars, which dwell alone."

A strong distinction grew up in the earliest times between the Arabs who "held towns and castles," and
those who "dwelt in tents."  Some of the former occupied the fertile wadies, or valleys, scattered here and
there among the mountains, where these towns and castles were surrounded by vineyards and orchards, groves
of palm trees, fields of grain, and well-stocked pastures.
They were settled in their habits, devoting themselves to
the cultivation of the soil and the breeding of cattle.

Others of this class gave themselves up to commerce,
having ports and cities along the Red Sea; the southern
shores of the peninsula and the Gulf of Persia, and carrying on foreign trade by means of ships and caravans.
Such especially were the people of Yemen, or Arabia
the Happy, that land of spices, perfumes, and frankin-

cense; the Sabæa of the poets; the Sheba of the sacred
Scriptures. They were among the most active mercan-
tile navigators of the eastern seas. Their ships brought
to their shores the myrrh and balsams of the opposite
coast of Berbera, with the gold, the spices, and other rich
commodities of India and tropical Africa. These, with
the products of their own country, were transported by
caravans across the deserts to the semi-Arabian states of
Ammon, Moab, and Edom or Idumea, to the Phœnician
ports of the Mediterranean, and thence distributed to the
western world.

The camel has been termed the ship of the desert, the
caravan may be termed its fleet. The caravans of Yemen
were generally fitted out, manned, conducted, and guarded
by the nomadic Arabs, the dwellers in tents, who, in this
respect, might be called the navigators of the desert.
They furnished the innumerable camels required, and
also contributed to the freight by the fine fleeces of their
countless flocks. The writings of the prophets show the
importance, in Scriptural times, of this inland chain of
commerce, by which the rich countries of the south,
India, Ethiopia, and Arabia the Happy, were linked with
ancient Syria.

Ezekiel, in his lamentations for Tyre, exclaims, "Arabia
and all the princes of Kedar, they occupied with thee in
lambs, and rams, and goats; in these were they thy merchants. The merchants of Sheba and Raamah occupied
in thy fairs with chief of all spices, and with all precious

stones and gold. Haran, and Canneh, and Eden,* the merchants of Sheba, Asshur, and Chelmad, were thy merchants." And Isaiah, speaking to Jerusalem, says— "The multitude of camels shall cover thee; the dromedaries of Midian and Ephah; all they from Sheba shall come; they shall bring gold and incense. . . . . All the flocks of Kedar shall be gathered together unto thee; the rams of Nebaioth shall minister unto thee." (Isaiah lx. 6, 7.)

The agriculturing and trading Arabs, however, the dwellers in towns and cities, have never been considered the true type of the race. They became softened by settled and peaceful occupations, and lost much of their original stamp by an intercourse with strangers. Yemen, too, being more accessible than the other parts of Arabia, and offering greater temptation to the spoiler, had been repeatedly invaded and subdued.

It was among the other class of Arabs, the rovers of the desert, the "dwellers in tents," by far the most numerous of the two, that the national character was preserved in all its primitive force and freshness. Nomadic in their habits, pastoral in their occupations, and acquainted by experience and tradition with all the hidden resources of the desert, they led a wandering life, roaming from place to place in quest of those wells and springs which had been the resort of their forefathers

* Haran, Canna, and Aden, ports on the Indian Sea.

since the days of the patriarchs; encamping wherever they could find date-trees for shade, and sustenance and pasturage for their flocks, and herds, and camels; and shifting their abode whenever the temporary supply was exhausted.

These nomadic Arabs were divided and subdivided into innumerable petty tribes or families, each with its Sheikh or Emir, the representative of the patriarch of yore, whose spear, planted beside his tent, was the ensign of command. His office, however, though continued for many generations in the same family, was not strictly hereditary; but depended upon the good-will of the tribe. He might be deposed, and another of a different line elected in his place. His power, too, was limited, and depended upon his personal merit and the confidence reposed in him. His prerogative consisted in conducting negotiations of peace and war; in leading his tribe against the enemy; in choosing the place of encampment, and in receiving and entertaining strangers of note. Yet, even in these and similar privileges, he was controlled by the opinions and inclinations of his people.*

* In summer the wandering Arabs, says Burckhardt, seldom remain above three or four days on the same spot; as soon as their cattle have consumed the herbage near a watering place, the tribe removes in search of pasture, and the grass again springing up, serves for a succeeding camp. The encampments vary in the number of tents, from six to eight hundred; when the tents are but few, they are pitched in a circle; but more considerable numbers in a straight line, or a row of single tents, especially along a rivulet, sometimes three or four behind as many others. In winter, when water and pasture never fail, the whole tribe spreads

However numerous and minute might be the divisions of a tribe, the links of affinity were carefully kept in mind by the several sections. All the Sheikhs of the same tribe acknowledge a common chief called the Sheikh of Sheikhs, who, whether ensconced in a rock-built castle, or encamped amid his flocks and herds in the desert, might assemble under his standard all the scattered branches on any emergency affecting the common weal.

itself over the plain in parties of three or four tents each, with an interval of half an hour's distance between each party. The Sheikh's tent is always on the side on which enemies or guests may be expected. To oppose the former and to honor the latter, is the Sheikh's principal business. Every father of a family sticks his lance into the ground by the side of his tent, and ties his horse in front. There also his camels repose at night.—Burckhardt, *Notes on Bedouins*, vol. i. p. 33.

The following is descriptive of the Arabs of Assyria, though it is applicable, in a great degree, to the whole race:—

"It would be difficult to describe the appearance of a large tribe when migrating to new pastures. We soon found ourselves in the midst of wide-spreading flocks of sheep and camels. As far as the eye could reach, to the right, to the left, and in front, still the same moving crowd. Long lines of asses and bullocks, laden with black tents, huge cauldrons, and variegated carpets; aged women and men, no longer able to walk, tied on the heap of domestic furniture; infants crammed into saddle-bags, their tiny heads thrust through the narrow opening, balanced on the animal's back by kids or lambs tied on the opposite side; young girls clothed only in the close-fitting Arab shirt, which displayed rather than concealed their graceful forms; mothers with their children on their shoulders; boys driving flocks of lambs; horsemen armed with their long tufted spears, scouring the plain on their fleet mares; riders urging their dromedaries with their short-hooked sticks, and leading their high-bred steeds by the halter; colts galloping among the throng; such was the motley crowd through which we had to wend our way."—*Layard's Nineveh*, i. 4.

The multiplicity of these wandering tribes, each with its petty prince and petty territory, but without a national head, produced frequent collisions. Revenge, too, was almost a religious principle among them. To avenge a relative slain was the duty of his family, and often involved the honor of his tribe; and these debts of blood sometimes remained unsettled for generations, producing deadly feuds.

The necessity of being always on the alert to defend his flocks and herds, made the Arab of the desert familiar from his infancy with the exercise of arms. None could excel him in the use of the bow, the lance, and the scimitar, and the adroit and graceful management of the horse. He was a predatory warrior also; for though at times he was engaged in the service of the merchant, furnishing him with camels and guides and drivers for the transportation of his merchandise, he was more apt to lay contributions on the caravan, or plunder it outright in its toilful progress through the desert. All this he regarded as a legitimate exercise of arms; looking down upon the gainful sons of traffic as an inferior race, debased by sordid habits and pursuits.

Such was the Arab of the desert, the dweller in tents, in whom was fulfilled the prophetic destiny of his ancestor Ishmael. "He will be a wild man; his hand will be against every man, and every man's hand against him." *

* Genesis xvi. 12.

Nature had fitted him for his destiny. His form was light and meagre, but sinewy and active, and capable of sustaining great fatigue and hardship. He was temperate and even abstemious, requiring but little food, and that of the simplest kind. His mind, like his body, was light and agile. He eminently possessed the intellectual attributes of the Shemitic race, penetrating sagacity, subtle wit, a ready conception, and a brilliant imagination. His sensibilities were quick and acute, though not lasting; a proud and daring spirit was stamped on his sallow visage and flashed from his dark and kindling eye. He was easily aroused by the appeals of eloquence, and charmed by the graces of poetry. Speaking a language copious in the extreme, the words of which have been compared to gems and flowers, he was naturally an orator; but he delighted in proverbs and apothegms, rather than in sustained flights of declamation, and was prone to convey his ideas in the oriental style, by apologue and parable.

Though a restless and predatory warrior, he was generous and hospitable. He delighted in giving gifts; his door was always open to the wayfarer, with whom he was ready to share his last morsel; and his deadliest foe, having once broken bread with him, might repose securely beneath the inviolable sanctity of his tent.

In religion the Arabs, in what they term the Days of Ignorance, partook largely of the two faiths, the Sabean and the Magian, which at that time prevailed over the eastern world. The Sabean, however, was the one to which they most adhered. They pretended to derive it from Sabi the son of Seth, who, with his father and his brother Enoch, they suppose to be buried in the pyramids. Others derive the name from the Hebrew word, Saba, or the stars, and trace the origin of the faith to the Assyrian shepherds, who as they watched their flocks by night on their level plains, and beneath their cloudless skies, noted the aspects and movements of the heavenly bodies, and formed theories of their good and evil influences on human affairs; vague notions which the Chaldean philosophers and priests reduced to a system, supposed to be more ancient even than that of the Egyptians.

By others it is derived from still higher authority, and claimed to be the religion of the antediluvian world. It survived, say they, the Deluge, and was continued among the patriarchs. It was taught by Abraham, adopted by his descendants, the children of Israel, and sanctified and confirmed in the tablets of the law delivered unto Moses, amid the thunder and lightning of Mount Sinai.

In its original state the Sabean faith was pure and spiritual; inculcating a belief in the unity of God, the doctrine of a future state of rewards and punishments, and the necessity of a virtuous and holy life to obtain a happy immortality. So profound was the reverence of the Sabeans for the Supreme Being, that they never mentioned his name, nor did they venture to approach him, but through intermediate intelligences or angels. These were supposed to inhabit and animate the heavenly bodies in the same way as the human body is inhabited and animated by a soul. They were placed in their respective spheres to supervise and govern the universe in subserviency to the Most High. In addressing themselves to the stars and other celestial luminaries, therefore, the Sabeans did not worship them as deities, but sought only to propitiate their angelic occupants as intercessors with the Supreme Being; looking up through these created things to God the great Creator.

By degrees this religion lost its original simplicity and purity, and became obscured by mysteries, and degraded by idolatries. The Sabeans, instead of regarding the heavenly bodies as the habitations of intermediate agents, worshipped them as deities; set up graven images in honor of them, in sacred groves and in the gloom of forests; and at length enshrined these idols in temples, and worshipped them as if instinct with divinity. The Sabean faith too underwent changes and modifications in the various countries through which it was diffused. Egypt has long been accused of reducing it to the most abject state of degradation; the statues, hieroglyphics, and painted sepulchres of that mysterious country, being considered records of the worship, not merely of celestial intelligences, but of the lowest order of created beings, and even of inanimate objects. Modern investigation and research, however, are gradually rescuing the most intellectual nation of antiquity from this aspersion, and as they slowly lift the veil of mystery which hangs over the tombs of Egypt, are discovering that all these apparent objects of adoration were but symbols of the varied attributes of the one Supreme Being, whose name was too sacred to be pronounced by mortals. Among the Arabs the Sabean faith became mingled with wild superstitions, and degraded by gross idolatry. Each tribe worshipped its particular star or planet, or set up its particular idol. Infanticide mingled its horrors with their religious rites. Among the nomadic tribes the birth of a daughter was considered a misfortune, her sex rendering her of little service in a wandering and predatory life, while she might bring disgrace upon her family by misconduct or captivity. Motives of unnatural policy, therefore, may have mingled with their religious feelings, in offering up female infants as sacrifices to their idols, or in burying them alive.

The rival sect of Magians or Guebres (fire worshippers), which, as we have said, divided the religious empire of the East, took its rise in Persia, where, after a while, its oral doctrines were reduced to writing by its great prophet and teacher Zoroaster, in his volume of the Zend-avesta. The creed, like that of the Sabeans, was originally simple and spiritual, inculcating a belief in one supreme and eternal God, in whom and by whom the universe exists; that he produced, through his creating word, two active principles, Ormusd, the principle or angel of light or good, and Ahriman, the principle or angel of darkness or evil : that these formed the world out of a mixture of their opposite elements, and were engaged in a perpetual contest in the regulation of its affairs. Hence the vicissitudes of good and evil, accordingly as the angel of light or darkness has the upper hand : this contest would continue until the end of the world, when there would be a general resurrection and a day of judgment; the angel of darkness and his disciples would then be banished to an abode of woful gloom, and their opponents would enter the blissful realms of ever-during light.

The primitive rites of this religion were extremely simple. The Magians had neither temples, altars, nor religious symbols of any kind, but addressed their prayers and hymns directly to the Deity, in what they conceived to be his residence, the sun. They reverenced this luminary as being his abode, and as the source of the light and heat of which all the other heavenly bodies were composed; and they kindled fires upon the mountain tops to supply light during its absence. Zoroaster first introduced the use of temples, wherein sacred fire, pretended to be derived from heaven, was kept perpetually alive through the guardianship of priests, who maintained a watch over it night and day.

In process of time this sect, like that of the Sabeans, lost sight of the Divine principle in the symbol, and came to worship light or fire, as the real Deity, and to abhor darkness as Satan or the devil. In their fanatic zeal the Magians would seize upon unbelievers and offer them up in the flames to propitiate their fiery deity.

To the tenets of these two sects reference is made in that beautiful text of the "Wisdom of Solomon:" "Surely vain are all men by nature who are ignorant of God, and could not, by considering the work, acknowledge the work-master; but deemed either fire, or wind, or the swift air, or the circle of the stars, or the violent water, or the lights of heaven, to be gods which govern the world."

Of these two faiths the Sabean, as we have before observed, was much the most prevalent among the Arabs; but in an extremely degraded form, mingled with all kinds of abuses and varying among the various tribes. The Magian faith prevailed among those tribes which, from their frontier position, had frequent intercourse with Persia; while other tribes partook of the superstitions and idolatries of the nations on which they bordered.

Judaism had made its way into Arabia at an early period, but very vaguely and imperfectly. Still many of its rites and ceremonies, and fanciful traditions, became implanted in the country. At a later day, however, when Palestine was ravaged by the Romans, and the city of Jerusalem taken and sacked, many of the Jews took refuge among the Arabs; became incorporated with the native tribes; formed themselves into communities; acquired possession of fertile tracts; built castles and strongholds, and rose to considerable power and influence.

The Christian religion had likewise its adherents

among the Arabs. St. Paul himself declares in his Epistle to the Galatians, that soon after he had been called to preach Christianity among the heathens, he "went into Arabia." The dissensions, also, which rose in the Eastern church, in the early part of the third century, breaking it up into sects, each persecuting the others as it gained the ascendency, drove many into exile into remote parts of the East; filled the deserts of Arabia with anchorites, and planted the Christian faith among some of the principal tribes.

The foregoing circumstances, physical and moral, may give an idea of the causes which maintained the Arabs for ages in an unchanged condition. While their isolated position and their vast deserts protected them from conquest, their internal feuds, and their want of a common tie, political or religious, kept them from being formidable as conquerors. They were a vast aggregation of distinct parts; full of individual vigor, but wanting coherent strength. Although their nomadic life rendered them hardy and active; although the greater part of them were warriors from their infancy, yet their arms were only wielded against each other, excepting some of the frontier tribes, which occasionally engaged as mercenaries in external wars. While, therefore, the other nomadic races of Central Asia, possessing no greater aptness for warfare, had, during a course of ages, successively overrun and conquered the civilized world, this warrior race, unconscious of its power, remained disjointed and harmless in the depths of its native deserts.

The time at length arrived when its discordant tribes were to be united in one creed, and animated by one common cause ; when a mighty genius was to arise, who should bring together these scattered limbs, animate them with his own enthusiastic and daring spirit, and lead them forth, a giant of the desert, to shake and over-turn the empires of the earth.

## CHAPTER II.

AHOMET, the great founder of the faith of Islam, was born in Mecca, in April, in the year 569 of the Christian era. He was of the valiant and illustrious tribe of Koreish, of which there were two branches, descended from two brothers, Haschem and Abd Schems. Haschem, the progenitor of Mahomet, was a great benefactor of Mecca. This city is situated in the midst of a barren and stony country, and in former times was often subject to scarcity of provisions. At the beginning of the sixth century Haschem established two yearly caravans, one in the winter to South Arabia or Yemen; the other in the summer to Syria. By these means abundant supplies were brought to Mecca, as well as a great variety of merchandise. The city became a commercial mart, and the tribe of Koreish, which engaged largely in these expeditions, became wealthy and powerful. Haschem, at this time, was the guardian of the Caaba, the great shrine of Arabian pilgrimage and worship, the custody of which was confided to none but the most honorable tribes and families, in the same man-

ner, as in old times, the temple of Jerusalem was intrusted only to the care of the Levites. In fact the guardianship of the Caaba was connected with civil dignities
and privileges, and gave the holder of it the control of
the sacred city.

On the death of Haschem, his son, Abd al Motâlleb,
succeeded to his honors, and inherited his patriotism.
He delivered the holy city from an invading army of
troops and elephants, sent by the Christian princes of
Abyssinia, who at that time held Yemen in subjection.
These signal services rendered by father and son, confirmed the guardianship of the Caaba, in the line of Haschem; to the great discontent and envy of the line of
Abd Schems.

Abd al Motâlleb had several sons and daughters.
Those of his sons who figure in history were, Abu Taleb,
Abu Lahab, Abbas, Hamza, and Abdallah. The last
named was the youngest and best beloved. He married
Amina, a maiden of a distant branch of the same illustrious stock of Koreish. So remarkable was Abdallah for
personal beauty and those qualities which win the affections of women, that, if Moslem traditions are to be
credited, on the night of his marriage with Amina, two
hundred virgins of the tribe of Koreish died of broken
hearts.

Mahomet was the first and only fruit of the marriage
thus sadly celebrated. His birth, according to similar
traditions with the one just cited, was accompanied by

signs and portents announcing a child of wonder. His mother suffered none of the pangs of travail. At the moment of his coming into the world, a celestial light illumined the surrounding country, and the new-born child, raising his eyes to heaven, exclaimed: "God is great! There is no God but God, and I am his prophet."

Heaven and earth, we are assured, were agitated at his advent. The Lake Sawa shrank back to its secret springs, leaving its borders dry; while the Tigris, bursting its bounds, overflowed the neighboring lands. The palace of Khosru, the King of Persia, shook to its foundations, and several of its towers were toppled to the earth. In that troubled night the Kadhi, or Judge of Persia, beheld, in a dream, a ferocious camel conquered by an Arabian courser. He related his dream in the morning to the Persian monarch, and interpreted it to portend danger from the quarter of Arabia.

In the same eventful night the sacred fire of Zoroaster, which, guarded by the Magi, had burned without interruption for upwards of a thousand years, was suddenly extinguished, and all the idols in the world fell down. The demons, or evil genii, which lurk in the stars and the signs of the zodiac, and exert a malignant influence over the children of men, were cast forth by the pure angels, and hurled, with their arch-leader, Eblis, or Lucifer, into the depths of the sea.

The relatives of the new-born child, say the like authorities, were filled with awe and wonder. His mother's brother, an astrologer, cast his nativity, and predicted that he would rise to vast power, found an empire, and establish a new faith among men. His grandfather, Abd al Motâlleb, gave a feast to the principal Koreishites, the seventh day after his birth, at which he presented this child, as the dawning glory of their race, and gave him the name of Mahomet (or Muhamed), indicative of his future renown.

Such are the marvelous accounts given by Moslem writers of the infancy of Mahomet, and we have little else than similar fables about his early years. He was scarce two months old when his father died, leaving him no other inheritance than five camels, a few sheep, and a female slave of Ethiopia, named Barakat. His mother, Amina, had hitherto nurtured him, but care and sorrow dried the fountains of her breast, and the air of Mecca being unhealthy for children, she sought a nurse for him among the females of the neighboring Bedouin tribes. These were accustomed to come to Mecca twice a year, in spring and autumn, to foster the children of its inhabitants; but they looked for the offspring of the rich, where they were sure of ample recompense, and turned with contempt from this heir of poverty. At length Halêma, the wife of a Saadite shepherd, was moved to compassion, and took the helpless infant to her home. It was in one of the pastoral valleys of the mountains.*

* The Beni Sad (or children of Sad) date from the most remote antiquity, and, with the Katan Arabs, are the only remnants of the primitive

Many were the wonders related by Halêma of her infant charge. On the journey from Mecca, the mule which bore him became miraculously endowed with speech, and proclaimed aloud that he bore on his back the greatest of prophets, the chief of ambassadors, the favorite of the Almighty. The sheep bowed to him as he passed; as he lay in his cradle and gazed at the moon, it stooped to him in reverence.

The blessing of heaven, say the Arabian writers, rewarded the charity of Halêma. While the child remained under her roof, everything around her prospered. The wells and springs were never dried up; the pastures were always green; her flocks and herds increased tenfold; a marvelous abundance reigned over her fields, and peace prevailed in her dwelling.

The Arabian legends go on to extol the almost supernatural powers, bodily and mental, manifested by this wonderful child at a very early age. He could stand alone when three months old; run abroad when he was seven, and at ten could join other children in their sports with bows and arrows. At eight months he could speak so as to be understood; and in the course of another month could converse with fluency, displaying a wisdom astonishing to all who heard him.

At the age of three years, while playing in the fields with his foster-brother, Masroud, two angels in shining

tribes of Arabia. Their valley is among the mountains which range southwardly from the Tayef.—*Burckhardt on the Bedouins*, vol. ii. p. 47.

apparel appeared before them. They laid Mahomet gently upon the ground, and Gabriel, one of the angels, opened his breast, but without inflicting any pain. Then taking forth his heart, he cleansed it from all impurity, wringing from it those black and bitter drops of original sin, inherited from our forefather Adam, and which lurk in the hearts of the best of his descendants, inciting them to crime. When he had thoroughly purified it, he filled it with faith and knowledge and prophetic light, and replaced it in the bosom of the child. Now, we are assured by the same authorities, began to emanate from his countenance that mysterious light which had continued down from Adam, through the sacred line of prophets, till the time of Isaac and Ishmael; but which had laid dormant in the descendants of the latter until it thus shone forth with renewed radiance from the features of Mahomet.

At this supernatural visitation, it is added, was impressed between the shoulders of the child the seal of prophecy, which continued throughout life the symbol and credential of his divine mission; though unbelievers saw nothing in it but a large mole, the size of a pigeon's egg.

When the marvelous visitation of the angel was related to Halêma and her husband, they were alarmed lest some misfortune should be impending over the child, or that his supernatural visitors might be of the race of evil spirits or genii, which haunt the solitudes of the desert, wreaking mischief on the children of men. His Saadite nurse, therefore, carried him back to Mecca, and delivered him to his mother, Amina.

He remained with his parent until his sixth year, when she took him with her to Medina, on a visit to her relatives of the tribe of Adij; but on her journey homeward she died, and was buried at Abwa, a village between Medina and Mecca. Her grave, it will be found, was a place of pious resort and tender recollection to her son, at the latest period of his life.

The faithful Abyssinian slave Barakat, now acted as a mother to the orphan child, and conducted him to his grandfather Abd al Motâlleb, in whose household he remained for two years, treated with care and tenderness. Abd al Motâlleb was now well stricken in years; having outlived the ordinary term of human existence. Finding his end approaching, he called to him his eldest son Abu Taleb, and bequeathed Mahomet to his especial protection. The good Abu Taleb took his nephew to his bosom, and ever afterwards was to him as a parent. As the former succeeded to the guardianship of the Caaba at the death of his father, Mahomet continued for several years in a kind of sacerdotal household, where the rites and ceremonies of the sacred house were rigidly observed. And here we deem it necessary to give a more especial notice of the alleged origin of the Caaba and of the rites and traditions and superstitions connected with it, closely interwoven as they are with the faith of Islam and the story of its founder.

# CHAPTER III.

WHEN Adam and Eve were cast forth from Paradise, say Arabian traditions, they fell in different parts of the earth; Adam on a mountain of the island of Serendib, or Ceylon; Eve in Arabia on the borders of the Red Sea, where the port of Joddah is now situated. For two hundred years they wandered separate and lonely about the earth, until, in consideration of their penitence and wretchedness, they were permitted to come together again on Mount Arafat, not far from the present city of Mecca. In the depth of his sorrow and repentance, Adam, it is said, raised his hands and eyes to heaven, and implored the clemency of God; entreating that a shrine might be vouchsafed to him similar to that at which he had worshipped when in Paradise, and round which the angels used to move in adoring processions.

The supplication of Adam was effectual. A tabernacle or temple formed of radiant clouds was lowered down by the hands of angels, and placed immediately below its prototype in the celestial paradise. Towards this heaven-descended shrine, Adam thenceforth turned when in

43

prayer, and round it he daily made seven circuits in imitation of the rites of the adoring angels.

At the death of Adam, say the same traditions, the tabernacle of clouds passed away, or was again drawn up to heaven; but another, of the same form and in the same place, was built of stone and clay by Seth, the son of Adam. This was swept away by the deluge. Many generations afterwards, in the time of the patriarchs, when Hagar and her child Ishmael were near perishing with thirst in the desert, an angel revealed to them a spring or well of water, near to the ancient site of the tabernacle. This was the well of Zem Zem, held sacred by the progeny of Ishmael to the present day. Shortly afterwards two individuals of the gigantic race of the Amalekites, in quest of a camel which had strayed from their camp, discovered this well, and, having slaked their thirst, brought their companions to the place. Here they founded the city of Mecca, taking Ishmael and his mother under their protection. They were soon expelled by the proper inhabitants of the country, among whom Ishmael remained. When grown to man's estate, he married the daughter of the ruling prince, by whom he had a numerous progeny, the ancestors of the Arabian people. In process of time, by God's command he undertook to rebuild the Caaba, on the precise site of the original tabernacle of clouds. In this pious work he was assisted by his father Abraham. A miraculous stone served Abraham as a scaffold, rising and sinking with him as he built the walls of the sacred edifice. It still remains there an inestimable relic, and the print of the patriarch's foot is clearly to be perceived on it by all true believers.

While Abraham and Ishmael were thus occupied, the angel Gabriel brought them a stone, about which traditional accounts are a little at variance; by some it is said to have been one of the precious stones of Paradise, which fell to the earth with Adam, and was afterwards lost in the slime of the deluge, until retrieved by the angel Gabriel. The more received tradition is, that it was originally the guardian angel appointed to watch over Adam in Paradise, but changed into a stone and ejected thence with him at his fall, as a punishment for not having been more vigilant. This stone Abraham and Ishmael received with proper reverence, and inserted it in a corner of the exterior wall of the Caaba, where it remains to the present day, devoutly kissed by worshippers each time they make a circuit of the temple. When first inserted in the wall it was, we are told, a single jacinth of dazzling whiteness, but became gradually blackened by the kisses of sinful mortals. At the resurrection it will recover its angelic form, and stand forth a testimony before God in favor of those who have faithfully performed the rites of pilgrimage.

Such are the Arabian traditions, which rendered the Caaba and the well of Zem Zem objects of extraordinary veneration from the remotest antiquity among the people of the East, and especially the descendants of Ishmael.

Mecca, which incloses these sacred objects within its walls, was a holy city many ages before the rise of Mahometanism, and was the resort of pilgrims from all parts of Arabia. So universal and profound was the religious feeling respecting this observance, that four months in every year were devoted to the rites of pilgrimage, and held sacred from all violence and warfare. Hostile tribes then laid aside their arms; took the heads from their spears; traversed the late dangerous deserts in security; thronged the gates of Mecca clad in the pilgrim's garb; made their seven circuits round the Caaba in imitation of the angelic host; touched and kissed the mysterious black stone; drank and made ablutions at the well Zem Zem in memory of their ancestor Ishmael; and having performed all the other primitive rites of pilgrimage returned home in safety, again to resume their weapons and their wars.

Among the religious observances of the Arabs in these their "days of ignorance;" that is to say, before the promulgation of the Moslem doctrines, fasting and prayer had a foremost place. They had three principal fasts within the year; one of seven, one of nine, and one of thirty days. They prayed three times each day; about sunrise, at noon, and about sunset; turning their faces in the direction of the Caaba, which was their kebla or point of adoration. They had many religious traditions, some of them acquired in early times from the Jews, and they are said to have nurtured their devotional feelings with the book of Psalms, and with a book said to be by Seth, and filled with moral discourses.

Brought up, as Mahomet was, in the house of the guardian of the Caaba, the ceremonies and devotions connected with the sacred edifice may have given an early bias to his mind, and inclined it to those speculations in matters of religion by which it eventually became engrossed. Though his Moslem biographers would fain persuade us his high destiny was clearly foretold in his childhood by signs and prodigies, yet his education appears to have been as much neglected as that of ordinary Arab children; for we find that he was not taught either to read or write. He was a thoughtful child, however; quick to observe, prone to meditate on all that he observed, and possessed of an imagination fertile, daring, and expansive. The yearly influx of pilgrims from distant parts made Mecca a receptacle for all kinds of floating knowledge, which he appears to have imbibed with eagerness and retained in a tenacious memory; and as he increased in years, a more extended sphere of observation was gradually opened to him.

# CHAPTER IV.

MAHOMET was now twelve years of age, but, as we have shown, he had an intelligence far beyond his years. The spirit of inquiry was awake within him, quickened by intercourse with pilgrims from all parts of Arabia. His uncle Abu Taleb, too, beside his sacerdotal character as guardian of the Caaba, was one of the most enterprising merchants of the tribe of Koreish, and had much to do with those caravans set on foot by his ancestor Haschem, which traded to Syria and Yemen. The arrival and departure of those caravans, which thronged the gates of Mecca and filled its streets with pleasing tumult, were exciting events to a youth like Mahomet, and carried his imagination to foreign parts. He could no longer repress the ardent curiosity thus aroused; but once, when his uncle was about to mount his camel to depart with the caravan for Syria, clung to him, and entreated to be permitted to accompany him. "For who, O my uncle," said he, "will take care of me when thou art away?"

The appeal was not lost upon the kind-hearted Abu

Taleb. He bethought him, too, that the youth was of an age to enter upon the active scenes of Arab life, and of a capacity to render essential service in the duties of the caravan; he readily, therefore, granted his prayer, and took him with him on the journey to Syria.

The route lay through regions fertile in fables and traditions, which it is the delight of the Arabs to recount in the evening halts of the caravan. The vast solitudes of the desert, in which that wandering people pass so much of their lives, are prone to engender superstitious fancies; they have accordingly peopled them with good and evil genii, and clothed them with tales of enchantment, mingled up with wonderful events which happened in days of old. In these evening halts of the caravan, the youthful mind of Mahomet doubtless imbibed many of those superstitions of the desert which ever afterwards dwelt in his memory, and had a powerful influence over his imagination. We may especially note two traditions which he must have heard at this time, and which we find recorded by him in after years in the Koran. One related to the mountainous district of Hedjar. Here, as the caravan wound its way through silent and deserted valleys, caves were pointed out in the sides of the mountains once inhabited by the Beni Thamud, or children of Thamud, one of the "lost tribes" of Arabia; and this was the tradition concerning them.

They were a proud and gigantic race, existing before the time of the patriarch Abraham. Having fallen into blind idolatry, God sent a prophet of the name of Saleh, to restore them to the right way. They refused, however, to listen to him, unless he should prove the divinity of his mission by causing a camel, big with young, to issue from the entrails of a mountain. Saleh accordingly prayed, and lo! a rock opened, and a female camel came forth, which soon produced a foal. Some of the Thamudites were convinced by the miracle, and were converted by the prophet from their idolatry; the greater part, however, remained in unbelief. Saleh left the camel among them as a sign, warning them that a judgment from heaven would fall on them, should they do her any harm. For a time the camel was suffered to feed quietly in their pastures, going forth in the morning, and returning in the evening. It is true, that when she bowed her head to drink from a brook or well, she never raised it until she had drained the last drop of water; but then in return she yielded milk enough to supply the whole tribe. As, however, she frightened the other camels from the pasture, she became an object of offense to the Thamudites, who hamstrung and slew her. Upon this there was a fearful cry from heaven, and great claps of thunder, and in the morning all the offenders were found lying on their faces dead. Thus the whole race was swept from the earth, and their country was laid for ever afterward under the ban of heaven.

This story made a powerful impression on the mind of Mahomet, insomuch that, in after years, he refused to let his people encamp in the neighborhood, but hurried them away from it as an accursed region.

Another tradition, gathered on this journey, related to the city of Eyla, situated near the Red Sea. This place, he was told, had been inhabited in old times by a tribe of Jews, who lapsed into idolatry and profaned the Sabbath, by fishing on that sacred day; whereupon the old men were transformed into swine, and the young men into monkeys.

We have noted these two traditions especially, because they are both cited by Mahomet as instances of divine judgment on the crime of idolatry, and evince the bias his youthful mind was already taking on that important subject.

Moslem writers tell us, as usual, of wonderful circumstances which attended the youth throughout this journey, giving evidence of the continual guardianship of heaven. At one time, as he traversed the burning sands of the desert, an angel hovered over him unseen, sheltering him with his wings; a miracle, however, which evidently does not rest on the evidence of an eye-witness; at another time he was protected by a cloud which hung over his head during the noontide heat; and on another occasion, as he sought the scanty shade of a withered tree, it suddenly put forth leaves and blossoms.

After skirting the ancient domains of the Moabites and the Ammonites, often mentioned in the sacred Scriptures, the caravan arrived at Bosra, or Bostra, on the confines

of Syria, in the country of the tribe of Manasseh, beyond
the Jordan. In Scripture days it had been a city of the
Levites, but now was inhabited by Nestorian Christians.
It was a great mart, annually visited by the caravans;
and here our wayfarers came to a halt, and encamped
near a convent of Nestorian monks.

By this fraternity Abu Taleb and his nephew were entertained with great hospitality. One of the monks, by
some called Sergius, by others Bahira, * on conversing
with Mahomet, was surprised at the precocity of his intellect, and interested by his eager desire for information,
which appears to have had reference, principally, to matters of religion. They had frequent conversations together on such subjects, in the course of which the efforts
of the monk must have been mainly directed against that
idolatry in which the youthful Mahomet had hitherto
been educated; for the Nestorian Christians were strenuous in condemning not merely the worship of images, but
even the casual exhibition of them; indeed, so far did
they carry their scruples on this point, that even the
cross, that general emblem of Christianity, was in a great
degree included in this prohibition.

Many have ascribed that knowledge of the principles
and traditions of the Christian faith displayed by Mahomet in after life, to those early conversations with this
monk; it is probable, however, that he had further in-

* Some assert that these two names indicate two monks who held conversations with Mahomet.

tercourse with the latter in the course of subsequent visits which he made to Syria.

Moslem writers pretend that the interest taken by the monk in the youthful stranger, arose from his having accidentally perceived between his shoulders the seal of prophecy. He warned Abu Taleb, say they, when about to set out on his return to Mecca, to take care that his nephew did not fall into the hands of the Jews ; foreseeing with the eye of prophecy the trouble and opposition he was to encounter from that people.

It required no miraculous sign, however, to interest a sectarian monk, anxious to make proselytes, in an intelligent and inquiring youth, nephew of the guardian of the Caaba, who might carry back with him to Mecca the seeds of Christianity sown in his tender mind; and it was natural that the monk should be eager to prevent his hoped-for convert, in the present unsettled state of his religious opinions, from being beguiled into the Jewish faith.

Mahomet returned to Mecca, his imagination teeming with the wild tales and traditions picked up in the desert, and his mind deeply impressed with the doctrines imparted to him in the Nestorian convent. He seems ever afterwards to have entertained a mysterious reverence for Syria, probably from the religious impressions received there. It was the land whither Abraham the patriarch had repaired from Chaldea, taking with him the primitive worship of the one true God. "Verily," he used to say in after years, "God has ever maintained guardians of his word in Syria; forty in number; when one dies another is sent in his room; and through them the land is blessed." And again—"Joy be to the people of Syria, for the angels of the kind God spread their wings over them." *

* *Mishcât-ul-Masâbih,* vol. ii. p. 812.

NOTE.—The conversion of Abraham from the idolatry into which the world had fallen after the deluge, is related in the sixth chapter of the Koran. Abraham's father, Azer, or Zerah, as his name is given in the Scriptures, was a statuary and an idolater.

"And Abraham said unto his father Azer, 'Why dost thou take graven images for gods? Verily, thou and thy people are in error.'

"Then was the firmament of heaven displayed unto Abraham, that he might see how the world was governed.

"When night came, and darkness overshadowed the earth, he beheld a bright star shining in the firmament, and cried out to his people who were astrologers: 'This, according to your assertions, is the Lord.'

"But the star set, and Abraham said, 'I have no faith in gods that set.'

"He beheld the moon rising, and exclaimed, 'Assuredly, this is the Lord.' But the moon likewise set, and he was confounded, and prayed unto God, saying, 'Direct me, lest I become as one of these people, who go astray.'

"When he saw the sun rising, he cried out, 'This is the most glorious of all; this of a certainty is the Lord.' But the sun also set. Then said Abraham, 'I believe not, my people, in those things which ye call gods. Verily, I turn my face unto Him, the Creator, who hath formed both the heavens and the earth.'"

## CHAPTER V.

COMMERCIAL OCCUPATIONS OF MAHOMET.—HIS MARRIAGE WITH CADIJAH.

AHOMET was now completely launched in active life, accompanying his uncles in various expeditions. At one time, when about sixteen years of age, we find him with his uncle Zobier, journeying with the caravan to Yemen; at another time acting as armor-bearer to the same uncle, who led a warlike expedition of Koreishites in aid of the Kenanites against the tribe of Hawazan. This is cited as Mahomet's first essay in arms, though he did little else than supply his uncle with arrows in the heat of the action, and shield him from the darts of the enemy. It is stigmatized among Arabian writers as al Fadjar, or the impious war, having been carried on during the sacred months of pilgrimage.

As Mahomet advanced in years, he was employed by different persons as commercial agent or factor in caravan journeys to Syria, Yemen, and elsewhere; all which tended to enlarge the sphere of his observation, and to give him a quick insight into character and a knowledge of human affairs.

He was a frequent attender of fairs also, which, in
Arabia, were not always mere resorts of traffic, but occasionally scenes of poetical contests between different
tribes, where prizes were adjudged to the victors, and
their prize poems treasured up in the archives of princes.
Such, especially, was the case with the fair of Ocadh;
and seven of the prize poems adjudged there, were hung
up as trophies in the Caaba. At these fairs, also, were
recited the popular traditions of the Arabs, and inculcated the various religious faiths which were afloat in
Arabia. From oral sources of this kind, Mahomet gradually accumulated much of that varied information as to
creeds and doctrines which he afterwards displayed.

There was at this time residing in Mecca a widow,
named Cadijah (or Khadijah), of the tribe of Koreish.
She had been twice married. Her last husband, a
wealthy merchant, had recently died, and the extensive
concerns of the house were in need of a conductor. A
nephew of the widow, named Chuzima, had become acquainted with Mahomet in the course of his commercial
expeditions, and had noticed the ability and integrity
with which he acquitted himself on all occasions. He
pointed him out to his aunt as a person well qualified to
be her factor. The personal appearance of Mahomet
may have strongly seconded this recommendation; for
he was now about twenty-five years of age, and extolled
by Arabian writers for his manly beauty and engaging
manners. So desirous was Cadijah of securing his ser-

vices, that she offered him double wages to conduct a caravan which she was on the point of sending off to Syria. Mahomet consulted his uncle Abu Taleb, and by his advice accepted the offer. He was accompanied and aided in the expedition by the nephew of the widow, and by her slave Maïsara, and so highly satisfied was Cadijah with the way in which he discharged his duties, that, on his return, she paid him double the amount of his stipulated wages. She afterwards sent him to the southern parts of Arabia on similar expeditions, in all which he gave like satisfaction.

Cadijah was now in her fortieth year, a woman of judgment and experience. The mental qualities of Mahomet rose more and more in her estimation, and her heart began to yearn toward the fresh and comely youth. According to Arabian legends, a miracle occurred most opportunely to confirm and sanctify the bias of her inclinations. She was one day with her handmaids, at the hour of noon, on the terraced roof of her dwelling, watching the arrival of a caravan conducted by Mahomet. As it approached, she beheld, with astonishment, two angels overshadowing him with their wings to protect him from the sun. Turning, with emotion, to her handmaids, "Behold!" said she, "the beloved of Allah, who sends two angels to watch over him!"

Whether or not the handmaidens looked forth with the same eyes of devotion as their mistress, and likewise discerned the angels, the legend does not mention. Suffice it to say, the widow was filled with a lively faith in the superhuman merits of her youthful steward, and forthwith commissioned her trusty slave, Maïsara, to offer him her hand. The negotiation is recorded with simple brevity. "Mahomet," demanded Maïsara, "why dost thou not marry?" "I have not the means," replied Mahomet. "Well, but if a wealthy dame should offer thee her hand: one also who is handsome and of high birth?" "And who is she?" "Cadijah!" "How is that possible?" "Let me manage it." Maïsara returned to his mistress and reported what had passed. An hour was appointed for an interview, and the affair was brought to a satisfactory arrangement with that promptness and sagacity which had distinguished Mahomet in all his dealings with the widow. The father of Cadijah made some opposition to the match, on account of the poverty of Mahomet, following the common notion that wealth should be added to wealth : but the widow wisely considered her riches only as the means of enabling her to follow the dictates of her heart. She gave a great feast, to which were invited her father and the rest of her relatives, and Mahomet's uncles Abu Taleb and Hamza, together with several other of the Koreishites. At this banquet wine was served in abundance, and soon diffused good humor round the board. The objections to Mahomet's poverty were forgotten; speeches were made by Abu Taleb on the one side, and by Waraka, a kinsman of Cadijah, on the other, in praise of the proposed nuptials; the dowry was arranged, and the marriage formally concluded.

Mahomet then caused a camel to be killed before his door, and the flesh distributed among the poor. The house was thrown open to all comers; the female slaves of Cadijah danced to the sound of timbrels, and all was revelry and rejoicing. Abu Taleb, forgetting his age and his habitual melancholy, made merry on the occasion. He had paid down from his purse a dower of twelve and a half okks of gold, equivalent to twenty young camels. Halêma, who had nursed Mahomet in his infancy, was summoned to rejoice at his nuptials, and was presented with a flock of forty sheep, with which she returned, enriched and contented, to her native valley, in the desert of the Saadites.

# CHAPTER VI.

CONDUCT OF MAHOMET AFTER HIS MARRIAGE.—BECOMES ANXIOUS FOR RELIG-
IOUS REFORM.—HIS HABITS OF SOLITARY ABSTRACTION.—THE VISION OF
THE CAVE.—HIS ANNUNCIATION AS A PROPHET.

HE marriage with Cadijah placed Mahomet among the most wealthy of his native city. His moral worth also gave him great influence in the community. Allah, says the historian Abulfeda, had endowed him with every gift necessary to accomplish and adorn an honest man; he was so pure and sincere, so free from every evil thought, that he was commonly known by the name of Al Amin or The Faithful.

The great confidence reposed in his judgment and probity, caused him to be frequently referred to as arbiter in disputes between his townsmen. An anecdote is given as illustrative of his sagacity on such occasions. The Caaba having been injured by fire, was undergoing repairs, in the course of which the sacred black stone was to be replaced. A dispute arose among the chiefs of the various tribes, as to which was entitled to perform so august an office, and they agreed to abide by the decision of the first person who should enter by the gate Al

Harâm. That person happened to be Mahomet. Upon hearing their different claims, he directed that a great cloth should be spread upon the ground, and the stone laid thereon; and that a man from each tribe should take hold of the border of the cloth. In this way the sacred stone was raised equally and at the same time by them all to a level with its allotted place, in which Mahomet fixed it with his own hands.

Four daughters and one son, were the fruit of the marriage with Cadijah. The son was named Kasim, whence Mahomet was occasionally called Abu Kasim, or the father of Kasim, according to Arabian nomenclature. This son, however, died in his infancy.

For several years after his marriage he continued in commerce, visiting the great Arabian fairs, and making distant journeys with the caravans. His expeditions were not as profitable as in the days of his stewardship, and the wealth acquired with his wife diminished, rather than increased in the course of his operations. That wealth, in fact, had raised him above the necessity of toiling for subsistence, and given him leisure to indulge the original bias of his mind—a turn for reverie and religious speculation, which he had evinced from his earliest years. This had been fostered in the course of his journeyings by his intercourse with Jews and Christians, originally fugitives from persecution, but now gathered into tribes, or forming part of the population of cities. The Arabian deserts too, rife as we have shown

them with fanciful superstitions, had furnished aliment
for his enthusiastic reveries. Since his marriage with
Cadijah, also, he had a household oracle to influence him
in his religious opinions. This was his wife's cousin
Waraka, a man of speculative mind and flexible faith;
originally a Jew; subsequently a Christian; and withal
a pretender to astrology. He is worthy of note as being
the first on record to translate parts of the Old and New
Testament into Arabic. From him Mahomet is supposed
to have derived much of his information respecting those
writings, and many of the traditions of the Mishnu and
the Talmud, on which he draws so copiously in his
Koran.

The knowledge thus variously acquired and treasured
up in an uncommonly retentive memory, was in direct
hostility to the gross idolatry prevalent in Arabia, and
practiced at the Caaba. That sacred edifice had gradually become filled and surrounded by idols, to the number of three hundred and sixty, being one for every day
of the Arab year. Hither had been brought idols from
various parts, the deities of other nations, the chief of
which, Hobal, was from Syria, and supposed to have the
power of giving rain. Among these idols, too, were
Abraham and Ishmael, once revered as prophets and
progenitors, now represented with divining arrows in
their hands, symbols of magic.

Mahomet became more and more sensible of the gross-
ness and absurdity of this idolatry, in proportion as his

intelligent mind contrasted it with the spiritual religions, which had been the subject of his inquiries. Various passages in the Koran show the ruling idea which gradually sprang up in his mind, until it engrossed his thoughts and influenced all his actions. That idea was a religious reform. It had become his fixed belief, deduced from all that he had learnt and meditated, that the only true religion had been revealed to Adam at his creation, and been promulgated and practiced in the days of innocence. That religion inculcated the direct and spiritual worship of one true and only God, the Creator of the universe.

It was his belief, furthermore, that this religion, so elevated and simple, had repeatedly been corrupted and debased by man, and especially outraged by idolatry; wherefore a succession of prophets, each inspired by a revelation from the Most High, had been sent from time to time, and at distant periods, to restore it to its original purity. Such was Noah, such was Abraham, such was Moses, and such was Jesus Christ. By each of these, the true religion had been reinstated upon earth, but had again been vitiated by their followers. The faith, as taught and practiced by Abraham when he came out of the land of Chaldea, seems especially to have formed a religious standard in his mind, from his veneration for the patriarch as the father of Ishmael, the progenitor of his race.

It appeared to Mahomet that the time for another re-

form was again arrived. The world had once more lapsed
into blind idolatry. It needed the advent of another
prophet, authorized by a mandate from on high, to restore the erring children of men to the right path, and to
bring back the worship of the Caaba to what it had been
in the days of Abraham and the patriarchs. The proba-
bility of such an advent with its attendant reforms, seems
to have taken possession of his mind, and produced habits of reverie and meditation, incompatible with the ordinary concerns of life and the bustle of the world. We are
told that he gradually absented himself from society, and
sought the solitude of a cavern on Mount Hara, about
three leagues north of Mecca, where, in emulation of the
Christian anchorites of the desert, he would remain days
and nights together, engaged in prayer and meditation.
In this way he always passed the month of Ramadhan,
the holy month of the Arabs. Such intense occupation
of the mind on one subject, accompanied by fervent enthusiasm of spirit, could not but have a powerful effect
upon his frame. He became subject to dreams, to ecstasies, and trances. For six months successively, according
to one of his historians, he had constant dreams bearing
on the subject of his waking thoughts. Often he would
lose all consciousness of surrounding objects, and lie
upon the ground as if insensible. Cadijah, who was
sometimes the faithful companion of his solitude, beheld
these paroxysms with anxious solicitude, and entreated
to know the cause; but he evaded her inquiries, or an-

swered them mysteriously. Some of his adversaries have attributed them to epilepsy, but devout Moslems declare them to have been the workings of prophecy; for already, say they, the intimations of the Most High began to dawn, though vaguely, on his spirit; and his mind labored with conceptions too great for mortal thought. At length, say they, what had hitherto been shadowed out in dreams, was made apparent and distinct by an angelic apparition and a divine annunciation.

It was in the fortieth year of his age, when this famous revelation took place. Accounts are given of it by Moslem writers as if received from his own lips, and it is alluded to in certain passages of the Koran. He was passing, as was his wont, the month of Ramadhan in the cavern of Mount Hara, endeavoring by fasting, prayer, and solitary meditation to elevate his thoughts to the contemplation of divine truth. It was on the night called by Arabs Al Kader, or the Divine Decree; a night in which, according to the Koran, angels descend to earth, and Gabriel brings down the decrees of God. During that night there is peace on earth, and a holy quiet reigns over all nature until the rising of the morn.

As Mahomet, in the silent watches of the night, lay wrapped in his mantle, he heard a voice calling upon him; uncovering his head, a flood of light broke upon him of such intolerable splendor that he swooned away. On regaining his senses, he beheld an angel in a human form, which, approaching from a distance, displayed a silken cloth covered with written characters. "Read!" said the angel.

"I know not how to read!" replied Mahomet.

"Read!" repeated the angel, "in the name of the Lord, who has created all things; who created man from a clot of blood. Read, in the name of the Most High, who taught man the use of the pen; who sheds on his soul the ray of knowledge, and teaches him what before he knew not."

Upon this Mahomet instantly felt his understanding illumined with celestial light, and read what was written on the cloth, which contained the decrees of God, as afterwards promulgated in the Koran. When he had finished the perusal, the heavenly messenger announced, "O Mahomet, of a verity, thou art the prophet of God! and I am his angel Gabriel."

Mahomet, we are told, came trembling and agitated to Cadijah in the morning, not knowing whether what he had heard and seen was indeed true, and that he was a prophet decreed to effect that reform so long the object of his meditations; or whether it might not be a mere vision, a delusion of the senses, or worse than all, the apparition of an evil spirit.

Cadijah, however, saw everything with the eye of faith, and the credulity of an affectionate woman. She saw in it the fruition of her husband's wishes, and the end of his paroxysms and privations. "Joyful tidings dost thou bring!" exclaimed she. "By him, in whose hand is the soul of Cadijah, I will henceforth regard thee as the prophet of our nation. Rejoice," added she, seeing him still cast down; "Allah will not suffer thee to fall to shame. Hast thou not been loving to thy kinsfolk, kind to thy neighbors, charitable to the poor, hospitable to the stranger, faithful to thy word, and ever a defender of the truth?"

Cadijah hastened to communicate what she had heard to her cousin Waraka, the translator of the Scriptures; who, as we have shown, had been a household oracle of Mahomet in matters of religion. He caught at once, and with eagerness, at this miraculous annunciation. "By him in whose hand is the soul of Waraka," exclaimed he; "thou speakest true, O Cadijah! The angel who has appeared to thy husband is the same who, in days of old, was sent to Moses the son of Amram. His annunciation is true. Thy husband is indeed a prophet!"

The zealous concurrence of the learned Waraka, is said to have had a powerful effect in fortifying the dubious mind of Mahomet.

NOTE.—Dr. Gustav Weil, in a note to *Mohammed der Prophet*, discusses the question of Mahomet's being subject to attacks of epilepsy; which has generally been represented as a slander of his enemies and of Christian writers. It appears, however, to have been asserted by some of the oldest Moslem biographers, and given on the authority of persons about him. He would be seized, they said, with violent trembling, followed by a kind of swoon, or rather convulsion, during which perspiration would stream from his forehead in the coldest weather; he would lie with his eyes closed, foaming at the mouth and bellowing like a young camel. Ayesha, one of his wives, and Zeid, one of his disciples, are among the persons cited as testifying to that effect.   They considered him at such times as under the influence of a revelation.   He had such attacks, however, in Mecca, before the Koran was revealed to him.   Cadijah feared that he was possessed by evil spirits, and would have called in the aid of a conjurer to exorcise them, but he forbade her.   He did not like that any one should see him during these paroxysms.   His visions, however, were not always preceded by such attacks.   Hareth Ibn Haschem, it is said, once asked him in what manner the revelations were made.   "Often," replied he, "the angel appears to me in a human form, and speaks to me.   Sometimes I hear sounds like the tinkling of a bell, but see nothing.   [A ringing in the ears is a symptom of epilepsy.]   When the invisible angel has departed, I am possessed of what he has revealed."   Some of his revelations he professed to receive direct from God, others in dreams ; for the dreams of prophets, he used to say, are revelations.

The reader will find this note of service in throwing some degree of light upon the enigmatical career of this extraordinary man.

# CHAPTER VII.

MAHOMET INCULCATES HIS DOCTRINES SECRETLY AND SLOWLY.—RECEIVES
FURTHER REVELATIONS AND COMMANDS.—ANNOUNCEMENT TO HIS KIN-
DRED.—MANNER IN WHICH IT WAS RECEIVED.—ENTHUSIASTIC DEVOTION
OF ALL.—CHRISTIAN PORTENTS.

OR a time Mahomet confided his revelations
merely to his own household. One of the first
to avow himself a believer, was his servant
Zeid, an Arab of the tribe of Kalb. This youth had been
captured in childhood by a freebooting party of Koreishites, and had come by purchase or lot into the possession of Mahomet. Several years afterwards his father,
hearing of his being in Mecca, repaired thither and offered a considerable sum for his ransom. "If he chooses
to go with thee," said Mahomet, "he shall go without
ransom : but if he chooses to remain with me, why should
I not keep him?" Zeid preferred to remain, having
ever, he said, been treated more as a son than as a slave.
Upon this, Mahomet publicly adopted him, and he had
ever since remained with him in affectionate servitude.
Now, on embracing the new faith, he was set entirely
free, but it will be found that he continued through life

69

that devoted attachment which Mahomet seems to have had the gift of inspiring in his followers and dependents.

The early steps of Mahomet in his prophetic career, were perilous and doubtful, and taken in secrecy. He had hostility to apprehend on every side; from his immediate kindred, the Koreishites of the line of Haschem, whose power and prosperity were identified with idolatry; and still more from the rival line of Abd Schems, who had long looked with envy and jealousy on the Haschemites, and would eagerly raise the cry of heresy and impiety to dispossess them of the guardianship of the Caaba. At the head of this rival branch of Koreish was Abu Sofian, the son of Harb, grandson of Omeya, and great-grandson of Abd Schems. He was an able and ambitious man, of great wealth and influence, and will be found one of the most persevering and powerful opponents of Mahomet.*

Under these adverse circumstances the new faith was propagated secretly and slowly, insomuch that for the first three years the number of converts did not exceed forty; these, too, for the most part, were young persons, strangers, and slaves. Their meetings for prayer were held in private, either at the house of one of the initiated,

---

* Niebuhr (*Travels*, vol. ii.) speaks of the tribe of Harb, which possessed several cities and a number of villages in the highlands of Hedjas, a mountainous range between Mecca and Medina. They have castles on precipitous rocks, and harass and lay under contribution the caravans. It is presumed that this tribe takes its name from the father of Abu Sofian; as did the great line of the Omeyades from his grandfather.

or in a cave near Mecca. Their secrecy, however, did not protect them from outrage. Their meetings were discovered; a rabble broke into their cavern and a scuffle ensued. One of the assailants was wounded in the head by Saad, an armorer, thenceforth renowned among the faithful, as the first of their number who shed blood in the cause of Islam.

One of the bitterest opponents of Mahomet was his uncle Abu Lahab, a wealthy man, of proud spirit and irritable temper. His son Otha had married Mahomet's third daughter, Rokaia, so that they were doubly allied. Abu Lahab, however, was also allied to the rival line of Koreish, having married Omm Jemil, sister of Abu Sofian, and he was greatly under the control of his wife and his brother-in-law. He reprobated what he termed the heresies of his nephew, as calculated to bring disgrace upon their immediate line, and to draw upon it the hostilities of the rest of the tribe of Koreish. Mahomet was keenly sensible of the rancorous opposition of this uncle, which he attributed to the instigations of his wife, Omm Jemil. He especially deplored it, as he saw that it affected the happiness of his daughter Rokaia, whose inclination to his doctrines brought on her the reproaches of her husband and his family.

These and other causes of solicitude preyed upon his spirits, and increased the perturbation of his mind. He became worn and haggard, and subject more and more to fits of abstraction. Those of his relatives who were attached to him, noticed his altered mien, and dreaded an attack of illness; others scoffingly accused him of mental hallucination; and the foremost among these scoffers was his uncle's wife, Omm Jemil, the sister of Abu Sofian.

The result of this disordered state of mind and body was another vision, or revelation, commanding him to "arise, preach, and magnify the Lord." He was now to announce, publicly and boldly, his doctrines, beginning with his kindred and tribe. Accordingly, in the fourth year of what is called his mission, he summoned all the Koreishites of the line of Haschem to meet him on the hill of Safa, in the vicinity of Mecca, when he would unfold matters important to their welfare. They assembled there, accordingly, and among them came Mahomet's hostile uncle Abu Lahab, and with him his scoffing wife, Omm Jemil. Scarce had the prophet begun to discourse of his mission, and to impart his revelations, when Abu Lahab started up in a rage, reviled him for calling them together on so idle an errand, and catching up a stone, would have hurled it at him. Mahomet turned upon him a withering look; cursed the hand thus raised in menace, and predicted his doom to the fire of Jehennam; with the assurance that his wife, Omm Jemil, would bear the bundle of thorns with which the fire would be kindled.

The assembly broke up in confusion. Abu Lahab and his wife, exasperated at the curse dealt out to them, compelled their son, Otha, to repudiate his wife, Rokaia, and sent her back weeping to Mahomet. She was soon indemnified, however, by having a husband of the true faith, being eagerly taken to wife by Mahomet's zealous disciple, Othman Ibn Affan.

Nothing discouraged by the failure of his first attempt, Mahomet called a second meeting of the Haschemites at his own house, where, having regaled them with the flesh of a lamb, and given them milk to drink, he stood forth and announced, at full length, his revelations received from heaven, and the divine command to impart them to those of his immediate line.

"O children of Abd al Motâlleb," cried he, with enthusiasm, "to you, of all men, has Allah vouchsafed these most precious gifts. In his name I offer you the blessings of this world, and endless joys hereafter. Who among you will share the burden of my offer? Who will be my brother, my lieutenant, my vizier?"

All remained silent; some wondering; others smiling with incredulity and derision. At length Ali, starting up with youthful zeal, offered himself to the service of the prophet, though modestly acknowledging his youth and physical weakness.* Mahomet threw his arms around the generous youth, and pressed him to his bosom. "Behold my brother, my vizier, my vicegerent," exclaimed he; "let all listen to his words, and obey him."

The outbreak of such a stripling as Ali, however, was

---

* By an error of translators, Ali is made to accompany his offer of adhesion by an extravagant threat against all who should oppose Mahomet.

answered by a scornful burst of laughter of the Koreishites ; who taunted Abu Taleb, father of the youthful
proselyte, with having to bow down before his son, and
yield him obedience.

But though the doctrines of Mahomet were thus un-
graciously received by his kindred and friends, they
found favor among the people at large, especially among
the women, who are ever prone to befriend a persecuted
cause. Many of the Jews, also, followed him for a time,
but when they found that he permitted his disciples to
eat the flesh of the camel, and of other animals forbidden
by their law, they drew back and rejected his religion as
unclean.

Mahomet now threw off all reserve, or rather was inspired with increasing enthusiasm, and went about
openly and earnestly proclaiming his doctrines, and
giving himself out as a prophet, sent by God to put an
end to idolatry, and to mitigate the rigor of the Jewish
and the Christian law. The hills of Safa and Kubeis,
sanctified by traditions concerning Hagar and Ishmael,
were his favorite places of preaching, and Mount Hara
was his Sinai, whither he retired occasionally, in fits of
excitement and enthusiasm, to return from its solitary
cave with fresh revelations of the Koran.

The good old Christian writers, on treating of the advent of one whom they denounce as the Arab enemy of
the church, make superstitious record of divers prodigies
which occurred, about this time, awful forerunners of

the troubles about to agitate the world. In Constantinople, at that time the seat of Christian empire, were several monstrous births and prodigious apparitions, which struck dismay into the hearts of all beholders. In certain religious processions in that neighborhood, the crosses on a sudden moved of themselves, and were violently agitated, causing astonishment and terror. The Nile, too, that ancient mother of wonders, gave birth to two hideous forms, seemingly man and woman, which rose out of its waters, gazed about them for a time with terrific aspect, and sank again beneath the waves. For a whole day the sun appeared to be diminished to one third of its usual size, shedding pale and baleful rays. During a moonless night a furnace light glowed throughout the heavens, and bloody lances glittered in the sky.

All these, and sundry other like marvels, were interpreted into signs of coming troubles. The ancient servants of God shook their heads mournfully, predicting the reign of antichrist at hand; with vehement persecution of the Christian faith, and great desolation of the churches; and to such holy men who have passed through the trials and troubles of the faith, adds the venerable Padre Jayme Bleda, it is given to understand and explain these mysterious portents, which forerun disasters of the church; even as it is given to ancient mariners to read in the signs of the air, the heavens and the deep, the coming tempest which is to overwhelm their bark.

Many of these sainted men were gathered to glory
before the completion of their prophecies. There, seated
securely in the empyreal heavens, they may have looked
down with compassion upon the troubles of the Christian
world; as men on the serene heights of mountains look
down upon the tempests which sweep the earth and sea,
wrecking tall ships, and rending lofty towers.

# CHAPTER VIII.

OUTLINES OF THE MAHOMETAN FAITH.

THOUGH it is not intended in this place to go fully into the doctrines promulgated by Mahomet, yet it is important to the right appreciation of his character and conduct, and of the events and circumstances set forth in the following narrative, to give their main features.

It must be particularly borne in mind, that Mahomet did not profess to set up a new religion; but to restore that derived in the earliest times from God himself. "We follow," says the Koran, "the religion of Abraham the orthodox, who was no idolater. We believe in God and that which hath been sent down to us, and that which hath been sent down unto Abraham and Ishmael, and Isaac and Jacob and the tribes, and that which was delivered unto Moses and Jesus, and that which was delivered unto the prophets from the Lord: we make no distinction between any of them, and to God we are resigned." *

* *Koran*, chap. ii.

77

The Koran,\* which was the great book of his faith, was delivered in portions from time to time, according to the excitement of his feelings, or the exigency of circumstances. It was not given as his own work, but as a divine revelation; as the very words of God. The Deity is supposed to speak in every instance. "We have sent thee down the book of truth, confirming the scripture which was revealed before it, and preserving the same in its purity." †

The law of Moses, it was said, had for a time been the guide and rule of human conduct. At the coming of Jesus Christ it was superseded by the Gospel; both were now to give place to the Koran, which was more full and explicit than the preceding codes, and intended to reform the abuses which had crept into them through the negligence or the corruptions of their professors. It was the completion of the Law; after it there would be no more divine revelations. Mahomet was the last, as he was the greatest, of the line of prophets sent to make known the will of God.

The unity of God was the corner-stone of this reformed religion. "There is no God but God," was its leading dogma. Hence, it received the name of the religion of Islam,‡ an Arabian word, implying submission to God.

---

\* Derived from the Arabic word Kora, to read or teach.

† *Koran*, ch. v.

‡ Some etymologists derive Islam from Salem or Aslama, which signifies salvation. The Christians form from it the term Islamism, and the

To this leading dogma, was added, "Mahomet is the prophet of God;" an addition authorized, as it was maintained, by the divine annunciation, and important to procure a ready acceptation of his revelations.

Beside the unity of God, a belief was inculcated in his angels or ministering spirits; in his prophets; in the resurrection of the body; in the last judgment and a future state of rewards and punishments, and in predestination. Much of the Koran may be traced to the Bible, the Mishnu and the Talmud of the Jews,* especially its wild though often beautiful traditions concerning the angels, the prophets, the patriarchs, and the good

Jews have varied it into Ismailism, which they intend as a reproach, and an allusion to the origin of the Arabs as descendants of Ishmael.

From Islam the Arabians drew the terms Moslem or Muslem, and Musulman, a professor of the faith of Islam. These terms are in the singular number and make Musliman in the dual, and Muslimen in the plural. The French and some other nations follow the idioms of their own languages in adopting or translating the Arabic terms, and form the plural by the addition of the letter *s* ; writing Musulman and Musulmans. A few English writers, of whom Gibbon is the chief, have imitated them, imagining that they were following the Arabian usage. Most English authors, however, follow the idiom of their own language, writing Moslem and Moslems, Musulman and Musulmen ; this usage is also the more harmonious.

\* *The Mishnu* of the Jews, like the Sonna of the Mahometans, is a collection of traditions forming the Oral Law. It was compiled in the second century by Judah Hakkodish, a learned Jewish Rabbi, during the reign of Antoninus Pius, the Roman Emperor.

The Jerusalem Talmud and the Babylonish Talmud, are both commentaries on the Mishnu. The former was compiled at Jerusalem, about three hundred years after Christ, and the latter in Babylonia, about two centuries later. The Mishnu is the most ancient record possessed by the Jews except the Bible.

and evil genii. He had at an early age imbibed a reverence for the Jewish faith, his mother, it is suggested,
having been of that religion.

The system laid down in the Koran, however, was es-
sentially founded on the Christian doctrines inculcated
in the New Testament; as they had been expounded to
him by the Christian sectarians of Arabia. Our Saviour
was to be held in the highest reverence as an inspired
prophet, the greatest that had been sent before the time
of Mahomet, to reform the Law; but all idea of his divinity was rejected as impious, and the doctrine of the
Trinity was denounced as an outrage on the unity of God.
Both were pronounced errors and interpolations of the
expounders; and this, it will be observed, was the opinion of some of the Arabian sects of Christians.

The worship of saints and the introduction of images
and paintings representing them, were condemned as
idolatrous lapses from the pure faith of Christ, and such,
we have already observed, were the tenets of the Nestorians with whom Mahomet is known to have had much
communication.

All pictures representing living things were prohibited. Mahomet used to say, that the angels would not
enter a house in which there were such pictures, and
that those who made them would be sentenced in the
next world, to find souls for them, or be punished.

Most of the benignant precepts of our Saviour were
incorporated in the Koran. Frequent alms-giving was

enjoined as an imperative duty, and the immutable law of right and wrong, "Do unto another, as thou wouldst he should do unto thee," was given for the moral conduct of the faithful.

"Deal not unjustly with others," says the Koran, "and ye shall not be dealt with unjustly. If there be any debtor under a difficulty of paying his debt, let his creditor wait until it be easy for him to do it; but if he remit it in alms, it will be better for him."

Mahomet inculcated a noble fairness and sincerity in dealing. "O merchants!" would he say, "falsehood and deception are apt to prevail in traffic, purify it therefore with alms; give something in charity as an atonement; for God is incensed by deceit in dealing, but charity appeases his anger. He who sells a defective thing, concealing its defect, will provoke the anger of God and the curses of the angels.

"Take not advantage of the necessities of another to buy things at sacrifice; rather relieve his indigence.

"Feed the hungry; visit the sick, and free the captive if confined unjustly.

"Look not scornfully upon thy fellow man; neither walk the earth with insolence; for God loveth not the arrogant and vainglorious. Be moderate in thy pace, and speak with a moderate tone; for the most ungrateful of all voices is the voice of asses." *

* The following words of Mahomet, treasured up by one of his disciples, appear to have been suggested by a passage in Matthew xxv. 35–45:

Idolatry of all kinds was strictly forbidden; indeed it was what Mahomet held in most abhorrence. Many of the religious usages, however, prevalent since time immemorial among the Arabs, to which he had been accustomed from infancy, and which were not incompatible with the doctrine of the unity of God, were still retained. Such was the pilgrimage to Mecca, including all the rites connected with the Caaba, the well of Zem Zem, and other sacred places in the vicinity; apart from any worship of the idols by which they had been profaned.

The old Arabian rite of prayer, accompanied or rather preceded by ablution, was still continued. Prayers indeed were enjoined at certain hours of the day and night; they were simple in form and phrase, addressed directly to the Deity with certain inflexions, or at times a total

"Verily, God will say at the day of resurrection, 'O sons of Adam! I was sick, and ye did not visit me.' Then they will say, 'How could we visit thee? for thou art the Lord of the universe, and art free from sickness.' And God will reply, 'Knew ye not that such a one of my servants was sick, and ye did not visit him? Had you visited that servant, it would have been counted to you as righteousness.' And God will say, 'O sons of Adam! I asked you for food, and ye gave it me not.' And the sons of Adam will say, 'How could we give thee food, seeing thou art the sustainer of the universe, and art free from hunger?' And God will say, 'Such a one of my servants asked you for bread, and ye refused it. Had you given him to eat, ye would have received your reward from me.' And God will say, 'O sons of Adam, I asked you for water, and ye gave it me not.' They will reply, 'O, our supporter! How could we give thee water, seeing thou art the sustainer of the universe, and not subject to thirst?' And God will say, 'Such a one of my servants asked you for water, and ye did not give it to him. Had ye done so, ye would have received your reward from me.'"

prostration of the body, and with the face turned towards the Kebla, or point of adoration.

At the end of each prayer, the following verse from the second chapter of the Koran was recited. It is said to have great beauty in the original Arabic, and is engraved on gold and silver ornaments, and on precious stones worn as amulets. "God! There is no God but He, the living, the ever living; he sleepeth not, neither doth he slumber. To him belongeth the heavens, and the earth, and all that they contain. Who shall intercede with him unless by his permission? He knoweth the past and the future, but no one can comprehend anything of his knowledge but that which he revealeth. His sway extendeth over the heavens and the earth, and to sustain them both is no burthen to him. He is the High, the Mighty!"

Mahomet was strenuous in enforcing the importance and efficacy of prayer. "Angels," said he, "come among you both by night and day; after which those of the night ascend to heaven, and God asks them how they left his creatures. We found them, say they, at their prayers, and we left them at their prayers."

The doctrines in the Koran respecting the resurrection and final judgment, were in some respects similar to those of the Christian religion, but were mixed up with wild notions derived from other sources; while the joys of the Moslem heaven, though partly spiritual, were clogged and debased by the sensualities of earth, and infinitely below the ineffable purity and spiritual blessedness of the heaven promised by our Saviour.

Nevertheless, the description of the last day, as contained in the eighty-first chapter of the Koran, and which must have been given by Mahomet at the outset of his mission at Mecca, as one of the first of his revelations, partakes of sublimity.

"In the name of the all merciful God! a day shall come when the sun will be shrouded, and the stars will fall from the heavens.

"When the camels about to foal will be neglected, and wild beasts will herd together through fear.

"When the waves of the ocean will boil, and the souls of the dead again be united to the bodies.

"When the female infant that has been buried alive will demand, For what crime was I sacrificed? and the eternal books will be laid open.

"When the heavens will pass away like a scroll, and hell will burn fiercely; and the joys of paradise will be made manifest.

"On that day shall every soul make known that which it hath performed.

"Verily, I swear to you by the stars which move swiftly and are lost in the brightness of the sun, and by the darkness of the night, and by the dawning of the day, these are not the words of an evil spirit, but of an angel of dignity and power, who possesses the confidence of Allah, and is revered by the angels under his command.

Neither is your companion, Mahomet, distracted. He beheld the celestial messenger in the light of the clear horizon, and the words revealed to him are intended as an admonition unto all creatures."

NOTE.—To exhibit the perplexed maze of controversial doctrines from which Mahomet had to acquire his notions of the Christian faith, we subjoin the leading points of the jarring sects of oriental Christians alluded to in the foregoing article; all of which have been pronounced heretical or schismatic.

The Sabellians, so called from Sabellius, a Libyan priest of the third century, believed in the unity of God, and that the Trinity expressed but three different states or relations, Father, Son, and Holy Ghost, all forming but one substance, as a man consists of body and soul.

The Arians, from Arius, an ecclesiastic of Alexandria in the fourth century, affirmed Christ to be the Son of God, but distinct from him and inferior to him, and denied the Holy Ghost to be God.

The Nestorians, from Nestorius, Bishop of Constantinople in the fifth century, maintained that Christ had two distinct natures, divine and human; that Mary was only his mother, and Jesus a man, and that it was an abomination to style her, as was the custom of the church, the Mother of God.

The Monophysites maintained the single nature of Christ, as their name betokens. They affirmed that he was combined of God and man, so mingled and united as to form but one nature.

The Eutychians, from Eutyches, abbot of a convent in Constantinople in the fifth century, were a branch of the Monophysites, expressly opposed to the Nestorians. They denied the double nature of Christ, declaring that he was entirely God previous to the incarnation, and entirely man during the incarnation.

The Jacobites, from Jacobus, bishop of Edessa, in Syria, in the sixth century, were a very numerous branch of the Monophysites, varying but little from the Eutychians. Most of the Christian tribes of Arabs were Jacobites.

The Mariamites, or worshippers of Mary, regarded the Trinity as consisting of God the Father, God the Son, and God the Virgin Mary.

The Collyridians were a sect of Arabian Christians, composed chiefly of females. They worshipped the Virgin Mary as possessed of divinity, and made offerings to her of a twisted cake, called collyris, whence they derived their name.

The Nazaræans, or Nazarenes, were a sect of Jewish Christians, who considered Christ as the Messiah, as born of a Virgin by the Holy Ghost, and as possessing something of a divine nature ; but they conformed in all other respects to the rites and ceremonies of the Mosaic law.

The Ebionites, from Ebion, a converted Jew, who lived in the first century, were also a sect of judaizing Christians, little differing from the Nazaræans. They believed Christ to be a pure man, the greatest of the prophets, but denied that he had any existence previous to being born of the Virgin Mary. This sect, as well as that of the Nazaræans, had many adherents in Arabia.

Many other sects might be enumerated, such as the Corinthians, Maronites, and Marcionites, who took their names from learned and zealous leaders ; and the Docetes and Gnostics, who were subdivided into various sects of subtle enthusiasts. Some of these asserted the immaculate purity of the Virgin Mary, affirming that her conception and delivery were effected like the transmission of the rays of light through a pane of glass, without impairing her virginity: an opinion still maintained strenuously in substance by Spanish Catholics.

Most of the Docetes asserted that Jesus Christ was of a nature entirely divine; that a phantom, a mere form without substance, was crucified by the deluded Jews, and that the crucifixion and resurrection were deceptive mystical exhibitions at Jerusalem for the benefit of the human race.

The Carpocratians, Basilidians, and Valentinians, named after three Egyptian controversialists, contended that Jesus Christ was merely a wise and virtuous mortal, the son of Joseph and Mary, selected by God to reform and instruct mankind ; but that a divine nature was imparted to him at the maturity of his age, and period of his baptism, by St. John. The former part of this creed, which is that of the Ebionites, has been revived, and is professed by some of the Unitarian Christians, a numerous and increasing sect of Protestants of the present day.

It is sufficient to glance at these dissensions, which we have not arranged in chronological order, but which convulsed the early Christian church, and continued to prevail at the era of Mahomet, to acquit him of any charge of conscious blasphemy in the opinions he inculcated concerning the nature and mission of our Saviour.

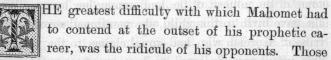HE greatest difficulty with which Mahomet had to contend at the outset of his prophetic ca- reer, was the ridicule of his opponents. Those who had known him from his infancy—who had seen him a boy about the streets of Mecca; and afterwards occu- pied in all the ordinary concerns of life, scoffed at his as- sumption of the apostolic character. They pointed with a sneer at him as he passed, exclaiming, "Behold the grandson of Abd al Motâlleb, who pretends to know what is going on in heaven!" Some who had witnessed his fits of mental excitement and ecstasy, considered him in- sane; others declared that he was possessed of a devil, and some charged him with sorcery and magic.

When he walked the streets he was subject to those jeers, and taunts, and insults which the vulgar are apt to vent upon men of eccentric conduct and unsettled mind. If he attempted to preach, his voice was drowned by dis-

87

cordant noises and ribald songs: nay, dirt was thrown upon him when he was praying in the Caaba.

Nor was it the vulgar and ignorant alone who thus insulted him. One of his most redoubtable assailants was a youth named Amru; and as he subsequently made a distinguished figure in Mahometan history, we would impress the circumstances of this, his first appearance, upon the mind of the reader. He was the son of a courtesan of Mecca; who seems to have rivaled in fascination the Phrynes and Aspasias of Greece, and to have numbered some of the noblest of the land among her lovers. When she gave birth to this child, she mentioned several of the tribe of Koreish who had equal claims to the paternity. The infant was declared to have most resemblance to Aass, the oldest of her admirers, whence, in addition to his name of Amru, he received the designation of Ibn al Aass, the son of Aass.

Nature had lavished her choicest gifts upon this natural child, as if to atone for the blemish of his birth. Though young, he was already one of the most popular poets of Arabia, and equally distinguished for the pungency of his satirical effusions and the captivating sweetness of his serious lays.

When Mahomet first announced his mission, this youth assailed him with lampoons and humorous madrigals; which, falling in with the poetic taste of the Arabs, were widely circulated, and proved greater impediments to the growth of Islamism than the bitterest persecution.

Those who were more serious in their opposition demanded of Mahomet supernatural proofs of what he asserted. " Moses, and Jesus, and the rest of the prophets," said they, " wrought miracles to prove the divinity of their missions. If thou art indeed a prophet, greater than they, work the like miracles."

The reply of Mahomet may be gathered from his own words in the Koran. " What greater miracle could they have than the Koran itself ; a book revealed by means of an unlettered man ; so elevated in language, so incontrovertible in argument, that the united skill of men and devils could compose nothing comparable. What greater proof could there be that it came from none but God himself? The Koran itself is a miracle."

They demanded, however, more palpable evidence ; miracles addressed to the senses ; that he should cause the dumb to speak, the deaf to hear, the blind to see, the dead to rise ; or that he should work changes in the face of nature ; cause fountains to gush forth ; change a sterile place into a garden, with palm-trees, and vines, and running streams ; cause a palace of gold to rise, decked with jewels and precious stones ; or ascend by a ladder into heaven in their presence. Or, if the Koran did indeed, as he affirmed, come down from heaven, that they might see it as it descended, or behold the angel who brought it ; and then they would believe.

Mahomet replied sometimes by arguments, sometimes by denunciations. He claimed to be nothing more than a man sent by God as an apostle.  Had angels, said he, walked familiarly on earth, an angel had assuredly been sent on this mission; but woful had been the case of those who, as in the present instance, doubted his word. They would not have been able, as with me, to argue, and dispute, and take time to be convinced; their perdition would have been instantaneous.  "God," added he, "needs no angel to enforce my mission.  He is a sufficient witness between you and me.  Those whom he shall dispose to be convinced, will truly believe; those whom he shall permit to remain in error, will find none to help their unbelief.  On the day of resurrection they will appear blind, and deaf, and dumb, and groveling on their faces.  Their abode will be in the eternal flames of Jehennam.  Such will be the reward of their unbelief.

"You insist on miracles.  God gave to Moses the power of working miracles.  What was the consequence? Pharaoh disregarded his miracles, accused him of sorcery, and sought to drive him and his people from the land; but Pharaoh was drowned, and with him all his host.  Would ye tempt God to miracles, and risk the punishment of Pharaoh?"

It is recorded by Al Maalem, an Arabian writer, that some of Mahomet's disciples at one time joined with the multitude in this cry for miracles, and besought him to prove, at once, the divinity of his mission, by turning the hill of Safa into gold.  Being thus closely urged, he betook himself to prayer; and having finished, assured his followers that the angel Gabriel had appeared to him, and informed him that, should God grant his prayer, and work the desired miracle, all who disbelieved it would be exterminated. In pity to the multitude, therefore, who appeared to be a stiff-necked generation, he would not expose them to destruction : so the hill of Safa was permitted to remain in its pristine state.

Other Moslem writers assert that Mahomet departed from his self-prescribed rule, and wrought occasional miracles, when he found his hearers unusually slow of belief. Thus we are told that, at one time, in presence of a multitude, he called to him a bull, and took from his horns a scroll containing a chapter of the Koran, just sent down from heaven. At another time, while discoursing in public, a white dove hovered over him, and, alighting on his shoulder, appeared to whisper in his ear ; being, as he said, a messenger from the Deity. On another occasion he ordered the earth before him to be opened, when two jars were found, one filled with honey, the other with milk, which he pronounced emblems of the abundance promised by heaven to all who should obey his law.

Christian writers have scoffed at these miracles ; suggesting that the dove had been tutored to its task, and sought grains of wheat which it had been accustomed to find in the ear of Mahomet ; that the scroll had previously been tied to the horns of the bull, and the vessels of milk and honey deposited in the ground. The true course would be to discard these miraculous stories altogether, as fables devised by mistaken zealots; and such they have been pronounced by the ablest of the Moslem commentators.

There is no proof that Mahomet descended to any artifices of the kind to enforce his doctrines or establish his apostolic claims. He appears to have relied entirely on reason and eloquence, and to have been supported by religious enthusiasm in this early and dubious stage of his career. His earnest attacks upon the idolatry which had vitiated and superseded the primitive worship of the Caaba, began to have a sensible effect, and alarmed the Koreishites. They urged Abu Taleb to silence his nephew or to send him away; but finding their entreaties unavailing, they informed the old man that if this pretended prophet and his followers persisted in their heresies, they should pay for them with their lives.

Abu Taleb hastened to inform Mahomet of these menaces, imploring him not to provoke against himself and family such numerous and powerful foes.

The enthusiastic spirit of Mahomet kindled at the words. "O my uncle!" exclaimed he, "though they should array the sun against me on my right hand, and the moon on my left, yet, until God should command me, or should take me hence, would I not depart from my purpose."

He was retiring with dejected countenance, when Abu Taleb called him back. The old man was as yet unconverted, but he was struck with admiration of the undaunted firmness of his nephew, and declared that, preach what he might, he would never abandon him to his enemies. Feeling that of himself he could not yield sufficient protection, he called upon the other descendants of Haschem and Abd al Motâlleb to aid in shielding their kinsman from the persecution of the rest of the tribe of Koreish; and so strong is the family tie among the Arabs, that though it was protecting him in what they considered a dangerous heresy, they all consented excepting his uncle Abu Lahab.

The animosity of the Koreishites became more and more virulent, and proceeded to personal violence. Mahomet was assailed and nearly strangled in the Caaba, and was rescued with difficulty by Abu Beker, who himself suffered personal injury in the affray. His immediate family became objects of hatred, especially his daughter Rokaia and her husband Othman Ibn Affan. Such of his disciples as had no powerful friends to protect them were in peril of their lives. Full of anxiety for their safety, Mahomet advised them to leave his dangerous companionship for the present, and take refuge in Abyssinia. The narrowness of the Red Sea made it easy to reach the African shore. The Abyssinians were Nestorian Christians, elevated by their religion above their barbarous neighbors. Their najashee or king was reputed to be tolerant and just. With him Mahomet trusted his daughter and his fugitive disciples would find refuge.

Othman Ibn Affan was the leader of this little band of
Moslems, consisting of eleven men and four women.
They took the way by the sea-coast to Jodda, a port
about two days' journey to the east of Mecca, where they
found two Abyssinian vessels at anchor, in which they
embarked, and sailed for the land of refuge.

This event, which happened in the fifth year of the
mission of Mahomet, is called the first Hegira or Flight,
to distinguish it from the second Hegira, the flight of the
prophet himself from Mecca to Medina.  The kind treatment experienced by the fugitives induced others of the
same faith to follow their example, until the number of
Moslem refugees in Abyssinia amounted to eighty-three
men and eighteen women, besides children.

The Koreishites finding that Mahomet was not to be
silenced, and was daily making converts, passed a law
banishing all who should embrace his faith.  Mahomet
retired before the storm, and took refuge in the house of
a disciple named Orkham, situated on the hill of Safa.
This hill, as has already been mentioned, was renowned
in Arabian tradition as the one on which Adam and Eve
were permitted to come once more together, after the
long solitary wandering about the earth which followed
their expulsion from paradise.  It was likewise connected
in tradition with the fortunes of Hagar and Ishmael.

Mahomet remained for a month in the house of Orkham, continuing his revelations and drawing to him sec-
taries from various parts of Arabia.  The hostility of the

Koreishites followed him to his retreat. Abu Jahl, an Arab of that tribe, sought him out, insulted him with opprobrious language, and even personally maltreated him. The outrage was reported to Hamza, an uncle of Mahomet, as he returned to Mecca from hunting. Hamza was no proselyte to Islamism, but he was pledged to protect his nephew. Marching with his bow unstrung in his hand to an assemblage of the Koreishites, where Abu Jahl was vaunting his recent triumph, he dealt the boaster a blow over the head, that inflicted a grievous wound. The kinsfolk of Abu Jahl rushed to his assistance, but the brawler stood in awe of the vigorous arm and fiery spirit of Hamza, and sought to pacify him. "Let him alone," said he to his kinsfolk; "in truth I have treated his nephew very roughly." He alleged in palliation of his outrage the apostasy of Mahomet; but Hamza was not to be appeased. "Well!" cried he, fiercely and scornfully, "I also do not believe in your gods of stone; can you compel me?" Anger produced in his bosom what reasoning might have attempted in vain. He forthwith declared himself a convert, took the oath of adhesion to the prophet, and became one of the most zealous and valiant champions of the new faith.

# CHAPTER X.

HE hatred of Abu Jahl to the prophet was increased by the severe punishment received at the hands of Hamza. He had a nephew named Omar Ibn al Khattâb; twenty-six years of age; of gigantic stature, prodigious strength, and great courage. His savage aspect appalled the bold, and his very walking-staff struck more terror into beholders than another man's sword. Such are the words of the Arabian historian, Abu Abdallah Mohamed Ibn Omal Alwakedi, and the subsequent feats of this warrior prove that they were scarce chargeable with exaggeration.

Instigated by his uncle Abu Jahl, this fierce Arab undertook to penetrate to the retreat of Mahomet, who was still in the house of Orkham, and to strike a poniard to his heart. The Koreishites are accused of having promised him one hundred camels and one thousand ounces of gold for this deed of blood; but this is improbable, nor did the vengeful nephew of Abu Jahl need a bribe.

As he was on his way to the house of Orkham he met a Koreishite, to whom he imparted his design. The Koreishite was a secret convert to Islamism, and sought to turn him from his bloody errand. "Before you slay Mahomet," said he, "and draw upon yourself the vengeance of his relatives, see that your own are free from heresy." "Are any of mine guilty of backsliding?" demanded Omar with astonishment. "Even so," was the reply; "thy sister Amina and her husband Seid."

Omar hastened to the dwelling of his sister, and entering it abruptly, found her and her husband reading the Koran. Seid attempted to conceal it, but his confusion convinced Omar of the truth of the accusation, and heightened his fury. In his rage he struck Seid to the earth; placed his foot upon his breast, and would have plunged his sword into it, had not his sister interposed. A blow on the face bathed her visage in blood. "Enemy of Allah!" sobbed Amina, "dost thou strike me thus for believing in the only true God? In despite of thee and thy violence, I will persevere in the true faith. Yes," added she with fervor, "'There is no God but God, and Mahomet is his prophet:'—And now, Omar, finish thy work!"

Omar paused; repented of his violence, and took his foot from the bosom of Seid.

"Show me the writing," said he. Amina, however, refused to let him touch the sacred scroll until he had washed his hands. The passage which he read, is said to have been the twentieth chapter of the Koran, which thus begins :—

"In the name of the most merciful God! We have not sent down the Koran to inflict misery on mankind, but as a monitor, to teach him to believe in the true God, the creator of the earth and the lofty heavens.

"The All Merciful is enthroned on high, to him belongeth whatsoever is in the heavens above, and in the earth beneath, and in the regions under the earth.

"Dost thou utter thy prayers with a loud voice? know that there is no need. God knoweth the secrets of thy heart; yea, that which is most hidden.

"Verily, I am God; there is none beside me. Serve me, serve none other. Offer up thy prayer to none but me."

The words of the Koran sank deep into the heart of Omar. He read farther, and was more and more moved; but when he came to the parts treating of the resurrection and of judgment, his conversion was complete.

He pursued his way to the house of Orkham, but with an altered heart. Knocking humbly at the door, he craved admission. "Come in, son of al Khattâb," exclaimed Mahomet, "what brings thee hither?"

"I come to enroll my name among the believers of God

and his prophet." So saying, he made the Moslem profession of faith.

He was not content until his conversion was publicly known. At his request, Mahomet accompanied him instantly to the Caaba, to perform openly the rites of Islamism. Omar walked on the left hand of the prophet, and Hamza on the right, to protect him from injury and insult, and they were followed by upwards of forty disciples. They passed in open day through the streets of Mecca, to the astonishment of its inhabitants. Seven times did they make the circuit of the Caaba, touching each time the sacred black stone, and complying with all the other ceremonials. The Koreishites regarded this procession with dismay, but dared not approach nor molest the prophet, being deterred by the looks of those terrible men of battle, Hamza and Omar; who, it is said, glared upon them like two lions that had been robbed of their young.

Fearless and resolute in everything, Omar went by himself the next day to pray as a Moslem in the Caaba, in open defiance of the Koreishites. Another Moslem, who entered the temple, was interrupted in his worship, and rudely treated; but no one molested Omar, because he was the nephew of Abu Jahl. Omar repaired to his uncle. "I renounce thy protection," said he. "I will not be better off than my fellow-believers." From that time he cast his lot with the followers of Mahomet, and was one of his most strenuous defenders.

Such was the wonderful conversion of Omar, afterwards
the most famous champion of the Islam faith.  So exasperated were the Koreishites by this new triumph of
Mahomet, that his uncle Abu Taleb feared they might attempt the life of his nephew, either by treachery or open
violence.  At his earnest entreaties, therefore, the latter,
accompanied by some of his principal disciples, withdrew
to a kind of castle, or stronghold, belonging to Abu Taleb,
in the neighborhood of the city.

The protection thus given by Abu Taleb, the head of
the Haschemites, and by others of his line, to Mahomet
and his followers, although differing from them in faith,
drew on them the wrath of the rival branch of the Koreishites, and produced a schism in the tribe.   Abu Sofian,
the head of that branch, availed himself of the heresies
of the prophet to throw discredit, not merely upon such
of his kindred as had embraced his faith, but upon the
whole line of Haschem, which, though dissenting from
his doctrines, had, through mere clannish feelings, protected him.   It is evident the hostility of Abu Sofian
arose, not merely from personal hatred or religious
scruples, but from family feud.   He was ambitious of
transferring to his own line the honors of the city so
long engrossed by the Haschemites.  The last measure of
the kind-hearted Abu Taleb, in placing Mahomet beyond
the reach of persecution, and giving him a castle as a
refuge, was seized upon by Abu Sofian and his adherents,
as a pretext for a general ban of the rival line.  They

accordingly issued a decree, forbidding the rest of the tribe of Koreish from intermarrying, or holding any intercourse, even of bargain or sale, with the Haschemites, until they should deliver up their kinsman, Mahomet, for punishment. This decree, which took place in the seventh year of what is called the mission of the prophet, was written on parchment, and hung up in the Caaba. It reduced Mahomet and his disciples to great straits, being almost famished at times in the stronghold in which they had taken refuge. The fortress was also beleaguered occasionally by the Koreishites, to enforce the ban in all its rigor, and to prevent the possibility of supplies.

The annual season of pilgrimage, however, when hosts of pilgrims repair from all parts of Arabia to Mecca, brought transient relief to the persecuted Moslems. During that sacred season, according to immemorial law and usage among the Arabs, all hostilities were suspended, and warring tribes met in temporary peace to worship at the Caaba. At such times Mahomet and his disciples would venture from their stronghold and return to Mecca. Protected also by the immunity of the holy month, Mahomet would mingle among the pilgrims and preach and pray; propound his doctrines, and proclaim his revelations. In this way he made many converts, who, on their return to their several homes, carried with them the seeds of the new faith to distant regions. Among these converts were occasionally the princes or heads of tribes, whose example had an influence on their adherents. Arabian legends give a pompous and extravagant account of the conversion of one of these princes; which, as it was attended by some of the most noted miracles recorded of Mahomet, may not be unworthy of an abbreviated insertion.

The prince in question was Habib Ibn Malec, surnamed the Wise on account of his vast knowledge and erudition; for he is represented as deeply versed in magic and the sciences, and acquainted with all religions, to their very foundations, having read all that had been written concerning them, and also acquired practical information, for he had belonged to them all by turns, having been Jew, Christian, and one of the Magi. It is true, he had had more than usual time for his studies and experience, having, according to Arabian legend, attained to the age of one hundred and forty years. He now came to Mecca at the head of a powerful host of twenty thousand men, bringing with him a youthful daughter, Satiha, whom he must have begotten in a ripe old age; and for whom he was putting up prayers at the Caaba, she having been struck dumb, and deaf, and blind, and deprived of the use of her limbs.

Abu Sofian and Abu Jahl, according to the legend, thought the presence of this very powerful, very idolatrous, and very wise old prince, at the head of so formidable a host, a favorable opportunity to effect the ruin of Mahomet. They accordingly informed Habib the Wise of the heresies of the pretended prophet; and prevailed upon the venerable prince to summon him into his presence, at his encampment in the Valley of Flints, there to defend his doctrines; in the hope that his obstinacy in error would draw upon him banishment or death.

The legend gives a magnificent account of the issuing forth of the idolatrous Koreishites, in proud array, on horseback and on foot, led by Abu Sofian and Abu Jahl, to attend the grand inquisition in the Valley of Flints; and of the oriental state in which they were received by Habib the Wise, seated under a tent of crimson, on a throne of ebony, inlaid with ivory and sandal-wood, and covered with plates of gold.

Mahomet was in the dwelling of Cadijah when he received a summons to this formidable tribunal. Cadijah was loud in her expressions of alarm; and his daughters hung about his neck, weeping and lamenting, for they thought him going to certain death; but he gently rebuked their fears, and bade them trust in Allah.

Unlike the ostentatious state of his enemies, Abu Sofian and Abu Jahl, he approached the scene of trial in simple guise, clad in a white garment, with a black turban, and a mantle which had belonged to his grandfather, Abd al Motâlleb, and was made of the stuff of Aden. His hair floated below his shoulders, the mysterious light of prophecy beamed from his countenance; and though he had not anointed his beard, nor used any perfumes, excepting a little musk and camphor for the hair of his upper lip, yet wherever he passed a bland odor diffused itself around, being, say the Arabian writers, the fragrant emanations from his person.

He was preceded by the zealous Abu Beker, clad in a scarlet vest and white turban; with his mantle gathered up under his arms, so as to display his scarlet slippers.

A silent awe, continues the legend, fell upon the vast assemblage as the prophet approached. Not a murmur, not a whisper was to be heard. The very brute animals were charmed to silence; and the neighing of the steed, the bellowing of the camel, and the braying of the ass were mute.

The venerable Habib received him graciously: his first question was to the point. "They tell thou dost pretend to be a prophet sent from God? Is it so?"

"Even so," replied Mahomet. "Allah has sent me to proclaim the veritable faith."

"Good," rejoined the wary sage, "but every prophet has given proof of his mission by signs and miracles. Noah had his rainbow: Solomon his mysterious ring: Abraham the fire of the furnace, which became cool at his command: Isaac the ram, which was sacrificed in his stead: Moses his wonder-working rod, and Jesus brought the dead to life, and appeased tempests with a word. If, then, thou art really a prophet, give us a miracle in proof."

The adherents of Mahomet trembled for him when they heard this request, and Abu Jahl clapped his hands, and extolled the sagacity of Habib the Wise. But the prophet rebuked him with scorn. "Peace! dog of thy race!" exclaimed he; "disgrace of thy kindred, and of thy tribe." He then calmly proceeded to execute the wishes of Habib.

The first miracle demanded of Mahomet was to reveal what Habib had within his tent, and why he had brought it to Mecca.

Upon this, says the legend, Mahomet bent toward the earth and traced figures upon the sand. Then raising his head, he replied, "O Habib! thou hast brought hither thy daughter, Satiha, deaf and dumb, and lame and blind, in the hope of obtaining relief of Heaven. Go to thy tent; speak to her, and hear her reply, and know that God is all-powerful."

The aged prince hastened to his tent. His daughter met him with light step and extended arms, perfect in all her faculties, her eyes beaming with joy, her face clothed with smiles, and more beauteous than the moon in an unclouded night.

The second miracle demanded by Habib was still more difficult. It was that Mahomet should cover the noontide heaven with supernatural darkness, and cause the moon to descend and rest upon the top of the Caaba.

The prophet performed this miracle as easily as the first. At his summons, a darkness blotted out the whole light of day. The moon was then seen straying from her course and wandering about the firmament. By the irresistible power of the prophet, she was drawn from the heavens and rested on the top of the Caaba. She then performed seven circuits about it, after the manner of the pilgrims, and having made a profound reverence to Mahomet, stood before him with lambent, wavering motion, like a flaming sword, giving him the salutation of peace, and hailing him as a prophet.

Not content with this miracle, pursues the legend, Mahomet compelled the obedient luminary to enter by the right sleeve of his mantle, and go out by the left; then to divide into two parts, one of which went towards the east, and the other towards the west, and meeting in the centre of the firmament reunited themselves into a round and glorious globe.

It is needless to say that Habib the Wise was convinced, and converted by these miracles, as were also four hundred and seventy of the inhabitants of Mecca. Abu Jahl, however, was hardened in unbelief, exclaiming that all was illusion and enchantment produced by the magic of Mahomet.

Note.—The miracles here recorded are not to be found in the pages of the accurate Abulfeda, nor are they maintained by any of the graver of the Moslem writers; but they exist in tradition, and are set forth with great prolixity by apocryphal authors, who insist that they are alluded to in the fifty-fourth chapter of the Koran. They are probably as true as many other of the wonders related of the prophet. It will be remembered that he himself claimed but one miracle, "the Koran."

# CHAPTER XI.

THE BAN OF NON-INTERCOURSE MYSTERIOUSLY DESTROYED.—MAHOMET EN-
ABLED TO RETURN TO MECCA.—DEATH OF ABU TALEB; OF CADIJAH.—
MAHOMET BETROTHS HIMSELF TO AYESHA.—MARRIES SAWDA.—THE KO-
REISHITES RENEW THEIR PERSECUTION.—MAHOMET SEEKS AN ASYLUM IN
TAYEF.—HIS EXPULSION THENCE.—VISITED BY GENII IN THE DESERT OF
NAKLAH.

HREE years had elapsed since Mahomet and his disciples took refuge in the castle of Abu Taleb. The ban or decree still existed in the Caaba, cutting them off from all intercourse with the rest of their tribe. The sect, as usual, increased under persecution. Many joined it in Mecca; murmurs arose against the unnatural feud engendered among the Koreishites, and Abu Sofian was made to blush for the lengths to which he had carried his hostility against some of his kindred.

All at once it was discovered that the parchment in the Caaba, on which the decree had been written, was so substantially destroyed, that nothing of the writing remained but the initial words, "In thy name, O Almighty God!" The decree was, therefore, declared to be annulled, and Mahomet and his followers were permitted to return to Mecca unmolested. The mysterious removal of this legal obstacle has been considered by pious Moslems, another miracle wrought by supernatural agency in favor of the prophet; though unbelievers have surmised that the document, which was becoming embarrassing in its effects to Abu Sofian himself, was secretly destroyed by mortal hands.

The return of Mahomet and his disciples to Mecca, was followed by important conversions, both of inhabitants of the city and of pilgrims from afar. The chagrin experienced by the Koreishites from the growth of this new sect, was soothed by tidings of victories of the Persians over the Greeks, by which they conquered Syria and a part of Egypt. The idolatrous Koreishites exulted in the defeat of the Christian Greeks, whose faith, being opposed to the worship of idols, they assimilated to that preached by Mahomet. The latter replied to their taunts and exultations, by producing the thirtieth chapter of the Koran, opening with these words: "The Greeks have been overcome by the Persians, but they shall overcome the latter in the course of a few years."

The zealous and believing Abu Beker made a wager of ten camels, that this prediction would be accomplished within three years. "Increase the wager, but lengthen the time," whispered Mahomet. Abu Beker staked one hundred camels, but made the time nine years. The prediction was verified and the wager won. This anecdote is confidently cited by Moslem doctors, as a proof that the

Koran came down from heaven, and that Mahomet possessed the gift of prophecy. The whole, if true, was no doubt a shrewd guess into futurity, suggested by a knowledge of the actual state of the warring powers.

Not long after his return to Mecca, Mahomet was summoned to close the eyes of his uncle Abu Taleb, then upwards of fourscore years of age, and venerable in character as in person. As the hour of death drew nigh, Mahomet exhorted his uncle to make the profession of faith necessary, according to the Islam creed, to secure a blissful resurrection.

A spark of earthly pride lingered in the breast of the dying patriarch. " O son of my brother ! " replied he, " should I repeat those words, the Koreishites would say, I did so through fear of death."

Abulfeda, the historian, insists that Abu Taleb actually died in the faith. Al Abbas, he says, hung over the bed of his expiring brother, and perceiving his lips to move, approached his ear to catch his dying words. They were the wished-for confession. Others affirm that his last words were, "I die in the faith of Abd al Motâlleb." Commentators have sought to reconcile the two accounts, by asserting that Abd al Motâlleb, in his latter days renounced the worship of idols, and believed in the unity of God.

Scarce three days had elapsed from the death of the venerable Abu Taleb, when Cadijah, the faithful and devoted wife of Mahomet, likewise sank into the grave.

She was sixty-five years of age.  Mahomet wept bitterly at her tomb, and clothed himself in mourning for her, and for Abu Taleb, so that this year was called the year of mourning.  He was comforted in his affliction, says the Arabian author, Abu Horaira, by an assurance from the angel Gabriel, that a silver palace was allotted to Cadijah in Paradise, as a reward for her great faith and her early services to the cause.

Though Cadijah had been much older than Mahomet at the time of their marriage, and past the bloom of years when women are desirable in the East, and though the prophet was noted for an amorous temperament, yet he is said to have remained true to her to the last; nor ever availed himself of the Arabian law, permitting a plurality of wives, to give her a rival in his house.  When, however, she was laid in the grave, and the first transport of his grief had subsided, he sought to console himself for her loss, by entering anew into wedlock; and henceforth indulged in a plurality of wives.  He permitted, by his law, four wives, to each of his followers; but did not limit himself to that number; for he observed that a prophet, being peculiarly gifted and privileged, was not bound to restrict himself to the same laws as ordinary mortals.

His first choice was made within a month after the death of Cadijah, and fell upon a beautiful child named Ayesha, the daughter of his faithful adherent, Abu Beker.  Perhaps he sought, by this alliance, to grapple Abu

Beker still more strongly to his side; he being one of the bravest and most popular of his tribe. Ayesha, however, was but seven years of age, and, though females soon bloom and ripen in those eastern climes, she was yet too young to enter into the married state. He was merely betrothed to her, therefore, and postponed their nuptials for two years, during which time he caused her to be carefully instructed in the accomplishments proper to an Arabian maiden of distinguished rank.

Upon this wife, thus chosen in the very blossom of her years, the prophet doted more passionately than upon any of those whom he subsequently married. All these had been previously experienced in wedlock; Ayesha, he said, was the only one who came a pure unspotted virgin to his arms.

Still, that he might not be without due solace while Ayesha was attaining the marriageable age, he took, as a wife, Sawda, the widow of Sokran, one of his followers. She had been nurse to his daughter Fatima, and was one of the faithful who fled into Abyssinia from the early persecutions of the people of Mecca. It is pretended that, while in exile, she had a mysterious intimation of the future honor which awaited her; for she dreamt that Mahomet laid his head upon her bosom. She recounted the dream to her husband Sokran, who interpreted it as a prediction of his speedy death, and of her marriage with the prophet.

The marriage, whether predicted or not, was one of

mere expediency. Mahomet never loved Sawda with the affection he manifested for his other wives. He would even have put her away in after years, but she implored to be allowed the honor of still calling herself his wife; proffering that, whenever it should come to her turn to share the marriage bed, she would relinquish her right to Ayesha. Mahomet consented to an arrangement which favored his love for the latter, and Sawda continued, as long as she lived, to be nominally his wife.

Mahomet soon became sensible of the loss he had sustained in the death of Abu Taleb; who had been not merely an affectionate relative, but a steadfast and powerful protector, from his great influence in Mecca. At his death there was no one to check and counteract the hostilities of Abu Sofian and Abu Jahl; who soon raised up such a spirit of persecution among the Koreishites, that Mahomet found it unsafe to continue in his native place. He set out, therefore, accompanied by his freedman Zeid, to seek a refuge at Tayef, a small walled town, about seventy miles from Mecca, inhabited by the Thakifites, or Arabs of the tribe of Thakeef. It was one of the favored places of Arabia, situated among vineyards and gardens. Here grew peaches and plums, melons and pomegranates; figs, blue and green, the nebeck-tree producing the lotus, and palm-trees with their clusters of green and golden fruit. So fresh were its pastures and fruitful its fields, contrasted with the sterility of the neighboring deserts, that the Arabs fabled it to have orignally been a part of Syria, broken off and floated hither at the time of the deluge.

Mahomet entered the gates of Tayef, with some degree of confidence, trusting for protection to the influence of his uncle Al Abbas, who had possessions there. He could not have chosen a worse place of refuge. Tayef was one of the strongholds of idolatry. Here was maintained in all its force the worship of El Lât, one of the female idols already mentioned. Her image of stone was covered with jewels and precious stones, the offerings of her votaries; it was believed to be inspired with life, and the intercession of El Lât was implored as one of the daughters of God.

Mahomet remained about a month in Tayef, seeking in vain to make proselytes among its inhabitants. When he attempted to preach his doctrines, his voice was drowned by clamors. More than once he was wounded by stones thrown at him, and which the faithful Zeid endeavored in vain to ward off. So violent did the popular fury become at last, that he was driven from the city, and even pursued for some distance beyond the walls by an insulting rabble of slaves and children.

Thus driven ignominiously from his hoped-for place of refuge, and not daring to return openly to his native city, he remained in the desert until Zeid should procure a secret asylum for him among his friends in Mecca. In this extremity, he had one of those visions or supernatural visitations which appear always to have occurred

in lonely or agitated moments, when we may suppose
him to have been in a state of mental excitement. It was
after the evening prayer, he says, in a solitary place in
the Valley of Naklah, between Mecca and Tayef. He was
reading the Koran, when he was overheard by a passing
company of Gins or Genii. These are spiritual beings,
some good, others bad, and liable like man to future
rewards and punishments. "Hark! give ear!" said the
Genii one to the other. They paused and listened as Mahomet continued to read. "Verily," said they at the end,
"we have heard an admirable discourse, which directeth
unto the right institution; wherefore we believe therein."

This spiritual visitation consoled Mahomet for his expulsion from Tayef, showing that though he and his doctrines might be rejected by men, they were held in reverence by spiritual intelligences. At least so we may
infer from the mention he makes of it in the forty-sixth
and seventy-second chapters of the Koran. Thence-
forward, he declared himself sent for the conversion of
these genii as well as of the human race.

NOTE.—The belief in genii was prevalent throughout the East, long
before the time of Mahomet. They were supposed to haunt solitary
places, particularly toward nightfall; a superstition congenial to the
habits and notions of the inhabitants of lonely and desert countries. The
Arabs supposed every valley and barren waste to have its tribe of genii,
who were subject to a dominant spirit, and roamed forth at night to
beset the pilgrim and the traveller. Whenever, therefore, they entered a
lonely valley toward the close of evening, they used to supplicate the pre-
siding spirit or lord of the place, to protect them from the evil genii
under his command.

Those columns of dust raised by whirling eddies of wind, and which sweep across the desert, are supposed to be caused by some evil genius or sprite of gigantic size.

The serpents which occasionally infest houses were thought to be often genii, some infidels and some believers. Mahomet cautioned his followers to be slow to kill a house serpent. "Warn him to depart ; if he do not obey, then kill him, for it is a sign that he is a mere reptile or an infidel genius."

It is fabled that in earlier times, the genii had admission to heaven, but were expelled on account of their meddling propensities. They have ever since been of a curious and prying nature, often attempting to clamber up to the constellations ; thence to peep into heaven, and see and overhear what is going on there. They are, however, driven thence by angels with flaming swords ; and those meteors called shooting stars are supposed by Mahometans to be darted by the guardian angels at these intrusive genii.

Other legends pretend that the earth was originally peopled by these genii, but they rebelled against the Most High, and usurped terrestrial dominion, which they maintained for two thousand years. At length, Azazil, or Lucifer, was sent against them and defeated them, overthrowing their mighty king, Gian ben Gian, the founder of the pyramids ; whose magic buckler of talismanic virtue fell subsequently into the hands of King Solomon the Wise, giving him power over the spells and charms of magicians and evil genii. The rebel spirits defeated and humiliated, were driven into an obscure corner of the earth. Then it was that God created man, with less dangerous faculties and powers, and gave him the world for a habitation.

The angels according to Moslem notions were created from bright gems ; the genii from fire without smoke, and Adam from clay.

Mahomet, when in the seventy-second chapter of the Koran, he alludes to the visitation of the genii in the Valley of Naklah, makes them give the following frank account of themselves.

"We formerly attempted to pry into what was transacting in heaven, but we found the same guarded by angels with flaming darts ; and we sat on some of the seats thereof to hear the discourse of its inhabitants ; but whoso listeneth now finds a flame prepared to guard the celestial confines. There are some among us who are Moslems, and there are others who swerve from righteousness. Whoso embraceth Islamism seeketh the true direction ; but those who swerve from righteousness shall be fuel for the fire of Jehennam."

# CHAPTER XII.

NIGHT JOURNEY OF THE PROPHET FROM MECCA TO JERUSALEM; AND THENCE
TO THE SEVENTH HEAVEN.

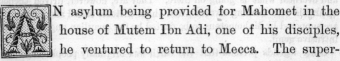N asylum being provided for Mahomet in the
house of Mutem Ibn Adi, one of his disciples,
he ventured to return to Mecca. The supernatural visitation of genii in the Valley of Naklah, was
soon followed by a vision or revelation far more extraordinary, and which has ever since remained a theme of
comment and conjecture among devout Mahometans.
We allude to the famous night journey to Jerusalem,
and thence to the seventh heaven. The particulars of it,
though given as if in the very words of Mahomet, rest
merely on tradition; some, however, cite texts corrobo-
rative of it, scattered here and there in the Koran.

We do not pretend to give this vision or revelation in
its amplitude and wild extravagance, but will endeavor to
seize upon its most essential features.

The night on which it occurred, is described as one of
the darkest and most awfully silent that had ever been
known. There was no crowing of cocks nor barking of
dogs; no howling of wild beasts nor hooting of owls.

116

The very waters ceased to murmur, and the winds to whistle; all nature seemed motionless and dead. In the mid watches of the night, Mahomet was roused by a voice crying, "Awake, thou sleeper!" The angel Gabriel stood before him. His forehead was clear and serene, his complexion white as snow, his hair floated on his shoulders; he had wings of many dazzling hues, and his robes were sown with pearls and embroidered with gold.

He brought Mahomet a white steed of wonderful form and qualities, unlike any animal he had ever seen; and in truth, it differs from any animal ever before described. It had a human face, but the cheeks of a horse: its eyes were as jacinths and radiant as stars. It had eagle's wings all glittering with rays of light; and its whole form was resplendent with gems and precious stones. It was a female, and from its dazzling splendor and incredible velocity was called Al Borak, or Lightning.

Mahomet prepared to mount this supernatural steed, but as he extended his hand, it drew back and reared.

"Be still, O Borak!" said Gabriel; "respect the prophet of God. Never wert thou mounted by mortal man more honored of Allah."

"O Gabriel!" replied Al Borak, who at this time was miraculously endowed with speech; "did not Abraham of old, the friend of God, bestride me when he visited his son Ishmael? O Gabriel! is not this the mediator, the intercessor, the author of the profession of faith?"

"Even so, O Borak, this is Mahomet Ibn Abdallah, of

one of the tribes of Arabia the Happy, and of the true faith. He is chief of the sons of Adam, the greatest of the divine legates, the seal of the prophets. All creatures must have his intercession before they can enter paradise. Heaven is on his right hand, to be the reward of those who believe in him; the fire of Jehennam is on his left hand, into which all shall be thrust who oppose his doctrines."

"O Gabriel!" entreated Al Borak; "by the faith existing between thee and him, prevail on him to intercede for me at the day of the resurrection."

"Be assured, O Borak!" exclaimed Mahomet, "that through my intercession thou shalt enter paradise."

No sooner had he uttered these words, than the animal approached and submitted to be mounted; then rising with Mahomet on its back, it soared aloft far above the mountains of Mecca.

As they passed like lightning between heaven and earth, Gabriel cried aloud, "Stop, O Mahomet! descend to the earth, and make the prayer with two inflections of the body."

They alighted on the earth, and having made the prayer—

"O friend and well beloved of my soul!" said Mahomet; "why dost thou command me to pray in this place?"

"Because it is Mount Sinai, on which God communed with Moses."

Mounting aloft, they again passed rapidly between heaven and earth, until Gabriel called out a second time, "Stop, O Mahomet! descend, and make the prayer with two inflections."

They descended, Mahomet prayed, and again demanded, "Why didst thou command me to pray in this place?"

"Because it is Bethlehem, where Jesus the Son of Mary was born."

They resumed their course through the air, until a voice was heard on the right, exclaiming, "O Mahomet, tarry a moment, that I may speak to thee; of all created beings I am most devoted to thee."

But Borak pressed forward, and Mahomet forbore to tarry, for he felt that it was not with him to stay his course, but with God the all-powerful and glorious.

Another voice was now heard on the left, calling on Mahomet in like words to tarry; but Borak still pressed forward, and Mahomet tarried not. He now beheld before him a damsel of ravishing beauty, adorned with all the luxury and riches of the earth. She beckoned him with alluring smiles: "Tarry a moment, O Mahomet, that I may talk with thee. I, who, of all beings, am the most devoted to thee." But still Borak pressed on, and Mahomet tarried not; considering that it was not with him to stay his course, but with God the all-powerful and glorious.

Addressing himself, however, to Gabriel, "What voices

are those I have heard?" said he; "and what damsel is this who has beckoned to me?"

"The first, O Mahomet, was the voice of a Jew; hadst thou listened to him, all thy nation would have been won to Judaism.

"The second was the voice of a Christian; hadst thou listened to him, thy people would have inclined to Christianity.

"The damsel was the world, with all its riches, its vanities, and allurements; hadst thou listened to her, thy nation would have chosen the pleasures of this life, rather than the bliss of eternity, and all would have been doomed to perdition."

Continuing their aerial course, they arrived at the gate of the holy temple at Jerusalem, where, alighting from Al Borak, Mahomet fastened her to the rings where the prophets before him had fastened her. Then entering the temple, he found there Abraham, and Moses, and Isa (Jesus), and many more of the prophets. After he had prayed in company with them for a time, a ladder of light was let down from heaven, until the lower end rested on the Shakra, or foundation-stone of the sacred house, being the stone of Jacob. Aided by the angel Gabriel, Mahomet ascended this ladder with the rapidity of lightning.

Being arrived at the first heaven, Gabriel knocked at the gate. "Who is there?" was demanded from within. "Gabriel." "Who is with thee?" "Mahomet." "Has he received his mission?" "He has." "Then he is welcome!" and the gate was opened.

The first heaven was of pure silver, and in its resplendent vault the stars are suspended by chains of gold. In each star an angel is placed sentinel, to prevent the demons from scaling the sacred abodes. As Mahomet entered, an ancient man approached him, and Gabriel said, "Here is thy father Adam, pay him reverence." Mahomet did so, and Adam embraced him, calling him the greatest among his children, and the first among the prophets.

In this heaven were innumerable animals of all kinds, which Gabriel said were angels, who, under these forms, interceded with Allah for the various races of animals upon earth. Among these was a cock of dazzling whiteness, and of such marvelous height, that his crest touched the second heaven, though five hundred years' journey above the first. This wonderful bird saluted the ear of Allah each morning with his melodious chant. All creatures on earth, save man, are awakened by his voice, and all the fowls of his kind chant hallelujahs in emulation of his note.*

* There are three to which, say the Moslem doctors, God always lends a willing ear: the voice of him who reads the Koran; of him who prays for pardon; and of this cock who crows to the glory of the Most High. When the last day is near, they add, Allah will bid this bird to close his wings and chant no more. Then all the cocks on earth will cease to crow, and their silence will be a sign that the great day of judgment is impending.

The Reverend Dr. Humphrey Prideaux, Dean of Norwich, in his *Life*

They now ascended to the second heaven. Gabriel, as before, knocked at the gate; the same questions and replies were exchanged; the door opened and they entered.

This heaven was all of polished steel, and dazzling splendor. Here they found Noah; who, embracing Mahomet, hailed him as the greatest among the prophets.

Arrived at the third heaven, they entered with the same ceremonies. It was all studded with precious stones, and too brilliant for mortal eyes. Here was seated an angel of immeasurable height, whose eyes were seventy thousand days' journey apart. He had at his command a hundred thousand battalions of armed men. Before him was spread a vast book, in which he was continually writing and blotting out.

"This, O Mahomet," said Gabriel, "is Asrael, the angel of death, who is in the confidence of Allah. In the book before him he is continually writing the names of those who are to be born, and blotting out the names of those who have lived their allotted time, and who, therefore, instantly die."

They now mounted to the fourth heaven, formed of the

of *Mahomet*, accuses him of having stolen this wonderful cock from the tract Bava Bartha of the Babylonish Talmud, "wherein," says he, "we have a story of such a prodigious bird, called Zig, which, standing with his feet on the earth, reacheth up to the heavens with his head, and with the spreading of his wings, darkeneth the whole orb of the sun, and causeth a total eclipse thereof. This bird the Chaldee paraphrast on the Psalms says is a cock, and that he crows before the Lord; and the Chaldee paraphrast on Job tells us of his crowing every morning before the Lord, and that God giveth him wisdom for that purpose."

finest silver. Among the angels who inhabited it was one five hundred days' journey in height. His countenance was troubled, and rivers of tears ran from his eyes. "This," said Gabriel, "is the angel of tears, appointed to weep over the children of men, and to predict the evils which await them."

The fifth heaven was of the finest gold. Here Mahomet was received by Aaron with embraces and congratulations. The avenging angel dwells in this heaven, and presides over the element of fire. Of all the angels seen by Mahomet, he was the most hideous and terrific. His visage seemed of copper, and was covered with wens and warts. His eyes flashed lightning, and ho grasped a flaming lance. He sat on a throne surrounded by flames, and before him was a heap of red-hot chains. Were he to alight upon earth in his true form, the mountains would be consumed, the seas dried up, and all the inhabitants would die with terror. To him, and the angels his ministers, is intrusted the execution of divine vengeance on infidels and sinners.

Leaving this awful abode, they mounted to the sixth heaven, composed of a transparent stone, called Hasala, which may be rendered carbuncle. Here was a great angel, composed half of snow and half of fire; yet the snow melted not, nor was the fire extinguished. Around him a choir of lesser angels continually exclaimed, "O Alla! who hast united snow and fire, unite all thy faithful servants in obedience to thy law."

"This, said Gabriel, "is the guardian angel of heaven and earth. It is he who despatches angels unto individuals of thy nation, to incline them in favor of thy mission, and call them to the service of God; and he will continue to do so until the day of resurrection."

Here was the prophet Musa (Moses), who, however, instead of welcoming Mahomet with joy, as the other prophets had done, shed tears at sight of him.

"Wherefore dost thou weep?" inquired Mahomet. "Because I behold a successor, who is destined to conduct more of his nation into paradise than ever I could of the backsliding children of Israel."

Mounting hence to the seventh heaven, Mahomet was received by the patriarch Abraham. This blissful abode is formed of divine light, and of such transcendent glory that the tongue of man cannot describe it. One of its celestial inhabitants will suffice to give an idea of the rest. He surpassed the whole earth in magnitude, and had seventy thousand heads; each head seventy thousand mouths; each mouth seventy thousand tongues; each tongue spoke seventy thousand different languages, and all these were incessantly employed in chanting the praises of the Most High.

While contemplating this wonderful being, Mahomet was suddenly transported aloft to the lotus-tree, called Sedrat, which flourishes on the right hand of the invisible throne of Allah. The branches of this tree extend wider than the distance between the sun and the earth.

Angels more numerous than the sands of the sea-shore, or of the beds of all the streams and rivers, rejoice beneath its shade. The leaves resemble the ears of an elephant; thousands of immortal birds sport among its branches, repeating the sublime verses of the Koran. Its fruits are milder than milk and sweeter than honey. If all the creatures of God were assembled, one of these fruits would be sufficient for their sustenance. Each seed incloses an houri, or celestial virgin, provided for the felicity of true believers. From this tree issue four rivers; two flow into the interior of paradise, two issue beyond it, and become the Nile and Euphrates.

Mahomet and his celestial guide now proceeded to Al Mamour, or the House of Adoration; formed of red jacinths or rubies, and surrounded by innumerable lamps, perpetually burning. As Mahomet entered the portal, three vases were offered him, one containing wine, another milk, and the third, honey. He took and drank of the vase containing milk.

"Well hast thou done; auspicious is thy choice," exclaimed Gabriel. "Hadst thou drunk of the wine, thy people had all gone astray."

The sacred house resembles in form the Caaba at Mecca, and is perpendicularly above it in the seventh heaven. It is visited every day by seventy thousand angels of the highest order. They were at this very time making their holy circuit, and Mahomet, joining with them, walked round it seven times.

Gabriel could go no further. Mahomet now traversed, quicker than thought, an immense space; passing through two regions of dazzling light, and one of profound darkness. Emerging from this utter gloom, he was filled with awe and terror at finding himself in the presence of Allah, and but two bow-shots from his throne. The face of the Deity was covered with twenty thousand veils, for it would have annihilated man to look upon its glory. He put forth his hands, and placed one upon the breast and the other upon the shoulder of Mahomet, who felt a freezing chill penetrate to his heart and to the very marrow of his bones. It was followed by a feeling of ecstatic bliss, while a sweetness and fragrance prevailed around, which none can understand, but those who have been in the divine presence.

Mahomet now received from the Deity himself, many of the doctrines contained in the Koran; and fifty prayers were prescribed as the daily duty of all true believers.

When he descended from the divine presence and again met with Moses, the latter demanded what Allah had required. "That I should make fifty prayers every day."

"And thinkest thou to accomplish such a task? I have made the experiment before thee. I tried it with the children of Israel, but in vain; return, then, and beg a diminution of the task."

Mahomet returned accordingly, and obtained a diminution of ten prayers; but when he related his success to Moses, the latter made the same objection to the daily amount of forty. By his advice Mahomet returned repeatedly, until the number was reduced to five.

Moses still objected. "Thinkest thou to exact five prayers daily from thy people? By Allah! I have had experience with the children of Israel, and such a demand is vain; return, therefore, and entreat still further mitigation of the task."

"No," replied Mahomet, "I have already asked indulgence until I am ashamed." With these words he saluted Moses and departed.

By the ladder of light he descended to the temple of Jerusalem, where he found Borak fastened as he had left her, and mounting, was borne back in an instant to the place whence he had first been taken.

This account of the vision, or nocturnal journey, is chiefly according to the words of the historians Abulfeda, Al Bokhari, and Abu Horeira, and is given more at large in the "Life of Mahomet," by Gagnier. The journey itself has given rise to endless commentaries and disputes among the doctors. Some affirm that it was no more than a dream or vision of the night; and support their assertion by a tradition derived from Ayesha, the wife of Mahomet, who declared that, on the night in question, his body remained perfectly still, and it was only in spirit that he made his nocturnal journey. In giving this tradition, however, they did not consider that at the time the journey was said to have taken place, Ayesha was still a child, and, though espoused, had not become the wife of Mahomet.

Others insist that he made the celestial journey bodily, and that the whole was miraculously effected in so short a space of time, that, on his return, he was able to prevent the complete overturn of a vase of water, which the angel Gabriel had struck with his wing on his departure.

Others say that Mahomet only pretended to have made the nocturnal journey to the temple of Jerusalem, and that the subsequent ascent to heaven was a vision. According to Ahmed ben Joseph, the nocturnal visit to the temple was testified by the patriarch of Jerusalem himself. "At the time," says he, "that Mahomet sent an envoy to the Emperor Heraclius, at Constantinople, inviting him to embrace Islamism, the patriarch was in the presence of the emperor. The envoy having related the nocturnal journey of the prophet, the patriarch was seized with astonishment, and informed the emperor of a circumstance coinciding with the narrative of the envoy. 'It is my custom,' said he, 'never to retire to rest at night until I have fastened every door of the temple. On the night here mentioned, I closed them according to my custom, but there was one which it was impossible to move. Upon this, I sent for the carpenters, who, having inspected the door, declared that the lintel over the portal, and the edifice itself, had settled to such a degree, that it was out of their power to close the door. I was obliged, therefore, to leave it open. Early in the morning, at the break of day, I repaired thither, and behold, the stone placed at the corner of the temple was perforated, and there were vestiges of the place where Al Borak had been fastened. Then, said I, to those present, this portal would not have remained fixed unless some prophet had been here to pray.'"

Traditions go on to say, that when Mahomet narrated his nocturnal journey to a large assembly in Mecca, many marveled yet believed, some were perplexed with doubt, but the Koreishites laughed it to scorn. "Thou sayest that thou hast been to the temple of Jerusalem," said Abu Jahl; "prove the truth of thy words, by giving a description of it."

For a moment Mahomet was embarrassed by the demand, for he had visited the temple in the night, when its form was not discernible; suddenly, however, the angel Gabriel stood by his side, and placed before his eyes an exact type of the sacred edifice, so that he was enabled instantly to answer the most minute questions.

The story still transcended the belief even of some of his disciples, until Abu Beker, seeing them wavering in their faith, and in danger of backsliding, roundly vouched for the truth of it; in reward for which support, Mahomet gave him the title of Al Seddek, or the Testifier to the Truth, by which he was thenceforth distinguished.

As we have already observed, this nocturnal journey

rests almost entirely upon tradition, though some of its circumstances are vaguely alluded to in the Koran. The whole may be a fanciful superstructure of Moslem fanatics on one of these visions or ecstasies to which Mahomet was prone, and the relations of which caused him to be stigmatized by the Koreishites as a madman.

# CHAPTER XIII.

MAHOMET MAKES CONVERTS OF PILGRIMS FROM MEDINA.—DETERMINES TO
FLY TO THAT CITY.—A PLOT TO SLAY HIM.—HIS MIRACULOUS ESCAPE.—
HIS HEGIRA, OR FLIGHT.—HIS RECEPTION AT MEDINA.

HE fortunes of Mahomet were becoming darker
and darker in his native place. Cadijah, his
original benefactress, the devoted companion
of his solitude and seclusion, the zealous believer in his
doctrines, was in her grave: so also was Abu Taleb, once
his faithful and efficient protector. Deprived of the sheltering influence of the latter, Mahomet had become, in a
manner, an outlaw in Mecca; obliged to conceal himself,
and remain a burthen on the hospitality of those whom
his own doctrines had involved in persecution. If
worldly advantage had been his object, how had it been
attained? Upwards of ten years had elapsed since first
he announced his prophetic mission; ten long years of
enmity, trouble, and misfortune. Still he persevered,
and now, at a period of life when men seek to enjoy in
repose the fruition of the past, rather than risk all in
new schemes for the future, we find him, after having
sacrificed ease, fortune, and friends, prepared to give

up home and country also, rather than his religious creed.

As soon as the privileged time of pilgrimage arrived, he emerged once more from his concealment, and mingled with the multitude assembled from all parts of Arabia. His earnest desire was to find some powerful tribe, or the inhabitants of some important city, capable and willing to receive him as a guest, and protect him in the enjoyment and propagation of his faith.

His quest was for a time unsuccessful. Those who had come to worship at the Caaba, drew back from a man stigmatized as an apostate; and the worldly-minded were unwilling to befriend one proscribed by the powerful of his native place.

At length, as he was one day preaching on the hill Al Akaba, a little to the north of Mecca, he drew the attention of certain pilgrims from the city of Yathreb. This city, since called Medina, was about two hundred and seventy miles north of Mecca. Many of its inhabitants were Jews and heretical Christians. The pilgrims in question were pure Arabs of the ancient and powerful tribe of Khazradites, and in habits of friendly intercourse with the Keneedites and Naderites, two Jewish tribes inhabiting Mecca, who claimed to be of the sacerdotal line of Aaron. The pilgrims had often heard their Jewish friends explain the mysteries of their faith, and talk of an expected Messiah. They were moved by the eloquence of Mahomet, and struck with the resemblance

of his doctrines to those of the Jewish law; insomuch
that when they heard him proclaim himself a prophet,
sent by Heaven to restore the ancient faith, they said,
one to another, " Surely this must be the promised Messiah of which we have been told." The more they listened, the stronger became their persuasion of the fact,
until in the end they avowed their conviction, and made
a final profession of the faith.

As the Khazradites belonged to one of the most powerful tribes of Yathreb, Mahomet sought to secure their
protection, and proposed to accompany them on their
return; but they informed him that they were at deadly
feud with the Awsites, another powerful tribe of that
city, and advised him to defer his coming until they
should be at peace. He consented; but on the return
home of the pilgrims, he sent with them Musab Ibn
Omeir, one of the most learned and able of his disciples,
with instructions to strengthen them in the faith, and to
preach it to their townsmen. Thus were the seeds of
Islamism first sown in the city of Medina. For a time
they thrived but slowly. Musab was opposed by the
idolaters, and his life threatened; but he persisted in his
exertions, and gradually made converts among the principal inhabitants. Among these were Saad Ibn Maads,
a prince or chief of the Awsites; and Osaid Ibn Hodheir,
a man of great authority in the city. Numbers of the
Moslems of Mecca, also, driven away by persecution,
took refuge in Medina, and aided in propagating the new

faith among its inhabitants, until it found its way into almost every household.

Feeling now assured of being able to give Mahomet an asylum in the city, upwards of seventy of the converts of Medina, led by Musab Ibn Omeir, repaired to Mecca with the pilgrims in the holy month of the thirteenth year of " the mission," to invite him to take up his abode in their city.    Mahomet gave them a midnight meeting on the hill Al Akaba.   His uncle Al Abbas, who, like the deceased Abu Taleb, took an affectionate interest in his welfare, though no convert to his doctrines, accompanied him to this secret conference, which he feared might lead him into danger.   He entreated the pilgrims from Medina not to entice his nephew to their city until more able to protect him : warning them that their open adoption of the new faith would bring all Arabia in arms against them.   His warnings and entreaties were in vain : a solemn compact was made between the parties.   Mahomet demanded that they should abjure idolatry, and worship the one true God openly and fearlessly.   For himself he exacted obedience in weal and woe ; and for the disciples who might accompany him, protection ; even such as they would render to their own wives and children.   On these terms he offered to bind himself to remain among them, to be the friend of their friends, the enemy of their enemies.   "But, should we perish in your cause," asked they, "what will be our reward ? " "Paradise ! " replied the prophet.

The terms were accepted; the emissaries from Medina placed their hands in the hands of Mahomet, and swore to abide by the compact. The latter then singled out twelve from among them, whom he designated as his apostles; in imitation, it is supposed, of the example of our Saviour. Just then a voice was heard from the summit of the hill, denouncing them as apostates, and menacing them with punishment. The sound of this voice, heard in the darkness of the night, inspired temporary dismay. "It is the voice of the fiend Iblis," said Mahomet, scornfully; "he is the foe of God: fear him not." It was probably the voice of some spy or eavesdropper of the Koreishites; for the very next morning they manifested a knowledge of what had taken place in the night; and treated the new confederates with great harshness as they were departing from the city.

It was this early accession to the faith, and this timely aid proffered and subsequently afforded to Mahomet and his disciples, which procured for the Moslems of Medina the appellation of Ansarians, or auxiliaries, by which they were afterwards distinguished.

After the departure of the Ansarians, and the expiration of the holy month, the persecutions of the Moslems were resumed with increased virulence, insomuch that Mahomet, seeing a crisis was at hand, and being resolved to leave the city, advised his adherents generally to provide for their safety. For himself, he still lingered in Mecca with a few devoted followers.

Abu Sofian, his implacable foe, was at this time governor of the city. He was both incensed and alarmed at the spreading growth of the new faith, and held a meeting of the chief of the Koreishites to devise some means of effectually putting a stop to it. Some advised that Mahomet should be banished the city; but it was objected that he might gain other tribes to his interest, or perhaps the people of Medina, and return at their head to take his revenge. Others proposed to wall him up in a dungeon, and supply him with food until he died; but it was surmised that his friends might effect his escape. All these objections were raised by a violent and pragmatical old man, a stranger from the province of Nedja, who, say the Moslem writers, was no other than the devil in disguise, breathing his malignant spirit into those present. At length it was declared by Abu Jahl, that the only effectual check on the growing evil was to put Mahomet to death. To this all agreed, and as a means of sharing the odium of the deed, and withstanding the vengeance it might awaken among the relatives of the victim, it was arranged that a member of each family should plunge his sword into the body of Mahomet.

It is to this conspiracy that allusion is made in the eighth chapter of the Koran. "And call to mind how the unbelievers plotted against thee, that they might either detain thee in bonds, or put thee to death, or expel thee the city; but God laid a plot against them; and God is the best layer of plots."

In fact, by the time the murderers arrived before the dwelling of Mahomet, he was apprised of the impending danger. As usual, the warning is attributed to the angel Gabriel, but it is probable it was given by some Koreishite, less bloody-minded than his confederates. It came just in time to save Mahomet from the hands of his enemies. They paused at his door, but hesitated to enter. Looking through a crevice they beheld, as they thought, Mahomet wrapped in his green mantle, and lying asleep on his couch. They waited for a while, consulting whether to fall on him while sleeping, or wait until he should go forth. At length they burst open the door and rushed toward the couch. The sleeper started up; but, instead of Mahomet, Ali stood before them. Amazed and confounded, they demanded, " Where is Mahomet ? " "I know not," replied Ali, sternly, and walked forth ; nor did any one venture to molest him. Enraged at the escape of their victim, however, the Koreishites proclaimed a reward of a hundred camels to any one who should bring them Mahomet alive or dead.

Divers accounts are given of the mode in which Mahomet made his escape from the house after the faithful Ali had wrapped himself in his mantle and taken his place upon the couch. The most miraculous account is, that he opened the door silently, as the Koreishites stood before it, and, scattering a handful of dust in the air, cast such blindness upon them, that he walked through the midst of them without being perceived. This, it is added, is confirmed by the verse of the 30th chapter of the Koran: "We have thrown blindness upon them, that they shall not see."

The most probable account is, that he clambered over the wall in the rear of the house, by the help of a servant, who bent his back for him to step upon it.

He repaired immediately to the house of Abu Beker, and they arranged for instant flight. It was agreed that they should take refuge in a cave in Mount Thor, about an hour's distance from Mecca, and wait there until they could proceed safely to Medina: and in the meantime the children of Abu Beker should secretly bring them food. They left Mecca while it was yet dark, making their way on foot by the light of the stars, and the day dawned as they found themselves at the foot of Mount Thor. Scarce were they within the cave, when they heard the sound of pursuit. Abu Beker, though a brave man, quaked with fear. "Our pursuers," said he, "are many, and we are but two." "Nay," replied Mahomet, "there is a third; God is with us!" And here the Moslem writers relate a miracle, dear to the minds of all true believers. By the time, say they, that the Koreishites reached the mouth of the cavern, an acacia-tree had sprung up before it, in the spreading branches of which a pigeon had made its nest, and laid its eggs, and over the whole a spider had woven its web. When the Koreishites beheld these signs of undisturbed quiet, they concluded that no one could recently have entered the cavern; so they turned away, and pursued their search in another direction.

Whether protected by miracle or not, the fugitives remained for three days undiscovered in the cave, and Asama, the daughter of Abu Beker, brought them food in the dusk of the evenings.

On the fourth day, when they presumed the ardor of pursuit had abated, the fugitives ventured forth, and set out for Medina, on camels which a servant of Abu Beker had brought in the night for them. Avoiding the main road usually taken by the caravans, they bent their course nearer to the coast of the Red Sea. They had not proceeded far, however, before they were overtaken by a troop of horse, headed by Soraka Ibn Malec. Abu Beker was again dismayed by the number of their pursuers; but Mahomet repeated the assurance, "Be not troubled; Allah is with us." Soraka was a grim warrior, with shagged iron-gray locks, and naked sinewy arms rough with hair. As he overtook Mahomet, his horse reared and fell with him. His superstitious mind was struck with it as an evil sign. Mahomet perceived the state of his feelings, and by an eloquent appeal wrought upon him to such a degree, that Soraka, filled with awe, entreated his forgiveness; and turning back with his troop, suffered him to proceed on his way unmolested.

The fugitives continued their journey without further interruption, until they arrived at Koba, a hill about two miles from Medina. It was a favorite resort of the inhabitants of the city, and a place to which they sent their sick and infirm, for the air was pure and salubrious. Hence, too, the city was supplied with fruit; the hill and its environs being covered with vineyards, and with groves of the date and lotus; with gardens producing citrons, oranges, pomegranates, figs, peaches, and apricots; and being irrigated with limpid streams.

On arriving at this fruitful spot, Al Kaswa, the camel of Mahomet, crouched on her knees, and would go no further. The prophet interpreted it as a favorable sign, and determined to remain at Koba, and prepare for entering the city. The place where his camel knelt is still pointed out by pious Moslems, a mosque named Al Takwa having been built there to commemorate the circumstance. Some affirm that it was actually founded by the prophet. A deep well is also shown in the vicinity, beside which Mahomet reposed under the shade of the trees, and into which he dropped his seal ring. It is believed still to remain there, and has given sanctity to the well; the waters of which are conducted by subterraneous conduits to Medina. At Koba he remained four days, residing in the house of an Awsite named Colthum Ibn Hadem. While at this village he was joined by a distinguished chief, Boreida Ibn Hoseib, with seventy followers, all of the tribe of Saham. These made profession of faith between the hands of Mahomet.

Another renowned proselyte who repaired to the prophet at this village, was Salman al Parsi (or the Persian). He is said to have been a native of a small place near Ispahan, and that, on passing one day by a Christian church, he was so much struck by the devotion of the people, and the solemnity of the worship, that he became disgusted with the idolatrous faith in which he had been brought up. He afterwards wandered about the East, from city to city, and convent to convent, in quest of a religion, until an ancient monk, full of years and infirmities, told him of a prophet who had arisen in Arabia to restore the pure faith of Abraham.

This Salman rose to power in after years, and was reputed by the unbelievers of Mecca to have assisted Mahomet in compiling his doctrine. This is alluded to in the sixteenth chapter of the Koran. "Verily, the idolaters say, that a certain man assisted to compose the Koran; but the language of this man is Ajami (or Persian), and the Koran is indited in the pure Arabian tongue."*

The Moslems of Mecca, who had taken refuge some time before in Medina, hearing that Mahomet was at hand, came forth to meet him at Koba; among these was the early convert Talha, and Zobeir, the nephew of Cadijah. These, seeing the travel-stained garments of Ma-

---

* The renowned and learned Humphrey Prideaux, Doctor of Divinity and Dean of Norwich, in his *Life of Mahomet,* confounds this Salman the Persian with Abdallah Ibn Salam, a learned Jew; by some called Abdias Ben Salan in the Hebrew dialect, and by others Abdallah Salen; who is accused by Christian writers of assisting Mahomet in fabricating his revelations.

homet and Abu Beker, gave them white mantles, with which to make their entrance into Medina. Numbers of the Ansarians, or auxiliaries, of Medina, who had made their compact with Mahomet in the preceding year, now hastened to renew their vow of fidelity.

Learning from them that the number of proselytes in the city was rapidly augmenting, and that there was a general disposition to receive him favorably, he appointed Friday, the Moslem sabbath, the sixteenth day of the month Rabi, for his public entrance.

Accordingly, on the morning of that day he assembled all his followers to prayer; and after a sermon, in which he expounded the main principles of his faith, he mounted his camel Al Kaswa, and set forth for that city which was to become renowned in after ages as his city of refuge.

Boreida Ibn al Hoseib, with his seventy horsemen of the tribe of Saham, accompanied him as a guard. Some of the disciples took turns to hold a canopy of palm-leaves over his head, and by his side rode Abu Beker. "O apostle of God!" cried Boreida, "thou shalt not enter Medina without a standard;" so saying, he unfolded his turban, and tying one end of it to the point of his lance, bore it aloft before the prophet.

The city of Medina was fair to approach, being extolled for beauty of situation, salubrity of climate, and fertility of soil; for the luxuriance of its palm-trees, and the fragrance of its shrubs and flowers. At a short distance from the city a crowd of new proselytes to the faith, came forth in sun and dust to meet the cavalcade. Most of them had never seen Mahomet, and paid reverence to Abu Beker through mistake; but the latter put aside the screen of palm-leaves, and pointed out the real object of homage, who was greeted with loud acclamations.

In this way did Mahomet, so recently a fugitive from his native city, with a price upon his head, enter Medina, more as a conqueror in triumph than an exile seeking an asylum. He alighted at the house of a Khazradite, named Abu Ayub, a devout Moslem, to whom moreover he was distantly related; here he was hospitably received, and took up his abode in the basement story.

Shortly after his arrival he was joined by the faithful Ali, who had fled from Mecca, and journeyed on foot, hiding himself in the day and travelling only at night, lest he should fall into the hands of the Koreishites. He arrived weary and wayworn, his feet bleeding with the roughness of the journey.

Within a few days more came Ayesha, and the rest of Abu Beker's household, together with the family of Mahomet, conducted by his faithful freedman Zeid, and by Abu Beker's servant Abdallah.

Such is the story of the memorable Hegira, or "Flight of the Prophet;"—the era of the Arabian calendar from which time is calculated by all true Moslems: it corresponds to the 622d year of the Christian era.

## CHAPTER XIV.

MAHOMET soon found himself at the head of a
numerous and powerful sect in Medina; partly
made up of those of his disciples who had fled
from Mecca, and were thence called Mohadjerins or
Fugitives, and partly of inhabitants of the place, who on
joining the faith were called Ansarians or Auxiliaries.
Most of these latter were of the powerful tribes of the
Awsites and Khazradites, which, though descended from
two brothers, Al Aws and Al Khazraj, had for a hundred
and twenty years distracted Medina by their inveterate
and mortal feuds, but had now become united in the
bonds of faith. With such of these tribes as did not immediately adopt his doctrines he made a covenant.

The Khazradites were very much under the sway of a
prince or chief named Abdallah Ibn Obba; who, it is
said, was on the point of being made king, when the
arrival of Mahomet and the excitement caused by his

doctrines, gave the popular feeling a new direction. Abdallah was stately in person, of a graceful demeanor, and ready and eloquent tongue; he professed great friendship for Mahomet, and with several companions of his own type and character, used to attend the meetings of the Moslems. Mahomet was captivated at first by their personal appearance, their plausible conversation, and their apparent deference; but he found in the end that Abdallah was jealous of his popularity and cherished secret animosity against him, and that his companions were equally false in their pretended friendship; hence, he stamped them with the name of "The Hypocrites." Abdallah Ibn Obba long continued his political rival in Medina.

Being now enabled publicly to exercise his faith and preach his doctrines, Mahomet proceeded to erect a mosque. The place chosen was a grave-yard or burying-ground, shaded by date-trees. He is said to have been guided in his choice by what he considered a favorable omen; his camel having knelt opposite to this place on his public entry into the city. The dead were removed, and the trees cut down to make way for the intended edifice. It was simple in form and structure, suited to the unostentatious religion which he professed and to the scanty and precarious means of its votaries. The walls were of earth and brick; the trunks of the palm-trees recently felled, served as pillars to support the roof, which was framed of their banches and thatched with their leaves. It was about a hundred ells square, and had three doors; one to the south, where the Kebla was afterwards established, another called the gate of Gabriel, and the third the gate of Mercy. A part of the edifice, called Soffat, was assigned as a habitation to such of the believers as were without a home.

Mahomet assisted with his own hands in the construction of this mosque. With all his foreknowledge, he little thought that he was building his own tomb and monument; for in that edifice his remains are deposited. It has in after times been repeatedly enlarged and beautified, but still bears the name Mesjed al Nebi (the Mosque of the Prophet), from having been founded by his hands. He was for some time at a loss in what manner his followers should be summoned to their devotions; whether with the sound of trumpets, as among the Jews, or by lighting fires on high places, or by the striking of timbrels. While in this perplexity, a form of words to be cried aloud, was suggested by Abdallah, the son of Zeid, who declared that it was revealed to him in a vision. It was instantly adopted by Mahomet, and such is given as the origin of the following summons, which is to this day heard from the lofty minarets throughout the East, calling the Moslems to the place of worship: "God is great! God is great! There is no God but God. Mahomet is the apostle of God. Come to prayers! come to prayers! God is great! God is great! There is no God but God." To which at dawn of day is added the exhortation, "Prayer is better than sleep! Prayer is better than sleep!"

Everything in this humble mosque was at first conducted with great simplicity. At night it was lighted up by splinters of the date-tree: and it was some time before lamps and oil were introduced. The prophet stood on the ground and preached, leaning with his back against the trunk of one of the date-trees, which served as pillars. He afterwards had a pulpit or tribune erected, to which he ascended by three steps, so as to be elevated above the congregation. Tradition asserts, that when he first ascended this pulpit, the deserted date-tree uttered a groan; whereupon, as a consolation, he gave it the choice either to be transplanted to a garden again to flourish, or to be transferred to paradise, there to yield fruit, in after life, to true believers. The date-tree wisely chose the latter, and was subsequently buried beneath the pulpit, there to await its blissful resurrection.

Mahomet preached and prayed in the pulpit, sometimes sitting, sometimes standing and leaning on a staff. His precepts as yet were all peaceful and benignant, inculcating devotion to God and humanity to man. He seems to have emulated for a time the benignity of the Christian faith. "He who is not affectionate to God's creatures, and to his own children," would he say, "God will not be affectionate to him. Every Moslem who clothes the naked of his faith, will be clothed by Allah in the green robes of paradise."

In one of his traditional sermons transmitted by his disciples, is the following apologue on the subject of charity: "When God created the earth it shook and trembled, until he put mountains upon it, to make it firm. Then the angels asked, 'O God, is there anything of thy creation stronger than these mountains?' And God replied, 'Iron is stronger than the mountains; for it breaks them.' 'And is there anything of thy creation stronger than iron?' 'Yes; fire is stronger than iron, for it melts it.' 'Is there anything of thy creation stronger than fire?' 'Yes; water, for it quenches fire.' 'O Lord, is there anything of thy creation stronger than water?' 'Yes, wind; for it overcomes water and puts it in motion.' 'O, our Sustainer! is there anything of thy creation stronger than wind?' 'Yes, a good man giving alms; if he give with his right hand and conceal it from his left, he overcomes all things.'"

His definition of charity embraced the wide circle of kindness. Every good act, he would say, is charity. Your smiling in your brother's face is charity; an exhortation of your fellow man to virtuous deeds is equal to alms-giving; your putting a wanderer in the right road is charity; your assisting the blind is charity; your removing stones and thorns and other obstructions from the road is charity; your giving water to the thirsty is charity.

"A man's true wealth hereafter is the good he does in this world to his fellow man. When he dies, people will say, What property has he left behind him? But the angels, who examine him in the grave, will ask, 'What good deeds hast thou sent before thee?'"

"O prophet!" said one of his disciples, "my mother Omm-Sad, is dead; what is the best alms I can send for the good of her soul?" "Water!" replied Mahomet, bethinking himself of the panting heats of the desert. "Dig a well for her, and give water to the thirsty." The man digged a well in his mother's name, and said "This well is for my mother, that its rewards may reach her soul."

Charity of the tongue, also, that most important and least cultivated of charities, was likewise earnestly inculcated by Mahomet. Abu Jaraiya, an inhabitant of Basrah, coming to Medina, and being persuaded of the apostolical office of Mahomet, entreated of him some great rule of conduct. "Speak evil of no one," answered the prophet. "From that time," says Abu Jaraiya, "I never did abuse any one, whether freeman or slave."

The rules of Islamism extended to the courtesies of life. Make a salam (or salutation) to a house on entering and leaving it. Return the salute of friends and acquaintances, and wayfarers on the road. He who rides must be the first to make the salute to him who walks; he who walks to him who is sitting; a small party to a large party, and the young to the old.

On the arrival of Mahomet at Medina, some of the Christians of the city promptly enrolled themselves among his followers; they were probably of those sectarians who held to the human nature of Christ, and found nothing repugnant in Islamism; which venerated Christ as the greatest among the prophets. The rest of the Christians resident there showed but little hostility to the new faith, considering it far better than the old idolatry. Indeed, the schisms and bitter dissensions among the Christians of the East had impaired their orthodoxy, weakened their zeal, and disposed them easily to be led away by new doctrines.

The Jews, of which there were rich and powerful families in Medina and its vicinity, showed a less favorable disposition. With some of them Mahomet made covenants of peace, and trusted to gain them in time to accept him as their promised Messiah or prophet. Biased, perhaps unconsciously, by such views, he had modeled many of his doctrines on the dogmas of their religion, and observed certain of their fasts and ordinances. He allowed such as embraced Islamism, to continue in the observance of their Sabbath, and of several of the Mosaic laws and ceremonies. It was the custom of the different religions of the East, to have each a Kebla or sacred point towards which they turned their faces in the act of adoration; the Sabeans toward the North Star; the Persian fire-worshipper towards the east, the place of the rising sun; the Jews toward their holy city of Jerusalem. Hitherto Mahomet had prescribed nothing of the kind; but now, out of deference to the Jews, he made Jerusalem the Kebla, toward which all Moslems were to turn their faces when in prayer.

While new converts were daily made among the inhabitants of Medina, sickness and discontent began to prevail among the fugitives from Mecca. They were not accustomed to the climate; many suffered from fevers, and in their sickness and debility languished after the home whence they were exiled.

To give them a new home, and link them closely with their new friends and allies, Mahomet established a brotherhood between fifty-four of them and as many of the inhabitants of Medina. Two persons thus linked together, were pledged to stand by each other in weal and woe; it was a tie which knit their interests more closely even than that of kindred, for they were to be heirs to each other in preference to blood relations.

This institution was one of expediency, and lasted only until the new comers had taken firm root in Medina; extended merely to those of the people of Mecca who had fled from persecution; and is alluded to in the following verse of the eighth chapter of the Koran: "They who have believed and have fled their country, and employed their substance and their persons in fighting for the faith, and they who have given the prophet a refuge among them, and have assisted him, these shall be deemed the one nearest of kin to the other."

In this shrewd, but simple way, were laid the foundations of that power which was soon to attain stupendous strength, and to shake the mightiest empires of the world.

## CHAPTER XV.

THE family relations of Mahomet had been much broken up by the hostility brought upon him by his religious zeal. His daughter Rokaia was still an exile with her husband, Othman Ibn Affan, in Abyssinia; his daughter Zeinab had remained in Mecca with her husband, Abul Aass, who was a stubborn opposer of the new faith. The family with Mahomet in Medina consisted of his recently wedded wife Sawda, and Fatima and Um Colthum, daughters of his late wife Cadijah. He had a heart prone to affection, and subject to female influence, but he had never entertained much love for Sawda; and though he always treated her with kindness, he felt the want of some one to supply the place of his deceased wife Cadijah.

"O Omar," said he one day, "the best of man's treasures is a virtuous woman, who acts by God's orders, and is obedient and pleasing to her husband: he regards her personal and mental beauties with delight; when he orders her to do anything she obeys him; and when he is absent she guards his right in property and honor."

He now turned his eyes upon his betrothed spouse Ayesha, the beautiful daughter of Abu Beker. Two years had elapsed since they were betrothed, and she had now attained her ninth year; an infantine age it would seem, though the female form is wonderfully precocious in the quickening climates of the East. Their nuptials took place a few months after their arrival in Medina, and were celebrated with great simplicity; the wedding supper was of milk, and the dowry of the bride was twelve okk of silver.

The betrothing of Fatima, his youngest daughter, with his loyal disciple Ali, followed shortly after, and their marriage at a somewhat later period. Fatima was between fifteen and sixteen years of age, of great beauty, and extolled by Arabian writers as one of the four perfect women with whom Allah has deigned to bless the earth. The age of Ali was about twenty-two.

Heaven and earth, say the Moslem writers, joined in paying honor to these happy espousals. Medina resounded with festivity, and blazed with illuminations, and the atmosphere was laden with aromatic odors. As Mahomet, on the nuptial night, conducted his daughter to her bridegroom, heaven sent down a celestial pomp to attend her; on her right hand was the archangel Gabriel; on her left was Michael, and she was followed by a train of seventy thousand angels, who all night kept watch round the mansion of the youthful pair.

Such are the vaunting exaggerations with which Moslem writers are prone to overlay every event in the history of the prophet, and destroy the real grandeur of his career, which consists in its simplicity. A more reliable account states that the wedding feast was of dates and olives; that the nuptial couch was a sheep-skin; that the portion of the bride consisted of two skirts, one head-tire, two silver armlets, one leathern pillow stuffed with palm-leaves, one beaker or drinking cup, one handmill, two large jars for water, and one pitcher. All this was in unison with the simplicity of Arab housekeeping, and with the circumstances of the married couple; and to raise the dowry required of him, Ali, it is said, had to sell several camels and some shirts of mail.

The style of living of the prophet himself was not superior to that of his disciple. Ayesha, speaking of it in after years, observed: "For a whole month together we did not light a fire to dress victuals; our food was nothing but dates and water, unless any one sent us meat. The people of the prophet's household never got wheatbread two successive days."

His food, in general, was dates and barley-bread, with milk and honey. He swept his chamber, lit his fire, mended his clothes, and was in fact his own servant. For each of his two wives he provided a separate house adjoining the mosque. He resided with them by turns, but Ayesha ever remained his favorite.

Mahomet has been extolled by Moslem writers for the chastity of his early life; and it is remarkable that, with all the plurality of wives indulged in by the Arabs, and which he permitted himself in subsequent years, and with all that constitutional fondness which he evinced for the sex, he remained single in his devotion to Cadijah to her dying day, never giving her a rival in his house, nor in his heart. Even the fresh and budding charms of Ayesha, which soon assumed such empire over him, could not obliterate the deep and mingled feeling of tenderness and gratitude for his early benefactress. Ayesha was piqued one day at hearing him indulge in these fond recollections: "O, apostle of God," demanded the youthful beauty, "was not Cadijah stricken in years? Has not Allah given thee a better wife in her stead?"

"Never!" exclaimed Mahomet, with an honest burst of feeling— "never did God give me a better! When I was poor, she enriched me; when I was pronounced a liar, she believed in me; when I was opposed by all the world, she remained true to me!"

# CHAPTER XVI.

THE SWORD ANNOUNCED AS THE INSTRUMENT OF FAITH.—FIRST FORAY
AGAINST THE KOREISHITES.—SURPRISAL OF A CARAVAN.

E come now to an important era in the career
of Mahomet. Hitherto he had relied on argument and persuasion to make proselytes; en-
joining the same on his disciples. His exhortations to
them to bear with patience and long-suffering the violence of their enemies, almost emulated the meek precept
of our Saviour, "if they smite thee on the one cheek,
turn to them the other also." He now arrived at a point
where he completely diverged from the celestial spirit of
the Christian doctrines, and stamped his religion with
the alloy of fallible mortality. His human nature was
not capable of maintaining the sublime forbearance he
had hitherto inculcated. Thirteen years of meek endur-
ance had been rewarded by nothing but aggravated injury and insult. His greatest persecutors had been those
of his own tribe, the Koreishites, especially those of the
rival line of Abd Schems; whose vindictive chief, Abu
Sofian, had now the sway at Mecca. By their virulent
hostility his fortunes had been blasted; his family de-
156

graded, impoverished, and dispersed, and he himself driven into exile. All this he might have continued to bear with involuntary meekness, had not the means of retaliation unexpectedly sprung up within his reach. He had come to Medina a fugitive seeking an asylum, and craving merely a quiet home. In a little while, and probably to his own surprise, he found an army at his command: for among the many converts daily made in Medina, the fugitives flocking to him from Mecca, and proselytes from the tribes of the desert, were men of resolute spirit, skilled in the use of arms, and fond of partisan warfare. Human passions and mortal resentments were awakened by this sudden accession of power. They mingled with that zeal for religious reform, which was still his predominant motive. In the exaltations of his enthusiastic spirit he endeavored to persuade himself, and perhaps did so effectually, that the power thus placed within his reach was intended as a means of effecting his great purpose, and that he was called upon by divine command to use it. Such, at least, is the purport of the memorable manifesto which he issued at this epoch, and which changed the whole tone and fortunes of his faith.

"Different prophets," said he, "have been sent by God to illustrate his different attributes: Moses his clemency and providence; Solomon his wisdom, majesty, and glory; Jesus Christ his righteousness, omniscience, and power;—his righteousness by purity of conduct; his omniscience by the knowledge he displayed of the secrets of all hearts; his power by the miracles he wrought. None of these attributes, however, have been sufficient to enforce conviction, and even the miracles of Moses and Jesus have been treated with unbelief. I, therefore, the last of the prophets, am sent with the sword! Let those who promulgate my faith enter into no argument nor discussion; but slay all who refuse obedience to the law. Whoever fights for the true faith, whether he fall or conquer, will assuredly receive a glorious reward."

"The sword," added he, "is the key of heaven and hell; all who draw it in the cause of the faith will be rewarded with temporal advantages; every drop shed of their blood, every peril and hardship endured by them, will be registered on high as more meritorious than even fasting and praying. If they fall in battle, their sins will at once be blotted out, and they will be transported to paradise, there to revel in eternal pleasures in the arms of black-eyed houris."

Predestination was brought to aid these belligerent doctrines. Every event, according to the Koran, was predestined from eternity, and could not be avoided. No man could die sooner or later than his allotted hour, and when it arrived, it would be the same, whether the angel of death should find him in the quiet of his bed, or amid the storm of battle.

Such were the doctrines and revelations which converted Islamism of a sudden from a religion of meekness and philanthropy, to one of violence and the sword. They were peculiarly acceptable to the Arabs, harmonizing with their habits, and encouraging their predatory propensities. Virtually pirates of the desert, it is not to be wondered at that, after this open promulgation of the Religion of the Sword, they should flock in crowds to the standard of the prophet. Still no violence was authorized by Mahomet against those who should persist in unbelief, provided they should readily submit to his temporal sway, and agree to pay tribute; and here we see the first indication of worldly ambition and a desire for temporal dominion dawning upon his mind. Still it will be found, that the tribute thus exacted was subsidiary to his ruling passion, and mainly expended by him in the extension of the faith.

The first warlike enterprises of Mahomet betray the lurking resentment we have noted. They were directed against the caravans of Mecca, belonging to his implacable enemies the Koreishites. The three first were headed by Mahomet in person, but without any material result. The fourth was confided to a Moslem, named Abdallah Ibn Jasch; who was sent out with eight or ten resolute followers on the road toward South Arabia. As it was now the holy month of Radjab, sacred from violence and rapine, Abdallah had sealed orders, not to be opened until the third day. These orders were vaguely yet significantly worded. Abdallah was to repair to the valley of Naklah, between Mecca and Tayef (the same in

which Mahomet had the revelation of the Genii), where
he was to watch for an expected caravan of the Koreishites. "Perhaps," added the letter of instructions
shrewdly,—"perhaps thou mayest be able to bring us
some tidings of it."

Abdallah understood the true meaning of the letter,
and acted up to it. Arriving in the valley of Naklah, he
descried the caravan, consisting of several camels laden
with merchandise, and conducted by four men. Following it at a distance, he sent one of his men, disguised as
a pilgrim, to overtake it. From the words of the latter
the Koreishites supposed his companions to be like himself, pilgrims bound to Mecca. Besides, it was the month
of Radjab, when the desert might be travelled in security.
Scarce had they come to a halt, however, when Abdallah
and his comrades fell on them; killed one and took two
prisoners; the fourth escaped. The victors then returned
to Medina with their prisoners and booty.

All Medina was scandalized at this breach of the holy
month. Mahomet, finding that he had ventured too far,
pretended to be angry with Abdallah, and refused to take
the share of the booty offered to him. Confiding in the
vagueness of his instructions, he insisted that he had not
commanded Abdallah to shed blood, or commit any violence during the holy month.

The clamor still continuing, and being echoed by the
Koreishites of Mecca, produced the following passage of
the Koran :—

"They will ask thee concerning the sacred month, whether they may make war therein. Answer: To war therein is grievous; but to deny God, to bar the path of God against his people, to drive true believers from his holy temple, and to worship idols, are sins far more grievous than to kill in the holy months."

Having thus proclaimed divine sanction for the deed, Mahomet no longer hesitated to take his share of the booty. He delivered one of the prisoners on ransom; the other embraced Islamism.

The above passage of the Koran, however satisfactory it may have been to devout Moslems, will scarcely serve to exculpate their prophet in the eyes of the profane. The expedition of Abdallah Ibn Jasch was a sad practical illustration of the new religion of the sword. It contemplated not merely an act of plunder and revenge, a venial act in the eyes of Arabs, and justified by the new doctrines by being exercised against the enemies of the faith, but an outrage also on the holy month, that period sacred from time immemorial against violence and bloodshed, and which Mahomet himself professed to hold in reverence. The craft and secrecy also with which the whole was devised and conducted, the sealed letter of instructions to Abdallah, to be opened only at the end of three days, at the scene of projected outrage, and couched in language vague, equivocal, yet sufficiently significant to the agent; all were in direct opposition to the conduct of Mahomet in the earlier part of his career, when he dared openly to pursue the path of duty, "though the sun should be arrayed against him on the right hand, and the moon on the left;" all showed that he was conscious of the turpitude of the act he was authorizing. His disavowal of the violence committed by Abdallah, yet his bringing the Koran to his aid to enable him to profit by it with impunity, give still darker shades to this transaction; which altogether shows how immediately and widely he went wrong the moment he departed from the benevolent spirit of Christianity, which he at first endeavored to emulate. Worldly passions and worldly interests were fast getting the ascendency over that religious enthusiasm which first inspired him. As has well been observed, the "first drop of blood shed in his name in the Holy Week, displayed him a man, in whom the slime of earth had quenched the holy flame of prophecy."

## CHAPTER XVII.

### THE BATTLE OF BEDER.

IN the second year of the Hegira, Mahomet received intelligence that his arch foe, Abu Sofian, with a troop of thirty horsemen, was conducting back to Mecca a caravan of a thousand camels, laden with the merchandise of Syria. Their route lay through the country of Medina, between the range of mountains and the sea. Mahomet determined to intercept them. About the middle of the month Ramadhan, therefore, he sallied forth with three hundred and fourteen men, of whom eighty-three were Mohadjerins, or exiles from Mecca; sixty-one Awsites, and a hundred and seventy Khazradites. Each troop had its own banner. There were but two horses in this little army,* but there were seventy fleet camels, which the

---

* "The Arabs of the desert," says Burckhardt, "are not rich in horses. Among the great tribes on the Red Sea, between Akaba and Mecca, and to the south and southeast of Mecca, as far as Yemen, horses are very scarce, especially among those of the mountainous districts. The settled inhabitants of Hedjaz and Yemen are not much in the habit of keeping horses. The tribes most rich in horses are those who dwell in the comparatively fertile plains of Mesopotamia, on the banks of the river Euphrates, and on the Syrian plains."—*Burckhardt*, ii. 50.

troop mounted by turns, so as to make a rapid march without much fatigue.

Othman Ibn Affan, the son-in-law of Mahomet, was now returned with his wife Rokaia from their exile in Abyssinia, and would have joined the enterprise, but his wife was ill almost unto death, so that he was obliged reluctantly to remain in Medina.

Mahomet for a while took the main road to Mecca, then leaving it to the left, turned toward the Red Sea and entered a fertile valley, watered by the brook Beder. Here he laid in wait near a ford, over which the caravans were accustomed to pass. He caused his men to dig a deep trench, and to divert the water therein, so that they might resort thither to slake their thirst, out of reach of the enemy.

In the meantime, Abu Sofian having received early intelligence that Mahomet had sallied forth to waylay him with a superior force, despatched a messenger named Omair, on a fleet dromedary, to summon instant relief from Mecca. The messenger arrived at the Caaba haggard and breathless. Abu Jahl mounted the roof and sounded the alarm. All Mecca was in confusion and consternation. Henda the wife of Abu Sofian, a woman of a fierce and intrepid nature, called upon her father Otha, her brother Al Walid, her uncle Shaiba, and all the warriors of her kindred, to arm and hasten to the relief of her husband. The brothers, too, of the Koreishite slain by Abdallah Ibn Jasch, in the valley of Naklah, seized their weapons to avenge his death. Motives of interest were mingled with eagerness for vengeance, for most of the Koreishites had property embarked in the caravan. In a little while a force of one hundred horse and seven hundred camels hurried forward on the road toward Syria. It was led by Abu Jahl, now threescore and ten years of age, a veteran warrior of the desert, who still retained the fire, and almost the vigor and activity of youth, combined with the rancor of old age.

While Abu Jahl, with his forces, was hurrying on in one direction, Abu Sofian was approaching in another. On arriving at the region of danger, he preceded his caravan a considerable distance, carefully regarding every track and footprint. At length he came upon the track of the little army of Mahomet. He knew it from the size of the kernels of the dates, which the troops had thrown by the wayside as they marched — those of Medina being remarkable for their smallness. On such minute signs do the Arabs depend in tracking their foes through the deserts.

Observing the course Mahomet had taken, Abu Sofian changed his route, and passed along the coast of the Red Sea until he considered himself out of danger. He then sent another messenger to meet any Koreishites that might have sallied forth, and to let them know that the caravan was safe, and they might return to Mecca.

The messenger met the Koreishites when in full march. On hearing that the caravan was safe, they came to a

halt and held council. Some were for pushing forward
and inflicting a signal punishment on Mahomet and his
followers ; others were for turning back. In this dilemma, they sent a scout to reconnoitre the enemy. He
brought back word that they were about three hundred
strong; this increased the desire of those who were for
battle. Others remonstrated. "Consider," said they,
"these are men who have nothing to lose ; they have
nothing but their swords ; not one of them will fall without slaying his man. Beside, we have relatives among
them ; if we conquer, we will not be able to look each
other in the face, in having slain each other's relatives."
These words were producing their effect, but the brothers
of the Koreishite who had been slain in the valley of
Naklah, were instigated by Abu Jahl to cry for revenge.
That fiery old Arab seconded their appeal. "Forward!"
cried he ; "let us get water from the brook Beder for the
feast with which we shall make merry over the escape of
our caravan." The main body of the troops, therefore, elevated their standards and resumed their march,
though a considerable number turned back to Mecca.

The scouts of Mahomet brought him notice of the approach of this force. The hearts of some of his followers
failed them ; they had come forth in the expectation of
little fighting and much plunder, and were dismayed at
the thoughts of such an overwhelming host; but Mahomet bade them be of good cheer, for Allah had promised him an easy victory.

The Moslems posted themselves on a rising ground, with water at the foot of it. A hut, or shelter of the branches of trees, had been hastily erected on the summit for Mahomet, and a dromedary stood before it, on which he might fly to Medina in case of defeat.

The vanguard of the enemy entered the valley panting with thirst, and hastened to the stream to drink; but Hamza, the uncle of Mahomet, set upon them with a number of his men, and slew the leader with his own hand. Only one of the vanguard escaped, who was afterwards converted to the faith.

The main body of the enemy now approached with sound of trumpet. Three Koreishite warriors advancing in front, defied the bravest of the Moslems to equal combat. Two of these challengers were Otha, the father-in-law of Abu Sofian, and Al Walid, his brother-in-law. The third challenger was Shaiba, the brother of Otha. These it will be recollected had been instigated to sally forth from Mecca, by Henda, the wife of Abu Sofian. They were all men of rank in their tribe.

Three warriors of Medina stepped forward and accepted their challenge; but they cried, "No! Let the renegades of our own city of Mecca, advance, if they dare." Upon this Hamza and Ali, the uncle and cousin of Mahomet, and Obeidah Ibn al Hareth, undertook the fight. After a fierce and obstinate contest, Hamza and Ali each slew his antagonist. They then went to the aid of Obeidah, who was severely wounded and nearly overcome by Otha. They slew the Koreishite and bore away their associate, but he presently died of his wounds.

The battle now became general. The Moslems, aware of the inferiority of their number, at first merely stood on the defensive, maintaining their position on the rising ground, and galling the enemy with flights of arrows whenever they sought to slake their intolerable thirst at the stream below. Mahomet remained in his hut on the hill, accompanied by Abu Beker, and earnestly engaged in prayer. In the course of the battle he had a paroxysm, or fell into a kind of trance. Coming to himself, he declared that God in a vision had promised him the victory. Rushing out of the hut, he caught up a handful of dust and cast it into the air toward the Koreishites, exclaiming, "May confusion light upon their faces." Then ordering his followers to charge down upon the enemy: "Fight, and fear not," cried he; " the gates of paradise are under the shade of swords. He will assuredly find instant admission, who falls fighting for the faith."

In the shock of battle which ensued, Abu Jahl, who was urging his horse into the thickest of the conflict, received a blow of a scimetar in the thigh, which brought him to the ground. Abdallah Ibn Masoud put his foot upon his breast, and while the fiery veteran was still uttering imprecations and curses on Mahomet, severed his head from his body.

The Koreishites now gave way and fled. Seventy remained dead on the field, and nearly the same number were taken prisoners. Fourteen Moslems were slain, whose names remain on record as martyrs to the faith.

This signal victory was easily to be accounted for on natural principles; the Moslems being fresh and unwearied, and having the advantage of a rising ground, and a supply of water; while the Koreishites were fatigued by a hasty march, parched with thirst, and diminished in force, by the loss of numbers who had turned back to Mecca. Moslem writers, however, attribute this early triumph of the faith to supernatural agency. When Mahomet scattered dust in the air, say they, three thousand angelic warriors in white and yellow turbans, and long dazzling robes, and mounted on black and white steeds, came rushing like a blast, and swept the Koreishites before them. Nor is this affirmed on Moslem testimony alone, but given on the word of an idolater, a peasant who was attending sheep on an adjacent hill. "I was with a companion, my cousin," said the peasant, "upon the fold of the mountain watching the conflict, and waiting to join with the conquerors and share the spoil. Suddenly, we beheld a great cloud sailing toward us, and within it were the neighing of steeds and the braying of trumpets. As it approached, squadrons of angels sallied forth, and we heard the terrific voice of the archangel as he urged his mare Haizum, 'Speed! speed! O Haizum!' At which awful sound the heart of my companion burst with terror, and he died on the spot; and I had well nigh shared his fate." *

When the conflict was over, Abdallah Ibn Masoud brought the head of Abu Jahl to Mahomet, who eyed the grisly trophy with exultation, exclaiming, "This man was the Pharaoh of our nation." The true name of this veteran warrior was Amru Ibn Hasham. The Koreishites had given him the surname of Abu 'lhoem, or Father of Wisdom, on account of his sagacity. The Moslems had changed it to Abu Jahl, Father of Folly. The latter appellation has adhered to him in history, and he is never mentioned by true believers without the ejaculation, "May he be accursed of God."

The Moslems who had fallen in battle were honorably interred; as to the bodies of the Koreishites, they were contemptuously thrown into a pit which had been digged for them. The question was how to dispose of the prisoners. Omar was for striking off their heads; but Abu Beker advised that they should be given up on ransom.

---

* This miraculous aid is repeatedly mentioned in the Koran, *e. g.*:—

"God had already given you the victory at Beder, when ye were inferior in number. When thou saidst unto the faithful, Is it not enough for you that your Lord should assist you with three thousand angels, sent down from heaven? Verily, if ye persevere, and fear God, and your enemies come upon you suddenly, your Lord will assist you with five thousand angels, distinguished by their horses and attire—

*   *   *   *   *   *   *

"O true believers, ye slew not those who were slain at Beder yourselves, but God slew them. Neither didst thou, O Mahomet, cast the gravel into their eyes, when thou didst seem to cast it; but God cast it."— Sale's *Koran*, chap. iii.

Mahomet observed that Omar was like Noah, who prayed for the destruction of the guilty by the deluge; but Abu Beker was like Abraham, who interceded for the guilty. He decided on the side of mercy. But two of the prisoners were put to death; one, named Nadhar, for having ridiculed the Koran as a collection of Persian tales and fables; the other, named Okba, for the attempt upon the life of Mahomet when he first preached in the Caaba, and when he was rescued by Abu Beker. Several of the prisoners who were poor, were liberated on merely making oath never again to take up arms against Mahomet or his followers. The rest were detained until ransoms should be sent by their friends.

Among the most important of the prisoners, was Al Abbas, the uncle of Mahomet. He had been captured by Abu Yaser, a man of small stature. As the bystanders scoffed at the disparity of size, Al Abbas pretended that he really had surrendered to a horseman of gigantic size, mounted on a steed the like of which he had never seen before. Abu Yaser would have steadily maintained the truth of his capture, but Mahomet, willing to spare the humiliation of his uncle, intimated that the captor had been aided by the angel Gabriel.

Al Abbas would have excused himself from paying ransom, alleging that he was a Moslem in heart, and had only taken part in the battle on compulsion; but his excuse did not avail. It is thought by many that he really had a secret understanding with his nephew, and was employed by him as a spy in Mecca, both before and after the battle of Beder.

Another prisoner of great importance to Mahomet was Abul Aass, the husband of his daughter Zeinab. The prophet would fain have drawn his son-in-law to him and enrolled him among his disciples, but Abul Aass remained stubborn in unbelief. Mahomet then offered to set him at liberty on condition of his returning to him his daughter. To this the infidel agreed; and Zeid, the faithful freedman of the prophet, was sent with several companions to Mecca, to bring Zeinab to Medina; in the meantime, her husband Abul Aass, remained a hostage for the fulfillment of the compact.

Before the army returned to Medina there was a division of the spoil; for, though the caravan of Abu Sofian had escaped, yet considerable booty of weapons and camels had been taken in the battle, and a large sum of money would accrue from the ransom of the prisoners. On this occasion Mahomet ordered that the whole should be equally divided among all the Moslems engaged in the enterprise; and though it was a long-established custom among the Arabs to give a fourth part of the booty to the chief, yet he contented himself with the same share as the rest. Among the spoil which fell to his lot was a famous sword of admirable temper, called Dhul Fakar, or the Piercer. He ever afterwards bore it when in battle; and his son-in-law Ali inherited it at his death.

This equal distribution of the booty caused great murmurs among the troops. Those who had borne the brunt
of the fight, and had been most active in taking the spoil,
complained that they had to share alike with those who
had stood aloof from the affray, and with the old men
who had remained to guard the camp. The dispute, observes Sale, resembles that of the soldiers of David in
relation to spoils taken from the Amalekites; those who
had been in the action insisting that they who tarried by
the stuff should have no share of the spoil. The decision
was the same—that they should share alike. (1 Samuel
xxx. 21–25.) Mahomet, from his knowledge of Bible
history, may have been guided by this decision. The
division of the spoils was an important point to settle,
for a leader about to enter on a career of predatory warfare. Fortunately, he had a timely revelation shortly
after his return to Mecca, regulating for the future the
division of all booty gained in fighting for the faith.

Such are the particulars of the famous battle of Beder,
the first victory of the Saracens under the standard of
Mahomet; inconsiderable, perhaps in itself, but stupendous in its results; being the commencement of a career
of victories which changed the destinies of the world.

# CHAPTER XVIII.

DEATH OF THE PROPHET'S DAUGHTER ROKAIA.—RESTORATION OF HIS DAUGH-
    TER ZEINAB.—EFFECT OF THE PROPHET'S MALEDICTION ON ABU LAHAB
    AND HIS FAMILY.—FRANTIC RAGE OF HENDA, THE WIFE OF ABU SOFIAN.—
    MAHOMET NARROWLY ESCAPES ASSASSINATION.—EMBASSY OF THE KORE-
    ISHITES.—THE KING OF ABYSSINIA.

AHOMET returned in triumph to Medina with
the spoils and prisoners taken in his first battle. His exultation, however, was checked by
domestic grief. Rokaia, his beloved daughter, so recently
restored from exile, was no more. The messenger who
preceded Mahomet with tidings of his victory, met the
funeral train at the gate of the city, bearing her body to
the tomb.

The affliction of the prophet was soothed shortly afterward by the arrival from Mecca of his daughter Zeinab,
conducted by the faithful Zeid. The mission of Zeid had
been attended with difficulties. The people of Mecca
were exasperated by the late defeat, and the necessity of
ransoming the prisoners. Zeid remained, therefore, without the walls, and sent in a message to Kenanah, the
brother of Abul Aass, informing him of the compact, and
appointing a place where Zeinab should be delivered into

his hands. Kenanah set out to conduct her thither in a litter. On the way he was beset by a throng of Koreish-ites, determined to prevent the daughter of Mahomet from being restored to him. In the confusion one Hab-bar Ibn Aswad made a thrust at the litter with a lance, which, had not Kenanah parried it with his bow, might have proved fatal to Zeinab. Abu Sofian was attracted to the place by the noise and tumult, and rebuked Ke-nanah for restoring Mahomet's daughter thus publicly, as it might be construed into a weak concession; Zeinab was taken back, therefore, to her home, and Kenanah delivered her up secretly to Zeid in the course of the following night.

Mahomet was so exasperated at hearing of the attack on his daughter, that he ordered whoever should take Habbar, to burn him alive. When his rage had subsided he modified this command. "It is for God alone," said he, "to punish man with fire. If taken, let Habbar be put to death with the sword."

The recent triumph of the Moslems at Beder struck the Koreishites of Mecca with astonishment and mortifi-cation. The man so recently driven a fugitive from their walls, had suddenly started up a powerful foe. Several of their bravest and most important men had fallen be-neath his sword; others were his captives, and awaited a humiliating ransom. Abu Lahab, the uncle of Mahomet, and always his vehement opposer, had been unable, from illness, to take the field. He died a few days after hearing of the victory, his death being hastened by the exasperation of his spirits. Pious Moslems, however, attribute it to the curse pronounced by Mahomet aforetime on him and his family, when he raised his hand to hurl a stone at the prophet on the hill of Safa. That curse, say they, fell heavily also on his son Otho, who had repudiated the prophet's daughter Rokaia; he was torn to pieces by a lion, in the presence of a whole caravan, when on a journey to Syria.

By no one was the recent defeat at Beder felt so severely as by Abu Sofian. He reached Mecca in safety with his caravan, it is true; but it was to hear of the triumph of the man he detested, and to find his home desolate. His wife Henda met him with frantic lamentations for the death of her father, her uncle, and her brother. Rage mingled with her grief, and she cried night and day for vengeance on Hamza and Ali, by whose hands they had fallen.*

---

* It is a received law among all the Arabs, that whoever sheds the blood of a man, owes blood on that account to the family of the slain person. This ancient law is sanctioned by the Koran. "O true believers, the law of retaliation is ordained to you for the slain; the free shall die for the free." The Blood-revenge, or Thar, as it is termed in Arabic, is claimed by the relatives of all who have been killed in open war, and not merely of the actual homicide, but of all his relations. For those killed in wars between two tribes, the price of blood is required from the persons who were known to have actually killed them.

The Arab regards this Blood-revenge as one of his most sacred rights, as well as duties; no earthly consideration could induce him to give it up. He has a proverbial saying, "Were hell-fire to be my lot, I would not relinquish the Thar."—See *Burckhardt*, v. i. 314, Notes.

Abu Sofian summoned two hundred fleet horsemen, each with a sack of meal at his saddle-bow, the scanty provisions of an Arab for a foray; as he sallied forth he vowed neither to anoint his head, perfume his beard, nor approach a female, until he had met Mahomet face to face. Scouring the country to within three miles of the gates of Medina, he slew two of the prophet's followers, ravaged the fields, and burnt the date-trees.

Mahomet sallied forth to meet him at the head of a superior force. Abu Sofian, regardless of his vow, did not wait his approach, but turned bridle and fled. His troop clattered after him, throwing off their sacks of meal in the hurry of their flight; whence this scampering affair was derisively called "The war of the meal sacks."

Moslem writers record an imminent risk of the prophet, while yet in the field on this occasion. He was one day sleeping alone at the foot of a tree, at a distance from his camp, when he was awakened by a noise, and beheld Durthur, a hostile warrior, standing over him with a drawn sword. "O Mahomet," cried he, "who is there now to save thee?" "God!" replied the prophet. Struck with conviction, Durthur let fall his sword, which was instantly seized upon by Mahomet. Brandishing the weapon, he exclaimed in turn, "Who is there now to save thee, O Durthur?" "Alas, no one!" replied the soldier. "Then learn from me to be merciful." So saying, he returned the sword. The heart of the warrior was overcome; he acknowledged Mahomet as the prophet of God, and embraced the faith.

As if the anecdote were not sufficiently marvelous, other devout Moslems affirm that the deliverance of Mahomet was through the intervention of the angel Gabriel, who, at the moment Durthur was about to strike, gave him a blow on the breast with his invisible hand, which caused him to let fall his sword.

About this time the Koreishites of Mecca bethought themselves of the relatives and disciples of Mahomet who had taken refuge from their persecutions in Abyssinia; most of whom still remained there under the protection of the Najashee or Abyssinian king. To this potentate the Koreishites sent an embassy to obtain the persons of the fugitives. One of the ambassadors was Abdallah Ibn Rabia; another was Amru Ibn Al Aass, the distinguished poet who had assailed Mahomet at the outset of his mission with lampoons and madrigals. He was now more matured in years, and as remarkable for his acute sagacity as for his poetic talents. He was still a redoubtable opponent of the faith of Islam, of which in after years he was to prove one of the bravest and most distinguished champions.

Amru and Abdallah opened their embassy in the oriental style by the parade of rich presents, and then requested, in the name of the Koreish authorities of Mecca, that the fugitives might be delivered up to them. The king was a just man, and summoned the Moslems before him to explain this new and dangerous heresy of which they were accused. Among their number was Giafar, or Jaafar, the son of Abu Taleb, and brother of Ali, consequently the cousin of Mahomet. He was a man of persuasive eloquence and a most prepossessing appearance. He stood forth on this occasion, and expounded the doctrines of Islam with zeal and power. The king, who, as has been observed, was a Nestorian Christian, found these doctrines so similar in many respects to those of his sect, and so opposed to the gross idolatry of the Koreishites, that, so far from giving up the fugitives, he took them more especially into favor and protection, and returning to Amru and Abdallah the presents they had brought, dismissed them from his court.

# CHAPTER XIX.

HE battle of Beder had completely changed the position of Mahomet; he was now a triumphant chief of a growing power. The idolatrous tribes of Arabia were easily converted to a faith which flattered their predatory inclinations with the hope of spoil, and which, after all, professed but to bring them back to the primitive religion of their ancestors; the first cavalcade, therefore, which entered the gates of Medina with the plunder of a camp, made converts of almost all its heathen inhabitants, and gave Mahomet the control of the city. His own tone now became altered, and he spoke as a lawgiver and a sovereign. The first evidence of this change of feeling was in his treatment of the Jews, of whom there were three principal and powerful families in Medina.

All the concessions made by him to that stiff-necked race had proved fruitless; they not only remained stub-

180

born in unbelief, but treated him and his doctrines with ridicule. Assma, the daughter of Merwan, a Jewish poetess, wrote satires against him. She was put to death by one of his fanatic disciples. Abu Afak, an Israelite, one hundred and twenty years of age, was likewise slain for indulging in satire against the prophet. Kaab Ibn Aschraf, another Jewish poet, repaired to Mecca after the battle of Beder, and endeavored to stir up the Koreishites to vengeance, reciting verses in which he extolled the virtues and bewailed the death of those of their tribe who had fallen in the battle. Such was his infatuation, that he recited these verses in public, on his return to Medina, and in the presence of some of the prophet's adherents who were related to the slain. Stung by this invidious hostility, Mahomet one day exclaimed in his anger, " Who will rid me of this son of Aschraf ? " Within a few days afterwards, Kaab paid for his poetry with his life ; being slain by a zealous Ansarian of the Awsite tribe.

An event at length occurred which caused the anger of Mahomet against the Jews to break out in open hostility. A damsel of one of the pastoral tribes of Arabs who brought milk to the city, was one day in the quarter inhabited by the Beni Kainoka, or children of Kainoka, one of the three principal Jewish families. Here she was accosted by a number of young Israelites, who having heard her beauty extolled, besought her to uncover her face. The damsel refused an act contrary to the

laws of propriety among her people. A young gold-
smith, whose shop was hard by, secretly fastened the
end of her veil to the bench on which she was sitting, so
that when she rose to depart, the garment remained, and
her face was exposed to view. Upon this there was
laughter and scoffing among the young Israelites, and the
damsel stood in the midst confounded and abashed. A
Moslem present, resenting the shame put upon her, drew
his sword, and thrust it through the body of the gold-
smith; he in his turn was instantly slain by the Israelites. The Moslems from a neighboring quarter flew to
arms, the Beni Kainoka did the same, but being inferior
in numbers, took refuge in a stronghold. Mahomet interfered to quell the tumult; but, being generally exasperated against the Israelites, insisted that the offending
tribe should forthwith embrace the faith. They pleaded
the treaty which he had made with them on his coming
to Medina, by which they were allowed the enjoyment of
their religion; but he was not to be moved. For some
time the Beni Kainoka refused to yield, and remained
obstinately shut up in their stronghold; but famine compelled them to surrender. Abdallah Ibn Obba Solul, the
leader of the Khazradites, who was a protector of this
Jewish tribe, interfered in their favor, and prevented
their being put to the sword; but their wealth and effects
were confiscated, and they were banished to Syria, to the
number of seven hundred men.

The arms and riches accruing to the prophet and his

followers from this confiscation, were of great avail in the
ensuing wars of the faith. Among the weapons which
fell to the share of Mahomet are enumerated three
swords : Medham, the Keen ; al Battar, the Trenchant ;
and Hatef, the Deadly. Two lances : al Monthari, the
Disperser ; and al Monthawi, the Destroyer. A cuirass
of silver, named al Fadha, and another named al Saadia,
said to have been given by Saul to David, when about to
encounter Goliath. There was a bow, too, called al Ca-
tûm, or the Strong ; but it did not answer to its name, for
in the first battle in which the prophet used it, he drew
it with such force that he broke it in pieces. In general,
he used the Arabian kind of bow, with appropriate arrows and lances, and forbade his followers to use those
of Persia.

Mahomet now sought no longer to conciliate the Jews ;
on the contrary, they became objects of his religious hostility. He revoked the regulation by which he had made
Jerusalem the Kebla or point of prayer, and established
Mecca in its place ; towards which, ever since, the Mahometans turn their faces when performing their devotions.

The death of the prophet's daughter Rokaia had been
properly deplored by her husband Othman. To console
the latter for his loss, Omar, his brother in arms, offered
him, in the course of the year, his daughter Hafza for
wife. She was the widow of Hobash, a Suhamite, eighteen years of age, and of tempting beauty, yet Othman

declined the match. Omar was indignant at what he conceived a slight to his daughter and to himself, and complained of it to Mahomet. "Be not grieved, Omar," replied the prophet, "a better wife is destined for Othman, and a better husband for thy daughter." He in effect gave his own daughter Omm Kolthum to Othman; and took the fair Hafza to wife himself. By these politic alliances he grappled both Othman and Omar more strongly to his side, while he gratified his own inclinations for female beauty. Hafza, next to Ayesha, was the most favored of his wives; and was intrusted with the coffer containing the chapters and verses of the Koran as they were revealed.

## CHAPTER XX.

AS the power of Mahomet increased in Medina, the hostility of the Koreishites in Mecca augmented in virulence. Abu Sofian held command in the sacred city, and was incessantly urged to warfare by his wife Henda, whose fierce spirit could take no rest, until "blood revenge" had been wreaked on those by whom her father and brother had been slain. Akrema, also, a son of Abu Jahl, and who inherited his father's hatred of the prophet, clamored for vengeance. In the third year of the Hegira, therefore, the year after the battle of Beder, Abu Sofian took the field at the head of three thousand men, most of them Koreishites, though there were also Arabs of the tribes of Kanana and Tehama. Seven hundred were armed with corselets and two hundred were horsemen. Akrema was one of the captains, as was also Khaled Ibn al Waled, a warrior of indomitable valor, who afterwards rose to great renown.

185

The banners were borne in front by the race of Abd al Dar, a branch of the tribe of Koreish, who had a hereditary right to the foremost place in council, the foremost rank in battle, and to bear the standard in the advance of the army.

In the rear of the host followed the vindictive Henda, with fifteen principal women of Mecca, relatives of those slain in the battle of Beder; sometimes filling the air with wailings and lamentations for the dead; at other times animating the troops with the sound of timbrels and warlike chants. As they passed through the village of Abwa, where Amina the mother of Mahomet was interred, Henda was with difficulty prevented from tearing the mouldering bones out of the grave.

Al Abbas, the uncle of Mahomet, who still resided in Mecca, and was considered hostile to the new faith, seeing that destruction threatened his nephew should that army come upon him by surprise, sent secretly a swift messenger to inform him of his danger. Mahomet was at the village of Koba, when the message reached him. He immediately hastened back to Medina, and called a council of his principal adherents. Representing the insufficiency of their force to take to the field, he gave it as his opinion that they should await an attack on Medina, where the very women and children could aid them by hurling stones from the house-tops. The elder among his followers joined in his opinion; but the young men, of heady valor at all times, and elated by the late victory at Beder, cried out for a fair fight in the open field.

Mahomet yielded to their clamors, but his forces, when mustered, were scarce a thousand men; one hundred only had cuirasses, and but two were horsemen. The hearts of those recently so clamorous to sally forth, now misgave them, and they would fain await the encounter within the walls. "No," replied Mahomet, "it becomes not a prophet when once he has drawn the sword to sheathe it; nor when once he has advanced, to turn back, until God has decided between him and the foe." So saying, he led forth his army. Part of it was composed of Jews and Khazradites, led by Abdallah Ibn Obba Solûl. Mahomet declined the assistance of the Jews, unless they embraced the faith of Islam, and as they refused, he ordered them back to Medina; upon which their protector, Abdallah, turned back also with his Khazradites; thus reducing the army to about seven hundred men.

With this small force Mahomet posted himself upon the hill of Ohod, about six miles from Medina. His position was partly defended by rocks and the asperities of the hill, and archers were stationed to protect him in flank and rear from the attacks of cavalry. He was armed with a helmet and two shirts of mail. On his sword was engraved, "Fear brings disgrace; forward lies honor. Cowardice saves no man from his fate." As he was not prone to take an active part in battle, he confided his sword to a brave warrior, Abu Dudjana, who swore to wield it as long as it had edge and temper. For himself, he, as usual, took a commanding stand whence he might overlook the field.

The Koreishites, confident in their numbers, came marching to the foot of the hill with banners flying. Abu Sofian led the centre; there were a hundred horsemen on each wing; the left commanded by Akrema, the son of Abu Jahl, the right by Khaled Ibn al Waled. As they advanced Henda and her companions struck their timbrels and chanted their war song; shrieking out at intervals the names of those who had been slain in the battle of Beder. "Courage, sons of Abd al Dar!" cried they to the standard-bearers, "forward to the fight! close with the foe! strike home and spare not. Sharp be your swords and pitiless your hearts!"

Mahomet restrained the impatience of his troops; ordering them not to commence the fight, but to stand firm and maintain their advantage of the rising ground. Above all, the archers were to keep their post, let the battle go as it might, lest the cavalry should fall upon his rear.

The horsemen of the left wing, led by Akrema, now attempted to take the Moslems in flank, but were repulsed by the archers, and retreated in confusion. Upon this Hamza set up the Moslem war-cry, Amit! amit! (Death! death!) and rushed down with his forces upon the centre. Abu Dudjana was at his right hand, armed with the sword of Mahomet, and having a red band round his head, on which was written, "Help comes from God! victory is ours!"

The enemy were staggered by the shock. Abu Dudjana dashed into the midst of them, dealing deadly blows on every side, and exclaiming, "The sword of God and his prophet!" Seven standard-bearers, of the race of Abd al Dar, were, one after the other, struck down, and the centre began to yield. The Moslem archers, thinking the victory secure, forgot the commands of Mahomet, and leaving their post, dispersed in quest of spoil, crying "Booty! booty!" Upon this Khaled, rallying the horse, got possession of the ground abandoned by the archers, attacked the Moslems in rear, put some to flight, and threw the rest in confusion. In the midst of the confusion a horseman, Obbij Ibn Chalaf by name, pressed through the throng, crying, "Where is Mahomet? There is no safety while he lives." But Mahomet, seizing a lance from an attendant, thrust it through the throat of the idolater, who fell dead from his horse. "Thus," says the pious Al Jannabi, "died this enemy of God, who, some years before, had menaced the prophet, saying, 'I shall find a day to slay thee.' 'Have care,' was the reply; 'if it please Allah, thou thyself shall fall beneath my hand.'"

In the midst of the mêlée a stone from a sling struck Mahomet on the mouth, cutting his lip and knocking out one of his front teeth; he was wounded in the face also by an arrow, the iron head of which remained in the wound. Hamza, too, while slaying a Koreishite, was transfixed by the lance of Waksa, an Ethiopian slave, who had been promised his freedom if he should revenge the death of his master, slain by Hamza in the battle of Beder. Mosaab Ibn Omair, also, who bore the standard of Mahomet, was laid low, but Ali seized the sacred banner and bore it aloft amidst the storm of battle.

As Mosaab resembled the prophet in person, a shout was put up by the enemy that Mahomet was slain. The Koreishites were inspired with redoubled ardor at the sound; the Moslems fled in despair, bearing with them Abu Beker and Omar, who were wounded. Raab, the son of Malek, however, beheld Mahomet lying among the wounded in a ditch, and knew him by his armor. "Oh believers!" cried he, "the prophet of God yet lives. To the rescue! to the rescue!" Mahomet was drawn forth and borne up the hill to the summit of a rock, where the Moslems prepared for a desperate defense. The Koreishites, however, thinking Mahomet slain, forbore to pursue them, contenting themselves with plundering and mutilating the dead. Henda and her female companions were foremost in the savage work of vengeance; and the ferocious heroine sought to tear out and devour the heart of Hamza. Abu Sofian bore a part of the mangled body upon his lance, and descending the hill in triumph, exclaimed, exultingly, "War has its vicissitudes. The battle of Ohod succeeds to the battle of Beder."

The Koreishites having withdrawn, Mahomet descended from the rock and visited the field of battle. At sight of the body of his uncle Hamza so brutally mangled and mutilated, he vowed to inflict like outrage on seventy of the enemy when in his power. His grief, we are told, was soothed by the angel Gabriel, who assured him that Hamza was enregistered an inhabitant of the seventh heaven, by the title of "The lion of God and of his prophet."

The bodies of the slain were interred two and two, and three and three, in the places where they had fallen. Mahomet forbade his followers to mourn for the dead by cutting off their hair, rending their garments, and the other modes of lamentation usual among the Arabs; but he consented that they should weep for the dead, as tears relieve the overladen heart.

The night succeeding the battle was one of great disquietude, lest the Koreishites should make another attack; or should surprise Medina. On the following day he marched in the direction of that city, hovering near the enemy, and on the return of night lighting numerous watch-fires. Abu Sofian, however, had received intelligence that Mahomet was still alive. He felt himself too weak to attack the city, therefore, while Mahomet was in the field, and might come to its assistance; and he feared that the latter might be reinforced by its inhabitants, and seek him with superior numbers. Contenting himself, therefore, with the recent victory, he made a truce with the Moslems for a year, and returned in triumph to Mecca.

Mahomet sought consolation for this mortifying defeat by taking to himself another wife, Hend, the daughter of Omeya, a man of great influence. She was a widow, and had, with her husband, been among the number of the fugitives in Abyssinia. She was now twenty-eight years of age, and had a son named Salma, whence she was commonly called Omm Salma, or the Mother of Salma. Being distinguished for grace and beauty, she had been sought by Abu Beker and Omar, but without success. Even Mahomet at first met with difficulty. "Alas!" said she, "what happiness can the prophet of God expect with me? I am no longer young; I have a son, and I am of a jealous disposition." "As to thy age," replied Mahomet, "thou art much younger than I. As to thy son, I will be a father to him; as to thy jealous disposition, I will pray Allah to root it from thy heart."

A separate dwelling was prepared for the bride, adjacent to the mosque. The household goods, as stated by a Moslem writer, consisted of a sack of barley, a handmill, a pan, and a pot of lard or butter. Such were as yet the narrow means of the prophet; or rather, such the frugality of his habits and the simplicity of Arab life.

# CHAPTER XXI.

THE defeat of Mahomet at the battle of Ohod,
acted for a time unfavorably to his cause
among some of the Arab and Jewish tribes,
as was evinced by certain acts of perfidy. The inhabitants of two towns, Adhal and Kara, sent a deputation to
him, professing an inclination to embrace the faith, and
requesting missionaries to teach them its doctrines. He
accordingly sent six disciples to accompany the deputation; but on the journey, while reposing by the brook
Radje within the boundaries of the Hodseitites, the
deputies fell upon the unsuspecting Moslems, slew four
of them, and carried the other two to Mecca, where they
gave them up to the Koreishites, who put them to death.

A similar act of treachery was practiced by the people
of the province of Nadjed. Pretending to be Moslems,
they sought succor from Mahomet against their enemies.
He sent a number of his followers to their aid, who were
attacked by the Beni Suleim or Suleimites, near the

brook Manna, about four days' journey from Medina,
and slain almost to a man.   One of the Moslems, Amru
Ibn Omeya, escaped the carnage and made for Medina.
On the way he met two unarmed Jews of the Beni Amir;
either mistaking these for enemies, or provoked to
wanton rage by the death of his comrades, he fell upon
them and slew them.   The tribe, who were at peace with
Mahomet, called upon him for redress.   He referred the
matter to the mediation of another Jewish tribe, the
Beni Nadher, who had rich possessions and a castle,
called Zohra, within three miles of Medina.   This tribe
had engaged by a treaty, when he came a fugitive from
Mecca, to maintain a neutrality between him and his
opponents.   The chief of this tribe being now applied to
as a mediator, invited Mahomet to an interview.   He
went, accompanied by Abu Beker, Omar, Ali, and a few
others.   A repast was spread in the open air before the
mansion of the chief.   Mahomet, however, received private information that he had been treacherously decoyed
hither, and was to be slain as he sat at the repast : it is
said that he was to be crushed by a mill-stone, flung
from the terraced roof of the house.   Without intimating
his knowledge of the treason, he left the company abruptly, and hastened back to Medina.

His rage was now kindled against the whole race of
Nadher, and he ordered them to leave the country within
ten days on pain of death.   They would have departed,
but Abdallah the Khazradite secretly persuaded them to

stay by promising them aid. He failed in his promise. The Beni Nadher, thus disappointed by the "Chief of the Hypocrites," shut themselves up in their castle of Zohra, where they were besieged by Mahomet, who cut down and burnt the date-trees, on which they depended for supplies. At the end of six days they capitulated, and were permitted to depart, each with a camel load of effects, arms excepted. Some were banished to Syria, others to Khaïbar, a strong Jewish city and fortress, distant several days' journey from Medina. As the tribe was wealthy, there was great spoil, which Mahomet took entirely to himself. His followers demurred that this was contrary to the law of partition revealed in the Koran; but he let them know that according to another revelation, all booty gained, like the present, without striking a blow, was not won by man, but was a gift from God, and must be delivered over to the prophet to be expended by him in good works, and the relief of orphans, of the poor, and the traveller. Mahomet, in effect, did not appropriate it to his own benefit, but shared it among the Mohadjerins, or exiles from Mecca ; two Nadherite Jews who had embraced Islamism, and two or three Ansarians or Auxiliaries of Medina, who had proved themselves worthy, and were poor.

We forbear to enter into details of various petty expeditions of Mahomet about this time, one of which extended to the neighborhood of Tabuk, on the Syrian frontier, to punish a horde which had plundered the caravans of Medina. These expeditions were checkered in their results, though mostly productive of booty; which now began to occupy the minds of the Moslems, almost as much as the propagation of the faith. The spoils thus suddenly gained may have led to riot and debauchery, as we find a revelation of the passage of the Koran, forbidding wine and games of hazard, those fruitful causes of strife and insubordination in predatory camps.

During this period of his career, Mahomet in more than one instance narrowly escaped falling by the hand of an assassin. He himself is charged with the use of insidious means to rid himself of an enemy; for it is said that he sent Amru Ibn Omeya on a secret errand to Mecca, to assassinate Abu Sofian, but that the plot was discovered, and the assassin only escaped by rapid flight. The charge, however, is not well substantiated, and is contrary to his general character and conduct.

If Mahomet had relentless enemies, he had devoted friends, an instance of which we have in the case of his freedman and adopted son Zeid Ibn Horeth. He had been one of the first converts to the faith, and one of its most valiant champions. Mahomet consulted him on all occasions, and employed him in his domestic concerns. One day he entered his house with the freedom with which a father enters the dwelling of a son. Zeid was absent, but Zeinab his wife, whom he had recently married, was at home. She was the daughter of Djasch, of the country of Kaiba, and considered the fairest of her tribe. In the privacy of home she had laid aside her veil and part of her attire, so that her beauty stood revealed to the gaze of Mahomet on his sudden entrance. He could not refrain from expressions of wonder and admiration, to which she made no reply, but repeated them all to her husband on his return. Zeid knew the amorous susceptibility of Mahomet, and saw that he had been captivated by the beauty of Zeinab. Hastening after him, he offered to repudiate his wife; but the prophet forbade it as contrary to the law. The zeal of Zeid was not to be checked; he loved his beautiful wife, but he venerated the prophet, and he divorced himself without delay. When the requisite term of separation had elapsed, Mahomet accepted with gratitude his pious sacrifice. His nuptials with Zeinab surpassed in splendor all his other marriages. His doors were open to all comers; they were feasted with the flesh of sheep and lambs, with cakes of barley, with honey, and fruits, and favorite beverages; so they ate and drank their fill and then departed—railing against the divorce as shameful, and the marriage as incestuous.

At this critical juncture was revealed that part of the thirty-third chapter of the Koran, distinguishing relatives by adoption from relatives by blood, according to which there was no sin in marrying one who had been the wife of an adopted son. This timely revelation pacified the faithful; but, to destroy all shadow of a scruple,

Mahomet revoked his adoption, and directed Zeid to resume his original appellation of Ibn Hareth, after his natural father. The beautiful Zeinab, however, boasted thenceforth a superiority over the other wives of the prophet on the score of the revelation, alleging that her marriage was ordained by heaven.*

* This was Mahomet's second wife of the name of Zeinab; the first, who had died some time previous, was the daughter of Chuzeima.

# CHAPTER XXII

EXPEDITION OF MAHOMET AGAINST THE BENI MOSTALEK.—HE ESPOUSES BARRA,
A CAPTIVE.—TREACHERY OF ABDALLAH IBN OBBA.—AYESHA SLANDERED.—
HER VINDICATION.—HER INNOCENCE PROVED BY A REVELATION.

MONG the Arab tribes which ventured to take up arms against Mahomet after his defeat at Ohod, were the Beni Mostalek, a powerful race of Koreishite origin. Mahomet received intelligence of their being assembled in warlike guise under their prince Al Hareth, near the wells of Moraïsi, in the territory of Kedaid, and within five miles of the Red Sea. He immediately took the field at the head of a chosen band of the faithful, accompanied by numbers of the Khazradites, led by their chief Abdallah Ibn Obba. By a rapid movement he surprised the enemy; Al Hareth was killed at the onset by the flight shot of an arrow; his troops fled in confusion after a brief resistance, in which a few were slain. Two hundred prisoners, five thousand sheep, and one thousand camels, were the fruits of this easy victory. Among the captives was Barra, the daughter of Al Hareth, and wife to a young Arab of her kin. In the division of the spoil she fell to the lot of Thabet Ibn Reis, who demanded a high ransom. The captive ap-

pealed to Mahomet against this extortion, and prayed
that the ransom might be mitigated. The prophet regarded her with eyes of desire, for she was fair to look
upon. "I can serve thee better," said he, "than by abat-
ing thy ransom: be my wife." The beautiful Barra gave
ready consent; her ransom was paid by the prophet to
Thabet; her kindred were liberated by the Moslems, to
whose lot they had fallen; most of them embraced the
faith, and Barra became the wife of Mahomet after his
return to Medina.

After the battle, the troops crowded round the wells of
Moraïsi to assuage their thirst. In the press a quarrel
rose between some of the Mohajerins, or exiles of Mecca,
and the Khazradites, in which one of the latter received
a blow. His comrades rushed to revenge the insult, and
blood would have been shed but for the interference of
Mahomet. The Khazradites remained incensed, and
other of the people of Medina made common cause with
them. Abdallah Ibn Obba, eager to take advantage of
every circumstance adverse to the rising power of Mahomet, drew his kindred and townsfolk apart. "Behold,"
said he, "the insults you have brought upon yourselves
by harboring these fugitive Koreishites. You have
taken them to your houses, and given them your goods,
and now they turn upon and maltreat you. They would
make themselves your masters even in your own house;
but by Allah, when we return to Medina, we will see
which of us is strongest."

Secret word was brought to Mahomet of this seditious speech. Omar counselled him at once to make way with Abdallah; but the prophet feared to excite the vengeance of the kindred and adherents of the powerful Khazradite. To leave no time for mutiny, he set off immediately on the homeward march, although it was in the heat of the day, and continued on throughout the night, nor halted until the following noon, when the wearied soldiery cared for nothing but repose.

On arriving at Medina, he called Abdallah to account for his seditious expressions. He flatly denied them, pronouncing the one who had accused him a liar. A revelation from heaven, however, established the charge against him and his adherents. "These are the men," says the Koran, "who say to the inhabitants of Medina, do not bestow anything on the refugees who are with the apostle of God, that they may be compelled to separate from him. They say, verily, if we return to Medina, the worthier will expel thence the meaner. God curse them! how are they turned aside from the truth."

Some of the friends of Abdallah, convinced by this revelation, advised him to ask pardon of the prophet; but he spurned their counsel. "You have already," said he, "persuaded me to give this man my countenance and friendship, and now you would have me put myself beneath his very feet."

Nothing could persuade him that Mahomet was not an idolater at heart, and his revelations all imposture and deceit. He considered him, however, a formidable rival, and sought in every way to injure and annoy him. To this implacable hostility is attributed a scandalous story which he propagated about Ayesha, the favorite wife of the prophet.

It was the custom with Mahomet always to have one of his wives with him, on his military expeditions, as companion and solace; she was taken by lot, and on the recent occasion the lot had fallen on Ayesha. She travelled in a litter, inclosed by curtains, and borne on the back of a camel, which was led by an attendant. On the return homeward the army, on one occasion, coming to a halt, the attendants of Ayesha were astonished to find the litter empty. Before they had recovered from their surprise, she arrived on a camel, led by a youthful Arab named Safwan Ibn al Moattel. This circumstance having come to the knowledge of Abdallah, he proclaimed it to the world after his return to Medina, affirming that Ayesha had been guilty of wantonness with the youthful Safwan.

The story was eagerly caught up and circulated by Hamna, the sister of the beautiful Zeinab, whom Mahomet had recently espoused, and who hoped to benefit her sister by the downfall of her deadly rival Ayesha; it was echoed also by Mistah, a kinsman of Abu Beker, and was celebrated in satirical verses by a poet named Hasan.

It was some time before Ayesha knew of the scandal thus circulating at her expense. Sickness had confined her to the house on her return to Medina, and no one ventured to tell her of what she was accused. She remarked, however, that the prophet was stern and silent, and no longer treated her with his usual tenderness. On her recovery, she heard with consternation the crime alleged against her, and protested her innocence. The following is her version of the story.

The army, on its homeward march, had encamped not far from Medina, when orders were given in the night to march. The attendants, as usual, brought a camel before the tent of Ayesha, and placing the litter on the ground, retired until she could take her seat within it. As she was about to enter, she missed her necklace, and returned into the tent to seek it. In the meantime the attendants lifted the litter upon the camel and strapped it fast, not perceiving that it was empty; she being slender and of light weight. When she returned from seeking the necklace, the camel was gone, and the army was on the march; whereupon she wrapped herself in her mantle and sat down, trusting that, when her absence should be discovered, some persons would be sent back in quest of her.

While thus seated, Safwan Ibn al Moattel, the young Arab, being one of the rear-guard, came up, and, recognizing her, accosted her with the usual Moslem salutation. "To God we belong, and to God we must return! Wife of the prophet, why dost thou remain behind?"

Ayesha made no reply, but drew her veil closer over

her face. Safwan then alighted, aided her to mount the camel, and, taking the bridle, hastened to rejoin the army. The sun had risen, however, before he overtook it, just without the walls of Medina.

This account, given by Ayesha, and attested by Safwan Ibn al Moattel, was satisfactory to her parents and particular friends, but was scoffed at by Abdallah and his adherents, "the Hypocrites." Two parties thus arose on the subject, and great strife ensued. As to Ayesha, she shut herself up within her dwelling, refusing all food, and weeping day and night in the bitterness of her soul.

Mahomet was sorely troubled in mind, and asked counsel of Ali in his perplexity. The latter made light of the affair, observing that his misfortune was the frequent lot of man. The prophet was but little consoled by this suggestion. He remained separated from Ayesha for a month; but his heart yearned toward her; not merely on account of her beauty, but because he loved her society. In a paroxysm of grief, he fell into one of those trances, which unbelievers have attributed to epilepsy; in the course of which he received a seasonable revelation, which will be found in a chapter of the Koran. It was to this effect :—

They who accuse a reputable female of adultery, and produce not four witnesses of the fact, shall be scourged with fourscore stripes, and their testimony rejected. As to those who have made the charge against Ayesha, have they produced four witnesses thereof? If they have not, they are liars in the sight of God. Let them receive, therefore, the punishment of their crime.

The innocence of the beautiful Ayesha being thus miraculously made manifest, the prophet took her to his bosom with augmented affection. Nor was he slow in dealing the prescribed castigation. It is true, Abdallah Ibn Obba was too powerful a personage to be subjected to the scourge, but it fell the heavier on the shoulders of his fellow calumniators. The poet Hasan was cured for some time of his propensity to make satirical verses, nor could Hamna, though a female, and of great personal charms, escape the infliction of stripes; for Mahomet observed that such beauty should have been accompanied by a gentler nature.

The revelation at once convinced the pious Ali of the purity of Ayesha; but she never forgot nor forgave that he had doubted; and the hatred thus implanted in her bosom was manifested to his great detriment in many of the most important concerns of his after life.

# CHAPTER XXIII.

THE BATTLE OF THE MOAT.—BRAVERY OF SAAD IBN MOAD.—DEFEAT OF THE
KOREISHITES.—CAPTURE OF THE JEWISH CASTLE OF KORAIDA.—SAAD DE-
CIDES AS TO THE PUNISHMENT OF THE JEWS.—MAHOMET ESPOUSES RI-
HANA, A JEWISH CAPTIVE.—HIS LIFE ENDANGERED BY SORCERY; SAVED
BY A REVELATION OF THE ANGEL GABRIEL.

URING the year of truce which succeeded the
battle of Ohod, Abu Sofian, the restless chief
of the Koreishites, formed a confederacy with
the Arab tribe of Ghatafan and other tribes of the desert,
as well as with many of the Jews of the race of Nadher,
whom Mahomet had driven from their homes. The truce
being ended, he prepared to march upon Medina, with
these confederates, their combined forces amounting to
ten thousand men.

Mahomet had early intelligence of the meditated attack, but his late reverse at Ohod made him wary of
taking the field against such numbers; especially as he
feared the enemy might have secret allies in Medina;
where he distrusted the Jewish inhabitants and the
Hypocrites, the partisans of Abdallah Ibn Obba, who
were numerous and powerful.

Great exertions were now made to put the city in a

state of defense. Salmân the Persian, who had embraced the faith, advised that a deep moat should be digged at some distance beyond the wall, on the side on which the enemy would approach. This mode of defense, hitherto unused in Arabia, was eagerly adopted by Mahomet; who set a great number of men to dig the moat, and even assisted personally in the labor. Many miracles are recorded of him during the progress of this work. At one time, it is said, he fed a great multitude from a single basket of dates; which remained full after all were satisfied. At another time he feasted a thousand men upon a roasted lamb and a loaf of barley bread; yet enough remained for all his fellow-laborers in the moat. Nor must we omit to note the wonderful blows which he gave to a rock, with an iron mallet; striking off sparks which in one direction lighted up all Yemen, or Arabia the Happy; in another, revealed the imperial palace of Constantinople; and in a third, illumined the towers of the royal residents of Persia; all signs and portents of the future conquests of Islam.

Scarcely was the moat completed when the enemy appeared in great force on the neighboring hills. Leaving Ibn Omm Mactum, a trusty officer, to command in the city, and keep a vigilant eye on the disaffected, Mahomet sallied forth with three thousand men, whom he formed in battle array, having the deep moat in front. Abu Sofian advanced confidently with his combined force of Koreishites and Ghatafanites, but was unexpectedly checked by the moat, and by a galling fire from the Moslems drawn up beyond it. The enemy now encamped; the Koreishites in the lower part of the valley, and the Ghatafanites in the upper; and for some days the armies remained on each side of the moat, keeping up a distant combat with slings and stones, and flights of arrows.

In the meantime, spies brought word to Mahomet that a Jewish tribe, the Beni Koraida, who had a strong castle near the city, and had made a covenant of peace with him, were in secret league with the enemy. He now saw the difficulty, with his scanty forces, to man the whole extent of the moat; to guard against a perfidious attack from the Koraidites; and to maintain quiet in the city, where the Jews must have secret confederates. Summoning a council of war, he consulted with his captains on the policy of bribing the Ghatafanites to a separate peace, by offering them a third of the date-harvest of Medina. Upon this, Saad Ibn Moad, a stout leader of the Awsites of Medina, demanded: "Do you propose this by the command of Allah, or is it an idea of your own?" "If it had been a command of Allah," replied Mahomet, "I should never have asked your advice. I see you pressed by enemies on every side, and I seek to break their confederacy." "O prophet of God!" rejoined Saad, "when we were fellow-idolaters with these people of Ghatafan, they got none of our dates without paying for them; and shall we give them up gratuitously now that we are of the true faith, and led by thee? No, by Allah!

if they want our dates they must win them with their swords."

The stout Saad had his courage soon put to the proof. A prowling party of Koreishite horsemen, among whom was Akrema, the son of Abu Jahl, and Amru, uncle of Mahomet's first wife Cadijah, discovered a place where the moat was narrow, and putting spurs to their steeds succeeded in leaping over, followed by some of their comrades. They then challenged the bravest of the Moslems to equal combat. The challenge was accepted by Saad Ibn Moad, by Ali, and several of their companions. Ali had a close combat with Amru; they fought on horseback and on foot, until, grappling with each other, they rolled in the dust. In the end, Ali was victorious and slew his foe. The general conflict was maintained with great obstinacy; several were slain on both sides, and Saad Ibn Moad was severely wounded. At length the Koreishites gave way, and spurred their horses to recross the moat. The steed of one of them, Nawfal Ibn Abdallah, leaped short; his rider was assailed with stones while in the moat, and defied the Moslems to attack him with nobler weapons. In an instant Ali sprang down into the moat, and Nawfal soon fell beneath his sword. Ali then joined his companions in pursuit of the retreating foe, and wounded Akrema with a javelin. The skirmish was dignified with the name of the Battle of the Moat.

Mahomet, still unwilling to venture a pitched battle,

sent Rueim, a secretly converted Arab of the tribe of
Ghatafan, to visit the camps of the confederates, and
artfully to sow dissensions among them. Rueim first
repaired to the Koraidites, with whom he was in old
habits of friendship. "What folly is this," said he, "to
suffer yourselves to be drawn by the Koreishites of
Mecca into their quarrel! Bethink you how different is
your situation from theirs! If defeated, they have only
to retreat to Mecca, and be secure. Their allies from the
desert will also retire to their distant homes, and you
will be left to bear the whole brunt of the vengeance of
Mahomet and the people of Medina. Before you make
common cause with them, therefore, let them pledge
themselves and give hostages, never to draw back until
they have broken the power of Mahomet."

He then went to the Koreishites and the tribe of
Ghatafan, and warned them against confiding in the Jews
of Koraida, who intended to get hostages from them, and
deliver them up into the hands of Mahomet.

The distrust thus artfully sown among the confederates soon produced its effects. Abu Sofian sent word on
Friday evening, to the Koraidites, to be ready to join next
morning in a general assault. The Jews replied, that the
following day was their Sabbath, on which they could not
engage in battle; at the same time they declined to join
in any hostile act, unless their allies should give hostages
to stand by them to the end.

The Koreishites and Ghatafanites were now convinced

of the perfidy of the Koraidites, and dared not venture upon the meditated attack, lest these should fall upon them in the rear. While they lay idly in their camp a cold storm came on, with drenching rain, and sweeping blasts from the desert. Their tents were blown down; their camp-fires were extinguished; in the midst of the uproar the alarm was given that Mahomet had raised the storm by enchantment, and was coming upon them with his forces. All now was panic and confusion. Abu Sofian, finding all efforts vain to produce order, mounted his camel in despair, and gave the word to retreat. The confederates hurried off from the scene of tumult and terror, the Koreishites towards Mecca, the others to their homes in the desert.

Abu Sofian, in rage and mortification, wrote a letter to Mahomet, upbraiding him with his cowardice in lurking behind a ditch, a thing unknown in Arabian warfare; and threatening to take his revenge on some future day, when they might meet in open fight, as in the field of Ohod. Mahomet hurled back a defiance, and predicted that the day was approaching when he would break in pieces the idols of the Koreishites.

The invaders having disappeared, Mahomet turned to take vengeance on the Beni Koraida; who shut themselves up in their castle, and withstood a siege of many days. At length, pinched by famine, they implored the intercession of their ancient friends and protectors, the Awsites. The latter entreated the prophet to grant these

Hebrews the same terms he had formerly granted to the
Beni Kainoka, at the prayer of Abdallah the Khazradite.
Mahomet reflected a moment, and offered to leave their
fate to the decision of Saad Ibn Moad, the Awsite chief.
The Koraidites gladly agreed, knowing him to have been
formerly their friend. They accordingly surrendered
themselves, to the number of seven hundred, and were
conducted in chains to Medina. Unfortunately for them,
Saad considered their perfidious league with the enemy
as one cause of the recent hostility. He was still smart-
ing with the wound received in the battle of the Moat,
and in his moments of pain and anger had repeatedly
prayed that his life might be spared to see vengeance
wreaked on the Koraidites. Such was the state of his
feelings when summoned to decide upon their fate.

Being a gross, full-blooded man, he was with difficulty
helped upon an ass, propped up by a leather cushion,
and supported in his seat until he arrived at the tribunal
of justice. Before ascending it, he exacted an oath from
all present to abide by his decision. The Jews readily
took it, anticipating a favorable sentence. No sooner
was he helped into the tribunal, than, extending his hand,
he condemned the men to death, the women and children
to slavery, and their effects to be shared among the
victors.

The wretched Jews looked aghast, but there was no
appeal. They were conducted to a public place since
called the Market of the Koraidites, where great graves

had been digged. Into these they were compelled to descend, one by one, their prince Hoya Ibn Ahktab among the number, and were successively put to death. Thus the prayer of Saad Ibn Moad for vengeance on the Koraidites was fully gratified. He witnessed the execution of the men he had condemned, but such was his excitement that his wound broke out afresh, and he died shortly afterwards.

In the castle of Koraida was found a great quantity of pikes, lances, cuirasses, and other armor; and its lands were covered with flocks and herds and camels. In dividing the spoil each foot-soldier had one lot, each horseman three; two for his horse, and one for himself. A fifth part of the whole was set apart for the prophet.

The most precious prize in the eyes of Mahomet was Rihana, daughter of Simeon, a wealthy and powerful Jew; and the most beautiful female of her tribe. He took her to himself, and, having converted her to the faith, added her to the number of his wives.

But, though thus susceptible of the charms of the Israelitish women, Mahomet became more and more vindictive in his hatred of the men; no longer putting faith in their covenants, and suspecting them of the most insidious attempts upon his life. Moslem writers attribute to the spells of Jewish sorcerers a long and languishing illness, with which he was afflicted about this time, and which seemed to defy all remedy. They describe the very charm by which it was produced. It was prepared, say they, by a Jewish necromancer from the mountains, aided by his daughters, who were equally skilled in the diabolic art. They formed a small waxen effigy of Mahomet; wound round it some of his hair, and thrust through it eleven needles. They then made eleven knots in a bowstring, blowing with their breaths on each; and, winding the string round the effigy, threw the whole into a well.

Under the influence of this potent spell Mahomet wasted away, until his friend, the angel Gabriel, revealed the secret to him in a vision. On awaking, he sent Ali to the well, where the image was discovered. When it was brought to Mahomet, continues the legend, he repeated over it the two last chapters of the Koran, which had been communicated to him in the recent vision. They consist of eleven verses, and are to the following purport:

In the name of the all merciful God! I will fly for refuge to the Lord of the light of day.

That he may deliver me from the danger of beings and things created by himself.

From the dangers of the darksome night, and of the moon when in eclipse.

From the danger of sorcerers, who tie knots and blow on them with their breath.

From the danger of the envious, who devise deadly harm.

I will fly for refuge to Allah, the Lord of men.

To Allah, the King of men.

To Allah, the God of men.

That he may deliver me from the evil spirit who flies at the mention of his holy name.

Who suggests evil thoughts into the hearts of the children of men.

And from the evil Genii, and men who deal in magic.

At the repetition of each one of those verses, says the legend, a knot of the bowstring came loose, a needle fell from the effigy, and Mahomet gained strength. At the end of the eleventh verse he rose, renovated in health and vigor, as one restored to freedom after having been bound with cords.

The two final chapters of the Koran, which comprise these verses, are entitled the amulets, and considered by the superstitious Moslems effectual talismans against sorcery and magic charms.

The conduct of Mahomet in the affair narrated in this chapter, has been censured as weak and vacillating, and deficient in military decision, and his measures as wanting in true greatness of mind, and the following circumstances are adduced to support these charges. When threatened with violence from without, and perfidy from within, he is for bribing a part of his confederate foes to a separate peace ; but suffers himself to be, in a manner, hectored out of this crafty policy by Saad Ibn Moad ; yet, subsequently, he resorts to a scheme still more subtle and crafty, by which he sows dissension among his enemies. Above all, his conduct towards the

Jews has been strongly reprobated. His referring the appeal of the Beni Koraida for mercy, to the decision of one whom he knew to be bent on their destruction, has been stigmatized as cruel mockery ; and the massacre of those unfortunate men in the market-place of Medina, is pronounced one of the darkest pages of his history. In fact, his conduct towards this race from the time that he had power in his hands forms an exception to the general tenor of his disposition, which was forgiving and humane. He may have been especially provoked against them by proofs of treachery and deadly rancor on their part; but we see in this, as in other parts of his policy in this part of his career, instances of that worldly alloy which at times was debasing his spirit, now that he had become the Apostle of the Sword.

# CHAPTER XXIV.

MAHOMET UNDERTAKES A PILGRIMAGE TO MECCA.—EVADES KHALED AND A
   TROOP OF HORSE SENT AGAINST HIM.—ENCAMPS NEAR MECCA.—NEGO-
   TIATES WITH THE KOREISHITES FOR PERMISSION TO ENTER AND COMPLETE
   HIS PILGRIMAGE.—TREATY FOR TEN YEARS, BY WHICH HE IS PERMITTED
   TO MAKE A YEARLY VISIT OF THREE DAYS.—HE RETURNS TO MEDINA.

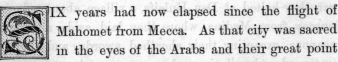

IX years had now elapsed since the flight of
Mahomet from Mecca. As that city was sacred
in the eyes of the Arabs and their great point
of pilgrimage, his long exile from it, and his open warfare with the Koreishites, who had charge of the Caaba,
prejudiced him in the opinion of many of the tribes, and
retarded the spread of his doctrines. His followers, too,
who had accompanied him in his flight, languished once
more to see their native home, and there was danger of
their faith becoming enfeebled under a protracted exile.

Mahomet felt more and more the importance of linking
the sacred city with his religion, and maintaining the
ancient usages of his race. Besides, he claimed but to
be a reformer, anxious to restore the simplicity and purity of the patriarchal faith. The month Doul Kaada was
at hand, the month of pilgrimage, when there was a truce
to warfare, and enemies might meet in peace within the

217

holy boundaries. A timely vision assured Mahomet that he and his followers might safely avail themselves of the protection of this venerable custom to revisit the ancient shrines of Arabian worship. The revelation was joyfully received by his followers, and in the holy month he set forth from Medina on his pilgrimage, at the head of fourteen hundred men; partly Mohadjerins or Fugitives, and partly Ansarians or Auxiliaries. They took with them seventy camels to be slain in sacrifice at the Caaba. To manifest publicly that they came in peace and not in war, they halted at Dsu Huleifa, a village about a day's journey from Medina, where they laid aside all their weapons, excepting their sheathed swords, and thence continued on in pilgrim garb.

In the meantime a confused rumor of this movement had reached Mecca. The Koreishites, suspecting hostilities, sent forth Khaled Ibn Waled with a powerful troop of horse, to take post in a valley about two days' journey from Mecca, and check the advance of the Moslems.

Mahomet, hearing that the main road was thus barred against him, took a rugged and difficult route through the defiles of the mountains, and, avoiding Khaled and his forces descended into the plain near Mecca; where he encamped at Hodeïba, within the sacred boundaries. Hence he sent assurances to the Koreishites of his peaceable intentions, and claimed the immunities and rights of pilgrimage.

Envoys from the Koreishites visited his camp to make

observations. They were struck with the reverence with which he was regarded by his followers. The water with which he performed his ablutions became sanctified; a hair falling from his head, or the paring of a nail, was caught up as a precious relic. One of the envoys, in the course of conversation, unconsciously touched the flowing beard of the prophet; he was thrust back by the disciples, and warned of the impiety of the act. In making his report to the Koreishites on his return, "I have seen the king of Persia, and the emperor of Constantinople, surrounded by their courts," said he, "but never did I behold a sovereign so revered by his subjects as is Mahomet by his followers."

The Koreishites were the more loth to admit into their city an adversary to their sect, so formidable in his influence over the minds and affections of his fellow-men. Mahomet sent repeated missions to treat for a safe access to the sacred shrines, but in vain. Othman Ibn Affan, his son-in-law, was his last envoy. Several days elapsed without his return, and it was rumored that he was slain. Mahomet determined to revenge his fall. Standing under a tree, and summoning his people around him, he exacted an oath to defend him even to the death, and never to desert the standard of the faith. This ceremony is known among Mahometans by the name of the Spontaneous Inauguration.

The reappearance of Othman in the camp restored tranquillity. He was accompanied by Solhail, an ambas-

sador from the Koreishites, to arrange a treaty of peace.
They perceived the impolicy of warring with a man
whose power was incessantly increasing, and who was
obeyed with such fanatic devotion. The treaty proposed
was for ten years; during which time Mahomet and his
adherents were to have free access to Mecca as pilgrims,
there to remain, three days at a time, in the exercise of
their religious rites. The terms were readily accepted,
and Ali was employed to draw up the treaty. Mahomet
dictated the words. "Write," said he, "these are the
conditions of peace made by Mahomet the apostle of
God." "Hold!" cried Solhail, the ambassador, "had I
believed thee to be the apostle of God, I should never
have taken up arms against thee. Write, therefore, sim-
ply thy name, and the name of thy father." Mahomet
was fain to comply, for he felt he was not sufficiently in
force at this moment to contend about forms; so he
merely denominated himself in the treaty, Mahomet Ibn
Abdallah (Mahomet the son of Abdallah), an abnegation
which gave some little scandal to his followers. Their
discontent was increased when he ordered them to shave
their heads, and to sacrifice on the spot the camels
brought to be offered up at the Caaba, as it showed he
had not the intention of entering Mecca; these rites
being properly done at the conclusion of the ceremonials
of pilgrimage. They reminded him of his vision which
promised a safe entrance of the sacred city; he replied,
that the present treaty was an earnest of its fulfillment,

which would assuredly take place on the following year. With this explanation they had to content themselves; and having performed the ceremony, and made the sacrifice prescribed, the camp was broken up, and the pilgrim host returned, somewhat disappointed and dejected, to Medina.

# CHAPTER XXV.

O console his followers for the check their religious devotion had experienced at Mecca, Mahomet now set on foot an expedition calculated
to gratify that love of plunder, which began to rival
fanaticism in attaching them to his standard.

About five days' journey to the northeast of Medina,
was situated the city of Khaïbar, and its dependent territory. It was inhabited by Jews, who had grown wealthy
by commerce, as well as agriculture. Their rich domain
was partly cultivated with grain, and planted with groves
of palm-trees; partly devoted to pasturage and covered
with flocks and herds; and it was fortified by several
castles. So venerable was its antiquity, that Abulfeda,
the Arabian historian, assures us that Moses, after the
passage of the Red Sea, sent an army against the Amalekites, inhabiting Gothreb (Medina), and the strong city
of Khaïbar.

222

This region had become a place of refuge for the hostile Jews, driven by Mahomet from Medina and its environs, and for all those who had made themselves obnoxious to his vengeance. These circumstances, together with its teeming wealth, pointed it out as a fit and ripe object for that warfare which he had declared against all enemies of the faith.

In the beginning of the seventh year of the Hegira, he departed on an expedition against Khaïbar, at the head of twelve hundred foot and two hundred horse, accompanied by Abu Beker, by Ali, by Omar, and other of his principal officers. He had two standards; one representing the sun, the other a black eagle; which last became famous in after years as the standard of Khaled.

Entering the fertile territory of Khaïbar, he began his warfare by assailing the inferior castles with which it was studded. Some of these capitulated without making resistance; in which cases, being considered "gifts from God," the spoils went to the prophet, to be disposed of by him the way before mentioned. Others of more strength and garrisoned by stouter hearts, had to be taken by storm.

After the capture of these minor fortresses, Mahomet advanced against the city of Khaïbar. It was strongly defended by outworks, and its citadel, Al Kamus, built on a steep rock, was deemed impregnable, insomuch that Kenana Ibn al Rabi, the chief or king of the nation, had made it the depository of all his treasures.

The siege of this city was the most important enter-prise the Moslems had yet undertaken. When Mahomet first came in sight of its strong and frowning walls, and its rock-built citadel, he is said to have put up the fol-lowing prayer :

"O Allah! Lord of the seven heavens, and of all things which they cover! Lord of the seven earths, and all which they sustain! Lord of the evil spirits, and of all whom they lead astray! Lord of the winds, and of all whom they scatter and disperse! We supplicate thee to deliver into our hands this city, and all that it contains, and the riches of all its lands. To thee we look for aid against this people, and against all the perils by which we are environed."

To give more solemnity to his prayers, he chose as his place of worship a great rock, in a stony place called Mansela, and, during all the time that he remained en-camped before Khaïbar, made daily seven circuits round it, as are made round the Caaba. A mosque was erected on this rock in after times in memorial of this devout ceremonial, and it became an object of veneration to all pious Moslems.

The siege of the citadel lasted for some time, and tasked the skill and patience of Mahomet and his troops, as yet but little practiced in the attack of fortified places. They suffered too from want of provisions, for the Arabs in their hasty expeditions seldom burden themselves with supplies, and the Jews on their approach had laid waste the level country, and destroyed the palm-trees round their capital.

Mahomet directed the attacks in person; the besiegers protected themselves by trenches, and brought battering-rams to play upon the walls; a breach was at length effected, but for several days every attempt to enter was vigorously repelled. Abu Beker at one time led the assault, bearing the standard of the prophet; but, after fighting with great bravery, was compelled to retreat. The next attack was headed by Omar Ibn Khattab, who fought until the close of day with no better success. A third attack was led by Ali, whom Mahomet armed with his own scimetar, called Dhu'l Fakar, or the Trenchant. On confiding to his hands the sacred banner, he pronounced him " a man who loved God and his prophet; and whom God and his prophet loved. A man who knew not fear, nor ever turned his back upon a foe."

And here it may be well to give a traditional account of the person and character of Ali. He was of the middle height, but robust and square, and of prodigious strength. He had a smiling countenance, exceedingly florid, with a bushy beard. He was distinguished for an amiable disposition, sagacious intellect, and religious zeal, and, from his undaunted courage, was surnamed the Lion of God.

Arabian writers dwell with fond exaggeration on the exploits, at Khaïbar, of this their favorite hero. He was clad, they say, in a scarlet vest, over which was buckled

VOL. I.—15

a cuirass of steel.  Scrambling with his followers up the great heap of stones and rubbish in front of the breach, he planted his standard on the top, determined never to recede until the citadel was taken.  The Jews sallied forth to drive down the assailants.  In the conflict which ensued, Ali fought hand to hand with the Jewish commander, Al Hareth, whom he slew.  The brother of the slain advanced to revenge his death.  He was of gigantic stature; with a double cuirass, a double turban, wound round a helmet of proof, in front of which sparkled an immense diamond.  He had a sword girt to each side, and brandished a three-pronged spear, like a trident. The warriors measured each other with the eye, and accosted each other in boasting oriental style.

"I," said the Jew, "am Marhab; armed at all points, and terrible in battle."

"And I am Ali, whom his mother, at his birth, surnamed Al Haïdara (the rugged lion)."

The Moslem writers make short work of the Jewish champion.  He made a thrust at Ali with his three-pronged lance, but it was dexterously parried; and before he could recover himself, a blow from the scimetar Dhu'l Fakar divided his buckler, passed through the helm of proof, through doubled turban and stubborn skull, cleaving his head even to his teeth.  His gigantic form fell lifeless to the earth.

The Jews now retreated into the citadel, and a general assault took place.  In the heat of the action the shield of Ali was severed from his arm, leaving his body exposed : wrenching a gate, however, from its hinges, he used it as a buckler through the remainder of the fight. Abu Râfe, a servant of Mahomet, testifies to the fact. "I afterwards," says he, "examined this gate in company with seven men, and all eight of us attempted in vain to wield it." *

The citadel being captured, every vault and dungeon was ransacked for the wealth said to be deposited there by Kenana, the Jewish prince. None being discovered, Mahomet demanded of him where he had concealed his treasure. He declared that it had all been expended in the subsistence of his troops, and in preparations for defense. One of his faithless subjects, however, revealed the place where a great amount had been hidden. It did not equal the expectations of the victors, and Kenana was put to the torture to reveal the rest of his supposed wealth. He either could not or would not make further discoveries, so he was delivered up to the vengeance of a Moslem, whose brother he had crushed to death by a piece of millstone hurled from the wall, and who struck off his head with a single blow of his sabre.†

While in the citadel of Khaïbar, Mahomet came near

---

* This stupendous feat is recorded by the historian Abulfeda, c. 24. "Abu Râfe," observes Gibbon, "was an eye-witness ; but who will be witness for Abu Râfe?" We join with the distinguished historian in his doubt ; yet if we scrupulously question the testimony of an eye-witness, what will become of history?

† The Jews inhabiting the tract of country called Khaïbar, are still

falling a victim to Jewish vengeance.    Demanding something to eat, a shoulder of lamb was set before him.    At the first mouthful he perceived something unusual in the taste, and spat it forth, but instantly felt acute internal pain.    One of his followers, named Baschar, who had eaten more freely, fell down and expired in convulsions. All now was confusion and consternation ; on diligent inquiry, it was found that the lamb had been cooked by Zaïnab, a female captive, niece to Marhab, the gigantic warrior slain by Ali.    Being brought before Mahomet, and charged with having infused poison into the viand, she boldly avowed it, vindicating it as a justifiable revenge for the ills he had brought upon her tribe and her family.    "I thought," said she, "if thou wert indeed a prophet, thou wouldst discover thy danger ; if but a chieftain, thou wouldst fall, and we should be delivered from a tyrant."

Arabian writers are divided as to the fate of this heroine.    According to some, she was delivered up to the vengeance of the relatives of Baschar, who had died of the poison.    According to others, her beauty pleaded in her behalf, and Mahomet restored her unharmed to her family.

The same writers seldom permit any remarkable event of Mahomet's life to pass without a miracle.    In the

known in Arabia by the name of Beni Kheibar.    They are divided into three tribes, under independent sheikhs, the Beni Messiad, Beni Schahan, and Beni Anaesse.    They are accused of pillaging the caravans.—*Niebuhr*, v. ii. p. 43.

present instance, they assure us that the poisoned shoulder of lamb became miraculously gifted with speech, and warned Mahomet of his danger. If so, it was rather slow of speech, for he had imbibed sufficient poison to injure his constitution throughout the remainder of his life; affecting him often with paroxysms of pain; and in his last moments he complained that the veins of his heart throbbed with the poison of Khaïbar. He experienced kinder treatment at the hands of Safiya (or Sophia), another female captive, who had still greater motives for vengeance than Zaïnab; for she was the recently espoused wife of Kenana, who had just been sacrificed for his wealth, and she was the daughter of Hoya Ibn Akhtab, prince of the Beni Koraida, who, with seven hundred of his people, had been put to death in the square of Medina, as has been related.

This Safiya was of great beauty; it is not surprising, therefore, that she should find instant favor in the eyes of Mahomet, and that he should seek, as usual, to add her to his harem; but it may occasion surprise that she should contemplate such a lot with complacency. Moslem writers, however, explain this by assuring us that she was supernaturally prepared for the event.

While Mahomet was yet encamped before the city, and carrying on the siege, she had a vision of the night, in which the sun descended from the firmament and nestled in her bosom. On recounting her dream to her husband Kenana in the morning, he smote her on the face, exclaiming, "Woman, you speak in parables of this Arab chief who has come against us."

The vision of Safiya was made true, for having converted her with all decent haste to the faith of Islam, Mahomet took her to wife before he left Khaïbar. Their nuptials took place on the homeward march, at Al Sahba, where the army halted for three days. Abu Ayub, one of the prophet's most ardent disciples and marshal of his household, patrolled around the nuptial tent throughout the night, sword in hand. Safiya was one of the most favored wives of Mahomet, whom she survived for forty years of widowhood.

Besides the marriages of affection which we have recorded, the prophet, about this time, made another of policy. Shortly after his return to Medina, he was gladdened by the arrival, from Abyssinia, of the residue of the fugitives. Among these was a comely widow, thirty years of age, whose husband, Abdallah, had died while in exile. She was generally known by the name of Omm Habiba, the mother of Habiba, from a daughter to whom she had given birth. This widow was the daughter of Mahomet's arch enemy, Abu Sofian; and the prophet conceived that a marriage with the daughter might soften the hostility of the father; a politic consideration, which is said to have been either suggested or sanctioned by a revelation of a chapter of the Koran.

When Abu Sofian heard of the espousals, "By heaven," exclaimed he, "this camel is so rampant that no muzzle can restrain him."

# CHAPTER XXVI.

URING the residue of the year, Mahomet remained at Medina, sending forth his trusty
disciples, by this time experienced captains, on
various military expeditions; by which refractory tribes
were rapidly brought into subjection. His views as a
statesman widened as his territories increased. Though
he professed, in cases of necessity, to propagate his religion by the sword, he was not neglectful of the peaceful measures of diplomacy, and sent envoys to various
princes and potentates, whose dominions bordered on his
political horizon, urging them to embrace the faith of
Islam; which was, in effect, to acknowledge him, through
his apostolic office, their superior.

Two of the most noted of these missions were to
Khosru II., King of Persia, and Heraclius, the Roman
Emperor, at Constantinople. The wars between the
Romans and the Persians, for the dominion of the East,
which had prevailed from time to time through several
centuries, had been revived by these two potentates with

varying fortunes, and for several years past had distracted the eastern world. Countries had been overrun by either power; states and kingdoms had changed hands under alternate invasions, and according to the conquests and defeats of the warring parties. At one time, Khosru with three armies, one vauntingly called the Fifty Thousand Golden Spears, had wrested Palestine, Cappadocia, Armenia, and several other great and wealthy provinces from the Roman emperor; had made himself master of Jerusalem, and carried off the Holy Cross to Persia; had invaded Africa, conquered Libya and Egypt, and extended his victories even to Carthage.

In the midst of his triumphant career, a Moslem envoy arrived bearing him a letter from Mahomet. Khosru sent for his secretary or interpreter, and ordered him to read it. The letter began as follows:

"In the name of the most merciful God! Mahomet, son of Abdallah, and apostle of God, to Khosru, King of Persia."

"What!" cried Khosru, starting up in haughty indignation, "does one who is my slave dare to put his name first in writing to me?" So saying, he seized the letter and tore it in pieces, without seeking to know its contents. He then wrote to his viceroy in Yemen, saying, "I am told there is in Medina a madman, of the tribe of Koreish, who pretends to be a prophet. Restore him to his senses; or if you cannot, send me his head."

When Mahomet was told how Khosru had torn his let-

ter, "Even so," said he, " shall Allah rend his empire in
pieces."

The letter from the prophet to Heraclius was more
favorably received, reaching him probably during his reverses. It was signed in characters of silver, Mahomet
Azzarel, Mahomet the messenger of God, and invited the
emperor to renounce Christianity, and embrace the faith
of Islam. Heraclius, we are told, deposited the epistle
respectfully upon his pillow, treated the envoy with distinction, and dismissed him with magnificent presents.
Engrossed, however, by his Persian wars, he paid no
further attention to this mission, from one whom he probably considered a mere Arab fanatic ; nor attached sufficient importance to his military operations, which may
have appeared mere predatory forays of the wild tribes
of the desert.

Another mission of Mahomet was to the Mukowkis, or
governor of Egypt, who had originally been sent there
by Heraclius to collect tribute ; but who, availing himself of the confusion produced by the wars between the
Romans and Persians, had assumed sovereign power, and
nearly thrown off all allegiance to the emperor. He received the envoy with signal honor, but evaded a direct
reply to the invitation to embrace the faith, observing
that it was a grave matter requiring much consideration.
In the meantime, he sent presents to Mahomet of precious jewels ; garments of Egyptian linen ; exquisite
honey and butter ; a white she-ass, called Yafur, a white

mule, called Daldal, and a fleet horse called Lazlos, or
the Prancer. The most acceptable of his presents, however, were two Coptic damsels, sisters, called Mariyah
(or Mary), and Shiren.

The beauty of Mariyah caused great perturbation in
the mind of the prophet. He would fain have made her
his concubine, but was impeded by his own law in the
seventeenth chapter of the Koran, ordaining that fornica-
tion should be punished with stripes.

He was relieved from his dilemma by another revelation, revoking the law in regard to himself alone, allowing him intercourse with his handmaid. It remained in
full force, however, against all other Moslems. Still, to
avoid scandal, and above all, not to excite the jealousy of
his wives, he carried on his intercourse with the beautiful Mariyah in secret; which may be one reason why she
remained long a favorite.

# CHAPTER XXVII.

MAHOMET'S PILGRIMAGE TO MECCA; HIS MARRIAGE WITH MAIMUNA.—KHALED
IBN AL WALED AND AMRU IBN AL AASS BECOME PROSELYTES.

THE time had now arrived when, by treaty with the Koreishites, Mahomet and his followers were permitted to make a pilgrimage to Mecca, and pass three days unmolested at the sacred shrines. He departed accordingly with a numerous and well-armed host, and seventy camels for sacrifices. His old adversaries would fain have impeded his progress, but they were overawed, and on his approach withdrew silently to the neighboring hills. On entering the bounds of Mecca, the pilgrims, according to compact and usage, laid aside all their warlike accoutrements excepting their swords, which they carried sheathed.

Great was their joy on beholding once more the walls and towers of the sacred city. They entered the gates in pilgrim garb, with devout and thankful hearts, and Mahomet performed all the ancient and customary rites, with a zeal and devotion which gratified beholders, and drew to him many converts. When he had complied with all the ceremonials he threw aside the Iram or pilgrim's garb, and withdrew to Sarif, a hamlet two leagues distant, and without the sacred boundaries. Here he had a ceremonial of a different kind to perform, but one in which he was prone to act with unfeigned devotion. It was to complete his marriage with Maimuna, the daughter of Al Hareth, the Helalite. He had become betrothed to her on his arrival at Mecca, but had postponed the nuptials until after he had concluded the rites of pilgrimage. This was doubtless another marriage of policy, for Maimuna was fifty-one years of age, and a widow, but the connection gained him two powerful proselytes. One was Khaled Ibn al Waled, a nephew of the widow, an intrepid warrior who had come near destroying Mahomet at the battle of Ohod. He now became one of the most victorious champions of Islamism, and by his prowess obtained the appellation of "The Sword of God."

The other proselyte was Khaled's friend, Amru Ibn al Aass; the same who assailed Mahomet with poetry and satire at the commencement of his prophetic career; who had been an ambassador from the Koreishites to the king of Abyssinia, to obtain the surrender of the fugitive Moslems, and who was henceforth destined with his sword to carry victoriously into foreign lands the faith he had once so strenuously opposed.

NOTE.—Maimuna was the last spouse of the prophet, and, old as she was at her marriage, survived all his other wives. She died many years after him, in a pavilion at Serif, under the same tree in the shade of which her nuptial tent had been pitched, and was there interred. The pious historian, Al Jannabi, who styles himself "a poor servant of Allah, hoping for the pardon of his sins through the mercy of God," visited her tomb on returning from a pilgrimage to Mecca, in the year of the Hegira 963, A.D. 1555. "I saw there," said he, "a dome of black marble erected in memory of Maimuna, on the very spot on which the apostle of God had reposed with her. God knows the truth! and also the reason of the black color of the stone. There is a place of ablution, and an oratory; but the building has fallen to decay."

# CHAPTER XXVIII.

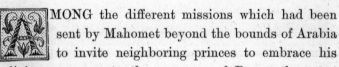MONG the different missions which had been
sent by Mahomet beyond the bounds of Arabia
to invite neighboring princes to embrace his
religion, was one to the governor of Bosra, the great
mart on the confines of Syria, to which he had made his
first caravan journey in the days of his youth. Syria had
been alternately under Roman and Persian domination,
but was at that time subject to the emperor, though
probably in a great state of confusion. The envoy of
Mahomet was slain at Muta, a town about three days'
journey eastward from Jerusalem. The one who slew
him was an Arab of the Christian tribe of Gassan, and son
to Shorhail, an emir, who governed Muta in the name of
Heraclius.

To revenge the death of his legate, and to insure respect to his envoys in future, Mahomet prepared to send
an army of three thousand men against the offending
city. It was a momentous expedition, as it might, for
the first time, bring the arms of Islam in collision with

those of the Roman Empire; but Mahomet presumed upon his growing power, the energy of his troops, and the disordered state of Syrian affairs. The command was intrusted to his freedman Zeid, who had given such signal proof of devotion in surrendering to him his beautiful wife Zeinab. Several chosen officers were associated with him. One was Mahomet's cousin Jaafar, son of Abu Taleb, and brother of Ali; the same who, by his eloquence, had vindicated the doctrines of Islam before the king of Abyssinia, and defeated the Koreishite embassy. He was now in the prime of life, and noted for great courage and manly beauty. Another of the associate officers was Abdallah Ibn Kawaha, the poet, but who had signalized himself in arms as well as poetry. A third was the new proselyte Khaled, who joined the expedition as a volunteer, being eager to prove by his sword the sincerity of his conversion.

The orders to Zeid were to march rapidly, so as to come upon Muta by surprise, to summon the inhabitants to embrace the faith, and to treat them with lenity. Women, children, monks, and the blind, were to be spared at all events; nor were any houses to be destroyed, nor trees cut down.

The little army sallied from Medina in the full confidence of coming upon the enemy unawares. On their march, however, they learned that a greatly superior force of Romans, or rather Greeks and Arabs, was advancing to meet them. A council of war was called.

Some were for pausing, and awaiting further orders from Mahomet : but Abdallah, the poet, was for pushing fearlessly forward without regard to numbers. "We fight for the faith !" cried he ; "if we fall, paradise is our reward. On, then, to victory or martyrdom !"

All caught a spark of the poet's fire, or rather, fanaticism. They met the enemy near Muta, and encountered them with fury rather than valor. In the heat of the conflict Zeid received a mortal wound. The sacred banner was falling from his grasp, but was seized and borne aloft by Jaafar. The battle thickened round him, for the banner was the object of fierce contention. He defended it with desperate valor. The hand by which he held it was struck off ; he grasped it with the other. That, too, was severed ; he embraced it with his bleeding arms. A blow from a scimetar cleft his skull ; he sank dead upon the field, still clinging to the standard of the faith. Abdallah the poet next reared the banner ; but he too fell beneath the sword. Khaled, the new convert, seeing the three Moslem leaders slain, now grasped the fatal standard, but in his hand it remained aloft. His voice rallied the wavering Moslems : his powerful arm cut its way through the thickest of the enemy. If his own account may be credited, and he was one whose deeds needed no exaggeration, nine scimetars were broken in his hand by the fury of the blows given by him in this deadly conflict.

Night separated the combatants. In the morning

Khaled, whom the army acknowledged as their commander, proved himself as wary as he was valiant. By dint of marches and countermarches, he presented his forces in so many points of view, that the enemy were deceived as to his number, and supposed he had received a strong reinforcement. At his first charge, therefore, they retreated : their retreat soon became a flight; in which they were pursued with great slaughter. Khaled then plundered their camp, in which was found great booty. Among the slain in the field of battle was found the body of Jaafar, covered with wounds, but all in front. Out of respect to his valor, and to his relationship with the prophet, Khaled ordered that his corpse should not be buried on the spot, but borne back for honorable interment at Medina.

The army, on its return, though laden with spoil, entered the city more like a funeral train than a triumphant pageant, and was received with mingled shouts and lamentations. While the people rejoiced in the success of their arms, they mourned the loss of three of their favorite generals. All bewailed the fate of Jaafar, brought home a ghastly corpse to that city whence they had so recently seen him sally forth in all the pride of valiant manhood, the admiration of every beholder. He had left behind him a beautiful wife and infant son. The heart of Mahomet was touched by her affliction. He took the orphan child in his arms and bathed it with his tears. But most he was affected when he beheld the young daughter of his faithful Zeid approaching him. He fell on her neck and wept in speechless emotion. A by-stander expressed surprise that he should give way to tears for a death which, according to Moslem doctrine, was but a passport to paradise. "Alas!" replied the prophet, "these are the tears of friendship for the loss of a friend!"

The obsequies of Jaafar were performed on the third day after the arrival of the army. By that time Mahomet had recovered his self-possession, and was again the prophet. He gently rebuked the passionate lamentations of the multitude, taking occasion to inculcate one of the most politic and consolatory doctrines of his creed. "Weep no more," said he, "over the death of this my brother. In place of the two hands lost in defending the standard of the faith, two wings have been given him to bear him to paradise; there to enjoy the endless delights insured to all believers who fall in battle."

It was in consequence of the prowess and generalship displayed by Khaled in this perilous fight, that he was honored by Mahomet with the appellation of "The Sword of God," by which he was afterwards renowned.

# CHAPTER XXIX.

MAHOMET, by force either of arms or eloquence, had now acquired dominion over a great number of the Arabian tribes. He had many thousand warriors under his command—sons of the desert inured to hunger, thirst, and the scorching rays of the sun, and to whom war was a sport rather than a toil. He had corrected their intemperance, disciplined their valor, and subjected them to rule. Repeated victories had given them confidence in themselves and in their leader; whose standard they followed with the implicit obedience of soldiers, and the blind fanaticism of disciples.

The views of Mahomet expanded with his means, and a grand enterprise now opened upon his mind. Mecca, his native city, the abode of his family for generations, the scene of his happiest years, was still in the hands of his implacable foes. The Caaba, the object of devotion and pilgrimage to all the children of Ishmæl, the shrine of his earliest worship, was still profaned by the emblems and rites of idolatry. To plant the standard of the faith

243

on the walls of his native city; to rescue the holy house from profanation; restore it to the spiritual worship of the one true God, and make it the rallying point of Islamism, formed now the leading object of his ambition.

The treaty of peace existing with the Koreishites was an impediment to any military enterprise; but some casual feuds and skirmishings soon gave a pretext for charging them with having violated the treaty stipulations. The Koreishites had by this time learned to appreciate and dread the rapidly increasing power of the Moslems, and were eager to explain away, or atone for, the quarrels and misdeeds of a few heedless individuals. They even prevailed on their leader, Abu Sofian, to repair to Medina as ambassador of peace, trusting that he might have some influence with the prophet through his daughter, Omm Habiba.

It was a sore trial to this haughty chief to come almost a suppliant to the man whom he had scoffed at as an impostor, and treated with inveterate hostility; and his proud spirit was doomed to still further mortification, for Mahomet, judging from his errand of the weakness of his party, and being secretly bent on war, vouchsafed him no reply.

Repressing his rage, Abu Sofian sought the intermediation of Abu Beker, of Omar, and Ali; but they all rebuked and repulsed him, for they knew the secret wishes of Mahomet. He next endeavored to secure the favor of

Fatima, the daughter of Mahomet and wife of Ali, by flattering a mother's pride, entreating her to let her son Hasan, a child but six years old, be his protector; but Fatima answered haughtily, "My son is too young to be a protector; and no protection can avail against the will of the prophet of God." Even his daughter, Omm Habiba, the wife of Mahomet, on whom Abu Sofian had calculated for influence, added to his mortification, for on his offering to seat himself on a mat in her dwelling, she hastily folded it up, exclaiming, "It is the bed of the prophet of God, and too sacred to be made the resting-place of an idolater."

The cup of humiliation was full to overflowing, and in the bitterness of his heart Abu Sofian cursed his daughter. He now turned again to Ali, beseeching his advice in the desperate state of his embassy.

"I can advise nothing better," replied Ali, "than for thee to promise, as the head of the Koreishites, a continuance of thy protection; and then to return to thy home."

"But thinkest thou that promise will be of any avail?"

"I think not," replied Ali, dryly; "but I know not to the contrary."

In pursuance of this advice, Abu Sofian repaired to the mosque, and made public declaration, in behalf of the Koreishites, that on their part the treaty of peace should be faithfully maintained; after which he returned to Mecca, deeply humiliated by the imperfect result of his mission. He was received with scoffs by the Koreishites, who observed that his declaration of peace availed nothing without the concurrence of Mahomet.

# CHAPTER XXX.

MAHOMET now prepared for a secret expedition to take Mecca by surprise. His allies were summoned from all quarters to Medina; but no intimation was given of the object he had in view. All the roads leading to Mecca were barred to prevent any intelligence of his movements being carried to the Koreishites. With all his precautions the secret came near being discovered. Among his followers, fugitives from Mecca, was one named Hateb, whose family had remained behind, and were without connections or friends to take an interest in their welfare. Hateb now thought to gain favor for them among the Koreishites, by betraying the plans of Mahomet. He accordingly wrote a letter revealing the intended enterprise, and gàve it in charge to a singing woman, named Sara, a Haschemite slave, who undertook to carry it to Mecca.

She was already on the road when Mahomet was apprised of the treachery. Ali and five others, well mounted, were sent in pursuit of the messenger. They soon overtook her, but searched her person in vain.

247

Most of them would have given up the search and turned back, but Ali was confident that the prophet of God could not be mistaken nor misinformed. Drawing his scimetar he swore to strike off the head of the messenger, unless the letter were produced. The threat was effectual. She drew forth the letter from among her hair.

Hateb, on being taxed with his perfidy, acknowledged it; but pleaded his anxiety to secure favor for his destitute family, and his certainty that the letter would be harmless, and of no avail against the purposes of the apostle of God. Omar spurned at his excuses and would have struck off his head; but Mahomet, calling to mind that Hateb had fought bravely in support of the faith in the battle of Beder, admitted his excuses and forgave him.

The prophet departed with ten thousand men on this momentous enterprise. Omar, who had charge of regulating the march, and appointing the encampments, led the army by lonely passes of the mountains; prohibiting the sound of attabal or trumpet, or anything else that could betray their movements. While on the march, Mahomet was joined by his uncle Al Abbas, who had come forth with his family from Mecca, to rally under the standard of the faith. Mahomet received him graciously, yet with a hint at his tardiness. "Thou art the last of the emigrants," said he, "as I am the last of the prophets." Al Abbas sent his family forward to Medina, while he turned and accompanied the expedition. The army reached the valley of Marr Azzahran, near to the sacred city, without being discovered. It was nightfall when they silently pitched their tents, and now Omar for the first time permitted them to light their watch-fires.

In the meantime, though Al Abbas had joined the standard of the faith in all sincerity, yet he was sorely disquieted at seeing his nephew advancing against Mecca, with such a powerful force and such hostile intent; and feared the entire destruction of the Koreishites, unless they could be persuaded in time to capitulate. In the dead of the night, he mounted Mahomet's white mule Fadda, and rode forth to reconnoitre. In skirting the camp, he heard the tramp of men and sound of voices. A scouting party were bringing in two prisoners captured near the city. Al Abbas approached, and found the captives to be Abu Sofian, and one of his captains. They were conducted to the watch-fire of Omar, who recognized Abu Sofian by the light. "God be praised," cried he, "that I have such an enemy in my hands, and without conditions." His ready scimetar might have given fatal significance to his words, had not Al Abbas stepped forward and taken Abu Sofian under his protection, until the will of the prophet should be known. Omar rushed forth to ascertain that will, or rather to demand the life of the prisoner; but Al Abbas, taking the latter up behind him, put spurs to his mule, and was the first to reach the tent of the prophet, followed hard by Omar, clamoring for the head of Abu Sofian.

Mahomet thus beheld in his power his inveterate enemy who had driven him from his home and country, and persecuted his family and friends; but he beheld in him the father of his wife Omm Habiba, and felt inclined to clemency. He postponed all decision in the matter until morning; giving Abu Sofian in charge of Al Abbas.

When the captain was brought before him on the following day: "Well, Abu Sofian," cried he, "is it not at length time to know that there is no other God but God?"

"That I already knew," replied Abu Sofian.

"Good! and is it not time for thee to acknowledge me as the apostle of God?"

"Dearer art thou to me than my father and my mother," replied Abu Sofian, using an oriental phrase of compliment; "but I am not yet prepared to acknowledge thee a prophet."

"Out upon thee!" cried Omar, "testify instantly to the truth, or thy head shall be severed from thy body."

To these threats were added the counsels and entreaties of Al Abbas, who showed himself a real friend in need. The rancor of Abu Sofian had already been partly subdued by the unexpected mildness of Mahomet; so, making a merit of necessity, he acknowledged the divinity of his mission; furnishing an illustration of the Moslem maxim, "To convince stubborn unbelievers, there is no argument like the sword."

Having now embraced the faith, Abu Sofian obtained favorable terms for the people of Mecca, in case of their submission. None were to be harmed who should remain quietly in their houses; or should take refuge in the houses of Abu Sofian and Hakim; or under the banner of Abu Rawaiha.

That Abu Sofian might take back to the city a proper idea of the force brought against it, he was stationed with Al Abbas at a narrow defile where the whole army passed in review. As the various Arab tribes marched by with their different arms and ensigns, Al Abbas explained the name and country of each. Abu Sofian was surprised at the number, discipline, and equipment of the troops; for the Moslems had been rapidly improving in the means and art of war; but when Mahomet approached, in the midst of a chosen guard, armed at all points and glittering with steel, his astonishment passed all bounds. "There is no withstanding this!" cried he to Al Abbas, with an oath—"truly thy nephew wields a mighty power."

"Even so," replied the other; "return then to thy people; provide for their safety, and warn them not to oppose the apostle of God."

Abu Sofian hastened back to Mecca, and assembling the inhabitants, told them of the mighty host at hand, led on by Mahomet; of the favorable terms offered in case of their submission, and of the vanity of all resistance. As Abu Sofian had been the soul of the opposition to Mahomet and his doctrines, his words had instant effect in producing acquiescence in an event which seemed to leave no alternative. The greater part of the inhabitants, therefore, prepared to witness, without resistance, the entry of the prophet.

Mahomet, in the meantime, who knew not what resistance he might meet with, made a careful distribution of his forces as he approached the city. While the main body marched directly forward, strong detachments advanced over the hills on each side. To Ali, who commanded a large body of cavalry, was confided the sacred banner, which he was to plant on Mount Hadjun, and maintain it there until joined by the prophet. Express orders were given to all the generals to practice forbearance, and in no instance to make the first attack; for it was the earnest desire of Mahomet to win Mecca by moderation and clemency, rather than subdue it by violence. It is true, all who offered armed resistance were to be cut down, but none were to be harmed who submitted quietly. Overhearing one of his captains exclaim, in the heat of his zeal, that "no place was sacred on the day of battle," he instantly appointed a cooler-headed commander in his place.

The main body of the army advanced without molestation. Mahomet brought up the rear guard, clad in a scarlet vest, and mounted on his favorite camel Al Kaswa. He proceeded but slowly, however; his movements being impeded by the immense multitude which thronged around him. Arrived on Mount Hadjun, where Ali had planted the standard of the faith, a tent was pitched for him. Here he alighted, put off his scarlet garment, and assumed the black turban and the pilgrim garb. Casting a look down into the plain, however, he beheld, with grief and indignation, the gleam of swords and lances, and Khaled, who commanded the left wing, in a full career of carnage. His troops, composed of Arab tribes converted to the faith, had been galled by a flight of arrows from a body of Koreishites; whereupon the fiery warrior charged into the thickest of them with sword and lance; his troops pressed after him; put the enemy to flight, entered the gates of Mecca pell-mell with them, and nothing but the swift commands of Mahomet preserved the city from a general massacre.

The carnage being stopped, and no further opposition manifested, the prophet descended from the mount and approached the gates, seated on his camel, accompanied by Abu Beker on his right hand, and followed by Osama, the son of Zeid. The sun was just rising as he entered the gates of his native city, with the glory of a conqueror, but the garb and humility of a pilgrim. He entered, repeating verses of the Koran, which he said had been revealed to him at Medina, and were prophetic of the event. He triumphed in the spirit of a religious zealot, not of a warrior. "Unto God," said he, "belong the hosts of heaven and earth, and God is mighty and wise. Now hath God verified unto his apostle the vision,

wherein he said, ye shall surely enter the holy temple of
Mecca in full security."

Without dismounting, Mahomet repaired directly to
the Caaba, the scene of his early devotions, the sacred
shrine of worship since the days of the patriarchs, and
which he regarded as the primitive temple of the one
true God.   Here he made the seven circuits round the
sacred edifice, a reverential rite from the days of religious purity; with the same devout feeling he each time
touched the black stone with his staff; regarding it as a
holy relic.   He would have entered the Caaba, but Othman Ibn Talha, the ancient custodian, locked the door.
Ali snatched the keys, but Mahomet caused them to be
returned to the venerable officer, and so won him by his
kindness, that he not merely threw open the doors, but
subsequently embraced the faith of Islam; whereupon
he was continued in his office.

Mahomet now proceeded to execute the great object
of his religious aspirations, the purifying of the sacred
edifice from the symbols of idolatry, with which it was
crowded.   All the idols in and about it, to the number
of three hundred and sixty, were thrown down and destroyed.   Among these, the most renowned was Hobal,
an idol brought from Balka, in Syria, and fabled to have
the power of granting rain.   It was, of course, a great
object of worship among the inhabitants of the thirsty
desert.   There were statues of Abraham and Ishmael
also, represented with divining arrows in their hands;

"an outrage on their memories," said Mahomet, "being symbols of a diabolical art which they had never practiced." In reverence of their memories, therefore, these statues were demolished. There were paintings, also, depicting angels in the guise of beautiful women. "The angels," said Mahomet, indignantly, "are no such beings. There are celestial houris provided in paradise for the solace of true believers; but angels are ministering spirits of the Most High, and of too pure a nature to admit of sex." The paintings were accordingly obliterated.

Even a dove, curiously carved of wood, he broke with his own hands, and cast upon the ground, as savoring of idolatry.

From the Caaba he proceeded to the well of Zem Zem. It was sacred in his eyes, from his belief that it was the identical well revealed by the angel to Hagar and Ishmael, in their extremity; he considered the rite connected with it as pure and holy, and continued it in his faith. As he approached the well, his uncle Al Abbas presented him a cruse of the water, that he might drink, and make the customary ablution. In commemoration of this pious act, he appointed his uncle guardian of the cup of the well; an office of sacred dignity, which his descendants retain to this day.

At noon one of his followers, at his command, summoned the people to prayer from the top of the Caaba, a custom continued ever since throughout Mahometan countries, from minarets or towers provided in every mosque. He also established the Kebla, toward which the faithful in every part of the world should turn their faces in prayer.

He afterwards addressed the people in a kind of sermon, setting forth his principal doctrines, and announcing the triumph of the faith as a fulfillment of prophetic promise. Shouts burst from the multitude in reply, "Allah Achbar, God is great!" cried they. "There is no God but God, and Mahomet is his prophet."

The religious ceremonials being ended, Mahomet took his station on the hill Al Safa, and the people of Mecca, male and female, passed before him, taking the oath of fidelity to him as the prophet of God, and renouncing idolatry. This was in compliance with a revelation in the Koran: "God hath sent his apostle with the direction and the religion of truth, that he may exalt the same over every religion. Verily, they who swear fealty to him, swear fealty unto God; the hand of God is over their hands." In the midst of his triumph, however, he rejected all homage paid exclusively to himself; and all regal authority. "Why dost thou tremble?" said he, to a man who approached with timid and faltering steps. "Of what dost thou stand in awe? I am no king, but the son of a Koreishite woman, who ate flesh dried in the sun."

His lenity was equally conspicuous. The once haughty chiefs of the Koreishites appeared with abject countenances before the man they had persecuted, for their lives were in his power.

"What can you expect at my hands?" demanded he sternly.

"Mercy, O generous brother! Mercy, O son of a generous line!"

"Be it so!" cried he, with a mixture of scorn and pity. "Away! begone! ye are free!"

Some of his followers who had shared his persecutions, were disappointed in their anticipations of a bloody revenge and murmured at his clemency; but he persisted in it, and established Mecca as an inviolable sanctuary, or place of refuge, so to continue until the final resurrection. He reserved to himself, however, the right on the present occasion, and during that special day, to punish a few of the people of the city, who had grievously offended, and been expressly proscribed; yet even these, for the most part, were ultimately forgiven.

Among the Koreishite women who advanced to take the oath, he descried Henda, the wife of Abu Sofian; the savage woman who had animated the infidels at the battle of Ohod, and had gnawed the heart of Hamza, in revenge for the death of her father. On the present occasion she had disguised herself to escape detection; but seeing the eyes of the prophet fixed on her, she threw herself at his feet, exclaiming, "I am Henda: pardon! pardon!" Mahomet pardoned her—and was requited for his clemency by her making his doctrines the subject of contemptuous sarcasms.

Among those destined to punishment was Wacksa, the

Ethiopian, who had slain Hamza; but he had fled from
Mecca on the entrance of the army. At a subsequent
period he presented himself before the prophet, and
made the profession of faith before he was recognized.
He was forgiven, and made to relate the particulars of
the death of Hamza; after which Mahomet dismissed
him with an injunction, never again to come into his
presence. He survived until the time of the Caliphat of
Omar, during whose reign he was repeatedly scourged
for drunkenness.

Another of the proscribed was Abdallah Ibn Saad, a
young Koreishite, distinguished for wit and humor, as
well as for warlike accomplishments. As he held the
pen of a ready writer, Mahomet had employed him to
reduce the revelations of the Koran to writing. In so
doing, he had often altered and amended the text; nay,
it was discovered that, through carelessness or design,
he had occasionally falsified it, and rendered it absurd.
He had even made his alterations and amendments matters of scoff and jest among his companions, observing
that if the Koran proved Mahomet to be a prophet, he
himself must be half a prophet. His interpolations being detected, he had fled from the wrath of the prophet,
and returned to Mecca, where he relapsed into idolatry.
On the capture of the city his foster-brother concealed
him in his house, until the tumult had subsided, when
he led him into the presence of the prophet, and supplicated for his pardon. This was the severest trial of

the lenity of Mahomet. The offender had betrayed his confidence; held him up to ridicule; questioned his apostolic mission, and struck at the very foundation of his faith. For some time he maintained a stern silence; hoping, as he afterwards declared, some zealous disciple might strike off the offender's head. No one, however, stirred; so, yielding to the entreaties of Othman, he granted a pardon. Abdallah instantly renewed his profession of faith, and continued a good Mussulman. His name will be found in the wars of the Caliphs. He was one of the most dexterous horsemen of his tribe, and evinced his ruling passion to the last, for he died repeating the hundredth chapter of the Koran, entitled "The War Steeds." Perhaps it was one which had experienced his interpolations.

Another of the proscribed was Akrema Ibn Abu Jahl, who on many occasions had manifested a deadly hostility to the prophet, inherited from his father. On the entrance of Mahomet into Mecca, Akrema threw himself upon a fleet horse, and escaped by an opposite gate, leaving behind him a beautiful wife, Omm Hakem, to whom he was recently married. She embraced the faith of Islam, but soon after learned that her husband, in attempting to escape by sea to Yemen, had been driven back to port. Hastening to the presence of the prophet, she threw herself on her knees before him, loose, dishevelled, and unveiled, and implored grace for her husband. The prophet, probably more moved by her beauty than her grief, raised her gently from the earth, and told her her prayer was granted. Hurrying to the sea-port, she arrived just as the vessel in which her husband had embarked was about to sail. She returned, mounted behind him, to Mecca, and brought him, a true believer, into the presence of the prophet. On this occasion, however, she was so closely veiled that her dark eyes alone were visible. Mahomet received Akrema's profession of faith ; made him commander of a battalion of Hawazenites, as the dower of his beautiful and devoted wife, and bestowed liberal donations on the youthful couple. Like many other converted enemies, Akrema proved a valiant soldier in the wars of the faith, and after signalizing himself on various occasions, fell in battle, hacked and pierced by swords and lances.

The whole conduct of Mahomet on gaining possession of Mecca, showed that it was a religious, more than a military triumph. His heart, too, softened toward his native place, now that it was in his power ; his resentments were extinguished by success, and his inclinations were all toward forgiveness.

The Ansarians, or Auxiliaries of Medina, who had aided him in his campaign, began to fear that its success might prove fatal to their own interests. They watched him anxiously, as one day, after praying on the hill Al Safa, he sat gazing down wistfully upon Mecca, the scene of his early struggles and recent glory : " Verily, " said he, " thou art the best of cities, and the most beloved of

Allah! Had I not been driven out from thee by my own tribe, never would I have left thee!" On hearing this, the Ansarians said, one to another, "Behold! Mahomet is conqueror and master of his native city; he will, doubtless, establish himself here, and forsake Medina!" Their words reached his ear, and he turned to them with reproachful warmth: "No!" cried he, "when you plighted to me your allegiance, I swore to live and die with you. I should not act as the servant of God, nor as his ambassador, were I to leave you."

He acted according to his words, and Medina, which had been his city of refuge, continued to be his residence to his dying day.

Mahomet did not content himself with purifying the Caaba, and abolishing idolatry from his native city; he sent forth his captains at the head of armed bands, to cast down the idols of different tribes set up in the neighboring towns and villages, and to convert their worshippers to his faith.

Of all these military apostles, none was so zealous as Khaled; whose spirit was still fermenting with recent conversion. Arriving at Naklah, the resort of the idolatrous Koreishites to worship at the shrine of Uzza, he penetrated the sacred grove, laid waste the temple, and cast the idol to the ground. A horrible hag, black and naked, with dishevelled hair, rushed forth, shrieking and wringing her hands; but Khaled severed her through the middle with one blow of his scimetar. He reported the deed to Mahomet, expressing a doubt whether she were priestess or evil spirit. "Of a truth," replied the prophet, "it was Uzza herself whom thou hast destroyed."

On a similar errand into the neighboring province of Tehama, Khaled had with him three hundred and fifty men, some of them of the tribe of Suleim, and was accompanied by Abda'lrahman, one of the earliest proselytes of the faith. His instructions from the prophet were to preach peace and good will, to inculcate the faith, and to abstain from violence, unless assailed. When about two days' journey on his way to Tehama, he had to pass through the country of the tribe of Jadsima. Most of the inhabitants had embraced the faith, but some were still of the Sabean religion. On a former occasion this tribe had plundered and slain an uncle of Khaled, also the father of Abda'lrahman, and several Suleimites, as they were returning from Arabia Felix. Dreading that Khaled and his host might take vengeance for these misdeeds, they armed themselves on their approach.

Khaled was secretly rejoiced at seeing them ride forth to meet him in this military array. Hailing them with an imperious tone, he demanded whether they were Moslems or infidels. They replied, in faltering accents, "Moslems." "Why then come ye forth to meet us with weapons in your hands?" "Because we have enemies among some of the tribes who may attack us unawares."

Khaled sternly ordered them to dismount and lay by

their weapons. Some complied, and were instantly seized and bound; the rest fled. Taking their flight as a confession of guilt, he pursued them with great slaughter; laid waste the country, and in the effervescence of his zeal even slew some of the prisoners.

Mahomet, when he heard of this unprovoked outrage, raised his hands to heaven, and called God to witness that he was innocent of it. Khaled, when upbraided with it on his return, would fain have shifted the blame on Abda'lrahman, but Mahomet rejected indignantly an imputation against one of the earliest and worthiest of his followers. The generous Ali was sent forthwith to restore to the people of Jadsima what Khaled had wrested from them, and to make pecuniary compensation to the relatives of the slain. It was a mission congenial with his nature, and he executed it faithfully. Inquiring into the losses and sufferings of each individual, he paid him to his full content. When every loss was made good, and all blood atoned for, he distributed the remaining money among the people, gladdening every heart by his bounty. So Ali received the thanks and praises of the prophet, but the vindictive Khaled was rebuked even by those whom he had thought to please.

"Behold!" said he, to Abda'lrahman, "I have avenged the death of thy father." "Rather say," replied the other, indignantly, "thou hast avenged the death of thine uncle. Thou hast disgraced the faith by an act worthy of an idolater."

# CHAPTER XXXI.

WHILE the military apostles of Mahomet were spreading his doctrines at the point of the sword in the plains, a hostile storm was gathering in the mountains. A league was formed among the Thakefites, the Hawazins, the Joshmites, the Saadites, and several of the hardy mountain tribes of Bedouins, to check a power which threatened to subjugate all Arabia. The Saadites, or Beni Sad, here mentioned, are the same pastoral Arabs among whom Mahomet had been nurtured in his childhood; and in whose valley, according to tradition, his heart had been plucked forth and purified by an angel. The Thakefites, who were foremost in the league, were a powerful tribe, possessing the strong mountain town of Tayef and its productive territory. They were bigoted idolaters; maintaining at their capital the far-famed shrine of the female idol Al Lat. The reader will remember the ignominious treatment of Mahomet, when he attempted to preach his doctrines at Tayef; being stoned in the public square, and ultimately driven with insult from the gates. It was probably a dread of vengeance at his hands, which now made the Thakefites so active in forming a league against him.

Malec Ibn Auf, the chief of the Thakefites, had the general command of the confederacy. He appointed the valley of Autas, between Honein and Tayef, as the place of assemblage and encampment; and as he knew the fickle nature of the Arabs, and their proneness to return home on the least caprice, he ordered them to bring with them their families and effects. They assembled, accordingly, from various parts, to the number of four thousand fighting men; but the camp was crowded with women and children, and encumbered with flocks and herds.

The expedient of Malec Ibn Auf to secure the adhesion of the warriors, was strongly disapproved by Doraid, the chief of the Joshmites. This was an ancient warrior, upwards of a hundred years old; meagre as a skeleton, almost blind, and so feeble that he had to be borne in a litter on the back of a camel. Still, though unable to mingle in the battle, he was potent in council from his military experience. This veteran of the desert advised that the women and children should be sent home forthwith, and the army relieved from all unnecessary incumbrances. His advice was not taken, and the valley of Autas continued to present rather the pastoral encampment of a tribe, than the hasty levy of an army.

In the meantime Mahomet, hearing of the gathering storm, had sallied forth to anticipate it, at the head of about twelve thousand troops, partly fugitives from Mecca, and auxiliaries from Medina, partly Arabs of the desert, some of whom had not yet embraced the faith.

In taking the field he wore 'a polished cuirass and helmet and rode his favorite white mule Daldal, seldom mounting a charger, as he rarely mingled in actual fight. His recent successes and his superiority in numbers, making him confident of an easy victory, he entered the mountains without precaution, and pushing forward for the enemy's camp at Mutas, came to a deep, gloomy valley on the confines of Honein. The troops marched without order through the rugged defile, each one choosing his own path. Suddenly they were assailed by showers of darts, stones and arrows, which lay two or three of Mahomet's soldiers dead at his feet, and wounded several others. Malec, in fact, had taken post with his ablest warriors about the heights commanding this narrow gorge. Every cliff and cavern was garrisoned with archers and slingers, and some rushed down to contend at close quarters.

Struck with a sudden panic, the Moslems turned and fled. In vain did Mahomet call upon them as their general, or appeal to them as the prophet of God. Each man sought but his own safety, and an escape from that horrible valley.

For a moment all seemed lost, and some recent but

unwilling converts betrayed an exultation in the supposed reverse of fortune of the prophet.

"By heavens!" cried Abu Sofian, as he looked after the flying Moslems, "nothing will stop them until they reach the sea."

"Ay," exclaimed another, "the magic power of Mahomet is at an end!"

A third, who cherished a lurking revenge for the death of his father, slain by the Moslems in the battle of Ohod, would have killed the prophet in the confusion, had he not been surrounded and protected by a few devoted followers. Mahomet himself, in an impulse of desperation, spurred his mule upon the enemy; but Al Abbas seized the bridle, stayed him from rushing to certain death, and at the same time put up a shout that echoed through the narrow valley. Al Abbas was renowned for strength of lungs, and at this critical moment it was the salvation of the army. The Moslems rallied when they heard his well-known voice, and finding they were not pursued, returned to the combat. The enemy had descended from the heights, and now a bloody conflict ensued in the defile. "The furnace is kindling," cried Mahomet exultingly, as he saw the glitter of arms and flash of weapons. Stooping from his saddle, and grasping a handful of dust, he scattered it in the air toward the enemy. "Confusion on their faces!" cried he, "may this dust blind them!" They were blinded accordingly, and fled in confusion, say the Moslem writers; though their defeat may rather be attributed to the Moslem superiority of force, and the zeal inspired by the exclamations of the prophet. Malec and the Thakefites took refuge in the distant city of Tayef, the rest retreated to the camp in the Valley of Autas.

While Mahomet remained in the Valley of Honein, he sent Abu Amir with a strong force to attack the camp. The Hawazins made a brave defense. Abu Amir was slain; but his nephew, Abu Musa, took the command, and obtained a complete victory, killing many of the enemy. The camp afforded great booty and many captives, from the unwise expedient of Malec Ibn Auf, in encumbering it with the families and effects, the flocks and herds of the confederates; and from his disregard of the sage advice of the veteran Doraid. The fate of that ancient warrior of the desert is worthy of mention. While the Moslem troops, scattered through the camp, were intent on booty, Rabia Ibn Rafi, a young Suleimite, observed a litter borne off on the back of a camel, and pursued it, supposing it to contain some beautiful female. On overtaking it and drawing the curtain, he beheld the skeleton form of the ancient Doraid. Vexed and disappointed, he struck at him with his sword, but the weapon broke in his hand. "Thy mother," said the old man sneeringly, "has furnished thee with wretched weapons; thou wilt find a better one hanging behind my saddle."

The youth seized it, but as he drew it from the scabbard, Doraid perceiving that he was a Suleimite, exclaimed, "Tell thy mother thou hast slain Doraid Ibn Simma, who has protected many women of her tribe in the day of battle." The words were ineffectual; the skull of the veteran was cloven with his own scimetar. When Rabia, on his return to Mecca, told his mother of the deed, "Thou hast indeed slain a benefactor of thy race," said she reproachfully. "Three women of thy family has Doraid Ibn Simma freed from captivity."

Abu Musa returned in triumph to Mahomet, making a great display of the spoils of the camp of Autas, and the women and children whom he had captured. One of the female captives threw herself at the feet of the prophet, and implored his mercy as his foster-sister Al Shima, the daughter of his nurse Halêma, who had nurtured him in the Saadite valley. Mahomet sought in vain to recognize in her withered features the bright playmate of his infancy, but she laid bare her back, and showed a scar where he had bitten her in their childish gambols. He no longer doubted; but treated her with kindness, giving her the choice either to remain with him and under his protection, or to return to her home and kindred.

A scruple rose among the Moslems with respect to their female captives. Could they take to themselves such as were married, without committing the sin of adultery? The revelation of a text of the Koran put an end to the difficulty. "Ye shall not take to wife free women who are married, unless your right hand shall have made them slaves." According to this all women taken in war may be made the wives of the captors, though their former husbands be living. The victors of Honein failed not to take immediate advantage of this v.

Leaving the captives and the booty in a secure place, and properly guarded, Mahomet now proceeded in pursuit of the Thakefites who had taken refuge in Tayef. A sentiment of vengeance mingled with his pious ardor as he approached this idolatrous place, the scene of former injury and insult, and beheld the gate whence he had once been ignominiously driven forth. The walls were too strong, however, to be stormed, and there was a protecting castle; for the first time, therefore, he had recourse to catapults, battering-rams, and other engines used in sieges, but unknown in Arabian warfare. These were prepared under the direction of Salmân al Farsi, the converted Persian.

The besieged, however, repulsed every attack, galling the assailants with darts and arrows, and pouring down melted iron upon the shields of bull-hides, under covert of which they approached the walls. Mahomet now laid waste the fields, the orchards, and vineyards, and proclaimed freedom to all slaves who should desert from the city. For twenty days he carried on an ineffectual siege —daily offering up prayers midway between the tents of his wives Omm Salama and Zeinab, to whom it had fallen by lot to accompany him in this campaign. His hopes of success began to fail, and he was further discouraged by a dream, which was unfavorably interpreted by Abu Beker, renowned for his skill in expounding visions. He would have raised the siege, but his troops murmured; whereupon he ordered an assault upon one of the gates. As usual, it was obstinately defended; numbers were slain on both sides: Abu Sofian, who fought valiantly on the occasion, lost an eye, and the Moslems were finally repulsed.

Mahomet now broke up his camp, promising his troops to renew the siege at a future day, and proceeded to the place where were collected the spoils of his expedition. These, say Arabian writers, amounted to twenty-four thousand camels, forty thousand sheep, four thousand ounces of silver, and six thousand captives.

In a little while appeared a deputation from the Hawazins, declaring the submission of their tribe, and begging the restoration of their families and effects. With them came Halêma, Mahomet's foster-nurse, now well stricken in years. The recollections of his childhood again pleaded with his heart. "Which is dearest to you," said he to the Hawazins, "your families or your goods?" They replied, "Our families."

"Enough," rejoined he, "as far as it concerns Al Abbas and myself, we are ready to give up our share of the prisoners; but there are others to be moved. Come to me after noontide prayer, and say, 'we implore the ambassador of God that he counsel his followers to return us our wives and children; and we implore his followers that they intercede with him in our favor.'"

The envoys did as he advised. Mahomet and Al Abbas immediately renounced their share of the captives; their example was followed by all excepting the tribes of Tamim and Fazara, but Mahomet brought them to consent by promising them a sixfold share of the prisoners taken in the next expedition. Thus the intercession of Halêma procured the deliverance of all the captives of her tribe. A traditional anecdote shows the deference with which Mahomet treated this humble protector of his infancy. "I was sitting with the prophet," said one of his disciples, "when all of a sudden a woman presented herself, and he rose and spread his cloth for her to sit down upon. When she went away, it was observed, 'that woman suckled the prophet.'"

Mahomet now sent an envoy to Malec, who remained shut up in Tayef, offering the restitution of all the spoils taken from him at Honein, and a present of one hundred camels, if he would submit and embrace the faith. Malec was conquered and converted by this liberal offer, and brought several of his confederate tribes with him to the standard of the prophet. He was immediately made their chief, and proved, subsequently, a severe scourge in the cause of the faith to his late associates the Thakefites.

The Moslems now began to fear that Mahomet, in these magnanimous impulses, might squander away all the gains of their recent battles; thronging around him, therefore, they clamored for a division of the spoils and captives. Regarding them, indignantly, "Have you ever," said he, "found me avaricious, or false, or disloyal?" Then plucking a hair from the back of a camel, and raising his voice, "By Allah!" cried he, "I have never taken from the common spoil the value of that camel's hair more than my fifth; and that fifth has always been expended for your good."

He then shared the booty as usual; four-fifths among the troops; but his own fifth he distributed among those whose fidelity he wished to insure. The Koreishites he considered dubious allies; perhaps he had overheard the exultation of some of them in anticipation of his defeat; he now sought to rivet them to him by gifts. To Abu Sofian he gave one hundred camels and forty okks of silver, in compensation for the eye lost in the attack on the gate of Tayef. To Akrema Ibn Abu Jahl, and others of like note, he gave in due proportions, and all from his own share.

Among the lukewarm converts thus propitiated, was Abbas Ibn Mardas, a poet. He was dissatisfied with his share, and vented his discontent in satirical verses. Mahomet overheard him. "Take that man hence," said he, "and cut out his tongue." Omar, ever ready for rigorous measures, would have executed the sentence literally, and on the spot; but others, better instructed in the prophet's meaning, led Abbas, all trembling, to the pub-

lic square where the captured cattle were collected, and
bade him choose what he liked from among them.

"What!" cried the poet, joyously, relieved from the
horrors of mutilation, "is this the way the prophet
would silence my tongue? By Allah! I will take nothing." Mahomet, however, persisted in his politic generosity, and sent him sixty camels. From that time forward the poet was never weary of chanting the liberality
of the prophet.

While thus stimulating the good-will of lukewarm proselytes of Mecca, Mahomet excited the murmurs of his
auxiliaries of Medina. "See," said they, "how he lav-
ishes gifts upon the treacherous Koreishites, while we,
who have been loyal to him through all dangers, receive
nothing but our naked share. What have we done that
we should be thus thrown into the background?"

Mahomet was told of their murmurs, and summoned
their leaders to his tent. "Hearken, ye men of Medina,"
said he; "were ye not in discord among yourselves, and
have I not brought you into harmony? Were ye not in
error, and have I not brought you into the path of truth?
Were ye not poor, and have I not made you rich?"

They acknowledged the truth of his words. "Look
ye!" continued he, "I came among you stigmatized as
a liar, yet you believed in me; persecuted, yet you protected me; a fugitive, yet you sheltered me; helpless,
yet you aided me. Think you I do not feel all this?
Think you I can be ungrateful? You complain that I

bestow gifts upon these people, and give none to you. It is true, I give them worldly gear, but it is to win their worldly hearts. To you, who have been true, I give— myself! They return home with sheep and camels; ye return with the prophet of God among you. For by him in whose hands is the soul of Mahomet, though the whole world should go one way and ye another, I would remain with you! Which of you, then, have I most rewarded?"

The auxiliaries were moved even to tears by this appeal. "O prophet of God," exclaimed they, "we are content with our lot!"

The booty being divided, Mahomet returned to Mecca, not with the parade and exultation of a conqueror, but in pilgrim garb, to complete the rites of his pilgrimage. All these being scrupulously performed, he appointed Moad Ibn Jabal as iman, or pontiff, to instruct the people in the doctrines of Islam, and gave the government of the city into the hands of Otab, a youth but eighteen years of age; after which he bade farewell to his native place, and set out with his troops on the return to Medina.

Arriving at the village of Al Abwa, where his mother was buried, his heart yearned to pay a filial tribute to her memory, but his own revealed law forbade any respect to the grave of one who had died in unbelief. In the strong agitation of his feelings he implored from heaven a relaxation of this law. If there was any deception on an occasion of this kind, one would imagine it must have been self-deception, and that he really believed in a fancied intimation from heaven relaxing the law, in part, in the present instance, and permitting him to visit the grave. He burst into tears on arriving at this trying place of the tenderest affections; but tears were all the filial tribute he was permitted to offer. "I asked leave of God," said he, mournfully, "to visit my mother's grave, and it was granted; but when I asked leave to pray for her, it was denied me!"

# CHAPTER XXXII.

SHORTLY after his return to Medina, Mahomet was afflicted by the death of his daughter Zeinab, the same who had been given up to him in exchange for her husband Abul Aass, the unbeliever, captured at the battle of Beder. The domestic affections of the prophet were strong, and he felt deeply this bereavement; he was consoled, however, by the birth of a son, by his favorite concubine Mariyah. He called the child Ibrahim, and rejoiced in the hope, that this son of his old age, his only male issue living, would continue his name to after generations.

His fame, either as a prophet or a conqueror, was now spreading to the uttermost parts of Arabia, and deputations from distant tribes were continually arriving at Medina, some acknowledging him as a prophet and embracing Islamism, others submitting to him as a temporal sovereign, and agreeing to pay tribute. The talents of Mahomet rose to the exigency of the moment; his views expanded with his fortunes, and he now proceeded with statesmanlike skill to regulate the fiscal concerns of his rapidly growing empire. Under the specious appellation of alms, a contribution was levied on true believers, amounting to a tithe of the productions of the earth, where it was fertilized by brooks and rain; and a twentieth part where its fertility was the result of irrigation. For every ten camels, two sheep were required; for forty head of cattle, one cow; for thirty head, a two years' calf; for every forty sheep, one; whoever contributed more than at this rate, would be considered so much the more devout, and would gain a proportionate favor in the eyes of God.

The tribute exacted from those who submitted to temporal sway, but continued in unbelief, was at the rate of one dinar in money or goods, for each adult person, bond or free.

Some difficulty occurred in collecting the charitable contributions; the proud tribe of Tamim openly resisted them, and drove away the collector. A troop of Arab horse was sent against them, and brought away a number of men, women and children, captives. A deputation of the Tamimites came to reclaim the prisoners. Four of the deputies were renowned as orators and poets, and instead of humbling themselves before Mahomet, proceeded to declaim in prose and verse, defying the Moslems to a poetical contest.

"I am not sent by God as a poet," replied Mahomet, "neither do I seek fame as an orator."

Some of his followers, however, accepted the challenge, and a war of ink ensued, in which the Tamimites acknowledged themselves vanquished. So well pleased was Mahomet with the spirit of their defiance, with their poetry, and with their frank acknowledgment of defeat, that he not merely gave them up the prisoners, but dismissed them with presents.

Another instance of his susceptibility to the charms of poetry is recorded in the case of Caab Ibn Zohair, a celebrated poet of Mecca, who had made him the subject of satirical verses, and had consequently been one of the proscribed; but had fled on the capture of the sacred city. Caab now came to Medina to make his peace, and approaching Mahomet when in the mosque, began chanting his praises in a poem afterwards renowned among the Arabs as a masterpiece. He concluded by especially extolling his clemency, "for with the prophet of God the pardon of injuries is, of all his virtues, that on which one can rely with the greatest certainty."

Captivated with the verse, and soothed by the flattery, Mahomet made good the poet's words, for he not merely forgave him, but taking off his own mantle, threw it upon his shoulders. The poet preserved the sacred garment to the day of his death, refusing golden offers for it. The

Caliph Moawyah purchased it of his heirs for ten thousand drachmas, and it continued to be worn by the Caliphs in processions and solemn ceremonials, until the thirty-sixth Caliphat, when it was torn from the back of the Caliph Al-Most'-asem Billah, by Holâgu, the Tartar conqueror, and burnt to ashes.

While town after town, and castle after castle of the Arab tribes were embracing the faith, and professing allegiance to Mahomet, Tayef, the stronghold of the Thakefites, remained obstinate in the worship of its boasted idol Al Lat. The inhabitants confided in their mountain position, and in the strength of their walls and castle. But, though safe from assault, they found themselves gradually hemmed in and isolated by the Moslems, so that at length they could not stir beyond their walls without being attacked. Thus threatened and harassed, they sent ambassadors to Mahomet to treat for peace.

The prophet cherished a deep resentment against this stiff-necked and most idolatrous city, which had at one time ejected him from its gates, and at another time repulsed him from its walls. His terms were conversion and unqualified submission. The ambassadors readily consented to embrace Islamism themselves, but pleaded the danger of suddenly shocking the people of Tayef, by a demand to renounce their ancient faith. In their name, therefore, they entreated permission for three years longer, to worship their ancient idol Al Lat. The request was peremptorily denied. They then asked at least one month's delay, to prepare the public mind. This likewise was refused, all idolatry being incompatible with the worship of God. They then entreated to be excused from the observance of the daily prayers.

"There can be no true religion without prayer," replied Mahomet. In fine, they were compelled to make an unconditional submission.

Abu Sofian, Ibn Harb, and Al Mogheira, were sent to Tayef, to destroy the idol Al Lat, which was of stone. Abu Sofian struck at it with a pick-axe, but missing his blow fell prostrate on his face. The populace set up a shout, considering it a good augury; but Al Mogheira demolished their hopes, and the statue, at one blow of a sledge-hammer. He then stripped it of the costly robes, the bracelets, the necklace, the ear-rings, and other ornaments of gold and precious stones wherewith it had been decked by its worshippers, and left it in fragments on the ground, with the women of Tayef weeping and lamenting over it.*

Among those who still defied the power of Mahomet, was the Bedouin chief Amir Ibn Tufiel, head of the powerful tribe of Amir. He was renowned for personal

---

* The Thakefites continue a powerful tribe to this day; possessing the same fertile region on the eastern declivity of the Hedjas chain of mountains. Some inhabit the ancient town of Tayef, others dwell in tents and have flocks of goats and sheep. They can raise two thousand matchlocks, and defended their stronghold of Tayef in the wars with the Wahabys.— *Burckhardt's Notes*, v. 2.

beauty and princely magnificence; but was of a haughty spirit, and his magnificence partook of ostentation. At the great fair of Okaz, between Tayef and Naklah, where merchants, pilgrims, and poets, were accustomed to assemble from all parts of Arabia, a herald would proclaim: "Whoso wants a beast of burden, let him come to Amir; is any one hungry, let him come to Amir, and he will be fed; is he persecuted, let him fly to Amir, and he will be protected."

Amir had dazzled every one by his generosity, and his ambition had kept pace with his popularity. The rising power of Mahomet inspired him with jealousy. When advised to make terms with him; "I have sworn," replied he haughtily, "never to rest until I had won all Arabia; and shall I do homage to this Koreishite?"

The recent conquests of the Moslems, however, brought him to listen to the counsels of his friends. He repaired to Medina, and coming into the presence of Mahomet, demanded frankly, "Wilt thou be my friend?"

"Never, by Allah!" was the reply, "unless thou dost embrace the faith of Islam?"

"And if I do, wilt thou content thyself with the sway over the Arabs of the cities, and leave to me the Bedouins of the deserts?"

Mahomet replied in the negative.

"What then will I gain by embracing thy faith?"

"The fellowship of all true believers."

"I covet no such fellowship!" replied the proud

Amir; and with a warlike menace he returned to his tribe.

A Bedouin chieftain of a different character was Adi, a prince of the tribe of Taï. His father Hatim had been famous, not merely for warlike deeds, but for boundless generosity, insomuch that the Arabs were accustomed to say, "as generous as Hatim." Adi the son was a Christian; and however he might have inherited his father's generosity, was deficient in his valor. Alarmed at the ravaging expeditions of the Moslems, he ordered a young Arab, who tended his camels in the desert, to have several of the strongest and fleetest at hand, and to give instant notice of the approach of an enemy.

It happened that Ali, who was scouring that part of the country with a band of horsemen, came in sight, bearing with him two banners, one white, the other black. The young Bedouin beheld them from afar, and ran to Adi, exclaiming, "the Moslems are at hand. I see their banners at a distance!" Adi instantly placed his wife and children on the camels, and fled to Syria. His sister, surnamed Saffana, or the Pearl, fell into the hands of the Moslems, and was carried with other captives to Medina. Seeing Mahomet pass near to the place of her confinement, she cried to him:

"Have pity upon me, O ambassador of God! My father is dead, and he who should have protected has abandoned me. Have pity upon me, O ambassador of God, as God may have pity upon thee!"

"Who is thy protector?" asked Mahomet.

"Adi, the son of Hatim."

"He is a fugitive from God and his prophet," replied Mahomet, and passed on.

On the following day, as Mahomet was passing by, Ali, who had been touched by the woman's beauty and her grief, whispered to her to arise and entreat the prophet once more. She accordingly repeated her prayer. "O prophet of God! my father is dead; my brother, who should have been my protector, has abandoned me. Have mercy upon me, as God will have mercy upon thee."

Mahomet turned to her benignantly. "Be it so," said he; and he not only set her free, but gave her raiment and a camel, and sent her by the first caravan bound to Syria.

Arriving in the presence of her brother, she upbraided him with his desertion. He acknowledged his fault and was forgiven. She then urged him to make his peace with Mahomet; "he is truly a prophet," said she, "and will soon have universal sway; hasten, therefore, in time to win his favor."

The politic Adi listened to her counsel, and hastening to Medina, greeted the prophet, who was in the mosque. His own account of the interview presents a striking picture of the simple manners and mode of life of Mahomet, now in the full exercise of sovereign power, and the career of rapid conquest. "He asked me," says Adi, "my name, and when I gave it, invited me to accompany him to his home. On the way a weak emaciated woman accosted him. He stopped and talked to her of her affairs. This, thought I to myself, is not very kingly. When we arrived at his house, he gave me a leathern cushion stuffed with palm-leaves to sit upon, while he sat upon the bare ground. This, thought I, is not very princely!

"He then asked me three times to embrace Islamism. I replied, 'I have a faith of my own.' 'I know thy faith,' said he, 'better than thou dost thyself. As prince, thou takest one fourth of the booty from thy people. Is this Christian doctrine?' By these words I perceived him to be a prophet, who knew more than other men.

"'Thou dost not incline to Islamism,' continued he, 'because thou seest we are poor. The time is at hand when true believers will have more wealth than they will know how to manage. Perhaps thou art deterred by seeing the small number of the Moslems in comparison with the hosts of their enemies. By Allah! in a little while a Moslem woman will be able to make a pilgrimage on her camel, alone and fearless, from Kadesia to God's temple at Mecca. Thou thinkest, probably, that the might is in the hands of the unbelievers; know that the time is not far off when we will plant our standards on the white castles of Babylon.'"*

The politic Adi believed in the prophecy, and forthwith embraced the faith.

---

* Weil's *Mohammed*, p. 247.

# CHAPTER XXXIII.

AHOMET had now, either by conversion or conquest, made himself sovereign of almost all Arabia. The scattered tribes, heretofore dangerous to each other, but by their disunion powerless against the rest of the world, he had united into one nation, and thus fitted for external conquest. His prophetic character gave him absolute control of the formidable power thus conjured up in the desert, and he was now prepared to lead it forth for the propagation of the faith, and the extension of the Moslem power in foreign lands.

His numerous victories, and the recent affair at Muta. had at length, it is said, roused the attention of the Emperor Heraclius, who was assembling an army on the confines of Arabia to crush this new enemy. Mahomet determined to anticipate his hostilities, and to carry the standard of the faith into the very heart of Syria.

Hitherto he had undertaken his expeditions with secrecy; imparting his plans and intentions to none but his most confidential officers, and beguiling his followers into enterprises of danger. The present campaign, however, so different from the brief predatory excursions of the Arabs, would require great preparations; an unusual force was to be assembled, and all kinds of provision made for distant marches, and a long absence. He proclaimed openly, therefore, the object and nature of the enterprise.

There was not the usual readiness to flock to his standard. Many remembered the disastrous affair at Muta, and dreaded to come again in conflict with disciplined Roman troops. The time of year also was unpropitious for such a distant and prolonged expedition. It was the season of summer heat; the earth was parched, and the springs and brooks were dried up. The date-harvest too was approaching, when the men should be at home to gather the fruit, rather than abroad on predatory enterprises.

All these things were artfully urged upon the people by Abdallah Ibn Obba, the Khazradite, who continued to be the covert enemy of Mahomet, and seized every occasion to counteract his plans. "A fine season this," would he cry, "to undertake such a distant march in defiance of dearth and drought, and the fervid heat of the desert! Mahomet seems to think a war with Greeks quite a matter of sport; trust me, you will find it very different from a war of Arab against Arab.  By Allah! methinks I already see you all in chains."

By these and similar scoffs and suggestions, he wrought upon the fears and feelings of the Khazradites, his partisans, and rendered the enterprise generally unpopular.  Mahomet, as usual, had resort to revelation. "Those who would remain behind, and refuse to devote themselves to the service of God," said a timely chapter of the Koran, "allege the summer heat as an excuse. Tell them the fire of hell is hotter!  They may hug themselves in the enjoyment of present safety, but endless tears will be their punishment hereafter."

Some of his devoted adherents manifested their zeal at this lukewarm moment.  Omar, Al Abbas, and Abda'l-rahman, gave large sums of money; several female devotees brought their ornaments and jewels.  Othman delivered one thousand, some say ten thousand, dinars to Mahomet, and was absolved from his sins, past, present, or to come.  Abu Beker gave four thousand drachmas; Mahomet hesitated to accept the offer knowing it to be all that he possessed.  "What will remain," said he, "for thee and thy family?"  "God and his prophet," was the reply.

These devout examples had a powerful effect; yet it was with much difficulty that an army of ten thousand horse and twenty thousand foot was assembled.  Mahomet now appointed Ali governor of Medina during his absence, and guardian of both their families.  He accepted the trust with great reluctance, having been accustomed always to accompany the prophet, and share all his perils. All arrangements being completed, Mahomet marched forth from Medina on this momentous expedition. A part of his army was composed of Khazradites and their confederates, led by Abdallah Ibn Obba. This man, whom Mahomet had well denominated the Chief of the Hypocrites, encamped separately with his adherents at night, at some distance in the rear of the main army; and when the latter marched forward in the morning, lagged behind and led his troops back to Medina. Repairing to Ali, whose dominion in the city was irksome to him and his adherents, he endeavored to make him discontented with his position, alleging that Mahomet had left him in charge of Medina solely to rid himself of an incumbrance. Stung by the suggestion, Ali hastened after Mahomet, and demanded if what Abdallah and his followers said were true.

"These men," replied Mahomet, "are liars. They are the party of Hypocrites and Doubters, who would breed sedition in Medina. I left thee behind to keep watch over them, and to be a guardian to both our families. I would have thee to be to me what Aaron was to Moses; excepting that thou canst not be, like him, a prophet; I being the last of the prophets." With this explanation Ali returned contented to Medina.

Many have inferred from the foregoing, that Mahomet intended Ali for his Caliph or successor; that being the signification of the Arabic word used to denote the relation of Aaron to Moses.

The troops who had continued on with Mahomet soon began to experience the difficulties of braving the desert in this sultry season. Many turned back on the second day; and others on the third and fourth. Whenever word was brought to the prophet of their desertion, "Let them go," would be the reply; "if they are good for anything God will bring them back to us; if they are not, we are relieved from so many incumbrances."

While some thus lost heart upon the march, others who had remained at Medina repented of their faintheartedness. One, named Abu Khaithama, entering his garden during the sultry heat of the day, beheld a repast of viands and fresh water spread for him by his two wives in the cool shade of a tent. Pausing at the threshold, "At this moment," exclaimed he, "the prophet of God is exposed to the winds and heats of the desert, and shall Khaithama sit here in the shade beside his beautiful wives? By Allah! I will not enter the tent!" He immediately armed himself with sword and lance, and mounting his camel, hastened off to join the standard of the faith.

In the meantime the army, after a weary march of seven days, entered the mountainous district of Hajar, inhabited in days of old by the Thamudites, one of the lost tribes of Arabia. It was the accursed region, the tradition concerning which has already been related.

The advance of the army, knowing nothing of this tradition, and being heated and fatigued, beheld, with delight, a brook running through a verdant valley, and cool caves cut in the sides of the neighboring hills, once the abodes of the heaven-smitten Thamudites. Halting along the brook, some prepared to bathe, others began to cook and make bread, while all promised themselves cool quarters for the night in the caves.

Mahomet, in marching, had kept, as was his wont, in the rear of the army to assist the weak; occasionally taking up a wayworn laggard behind him. Arriving at the place where the troops had halted, he recollected it of old, and the traditions concerning it, which had been told to him when he passed here in the days of his boyhood. Fearful of incurring the ban which hung over the neighborhood, he ordered his troops to throw away the meat cooked with the water of the brook, to give the bread kneaded with it to the camels, and to hurry away from the heaven-accursed place. Then wrapping his face in the folds of his mantle, and setting spurs to his mule, he hastened through that sinful region; the army following him as if flying from an enemy.

The succeeding night was one of great suffering; the army had to encamp without water; the weather was intensely hot, with a parching wind from the desert; and intolerable thirst prevailed throughout the camp, as though the Thamudite ban still hung over it. The next day, however, an abundant rain refreshed and invigorated

both man and beast.  The march was resumed with new
ardor, and the army arrived, without further hardship, at
Tabuc, a small town on the confines of the Roman empire, about half way between Medina and Damascus, and
about ten days' journey from either city.

Here Mahomet pitched his camp in the neighborhood
of a fountain, and in the midst of groves and pasturage.
Arabian traditions affirm that the fountain was nearly
dry; insomuch that, when a small vase was filled for the
prophet, not a drop was left: having assuaged his thirst,
however, and made his ablutions, Mahomet threw what
remained in the vase back into the fountain; whereupon
a stream gushed forth sufficient for the troops and all the
cattle.

From this encampment Mahomet sent out his captains
to proclaim and enforce the faith, or to exact tribute.
Some of the neighboring princes sent embassies, either
acknowledging the divinity of his mission, or submitting
to his temporal sway.  One of these was Johanna Ibn
Ruba, prince of Eyla, a Christian city, near the Red Sea.
This was the same city about which the tradition is told,
that in days of old, when its inhabitants were Jews, the
old men were turned into swine, and the young men into
monkeys, for fishing on the Sabbath, a judgment solemnly recorded in the Koran.

The prince of Eyla made a covenant of peace with
Mahomet, agreeing to pay an annual tribute of three
thousand dinars or crowns of gold.  The form of the

covenant became a precedent in treating with other powers.

Among the Arab princes who professed the Christian faith, and refused to pay homage to Mahomet, was Okaïder Ibn Malec, of the tribe of Kenda. He resided in a castle at the foot of a mountain, in the midst of his domain. Khaled was sent with a troop of horse to bring him to terms. Seeing the castle was too strong to be carried by assault, he had recourse to stratagem. One moonlight night, as Okaïder and his wife were enjoying the fresh air on the terraced roof of the castle, they beheld an animal grazing, which they supposed to be a wild ass from the neighboring mountains. Okaïder, who was a keen huntsman, ordered horse and lance, and sallied forth to the chase, accompanied by his brother Hassan and several of his people. The wild ass proved to be a decoy. They had not ridden far before Khaled and his men rushed from ambush and attacked them. They were too lightly armed to make much resistance. Hassan was killed on the spot, and Okaïder taken prisoner; the rest fled back to the castle; which, however, was soon surrendered. The prince was ultimately set at liberty on paying a heavy ransom and becoming a tributary.

As a trophy of the victory, Khaled sent to Mahomet the vest stripped from the body of Hassan. It was of silk, richly embroidered with gold. The Moslems gathered round, and examined it with admiration. "Do you admire this vest?" said the prophet. "I swear by him in whose hands is the soul of Mahomet, the vest which Saad, the son of Maadi, wears at this moment in paradise, is far more precious." This Saad was the judge who passed sentence of death on seven hundred Jewish captives at Medina, at the conclusion of a former campaign.

His troops being now refreshed by the sojourn at Tabuc, and the neighboring country being brought into subjection, Mahomet was bent upon prosecuting the object of his campaign, and pushing forward into the heart of Syria. His ardor, however, was not shared by his followers. Intelligence of immense bodies of hostile troops, assembled on the Syrian borders, had damped the spirits of the army. Mahomet remarked the general discouragement, yet was loth to abandon the campaign when but half completed. Calling a council of war, he propounded the question whether or not to continue forward. To this Omar replied dryly, "If thou hast the command of God to proceed further, do so." "If I had the command of God to proceed further," observed Mahomet, "I should not have asked thy counsel."

Omar felt the rebuke. He then, in a respectful tone, represented the impolicy of advancing in the face of the overwhelming force said to be collected on the Syrian frontier; he represented, also, how much Mahomet had already effected in this campaign. He had checked the threatened invasion of the imperial arms, and had received the homage and submission of various tribes and people, from the head of the Red Sea to the Euphrates : he advised him, therefore, to be content for the present year with what he had achieved, and to defer the completion of the enterprise to a future campaign.

His counsel was adopted : for, whenever Mahomet was not under strong excitement, or fancied inspiration, he was rather prone to yield up his opinion in military matters to that of his generals. After a sojourn of about twenty days, therefore, at Tabuc, he broke up his camp, and conducted his army back to Medina.

# CHAPTER XXXIV.

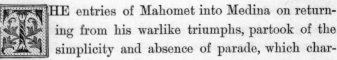HE entries of Mahomet into Medina on return-
ing from his warlike triumphs, partook of the
simplicity and absence of parade, which characterized all his actions. On approaching the city, when
his household came forth with the multitude to meet him,
he would stop to greet them, and take up the children of
the house behind him on his horse. It was in this simple way he entered Medina, on returning from the campaign against Tabuc.

The arrival of an army laden with spoil, gathered in the
most distant expedition ever undertaken by the soldiers
of Islam, was an event of too great moment, not to be
hailed with triumphant exultation by the community.
Those alone were cast down in spirit who had refused to
march forth with the army, or had deserted it when on
the march. All these were at first placed under an interdict; Mahomet forbidding his faithful followers to hold
any intercourse with them. Mollified, however, by their

contrition or excuses, he gradually forgave the greater part of them. Seven of those who continued under interdict, finding themselves cut off from communion with their acquaintance, and marked with opprobrium amid an exulting community, became desperate, and chained themselves to the walls of the mosque; swearing to remain there until pardoned. Mahomet, on the other hand, swore he would leave them there unless otherwise commanded by God. Fortunately he received the command in a revealed verse of the Koran; but, in freeing them from their self-imposed fetters, he exacted one third of their possessions, to be expended in the service of the faith.

Among those still under interdict were Kaab Ibn Malec, Murara Ibn Rabia, and Hilal Ibn Omeya. These had once been among the most zealous of professing Moslems; their defection was, therefore, ten times more heinous in the eyes of the prophet than that of their neighbors, whose faith had been lukewarm and dubious. Toward them, therefore, he continued implacable. Forty days they remained interdicted, and the interdict extended to communication with their wives.

The account given by Kaab Ibn Malec of his situation, while thus excommunicated, presents a vivid picture of the power of Mahomet over the minds of his adherents. Kaab declared that everybody shunned him, or regarded him with an altered mien. His two companions in disgrace did not leave their home; he, however, went about from place to place, but no one spake to him. He sought the mosque, sat down near the prophet, and saluted him, but his salutation was not returned. On the forty-first day came a command, that he should separate from his wife. He now left the city, and pitched a tent on the hill of Sala, determined there to undergo in its severest rigor the punishment meted out to him. His heart, however, was dying away; the wide world, he said, appeared to grow narrow to him. On the fifty-first day came a messenger holding out the hope of pardon. He hastened to Medina, and sought the prophet at the mosque, who received him with a radiant countenance, and said that God had forgiven him. The soul of Kaab was lifted up from the depths of despondency, and in the transports of his gratitude, he gave a portion of his wealth in atonement of his error.

Not long after the return of the army to Medina, Abdallah Ibn Obba, the Khazradite, "the chief of the Hypocrites," fell ill, so that his life was despaired of. Although Mahomet was well aware of the perfidy of this man, and the secret arts he had constantly practiced against him, he visited him repeatedly during his illness; was with him at his dying hour, and followed his body to the grave. There, at the urgent entreaty of the son of the deceased, he put up prayers that his sins might be forgiven.

Omar privately remonstrated with Mahomet for praying for a hypocrite; reminding him how often he had been slandered by Abdallah; but he was shrewdly answered by a text of the Koran: "Thou mayst pray for the 'Hypocrites' or not, as thou wilt; but though thou shouldst pray seventy times, yet will they not be forgiven."

The prayers at Abdallah's grave, therefore, were put up out of policy, to win favor with the Khazradites, and the powerful friends of the deceased; and in this respect the prayers were successful, for most of the adherents of the deceased became devoted to the prophet, whose sway was thenceforth undisputed in Medina. Subsequently he announced another revelation, which forbade him to pray by the death-bed or stand by the grave of any one who died in unbelief.

But though Mahomet exercised such dominion over his disciples, and the community at large, he had great difficulty in governing his wives, and maintaining tranquillity in his harem. He appears to have acted with tolerable equity in his connubial concerns, assigning to each of his wives a separate habitation, of which she was sole mistress, and passing the twenty-four hours with them by turns. It so happened, that on one occasion, when he was sojourning with Hafsa, the latter left her dwelling to visit her father. Returning unexpectedly, she surprised the prophet with his favorite and fortunate slave Mariyah, the mother of his son Ibrahim. The jealousy of Hafsa was vociferous. Mahomet endeavored to pacify her, dreading lest her outcries should rouse his whole harem to rebellion; but she was only to be appeased by an oath on his part never more to cohabit with Mariyah. On these terms she forgave the past, and promised secrecy.

She broke her promise, however, and revealed to Ayesha the infidelity of the prophet; and in a little while it was known throughout the harem. His wives now united in a storm of reproaches; until, his patience being exhausted, he repudiated Hafsa, and renounced all intercourse with the rest. For a month he lay alone on a mat in a separate apartment; but Allah, at length, in consideration of his lonely state, sent down the first and sixth chapters of the Koran, absolving him from the oath respecting Mariyah, who forthwith became the companion of his solitary chamber.

The refractory wives were now brought to a sense of their error, and apprised by the same revelation that the restrictions imposed on ordinary men did not apply to the prophet. In the end he took back Hafsa, who was penitent; and he was reconciled to Ayesha, whom he tenderly loved, and all the rest were in due time received into favor; but he continued to cherish Mariyah, for she was fair to look upon, and was the mother of his only son.

MAHOMET AND HIS SUCCESSORS. 302

# CHAPTER XXXV.

ABU BEKER CONDUCTS THE YEARLY PILGRIMAGE TO MECCA.—MISSION OF ALI
TO ANNOUNCE A REVELATION.

HE sacred month of yearly pilgrimage was now at hand, but Mahomet was too much occupied with public and domestic concerns to absent himself from Medina; he deputed Abu Beker, therefore, to act in his place as emir or commander of the pilgrims, who were to resort from Medina to the holy city. Abu Beker accordingly departed at the head of three hundred pilgrims, with twenty camels for sacrifice.

Not long afterwards Mahomet summoned his son-in-law and devoted disciple Ali, and, mounting him on Al Adha, or the slit-eared, the swiftest of his camels, urged him to hasten with all speed to Mecca, there to promulgate before the multitude of pilgrims assembled from all parts, an important sura, or chapter of the Koran, just received from heaven.

Ali executed his mission with his accustomed zeal and fidelity. He reached the sacred city in the height of the great religious festival. On the day of sacrifice, when the ceremonies of pilgrimage were completed by the slaying

of the victims in the Valley of Mina, and when Abu
Beker had preached and instructed the people in the doctrines and rites of Islamism, Ali rose before an immense
multitude assembled at the hill Al Akaba, and announced
himself a messenger from the prophet, bearing an important revelation.   He then read the sura, or chapter of the
Koran, of which he was the bearer; in which the religion
of the sword was declared in all its rigor.   It absolved
Mahomet from all truce or league with idolatrous and
other unbelievers, should they in anywise have been
false to their stipulations, or given aid to his enemies.   It
allowed unbelievers four months of toleration from the
time of this announcement, during which months they
might "go to and fro about the earth securely," but at
the expiration of that time all indulgence would cease;
war would then be made in every way, at every time and
in every place, by open force or by stratagem, against
those who persisted in unbelief : no alternative would be
left them but to embrace the faith, or pay tribute.   The
holy months and the holy places would no longer afford
them protection.   "When the months wherein ye are not
allowed to attack them  shall be passed," said the revelation, "kill the idolatrous wherever ye shall find them, or
take them prisoners ; besiege them, or lay in wait for
them." The ties of blood and friendship were to be alike
disregarded ; the faithful were to hold no communion
with their nearest relatives and dearest friends, should
they persist in idolatry.   After the expiration of the cur-

rent year, no unbeliever was to be permitted to tread the sacred bounds of Mecca, nor to enter the temple of Allah, a prohibition which continues to the present day.

This stringent chapter of the Koran is thought to have been provoked, in a great measure, by the conduct of some of the Jewish and idolatrous Arabs, with whom Mahomet had made covenants, but who had repeatedly played him false, and even made treacherous attempts upon his life. It evinces, however, the increased confidence he felt in consequence of the death of his insidious and powerful foe, Abdallah Ibn Obba, and the rapid conversion or subjugation of the Arab tribes. It was, in fact, a decisive blow for the exclusive domination of his faith.

When Abu Beker and Ali returned to Mecca, the former expressed surprise and dissatisfaction that he had not been made the promulgator of so important a revelation, as it seemed to be connected with his recent mission, but he was pacified by the assurance that all new revelations must be announced by the prophet himself, or by some one of his immediate family.

# CHAPTER XXXVI.

HE promulgation of the last-mentioned chapter
of the Koran, with the accompanying denunciation of exterminating war against all who
should refuse to believe or submit, produced hosts of
converts and tributaries; so that, towards the close of
the month, and in the beginning of the tenth year of the
Hegira, the gates of Medina were thronged with envoys
from distant tribes and princes. Among those who
bowed to the temporal power of the prophet was Farwa,
lieutenant of Heraclius, in Syria, and governor of Amon,
the ancient capital of the Ammonites. His act of submission, however, was disavowed by the emperor, and
punished with imprisonment.

Mahomet felt and acted more and more as a sovereign,
but his grandest schemes as a conqueror were always
sanctified by his zeal as an apostle. His captains were

304

sent on more distant expeditions than formerly, but it was always with a view to destroy idols, and bring idolatrous tribes to subjection ; so that his temporal power but kept pace with the propagation of his faith. He appointed two lieutenants to govern in his name in Arabia Felix ; but a portion of that rich and important country having shown itself refractory, Ali was ordered to repair thither at the head of three hundred horsemen, and bring the inhabitants to reason.

The youthful disciple expressed a becoming diffidence to undertake a mission where he would have to treat with men far older and wiser than himself ; but Mahomet laid one hand upon his lips, and the other upon his breast, and raising his eyes to heaven, exclaimed, "O, Allah! loosen his tongue and guide his heart!" He gave him one rule for his conduct as a judge. "When two parties come before thee, never pronounce in favor of one until thou hast heard the other." Then, giving into his hands the standard of the faith, and placing the turban on his head, he bade him farewell.

When the military missionary arrived in the heretical region of Yemen, his men, indulging their ancient Arab propensities, began to sack, to plunder, and destroy. Ali checked their excesses, and arresting the fugitive inhabitants, began to expound to them the doctrines of Islam. His tongue, though so recently consecrated by the prophet, failed to carry conviction, for he was answered by darts and arrows ; whereupon he returned to the old

argument of the sword, which he urged with such efficacy, that, after twenty unbelievers had been slain, the
rest avowed themselves thoroughly convinced. This
zealous achievement was followed by others of a similar kind, after each of which he despatched messengers to the prophet announcing a new triumph of the
faith.

While Mahomet was exulting in the tidings of success
from every quarter, he was stricken to the heart by one
of the severest domestic bereavements. Ibrahim, his son
by his favorite concubine Mariyah, a child but fifteen
months old, his only male issue, on whom reposed his
hope of transmitting his name to posterity, was seized
with a mortal malady, and expired before his eyes. Mahomet could not control a father's feelings as he bent in
agony over this blighted blossom of his hopes. Yet even
in this trying hour he showed that submission to the will
of God which formed the foundation of his faith. "My
heart is sad," murmured he, "and mine eyes overflow
with tears at parting with thee, O my son! And still
greater would be my grief, did I not know that I must
soon follow thee; for we are of God, from him we came,
and to him we must return."

Abd'lrahman seeing him in tears, demanded, "Hast
thou not forbidden us to weep for the dead?" "No,"
replied the prophet. "I have forbidden ye to utter
shrieks and outcries, to beat your faces, and rend your
garments; these are suggestions of the evil one: but

tears shed for a calamity are as balm to the heart, and are sent in mercy."

He followed his child to the grave, where, amidst the agonies of separation, he gave another proof that the elements of his religion were ever present to his mind. "My son! my son!" exclaimed he, as the body was committed to the tomb, "say God is my Lord! the prophet of God was my father, and Islamism is my faith!" This was to prepare his child for the questioning by examining angels as to religious belief, which, according to Moslem creed, the deceased would undergo while in the grave.*

An eclipse of the sun which happened about that time, was interpreted by some of his zealous followers as a celestial sign of mourning for the death of Ibrahim; but the afflicted father rejected such obsequious flattery. "The sun and moon," said he, "are among the wonders

---

* One of the funeral rites of the Moslems is for the Mulakken or priest to address the deceased, when in the grave, in the following words: "O servant of God! O son of a handmaid of God! know that, at this time, there will come down to thee two angels commissioned respecting thee and the like of thee; when they say to thee, 'Who is thy Lord?' answer them, 'God is my Lord,' in truth; and when they ask thee concerning thy prophet, or the man who hath been sent unto you, say to them, 'Mahomet is the apostle of God,' with veracity; and when they ask thee concerning thy religion, say to them, 'Islamism is my religion.' And when they ask thee concerning thy book of direction, say to them, 'The Koran is my book of direction, and the Moslems are my brothers;' and when they ask thee concerning thy Kebla, say to them, 'The Caaba is my Kebla, and I have lived and died in the assertion that there is no deity but God, and Mahomet is God's apostle;' and they will say, 'Sleep, O servant of God, in the protection of God!'"—See Lane's *Modern Egyptians*, vol. ii. p. 338.

of God, through which at times he signifies his will to his
servants ; but their eclipse has nothing to do either with
the birth or death of any mortal."

The death of Ibrahim was a blow which bowed him
toward the grave. His constitution was already impaired
by the extraordinary excitements and paroxysms of his
mind, and the physical trials to which he had been exposed ; the poison, too, administered to him at Khaïbar,
had tainted the springs of life, subjected him to excruciating pains, and brought on a premature old age. His religious zeal took the alarm from the increase of bodily
infirmities, and he resolved to expend his remaining
strength in a final pilgrimage to Mecca ; intended to serve
as a model for all future observances of the kind.

The announcement of his pious intention brought devotees from all parts of Arabia, to follow the pilgrim-
prophet. The streets of Medina were crowded with the
various tribes from the towns and cities, from the fastnesses of the mountains, and the remote parts of the
desert, and the surrounding valleys were studded with
their tents. It was a striking picture of the triumph of
a faith—these recently disunited, barbarous, and warring
tribes, brought together as brethren, and inspired by one
sentiment of religious zeal.

Mahomet was accompanied on this occasion by his nine
wives, who were transported on litters. He departed at
the head of an immense train, some say of fifty-five, others
ninety, and others a hundred and fourteen thousand pil-

grims. There was a large number of camels also, decorated with garlands of flowers and fluttering streamers, intended to be offered up in sacrifice.

The first night's halt was a few miles from Medina, at the village of Dhu'l Holaïfa, where, on former occasion, he and his followers had laid aside their weapons, and assumed the pilgrim garb. Early on the following morning, after praying in the mosque, he mounted his camel Al Aswa, and entering the plain of Baïda, uttered the prayer or invocation called in Arabic Talbijah, in which he was joined by all his followers. The following is the import of this solemn invocation: "Here am I in thy service, O God! Here am I in thy service! Thou hast no companion. To thee alone belongeth worship. From thee cometh all good. Thine alone is the kingdom. There is none to share it with thee."

This prayer, according to Moslem tradition, was uttered by the patriarch Abraham, when, from the top of the hill of Kubeis, near Mecca, he preached the true faith to the whole human race, and so wonderful was the power of his voice, that it was heard by every living being throughout the world; insomuch, that the very child in the womb responded, "Here am I in thy service, O God!"

In this way the pilgrim host pursued its course, winding in a lengthened train of miles, over mountain and valley, and making the deserts vocal at times with united prayers and ejaculations. There were no longer any hostile armies to impede or molest it, for by this time the Islam faith reigned serenely over all Arabia. Mahomet approached the sacred city over the same heights which he had traversed in capturing it, and he entered through the gate Beni Scheiba, which still bears the name of The Holy.

A few days after his arrival, he was joined by Ali, who had hastened back from Yemen ; and who brought with him a number of camels to be slain in sacrifice.

As this was to be a model pilgrimage, Mahomet rigorously observed all the rites which he had continued in compliance with patriarchal usage, or introduced in compliance with revelation. Being too weak and infirm to go on foot, he mounted his camel, and thus performed the circuits round the Caaba, and the journeyings to and fro between the hills of Safa and Merwa.

When the camels were to be offered up in sacrifice, he slew sixty-three with his own hand, one for each year of his age, and Ali, at the same time, slew thirty-seven on his own account.

Mahomet then shaved his head, beginning on the right side, and ending on the left. The locks thus shorn away were equally divided among his disciples, and treasured up as sacred relics. Khaled ever afterwards wore one in his turban, and affirmed that it gave him supernatural strength in battle.

Conscious that life was waning away within him, Mahomet, during this last sojourn in the sacred city of his faith, sought to engrave his doctrines deeply in the minds and hearts of his followers. For this purpose he preached frequently in the Caaba from the pulpit, or in the open air from the back of his camel. " Listen to my words," would he say, "for I know not whether, after this year, we shall ever meet here again. O, my hearers, I am but a man like yourselves : the angel of death may at any time appear, and I must obey his summons."

He would then proceed to inculcate not merely religious doctrines and ceremonies, but rules for conduct in all the concerns of life, public and domestic ; and the precepts laid down and enforced on this occasion have had a vast and durable influence on the morals, manners, and habitudes of the whole Moslem world.

It was doubtless in view of his approaching end, and in solicitude for the welfare of his relatives and friends after his death, and especially of his favorite Ali, who, he perceived, had given dissatisfaction in the conduct of his recent campaign in Yemen, that he took occasion, during a moment of strong excitement and enthusiasm among his hearers, to address to them a solemn adjuration.

" Ye believe," said he, "that there is but one God ; that Mahomet is his prophet and apostle ; that paradise and hell are truths ; that death and the resurrection are certain ; and that there is an appointed time when all who rise from the grave must be brought to judgment."

They all answered, "We believe these things." He

then adjured them solemnly by these dogmas of their faith ever to hold his family, and especially Ali, in love and reverence. "Whoever loves me," said he, "let him receive Ali as his friend. May God uphold those who befriend him, and may he turn from his enemies."

It was at the conclusion of one of his discourses in the open air, from the back of his camel, that the famous verse of the Koran is said to have come down from heaven in the very voice of the Deity. "Evil to those, this day, who have denied your religion. Fear them not, fear me. This day I have perfected your religion, and accomplished in you my grace. It is my good pleasure that Islamism be your faith."

On hearing these words, say the Arabian historians, the camel, El Karwa, on which the prophet was seated, fell on its knees in adoration. These words, add they, were the seal and conclusion of the law, for after them there were no further revelations.

Having thus fulfilled all the rites and ceremonies of pilgrimage, and made a full exposition of his faith, Mahomet bade a last farewell to his native city, and, putting himself at the head of his pilgrim army, set out on his return to Medina.

As he came in sight of it, he lifted up his voice and exclaimed, "God is great; God is great! There is but one God; he has no companion. His is the kingdom. To him alone belongeth praise. He is almighty. He hath fulfilled his promise.   He has stood by his servant, and alone dispersed his enemies.   Let us return to our homes, and worship and praise him!"

Thus ended what has been termed the valedictory pilgrimage, being the last made by the prophet.

# CHAPTER XXXVII.

OF THE TWO FALSE PROPHETS, AL ASWAD AND MOSEÏLMA.

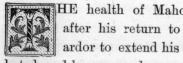HE health of Mahomet continued to decline after his return to Medina; nevertheless his ardor to extend his religious empire was unabated, and he prepared, on a great scale, for the invasion of Syria and Palestine. While he was meditating foreign conquest, however, two rival prophets arose to dispute his sway in Arabia. One was named Al Aswad, the other Moseïlma; they received from the faithful the well-merited appellation of "The Two Liars."

Al Aswad, a quick-witted man, and gifted with persuasive eloquence, was originally an idolater, then a convert to Islamism, from which he apostatized to set up for a prophet, and establish a religion of his own. His fickleness in matters of faith gained him the appellation of Ailhala, or "The Weathercock." In emulation of Mahomet he pretended to receive revelations from heaven through the medium of two angels. Being versed in juggling arts and natural magic, he astonished and confounded the multitude with spectral illusions, which he passed off as miracles, insomuch that certain Moslem writers believe he was really assisted by two evil genii or demons. His schemes, for a time, were crowned with great success, which shows how unsettled the Arabs were in those days in matters of religion, and how ready to adopt any new faith.

Budhan, the Persian whom Mahomet had continued as viceroy of Arabia Felix, died in this year; whereupon Al Aswad, now at the head of a powerful sect, slew his son and successor, espoused his widow after putting her father to death, and seized upon the reins of government. The people of Najran invited him to their city; the gates of Sanaa, the capital of Yemen, were likewise thrown open to him, so that, in a little while, all Arabia Felix submitted to his sway.

The news of this usurpation found Mahomet suffering in the first stages of a dangerous malady, and engrossed by preparations for the Syrian invasion. Impatient of any interruption to his plans, and reflecting that the whole danger and difficulty in question depended upon the life of an individual, he sent orders to certain of his adherents, who were about Al Aswad, to make way with him openly or by stratagem, either way being justifiable against enemies of the faith, according to the recent revelation promulgated by Ali. Two persons undertook the task, less, however, through motives of religion than revenge. One, named Rais, had received a mortal offense from the usurper; the other, named Firuz the Daïlemite, was cousin to Al Aswad's newly espoused wife, and nephew of her murdered father. They repaired to the woman, whose marriage with the usurper had probably been compulsory, and urged upon her the duty, according to the Arab law of blood, of avenging the deaths of her father and her former husband. With much difficulty they prevailed upon her to facilitate their entrance at the dead of night in the chamber of Al Aswad, who was asleep. Firuz stabbed him in the throat with a poniard. The blow was not effectual. Al Aswad started up, and his cries alarmed the guard. His wife, however, went forth and quieted them. "The prophet," said she, "is under the influence of divine inspiration." By this time the cries had ceased, for the assassins had stricken off the head of their victim. When the day dawned the standard of Mahomet floated once more on the walls of the city, and a herald proclaimed, by sound of trumpet, the death of Al Aswad, otherwise called the Liar and Impostor. His career of power began, and was terminated, within the space of four months. The people, easy of faith, resumed Islamism with as much facility as they had abandoned it.

Moseïlma, the other impostor, was an Arab of the tribe of Honeifa, and ruled over the city and province of Yamama, situated between the Red Sea and the Gulf of Persia. In the ninth year of the Hegira he had come to Mecca at the head of an embassy from his tribe, and had made profession of faith between the hands of Mahomet; but, on returning to his own country, had proclaimed that God had gifted him likewise with prophecy, and appointed him to aid Mahomet in converting the human race. To this effect he likewise wrote a Koran, which he gave forth as a volume of inspired truth. His creed was noted for giving the soul a humiliating residence in the region of the abdomen.

Being a man of influence and address, he soon made hosts of converts among his credulous countrymen. Rendered confident by success, he addressed an epistle to Mahomet, beginning as follows :

"From Moseïlma the prophet of Allah, to Mahomet the prophet of Allah! Come, now, and let us make a partition of the world, and let half be thine and half be mine."

This letter came also to the hands of Mahomet, while bowed down by infirmities and engrossed by military preparations. He contented himself for the present with the following reply :

"From Mahomet the prophet of God, to Moseïlma the Liar! The earth is the Lord's, and he giveth it as an inheritance to such of his servants as find favor in his sight. Happy shall those be who live in his fear."

In the urgency of other affairs, the usurpation of Moseïlma remained unchecked. His punishment was reserved for a future day.

# CHAPTER XXXVIII.

IT was early in the eleventh year of the Hegira
that, after unusual preparations, a powerful
army was ready to march for the invasion of
Syria. It would almost seem a proof of the failing powers of Mahomet's mind, that he gave the command of
such an army, on such an expedition, to Osama, a youth
but twenty years of age, instead of some one of his veteran and well-tried generals. It seems to have been a
matter of favor, dictated by tender and grateful recollections. Osama was the son of Zeid, Mahomet's devoted
freedman, who had given the prophet such a signal and
acceptable proof of devotion in relinquishing to him his
beautiful wife Zeinab. Zeid had continued to the last
the same zealous and self-sacrificing disciple, and had
fallen bravely fighting for the faith in the battle of
Muta.

Mahomet was aware of the hazard of the choice he had
made, and feared the troops might be insubordinate under

318

so young a commander. In a general review, therefore, he exhorted them to obedience, reminding them that Osama's father, Zeid, had commanded an expedition of this very kind, against the very same people, and had fallen by their hands; it was but a just tribute to his memory, therefore, to give his son an opportunity of avenging his death. Then placing his banner in the hands of the youthful general, he called upon him to fight valiantly the fight of the faith against all who should deny the unity of God. The army marched forth that very day, and encamped at Djorf, a few miles from Medina; but circumstances occurred to prevent its further progress.

That very night Mahomet had a severe access of the malady which for some time past had affected him, and which was ascribed by some to the lurking effects of the poison given to him at Khaïbar. It commenced with a violent pain in the head, accompanied by vertigo, and the delirium which seems to have mingled with all his paroxysms of illness. Starting up in the mid-watches of the night from a troubled dream, he called upon an attendant slave to accompany him; saying he was summoned by the dead who lay interred in the public burying-place of Medina to come and pray for them. Followed by the slave, he passed through the dark and silent city, where all were sunk in sleep, to the great burying-ground, outside of the walls.

Arrived in the midst of the tombs, he lifted up his voice and made a solemn apostrophe to their tenants.

"Rejoice, ye dwellers in the grave!" exclaimed he. "More peaceful is the morning to which ye shall awaken, than that which attends the living. Happier is your condition than theirs. God has delivered you from the storms with which they are threatened, and which shall follow one another like the watches of a stormy night, each darker than that which went before."

After praying for the dead, he turned and addressed his slave. "The choice is given me," said he, "either to remain in this world to the end of time, in the enjoyment of all its delights, or to return sooner to the presence of God; and I have chosen the latter."

From this time his illness rapidly increased, though he endeavored to go about as usual, and shifted his residence from day to day, with his different wives, as he had been accustomed to do. He was in the dwelling of Maïmona, when the violence of his malady became so great, that he saw it must soon prove fatal. His heart now yearned to be with his favorite wife Ayesha, and pass with her the fleeting residue of life. With his head bound up, and his tottering frame supported by Ali, and Fadhl the son of Al Abbas, he repaired to her abode. She, likewise, was suffering with a violent pain in the head, and entreated of him a remedy.

"Wherefore a remedy?" said he. "Better that thou shouldst die before me. I could then close thine eyes; wrap thee in thy funeral garb; lay thee in the tomb, and pray for thee."

"Yes," replied she, "and then return to my house and dwell with one of thy other wives, who would profit by my death."

Mahomet smiled at this expression of jealous fondness, and resigned himself into her care. His only remaining child, Fatima, the wife of Ali, came presently to see him. Ayesha used to say that she never saw any one resemble the prophet more in sweetness of temper, than this his daughter. He treated her always with respectful tenderness. When she came to him, he used to rise up, go towards her, take her by the hand, and kiss it, and would seat her in his own place. Their meeting on this occasion is thus related by Ayesha, in the traditions preserved by Abulfeda.

"'Welcome, my child,' said the prophet, and made her sit beside him! He then whispered something in her ear, at which she wept. Perceiving her affliction, he whispered something more, and her countenance brightened with joy.

"'What is the meaning of this?' said I to Fatima. 'The prophet honors thee with a mark of confidence never bestowed on any of his wives.' 'I cannot disclose the secret of the prophet of God,' replied Fatima. Nevertheless, after his death, she declared that at first he announced to her his impending death; but seeing her weep, consoled her with the assurance that she would shortly follow him, and become a princess in heaven, among the faithful of her sex."

In the second day of his illness Mahomet was tormented by a burning fever, and caused vessels of water to be emptied on his head and over his body; exclaiming amidst his paroxysms, "Now I feel the poison of Khaïbar rending my entrails."

When somewhat relieved, he was aided in repairing to the mosque, which was adjacent to his residence. Here, seated in his chair, or pulpit, he prayed devoutly; after which, addressing the congregation, which was numerous, "If any of you," said he, "have aught upon his conscience, let him speak out, that I may ask God's pardon for him."

Upon this a man, who had passed for a devout Moslem, stood forth and confessed himself a hypocrite, a liar, and a weak disciple. "Out upon thee!" cried Omar, "why dost thou make known what God had suffered to remain concealed?" But Mahomet turned rebukingly to Omar. "O son of Khattab," said he, "better is it to blush in this world than suffer in the next." Then lifting his eyes to heaven, and praying for the self-accused, "O God," exclaimed he, "give him rectitude and faith, and take from him all weakness in fulfilling such of thy commands as his conscience dictates."

Again addressing the congregation, "Is there any one among you," said he, "whom I have stricken; here is my back, let him strike me in return. Is there any one whose character I have aspersed; let him now cast reproach upon me. Is there any one from whom I have taken aught unjustly; let him now come forward and be indemnified."

Upon this, a man among the throng reminded Mahomet of a debt of three dinars of silver, and was instantly repaid with interest. "Much easier is it," said the prophet, "to bear punishment in this world than throughout eternity."

He now prayed fervently for the faithful, who had fallen by his side in the battle of Ohod, and for those who had suffered for the faith in other battles; interceding with them in virtue of the pact which exists between the living and the dead.

After this he addressed the Mohajerins or Exiles, who had accompanied him from Mecca, exhorting them to hold in honor the Ansarians, or allies of Medina. "The number of believers," said he, "will increase, but that of the allies never can. They were my family with whom I found a home. Do good to those who do good to them, and break friendship with those who are hostile to them."

He then gave three parting commands:

*First.*—Expel all idolaters from Arabia.

*Second.*—Allow all proselytes equal privileges with yourselves.

*Third.*—Devote yourselves incessantly to prayer.

His sermon and exhortation being finished, he was affectionately supported back to the mansion of Ayesha, but was so exhausted on arriving there that he fainted.

His malady increased from day to day, apparently with intervals of delirium, for he spoke of receiving visits from the angel Gabriel, who came from God to inquire after the state of his health; and told him that it rested with himself to fix his dying moment; the angel of death being forbidden by Allah to enter his presence without his permission.

In one of his paroxysms he called for writing implements, that he might leave some rules of conduct for his followers. His attendants were troubled, fearing he might do something to impair the authority of the Koran. Hearing them debate among themselves, whether to comply with his request, he ordered them to leave the room, and when they returned said nothing more on the subject.

On Friday, the day of religious assemblage, he prepared, notwithstanding his illness, to officiate in the mosque, and had water again poured over him to refresh and strengthen him, but on making an effort to go forth, fainted. On recovering, he requested Abu Beker to perform the public prayers; observing, "Allah has given his servant the right to appoint whom he pleases in his place." It was afterwards maintained by some that he thus intended to designate this long tried friend and adherent as his successor in office; but Abu Beker shrank from construing the words too closely.

Word was soon brought to Mahomet, that the appearance of Abu Beker in the pulpit had caused great agitation, a rumor being circulated that the prophet was dead. Exerting his remaining strength, therefore, and leaning on the shoulders of Ali and Al Abbas, he made his way into the mosque, where his appearance spread joy throughout the congregation. Abu Beker ceased to pray, but Mahomet bade him proceed, and taking his seat behind him in the pulpit, repeated the prayers after him. Then addressing the congregation, "I have heard," said he, "that a rumor of the death of your prophet filled you with alarm; but has any prophet before me lived for ever, that ye think I would never leave you? Everything happens according to the will of God, and has its appointed time, which is not to be hastened nor avoided. I return to him who sent me; and my last command to you is, that ye remain united; that ye love, honor, and uphold each other; that ye exhort each other to faith and constancy in belief, and to the performance of pious deeds; by these alone men prosper; all else leads to destruction."

In concluding his exhortation, he added, "I do but go before you; you will soon follow me. Death awaits us all; let no one then seek to turn it aside from me. My life has been for your good; so will be my death."

These were the last words he spake in public; he was again conducted back by Ali and Abbas to the dwelling of Ayesha.

On a succeeding day there was an interval during which he appeared so well that Ali, Abu Beker, Omar, and the rest of those who had been constantly about him, absented themselves for a time, to attend to their affairs. Ayesha alone remained with him. The interval was but illusive. His pains returned with redoubled violence. Finding death approaching, he gave orders that all his slaves should be restored to freedom, and all the money in the house distributed among the poor; then raising his eyes to heaven, "God be with me in the death struggle," exclaimed he.

Ayesha now sent in haste for her father and Hafza. Left alone with Mahomet, she sustained his head on her lap, watching over him with tender assiduity, and endeavoring to soothe his dying agonies. From time to time he would dip his hand in a vase of water, and with it feebly sprinkle his face. At length raising his eyes and gazing upward for a time with unmoving eyelids, "O Allah!" ejaculated he, in broken accents, "be it so!— among the glorious associates in paradise!"

"I knew by this," said Ayesha, who related the dying scene, "that his last moment had arrived, and that he had made choice of supernal existence."

In a few moments his hands were cold, and life was extinct. Ayesha laid his head upon the pillow, and beating her head and breast, gave way to loud lamentations. Her outcries brought the other wives of Mahomet, and their clamorous grief soon made the event known throughout the city. Consternation seized upon the people, as if some prodigy had happened. All business was suspended. The army which had struck its tents was ordered to halt, and Osama, whose foot was in the stirrup for the march, turned his steed to the gates of Medina, and planted his standard at the prophet's door.

The multitude crowded to contemplate the corpse, and agitation and dispute prevailed even in the chamber of death. Some discredited the evidence of their senses. "How can he be dead?" cried they. "Is he not our mediator with God? How then can he be dead? Impossible! He is but in a trance, and carried up to heaven like Isa (Jesus) and the other prophets."

The throng augmented about the house, declaring with clamor that the body should not be interred; when Omar, who had just heard the tidings, arrived. He drew his scimetar, and passing through the crowd, threatened to strike off the hands and feet of any one who should affirm that the prophet was dead. "He has but departed for a time," said he, "as Musa (Moses) the son of Imram went up forty days into the mountain; and like him he will return again."

Abu Beker, who had been in a distant part of the city, arrived in time to soothe the despair of the people and calm the transports of Omar. Passing into the chamber he raised the cloth which covered the corpse, and kissing the pale face of Mahomet, "O thou!" exclaimed he, "who wert to me as my father and my mother; sweet art thou even in death, and living odors dost thou exhale! Now livest thou in everlasting bliss, for never will Allah subject thee to a second death."

Then covering the corpse he went forth, and endeavored to silence Omar, but finding it impossible, he addressed the multitude. "Truly if Mahomet is the sole object of your adoration, he is dead; but if it be God you worship, he cannot die. Mahomet was but the prophet of God, and has shared the fate of the apostles and holy men who have gone before him. Allah, himself, has said in his Koran that Mahomet was but his ambassador, and was subject to death. What then! will you turn the heel upon him, and abandon his doctrine because he is dead? Remember your apostasy harms not God, but insures your own condemnation; while the blessings of God will be poured out upon those who continue faithful to him."

The people listened to Abu Beker with tears and sobbings, and as they listened their despair subsided. Even Omar was convinced but not consoled, throwing himself on the earth and bewailing the death of Mahomet, whom he remembered as his commander and his friend.

The death of the prophet, according to the Moslem historians Abulfeda and Al Jannabi, took place on his birthday, when he had completed his sixty-third year. It was in the eleventh year of the Hegira, and the 632d year of the Christian era.

The body was prepared for sepulture by several of the dearest relatives and disciples. They affirmed that a marvelous fragrance which, according to the evidence of his wives and daughters, emanated from his person during life, still continued; so that, to use the words of Ali,

" it seemed as if he were, at the same time, dead and living."

The body having been washed and perfumed, was wrapped in three coverings; two white, and the third of the striped cloth of Yemen. The whole was then perfumed with amber, musk, aloes, and odoriferous herbs. After this it was exposed in public, and seventy-two prayers were offered up.

The body remained three days unburied, in compliance with oriental custom, and to satisfy those who still believed in the possibility of a trance. When the evidences of mortality could no longer be mistaken, preparations were made for interment. A dispute now arose as to the place of sepulture. The Mohadjerins or disciples from Mecca contended for that city, as being the place of his nativity; the Ansarians claimed for Medina, as his asylum and the place of his residence during the last ten years of his life. A third party advised that his remains should be transported to Jerusalem, as the place of sepulture of the prophets. Abu Beker, whose word had always the greatest weight, declared it to have been the expressed opinion of Mahomet that a prophet should be buried in the place where he died. This in the present instance was complied with to the very letter, for a grave was digged in the house of Ayesha, beneath the very bed on which Mahomet had expired.

Note.—The house of Ayesha was immediately adjacent to the mosque, which was at that time a humble edifice with clay walls, and a roof thatched with palm leaves, and supported by the trunks of trees. It has since been included in a spacious temple, on the plan of a colonnade, inclosing an oblong square, 165 paces by 130, open to the heavens, with four gates of entrance. The colonnade, of several rows of pillars of various sizes covered with stucco and gayly painted, supports a succession of small white cupolas on the four sides of the square. At the four corners are lofty and tapering minarets.

Near the southeast corner of the square is an inclosure, surrounded by an iron railing, painted green, wrought with filigree work and interwoven with brass and gilded wire admitting no view of the interior excepting through small windows, about six inches square. This inclosure, the great resort of pilgrims, is called the Hadgira, and contains the tombs of Mahomet, and his two friends and early successors, Abu Beker and Omar. Above this sacred inclosure rises a lofty dome surmounted with a gilded globe and crescent, at the first sight of which, pilgrims, as they approach Medina, salute the tomb of the prophet with profound inclinations of the body and appropriate prayers. The marvelous tale, so long considered veritable, that the coffin of Mahomet remained suspended in the air without any support, and which Christian writers accounted for by supposing that it was of iron, and dexterously placed midway between two magnets, is proved to be an idle fiction.

The mosque has undergone changes. It was at one time partially thrown down and destroyed in an awful tempest, but was rebuilt by the Soldan of Egypt. It has been enlarged and embellished by various Caliphs, and in particular by Waled I., under whom Spain was invaded and conquered. It was plundered of its immense votive treasures by the Wahabees when they took and pillaged Medina. It is now maintained, though with diminished splendor, under the care of about thirty Agas, whose chief is called Sheikh Al Haram, or Chief of the Holy House. He is the principal personage in Medina. Pilgrimage to Medina, though considered a most devout and meritorious act, is not imposed on Mahometans, like pilgrimage to Mecca, as a religious duty, and has much declined in modern days.

The foregoing particulars are from Burckhardt, who gained admission into Medina, as well as into Mecca, in disguise and at great peril ; admittance into those cities being prohibited to all but Moslems.

# CHAPTER XXXIX.

PERSON AND CHARACTER OF MAHOMET, AND SPECULATIONS ON HIS PROPHETIC
CAREER.

AHOMET, according to accounts handed down
by tradition from his contemporaries, was of
the middle stature, square built and sinewy,
with large hands and feet. In his youth he was uncommonly strong and vigorous; in the latter part of his life
he inclined to corpulency. His head was capacious, well
shaped, and well set on a neck which rose like a pillar
from his ample chest. His forehead was high, broad at
the temples, and crossed by veins extending down to
the eyebrows, which swelled whenever he was angry or
excited. He had an oval face, marked and expressive
features, an aquiline nose, black eyes, arched eyebrows
which nearly met, a mouth large and inflexible, indicative of eloquence; very white teeth, somewhat parted
and irregular; black hair which waved without a curl on
his shoulders, and a long and very full beard.

His deportment, in general, was calm and equable; he
sometimes indulged in pleasantry, but more commonly
was grave and dignified; though he is said to have pos-

sessed a smile of captivating sweetness. His complexion was more ruddy than is usual with Arabs, and in his excited and enthusiastic moments there was a glow and radiance in his countenance, which his disciples magnified into the supernatural light of prophecy.

His intellectual qualities were undoubtedly of an extraordinary kind. He had a quick apprehension, a retentive memory, a vivid imagination, and an inventive genius. Owing but little to education, he had quickened and informed his mind by close observation, and stored it with a great variety of knowledge concerning the systems of religion current in his day, or handed down by tradition from antiquity. His ordinary discourse was grave and sententious, abounding with those aphorisms and apologues so popular among the Arabs; at times he was excited and eloquent, and his eloquence was aided by a voice musical and sonorous.

He was sober and abstemious in his diet, and a rigorous observer of fasts. He indulged in no magnificence of apparel, the ostentation of a petty mind; neither was his simplicity in dress affected; but the result of a real disregard to distinction from so trivial a source. His garments were sometimes of wool; sometimes of the striped cotton of Yemen, and were often patched. He wore a turban, for he said turbans were worn by the angels; and in arranging it he let one end hang down between his shoulders, which he said was the way they wore it. He forbade the wearing of clothes entirely of silk; but permitted a mixture of thread and silk. He forbade also red clothes and the use of gold rings. He wore a seal ring of silver, the engraved part under his finger close to the palm of his hand, bearing the inscription, " Mahomet the messenger of God." He was scrupulous as to personal cleanliness, and observed frequent ablutions. In some respects he was a voluptuary. "There are two things in this world," would he say, "which delight me, women and perfumes. These two things rejoice my eyes and render me more fervent in devotion." From his extreme cleanliness, and the use of perfumes and sweet-scented oil for his hair, probably arose that sweetness and fragrance of person, which his disciples considered innate and miraculous. His passion for the sex had an influence over all his affairs. It is said that when in the presence of a beautiful female, he was continually smoothing his brow and adjusting his hair, as if anxious to appear to advantage.

The number of his wives is uncertain. Abulfeda, who writes with more caution than other of the Arabian historians, limits it to fifteen, though some make it as much as twenty-five. At the time of his death he had nine, each in her separate dwelling, and all in the vicinity of the mosque at Medina. The plea alleged for his indulging in a greater number of wives than he permitted to his followers, was a desire to beget a race of prophets for his people. If such indeed were his desire, it was disappointed. Of all his children, Fatima the wife of Ali alone survived him, and she died within a short time after his death. Of her descendants, none excepting her eldest son Hassan ever sat on the throne of the Caliphs.

In his private dealings he was just. He treated friends and strangers, the rich and poor, the powerful and the weak, with equity, and was beloved by the common people for the affability with which he received them, and listened to their complaints.

He was naturally irritable, but had brought his temper under great control, so that even in the self-indulgent intercourse of domestic life he was kind and tolerant. "I served him from the time I was eight years old," said his servant Anas, "and he never scolded me for anything, though things were spoiled by me."

The question now occurs, was he the unprincipled impostor that he has been represented? Were all his visions and revelations deliberate falsehoods, and was his whole system a tissue of deceit? In considering this question we must bear in mind, that he is not chargeable with many extravagances which exist in his name. Many of the visions and revelations handed down as having been given by him are spurious. The miracles ascribed to him are all fabrications of Moslem zealots. He expressly and repeatedly disclaimed all miracles excepting the Koran; which, considering its incomparable merit, and the way in which it had come down to him from heaven, he pronounced the greatest of miracles. And here we must indulge a few observations on this famous document. While zealous Moslems and some of the most learned doctors of the faith draw proofs of its divine origin from the inimitable excellence of its style and composition, and the avowed illiteracy of Mahomet, less devout critics have pronounced it a chaos of beauties and defects; without method or arrangement; full of obscurities, incoherencies, repetitions, false versions of Scriptural stories, and direct contradictions. The truth is that the Koran as it now exists is not the same Koran delivered by Mahomet to his disciples, but has undergone many corruptions and interpolations. The revelations contained in it were given at various times, in various places, and before various persons; sometimes they were taken down by his secretaries or disciples on parchment, on palm-leaves, or the shoulder blades of sheep, and thrown together in a chest, of which one of his wives had charge; sometimes they were merely treasured up in the memories of those who heard them. No care appears to have been taken to systematize and arrange them during his life; and at his death they remained in scattered fragments, many of them at the mercy of fallacious memories. It was not until some time after his death that Abu Beker undertook to have them gathered together and transcribed. Zeid Ibn Thabet, who had been one of the secretaries of Mahomet, was employed for the purpose. He professed to know many parts of the Koran by heart, having written them down under the dictation of the prophet; other parts he col-

lected piecemeal from various hands, written down in
the rude way we have mentioned, and many parts he
took down as repeated to him by various disciples who
professed to have heard them uttered by the prophet
himself. The heterogeneous fragments thus collected
were thrown together without selection; without chronological order, and without system of any kind. The
volume thus formed during the Caliphat of Abu Beker
was transcribed by different hands, and many professed
copies put in circulation and dispersed throughout the
Moslem cities. So many errors, interpolations, and contradictory readings, soon crept into these copies, that
Othman, the third Caliph, called in the various manuscripts, and forming what he pronounced the genuine
Koran, caused all the others to be destroyed.

This simple statement may account for many of the incoherencies, repetitions, and other discrepancies charged
upon this singular document. Mahomet, as has justly
been observed, may have given the same precepts, or related the same apologue at different times, to different
persons in different words; or various persons may have
been present at one time, and given various versions of
his words; and reported his apologues and scriptural
stories in different ways, according to their imperfect
memoranda or fallible recollections. Many revelations
given by him as having been made in foregone times to
the prophets, his predecessors, may have been reported
as having been given as relations made to himself. It

has been intimated that Abu Beker, in the early days of his Caliphat, may have found it politic to interpolate many things in the Koran, calculated to aid him in emergencies, and confirm the empire of Islamism. What corruptions and interpolations may have been made by other and less scrupulous hands, after the prophet's death, we may judge by the daring liberties of the kind taken by Abdallah Ibn Saad, one of his secretaries, during his life-time.

From all these circumstance it will appear, that even the documentary memorials concerning Mahomet abound with vitiations, while the traditional are full of fable. These increase the difficulty of solving the enigma of his character and conduct. His history appears to resolve itself into two grand divisions. During the first part, up to the period of middle life, we cannot perceive what adequate object he had to gain by the impious and stupendous imposture with which he stands charged. Was it riches? His marriage with Cadijah had already made him wealthy, and for years preceding his pretended vision he had manifested no desire to increase his store. Was it distinction? He already stood high in his native place, as a man of intelligence and probity. He was of the illustrious tribe of Koreish, and of the most honored branch of that tribe. Was it power? The guardianship of the Caaba, and with it the command of the sacred city, had been for generations in his immediate family, and his situation and circumstances entitled him to look forward

with confidence to that exalted trust. In attempting to
subvert the faith in which he had been brought up, he
struck at the root of all these advantages. On that faith
were founded the fortunes and dignities of his family.
To assail it must draw on himself the hostility of his
kindred, the indignation of his fellow-citizens, and the
horror and odium of all his countrymen, who were worshippers at the Caaba.

Was there anything brilliant in the outset of his
prophetic career to repay him for these sacrifices, and to
lure him on? On the contrary, it was begun in doubt
and secrecy. For years it was not attended by any material success. In proportion as he made known his
doctrines and proclaimed his revelations, they subjected
him to ridicule, scorn, obloquy, and finally to an inveterate persecution; which ruined the fortunes of himself
and his friends; compelled some of his family and followers to take refuge in a foreign land; obliged him to
hide from sight in his native city, and finally drove him
forth a fugitive to seek an uncertain home elsewhere.
Why should he persist for years in a course of imposture
which was thus prostrating all his worldly fortunes, at a
time of life when it was too late to build them up anew?

In the absence of sufficient worldly motives, we are
compelled to seek some other explanation of his conduct
in this stage of his most enigmatical history; and this
we have endeavored to set forth in the early part of this
work; where we have shown his enthusiastic and vision-

ary spirit gradually wrought up by solitude, fasting, prayer, and meditation, and irritated by bodily disease into a state of temporary delirium, in which he fancies he receives a revelation from heaven, and is declared a prophet of the Most High. We cannot but think there was self-deception in this instance; and that he believed in the reality of the dream or vision; especially after his doubts had been combated by the zealous and confiding Cadijah, and the learned and crafty Waraka.

Once persuaded of his divine mission to go forth and preach the faith, all subsequent dreams and impulses might be construed to the same purport; all might be considered intimations of the divine will, imparted in their several ways to him as a prophet. We find him repeatedly subject to trances and ecstasies in times of peculiar agitation and excitement, when he may have fancied himself again in communication with the Deity, and these were almost always followed by revelations.

The general tenor of his conduct up to the time of his flight from Mecca, is that of an enthusiast acting under a species of mental delusion; deeply imbued with a conviction of his being a divine agent for religious reform: and there is something striking and sublime in the luminous path which his enthusiastic spirit struck out for itself through the bewildering maze of adverse faiths and wild traditions; the pure and spiritual worship of the one true God, which he sought to substitute for the blind idolatry of his childhood.

All the parts of the Koran supposed to have been promulgated by him at this time, incoherently as they have come down to us, and marred as their pristine beauty must be in passing through various hands, are of a pure and elevated character, and breathe poetical, if not religious, inspiration. They show that he had drunk deep of the living waters of Christianity, and if he had failed to imbibe them in their crystal purity, it might be because he had to drink from broken cisterns, and streams troubled and perverted by those who should have been their guardians. The faith he had hitherto inculcated was purer than that held forth by some of the pseudo-Christians of Arabia, and his life, so far, had been regulated according to its tenets.

Such is our view of Mahomet and his conduct during the early part of his career, while he was a persecuted and ruined man in Mecca. A signal change, however, took place, as we have shown in the foregoing chapters, after his flight to Medina, when, in place of the mere shelter and protection which he sought, he finds himself revered as a prophet, implicitly obeyed as a chief, and at the head of a powerful, growing, and warlike host of votaries. From this time worldly passions and worldly schemes too often give the impulse to his actions, instead of that visionary enthusiasm which, even if mistaken, threw a glow of piety on his earlier deeds. The old doctrines of forbearance, long-suffering, and resignation, are suddenly dashed aside ; he becomes vindictive towards those who have hitherto oppressed him, and ambitious of extended rule. His doctrines, precepts, and conduct, become marked by contradictions, and his whole course is irregular and unsteady. His revelations, henceforth, are so often opportune, and fitted to particular emergencies, that we are led to doubt his sincerity, and that he is any longer under the same delusion concerning them. Still, it must be remembered, as we have shown, that the records of these revelations are not always to be depended upon. What he may have uttered as from his own will, may have been reported as if given by the will of God. Often, too, as we have already suggested, he may have considered his own impulses as divine intimations; and that, being an agent ordained to propagate the faith, all impulses and conceptions toward that end might be part of a continued and divine inspiration.

If we are far from considering Mahomet the gross and impious impostor that some have represented him, so also are we indisposed to give him credit for vast forecast, and for that deeply concerted scheme of universal conquest which has been ascribed to him. He was, undoubtedly, a man of great genius and a suggestive imagination, but it appears to us that he was, in a great degree, the creature of impulse and excitement, and very much at the mercy of circumstances. His schemes grew out of his fortunes, and not his fortunes out of his schemes. He was forty years of age before he first broached his doctrines. He suffered year after year to

steal away before he promulgated them out of his own
family. When he fled from Mecca thirteen years had
elapsed from the announcement of his mission, and from
being a wealthy merchant he had sunk to be a ruined
fugitive. When he reached Medina he had no idea of the
worldly power that awaited him; his only thought was
to build a humble mosque where he might preach; and
his only hope that he might be suffered to preach with
impunity. When power suddenly broke upon him, he
used it for a time in petty forays and local feuds. His
military plans expanded with his resources, but were by
no means masterly, and were sometimes unsuccessful.
They were not struck out with boldness, nor executed
with decision; but were often changed in deference to
the opinions of warlike men about him, and sometimes
at the suggestion of inferior minds, who occasionally led
him wrong. Had he, indeed, conceived from the outset
the idea of binding up the scattered and conflicting
tribes of Arabia into one nation by a *brotherhood of faith*,
for the purpose of carrying out a scheme of external conquest, he would have been one of the first of military
projectors; but the idea of extended conquest seems to
have been an afterthought, produced by success. The
moment he proclaimed the religion of the sword, and
gave the predatory Arabs a taste of foreign plunder, that
moment he was launched in a career of conquest, which
carried him forward with its own irresistible impetus.
The fanatic zeal with which he had inspired his followers

did more for his success than his military science; their belief in his doctrine of predestination produced victories which no military calculation could have anticipated. In his dubious outset as a prophet, he had been encouraged by the crafty counsels of his scriptural oracle Waraka; in his career as a conqueror, he had Omar, Khaled, and other fiery spirits by his side to urge him on, and to aid him in managing the tremendous power which he had evoked into action. Even with all their aid, he had occasionally to avail himself of his supernatural machinery as a prophet, and in so doing may have reconciled himself to the fraud by considering the pious end to be obtained.

His military triumphs awakened no pride, no vainglory, as they would have done had they been effected for selfish purposes. In the time of his greatest power, he maintained the same simplicity of manners and appearance as in the days of his adversity. So far from affecting regal state, he was displeased if, on entering a room, any unusual testimonial of respect were shown him. If he aimed at universal dominion, it was the dominion of the faith: as to the temporal rule which grew up in his hands, as he used it without ostentation, so he took no step to perpetuate it in his family.

The riches which poured in upon him from tribute and the spoils of war, were expended in promoting the victories of the faith, and in relieving the poor among its votaries; insomuch that his treasury was often drained of its last coin. Omar Ibn Al Hareth declares that Mahomet, at his death, did not leave a golden dinar nor a silver dirhem, a slave nor a slave girl, nor anything but his gray mule Daldal, his arms, and the ground which he bestowed upon his wives, his children, and the poor. "Allah," says an Arabian writer, "offered him the keys of all the treasures of the earth, but he refused to accept them."

It is this perfect abnegation of self, connected with this apparently heartfelt piety, running throughout the various phases of his fortune, which perplex one in forming a just estimate of Mahomet's character. However he betrayed the alloy of earth after he had worldly power at his command, the early aspirations of his spirit continually returned and bore him above all earthly things. Prayer, that vital duty of Islamism, and that infallible purifier of the soul, was his constant practice. "Trust in God," was his comfort and support in times of trial and despondency. On the clemency of God, we are told, he reposed all his hopes of supernal happiness. Ayesha relates that on one occasion she inquired of him, "O prophet, do none enter paradise but through God's mercy?" "None—none—!" replied he, with earnest and emphatic repetition. "But you, O prophet, will not *you* enter excepting through his compassion?" Then Mahomet put his hand upon his head, and replied three times, with great solemnity, "Neither shall I enter paradise unless God cover me with his mercy!"

When he hung over the death-bed of his infant son Ibrahim, resignation to the will of God was exhibited in his conduct under this keenest of afflictions; and the hope of soon rejoining his child in paradise was his consolation. When he followed him to the grave, he invoked his spirit, in the awful examination of the tomb, to hold fast to the foundations of the faith, the unity of God, and his own mission as a prophet. Even in his own dying hour, when there could be no longer a worldly motive for deceit, he still breathed the same religious devotion, and the same belief in his apostolic mission. The last words that trembled on his lips ejaculated a trust of soon entering into blissful companionship with the prophets who had gone before him.

It is difficult to reconcile such ardent, persevering piety with an incessant system of blasphemous imposture; nor such pure and elevated and benignant precepts as are contained in the Koran, with a mind haunted by ignoble passions, and devoted to the grovelling interests of mere mortality; and we find no other satisfactory mode of solving the enigma of his character and conduct, than by supposing that the ray of mental hallucination which flashed upon his enthusiastic spirit during his religious ecstasies in the midnight cavern of Mount Hara, continued more or less to bewilder him with a species of monomania to the end of his career, and that he died in the delusive belief of his mission as a prophet.

When he hung over the death-bed of his infant son Ibrahim, resignation to the will of God was exhibited in his conduct under this keenest of afflictions; and the hope of soon rejoining his child in paradise was his consolation. When he followed him to the grave, he invoked his spirit, in the awful examination of the tomb, to hold fast to the foundations of the faith, the unity of God, and his own mission as a prophet. Even in his own dying hour, when there could be no longer a worldly motive for deceit, he still breathed the same religious devotion, and the same belief in his apostolic mission. The last words that trembled on his lips ejaculated a trust of soon entering into blissful companionship with the prophets who had gone before him.

It is difficult to reconcile such ardent, persevering piety with an incessant system of blasphemous imposture; nor such pure and elevated and benignant precepts as are contained in the Koran, with a mind haunted by ignoble passions, and devoted to the grovelling interests of mere mortality; and we find no other satisfactory mode of solving the enigma of his character and conduct than by supposing that the ray of mental hallucination which flashed upon his enthusiastic spirit during his religious ecstasies in the midnight cavern of Mount Hara, continued more or less to bewilder him with a specter of monomania to the end of his career, and that he died in the delusive belief of his mission as a prophet

# APPENDIX.

APPENDIX.

# APPENDIX.

## OF THE ISLAM FAITH.

In an early chapter of this work we have given such particulars of the faith inculcated by Mahomet as we deemed important to the understanding of the succeeding narrative : we now, though at the expense of some repetition, subjoin a more complete summary, accompanied by a few observations.

The religion of Islam, as we observed on the before-mentioned occasion, is divided into two parts ; FAITH and PRACTICE :—and first of Faith. This is distributed under six different heads, or articles, viz.: 1st, faith in God ; 2d, in his angels ; 3d, in his Scriptures or Koran ; 4th, in his prophets ; 5th, in the resurrection and final judgment ; 6th, in predestination. Of these we will briefly treat in the order we have enumerated them.

FAITH IN GOD.—Mahomet inculcated the belief that there is, was, and ever will be, one only God, the creator of all things ; who is single, immutable, omniscient, omnipotent, all-merciful, and eternal. The unity of God was specifically and strongly urged, in contradistinction to the Trinity of the Christians. It was designated, in the profession of faith, by raising one finger, and exclaiming, " La illaha il Allah !" There is no God but God ; to which was added, " Mohamed Resoul Allah !" Mahomet is the prophet of God.

FAITH IN ANGELS.—The beautiful doctrine of angels, or ministering spirits, which was one of the most ancient and universal of oriental

349

creeds, is interwoven throughout the Islam system. They are represented as ethereal beings, created from fire, the purest of elements, perfect in form and radiant in beauty, but without sex ; free from all gross or sensual passion, and all the appetites and infirmities of frail humanity; and existing in perpetual and unfading youth. They are various in their degrees and duties, and in their favor with the Deity. Some worship around the celestial throne ; others perpetually hymn the praises of Allah; some are winged messengers to execute his orders, and others intercede for the children of men.

The most distinguished of this heavenly host are four Archangels. Gabriel, the angel of revelations, who writes down the divine decrees ; Michael, the champion, who fights the battles of the faith ; Azraïl, the angel of death ; and Izrafil, who holds the awful commission to sound the trumpet on the day of resurrection. There was another angel named Azazil, the same as Lucifer, once the most glorious of the celestial band; but he became proud and rebellious. When God commanded his angels to worship Adam, Azazil refused, saying, "Why should I, whom thou hast created of fire, bow down to one whom thou hast formed of clay?" For this offense he was accursed and cast forth from paradise, and his name changed to Eblis, which signifies despair. In revenge of his abasement, he works all kinds of mischief against the children of men, and inspires them with disobedience and impiety.

Among the angels of inferior rank is a class called Moakkibat; two of whom keep watch upon each mortal, one on the right hand, the other on the left, taking note of every word and action. At the close of each day they fly up to heaven with a written report, and are replaced by two similar angels on the following day. According to Mahometan tradition, every good action is recorded ten times by the angel on the right ; and if the mortal commit a sin, the same benevolent spirit says to the angel on the left, "Forbear for seven hours to record it; peradventure he may repent and pray and obtain forgiveness."

Beside the angelic orders Mahomet inculcates a belief in spiritual beings called Gins or Genii, who, though likewise created of fire, partake of the appetites and frailties of the children of the dust, and like them are ultimately liable to death. By beings of this nature, which haunt the solitudes of the desert, Mahomet, as we have shown, professed to have been visited after his evening orisons in the solitary valley of Al Naklah.

When the angel Azazil rebelled and fell, and became Satan or Eblis, he still maintained sovereignty over these inferior spirits; who are divided by Orientalists into Dives and Peri : the former ferocious and gigantic ; the latter delicate and gentle, subsisting on perfumes. It would seem as if the Peri were all of the female sex, though on this point there rests obscurity. From these imaginary beings it is supposed the European fairies are derived.

Besides these there are other demi-spirits called Tacwins or Fates ; being winged females of beautiful forms, who utter oracles, and defend mortals from the assaults and machinations of evil demons.

There is vagueness and uncertainty about all the attributes given by Mahomet to these half-celestial beings ; his ideas on the subject having been acquired from various sources. His whole system of intermediate spirits has a strong, though indistinct infusion of the creeds and superstitions of the Hebrews, the Magians, and the Pagans or Sabeans.

*The third article of faith* is a belief in the KORAN, as a book of divine revelation. According to the Moslem creed, a book was treasured up in the seventh heaven, and had existed there from all eternity, in which were written down all the decrees of God, and all events, past, present, or to come. Transcripts from these tablets of the divine will were brought down to the lowest heaven by the angel Gabriel, and by him revealed to Mahomet from time to time, in portions adapted to some event or emergency. Being the direct words of God, they were all spoken in the first person.

Of the way in which these revelations were taken down or treasured up by secretaries and disciples, and gathered together by Abu Beker after the death of Mahomet, we have made sufficient mention. The compilation, for such in fact it is, forms the Moslem code of civil and penal, as well as religious law, and is treated with the utmost reverence by all true believers. A zealous pride is shown in having copies of it splendidly bound and ornamented. An inscription on the cover forbids any one to touch it who is unclean, and it is considered irreverent, in reading it, to hold it below the girdle. Moslems swear by it, and take omens from its pages, by opening it and reading the first text that meets the eye. With all its errors and discrepancies, if we consider it mainly as the work of one man, and that an unlettered man, it remains a stupendous monument of solitary legislation.

Beside the Koran or written law, a number of precepts and apologues which casually fell from the lips of Mahomet were collected after his death from ear-witnesses, and transcribed into a book called the Sonna or Oral Law. This is held equally sacred with the Koran by a sect of Mahometans thence called Sonnites ; others reject it as apocryphal; these last are termed Schiites. Hostilities and persecutions have occasionally taken place between these sects almost as virulent as those which, between Catholics and Protestants, have disgraced Christianity. The Sonnites are distinguished by white, the Schiites by red turbans; hence the latter have received from their antagonists the appellation of Kussilbachi, or Red Heads.

It is remarkable that circumcision, which is invariably practiced by the Mahometans, and forms a distinguishing rite of their faith, to which all proselytes must conform, is neither mentioned in the Koran nor the Sonna. It seems to have been a general usage in Arabia, tacitly adopted from the Jews, and is even said to have been prevalent throughout the East before the time of Moses.

It is said that the Koran forbids the making likenesses of any living thing, which has prevented the introduction of portrait-painting among Mahometans. The passage of the Koran, however, which is thought to contain the prohibition, seems merely an echo of the second commandment, held sacred by Jews and Christians, not to form images or pictures for worship. One of Mahomet's standards was a black eagle. Among the most distinguished Moslem ornaments of the Alhambra at Granada is a fountain supported by lions carved of stone, and some Moslem monarchs have had their effigies stamped on their coins.

Another and an important mistake with regard to the system of Mahomet, is the idea that it denies souls to the female sex, and excludes them from paradise. This error arises from his omitting to mention their en-joyments in a future state, while he details those of his own sex with the minuteness of a voluptuary. The beatification of virtuous females is al-luded to in the 56th Sura of the Koran, and also in other places, although from the vagueness of the language a cursory reader might suppose the houris of paradise to be intended.

*The fourth article of faith* relates to the PROPHETS. Their number amounts to two hundred thousand, but only six are super-eminent, as having brought new laws and dispensations upon earth, each abrogating those previously received wherever they varied or were contradictory. These six distinguished prophets were Adam, Noah, Abraham, Moses, Jesus, and Mahomet.

*The fifth article* of Islam faith is on the RESURRECTION and the FINAL JUDGMENT. On this awful subject Mahomet blended some of the Chris-tian belief with certain notions current among the Arabian Jews. One of the latter is the fearful tribunal of the Sepulchre. When Azraïl, the angel of death, has performed his office, and the corpse has been consigned to the tomb, two black angels, Munkar and Nakeer, of dismal and ap-palling aspect, present themselves as inquisitors ; during whose scrutiny the soul is reunited to the body. The defunct, being commanded to sit up, is interrogated as to the two great points of faith, the unity of God and the divine mission of Mahomet, and likewise as to the deeds done by him during life ; and his replies are recorded in books against the day of judgment. Should they be satisfactory, his soul is gently drawn forth from his lips, and his body left to its repose ; should they be other-wise, he is beaten about the brows with iron clubs, and his soul wrenched forth with racking tortures. For the convenience of this awful inquisi-tion, the Mahometans generally deposit their dead in hollow or vaulted sepulchres ; merely wrapped in funeral clothes, but not placed in coffins.

The space of time between death and resurrection is called Berzak, or the Interval. During this period the body rests in the grave, but the soul has a foretaste, in dreams or visions, of its future doom.

The souls of prophets are admitted at once into the full fruition of par-adise. Those of martyrs, including all who die in battle, enter into the bodies or crops of green birds, who feed on the fruits and drink of the streams of paradise. Those of the great mass of true believers are variously disposed of, but, according to the most received opinion, they hover, in a state of seraphic tranquillity, near the tombs. Hence the Moslem usage of visiting the graves of their departed friends and relatives, in the idea that their souls are the gratified witnesses of these testimonials of affection.

Many Moslems believe that the souls of the truly faithful assume the forms of snow-white birds, and nestle beneath the throne of Allah ; a belief in accordance with an ancient superstition of the Hebrews that the souls of the just will have a place in heaven under the throne of glory.

With regard to the souls of infidels, the most orthodox opinion is that they will be repulsed by angels both from heaven and earth, and cast into the cavernous bowels of the earth, there to await in tribulation the day of judgment.

THE DAY OF RESURRECTION will be preceded by signs and portents in heaven and earth. A total eclipse of the moon ; a change in the course of the sun, rising in the west instead of the east ; wars and tumults ; a universal decay of faith; the advent of Antichrist; the issuing forth of Gog and Magog to desolate the world ; a great smoke, covering the whole earth : these and many more prodigies and omens affrighting and harassing the souls of men, and producing a wretchedness of spirit and a weariness of life ; insomuch that a man passing by a grave shall envy the quiet dead, and say, " Would to God I were in thy place ! "

The last dread signal of the awful day will be the blast of a trumpet by the archangel Izrafil. At the sound thereof the earth will tremble ; castles and towers will be shaken to the ground, and mountains leveled with the plains. The face of heaven will be darkened ; the firmament will melt away, and the sun, the moon, and stars will fall into the sea. The ocean will be either dried up, or will boil and roll in fiery billows.

At the sound of that dreadful trump a panic will fall on the human race ; men will fly from their brothers, their parents, and their wives ; and mothers, in frantic terror abandon the infant at the breast. The savage beasts of the forests, and the tame animals of the pasture, will forget their fierceness and their antipathies, and herd together in affright.

The second blast of the trumpet is the blast of extermination. At that sound, all creatures in heaven and on earth and in the waters under the earth, angels and genii, and men and animals, all will die; excepting the chosen few especially reserved by Allah. The last to die will be Azraïl, the angel of death!

Forty days, or, according to explanations, forty years of continued rain will follow this blast of extermination; then will be sounded for the third time the trumpet of the archangel Izrafil; it is the call of judgment! At the sound of this blast, the whole space between heaven and earth will be filled with the souls of the dead flying in quest of their respective bodies. Then the earth will open; and there will be a rattling of dry bones, and a gathering together of scattered limbs; the very hairs will congregate together, and the whole body be reunited, and the soul will reënter it, and the dead will rise from mutilation, perfect in every part, and naked as when born. The infidels will grovel with their faces on the earth, but the faithful will walk erect; as to the truly pious, they will be borne aloft on winged camels, white as milk, with saddles of fine gold.

Every human being will then be put upon his trial as to the manner in which he has employed his faculties, and the good and evil actions of his life. A mighty balance will be poised by the angel Gabriel: in one of these scales, termed Light, will be placed his good actions ; in the other, termed Darkness, his evil deeds. An atom or a grain of mustard-seed will suffice to turn this balance, and the nature of the sentence will depend on the preponderance of either scale. At that moment retribution will be exacted for every wrong and injury. He who has wronged a fellow-mortal will have to repay him with a portion of his own good deeds, or, if he have none to boast of, will have to take upon himself a proportionate weight of the other's sins.

The trial of the balance will be succeeded by the ordeal of the bridge. The whole assembled multitude will have to follow Mahomet across the bridge Al Serát, as fine as the edge of a scimetar, which crosses the gulf of Jehennam or Hell. Infidels and sinful Moslems will grope along it darkling and fall into the abyss; but the faithful, aided by a beaming light, will cross with the swiftness of birds and enter the realms of paradise. The idea of this bridge, and of the dreary realm of Jehennam, is supposed to have been derived partly from the Jews, but chiefly from the Magians.

Jehennam is a region fraught with all kinds of horrors. The very trees have writhing serpents for branches, bearing for fruit the heads of demons. We forbear to dwell upon the particulars of this dismal abode, which are given with painful and often disgusting minuteness. It is described as consisting of seven stages, one below the other, and varying in the nature and intensity of torment. The first stage is allotted to Atheists, who deny creator and creation, and believe the world to be eternal. The second for Manicheans and others that admit two divine principles; and for the Arabian idolaters of the era of Mahomet. The third is for the Brahmins of India; the fourth for the Jews; the fifth for Christians; the sixth for the Magians or Ghebers of Persia; the seventh for hypocrites, who profess without believing in religion.

The fierce angel Thabeck, that is to say, the Executioner, presides over this region of terror.

We must observe that the general nature of Jehennam, and the distribution of its punishments, have given rise to various commentaries and expositions among the Moslem doctors. It is maintained by some, and it is a popular doctrine, that none of the believers in Allah and his prophets will be condemned to eternal punishment. Their sins will be expiated by proportionate periods of suffering, varying from nine hundred to nine thousand years.

Some of the most humane among the doctors contend against eternity of punishment to any class of sinners, saying that, as God is all merciful, even infidels will eventually be pardoned. Those who have an intercessor, as the Christians have in Jesus Christ, will be first redeemed. The liberality of these worthy commentators, however, does not extend so far as to admit them into paradise among true believers; but concludes that, after long punishment, they will be relieved from their torments by annihilation.

Between Jehennam and paradise is Al Araf or the Partition, a region destitute of peace or pleasure, destined for the reception of infants, lunatics, idiots, and such other beings as have done neither good nor evil. For such, too, whose good and evil deeds balance each other ; though these may be admitted to paradise through the intercession of Mahomet, on performing an act of adoration, to turn the scales in their favor. It is said that the tenants of this region can converse with their neighbors on either hand, the blessed and the condemned: and that Al Araf appears a paradise to those in hell, and a hell to those in paradise.

AL JANNAT, OR THE GARDEN.—When the true believer has passed through all his trials, and expiated all his sins, he refreshes himself at the pool of the Prophet. This is a lake of fragrant water, a month's journey in circuit, fed by the river Al Cauther, which flows from paradise. The water of this lake is sweet as honey, cold as snow, and clear as crystal; he who once tastes of it will never more be tormented by thirst; a blessing dwelt upon with peculiar zest by Arabian writers, accustomed to the parching thirst of the desert.

After the true believer has drunk of this water of life, the gate of paradise is open to him by the angel Rushvan. The same prolixity and minuteness which occur in the description of Jehennam, are lavished on the delights of paradise, until the imagination is dazzled and confused by the details. The soil is of the finest wheaten flour, fragrant with perfumes, and strewed with pearls and hyacinths instead of sands and pebbles.

Some of the streams are of crystal purity, running between green banks enamelled with flowers; others are of milk, of wine and honey; flowing over beds of musk, between margins of camphire, covered with moss and saffron ! The air is sweeter than the spicy gales of Sabea, and cooled by sparkling fountains. Here, too, is Taba, the wonderful tree of life, so large that a fleet horse would need a hundred years to cross its shade. The boughs are laden with every variety of delicious fruit, and bend to the hand of those who seek to gather.

The inhabitants of this blissful garden are clothed in raiment sparkling with jewels; they wear crowns of gold enriched with pearls and diamonds, and dwell in sumptuous palaces or silken pavilions, reclining on voluptuous couches. Here every believer will have hundreds of attendants, bearing dishes and goblets of gold, to serve him with every variety of exquisite viand and beverage. He will eat without satiety, and drink without inebriation; the last morsel and the last drop will be equally relished with the first; he will feel no repletion, and need no evacuation.

The air will resound with the melodious voice of Izrafil, and the songs of the daughters of paradise; the very rustling of the trees will produce ravishing harmony, while myriads of bells, hanging among their branches, will be put in dulcet motion by airs from the throne of Allah.

Above all, the faithful will be blessed with female society to the full extent even of oriental imaginings. Beside the wives he had on earth, who will rejoin him in all their pristine charms, he will be attended by the Hûr al Oyûn or Houris, so called from their large black eyes ; resplendent beings, free from every human defect or frailty; perpetually retaining their youth and beauty, and renewing their virginity. Seventy-two of these are allotted to every believer. The intercourse with them will be fruitful or not according to their wish, and the offspring will grow within an hour to the same stature with the parents.

That the true believer will be fully competent to the enjoyments of this blissful region, he will rise from the grave in the prime of manhood, at the age of thirty, of the stature of Adam, which was thirty cubits; with all his faculties improved to a state of preternatural perfection, with the abilities of a hundred men, and with desires and appetites quickened rather than sated by enjoyment.

These and similar delights are promised to the meanest of the faithful; there are gradations of enjoyment, however, as of merit; but, as to those prepared for the most deserving, Mahomet found the powers of description exhausted, and was fain to make use of the text from Scripture, that they should be such things "as eye hath not seen, ear hath not heard, neither hath it entered into the heart of man to conceive."

The expounders of the Mahometan law differ in their opinions as to the whole meaning of this system of rewards and punishments. One set understanding everything in a figurative, the other in a literal sense.

The former insist that the prophet spake in parable, in a manner suited to the coarse perceptions and sensual natures of his hearers ; and maintain that the joys of heaven will be mental as well as corporeal; the resurrection being of both soul and body. The soul will revel in a supernatural development and employment of all its faculties ; in a knowledge of all the arcana of nature ; the full revelation of everything past, present, and to come. The enjoyments of the body will be equally suited to its various senses, and perfected to a supernatural degree.

The same expounders regard the description of Jehennam as equally figurative; the torments of the soul consisting in the anguish of perpetual remorse for past crimes, and deep and ever-increasing despair for the loss of heaven; those of the body in excruciating and never-ending pain.

The other doctors, who construe everything in a literal sense, are considered the most orthodox, and their sect is beyond measure the most numerous. Most of the particulars in the system of rewards and punishments, as has been already observed, have close affinity to the superstitions of the Magians and the Jewish Rabbins. The Houri, or black-eyed nymphs, who figure so conspicuously in the Moslem's paradise, are said to be the same as the Huram Behest of the Persian Magi, and Mahomet is accused by Christian investigators of having purloined much of his description of heaven from the account of the New Jerusalem in the Apocalypse ; with such variation as is used by knavish jewellers, when they appropriate stolen jewels to their own use.

*The sixth and last article* of the Islam faith is PREDESTINATION, and on this Mahomet evidently reposed his chief dependence for the success of his military enterprises. He inculcated that every event had been predetermined by God, and written down in the eternal tablet previous to the creation of the world. That the destiny of every individual, and the hour of his death, were irrevocably fixed, and could neither be varied nor evaded by any effort of human sagacity or foresight. Under this persuasion, the Moslems engaged in battle without risk ; and, as death in battle was equivalent to martyrdom, and entitled them to an immediate admission into paradise, they had in either alternative, death or victory, a certainty of gain.

This doctrine, according to which men by their own free will can neither avoid sin nor avert punishment, is considered by many Mussulmen as derogatory to the justice and clemency of God ; and several sects have sprung up, who endeavor to soften and explain away this perplexing dogma ; but the number of these doubters is small, and they are not considered orthodox.

The doctrine of Predestination was one of those timely revelations to Mahomet, that were almost miraculous from their seasonable occurrence. It took place immediately after the disastrous battle of Ohod, in which many of his followers, and among them his uncle Hamza, were slain. Then it was, in a moment of gloom and despondency, when his followers around him were disheartened, that he promulgated this law, telling them that every man must die at the appointed hour, whether in bed or in the field of battle. He declared, moreover, that the angel Gabriel had announced to him the reception of Hamza into the seventh heaven, with the title of Lion of God and of the prophet. He added, as he contemplated the dead bodies, "I am witness for these, and for all who have been slain for the cause of God, and they shall appear in glory at the resurrection, with their wounds brilliant as vermilion and odoriferous as musk."

What doctrine could have been devised more calculated to hurry forward, in a wild career of conquest, a set of ignorant and predatory soldiers, than this assurance of booty if they survived, and paradise if they fell ?* It rendered almost irresistible the Moslem arms ; but it likewise contained the poison that was to destroy their dominion. From the moment the successors of the Prophet ceased to be aggressors and conquerors, and sheathed the sword definitely, the doctrine of predestination began its baneful work. Enervated by peace, and the sensuality permitted by the Koran,—which so distinctly separates its doctrines from the pure and self-denying religion of the Messiah,—the Moslem regarded every reverse as preordained by Allah, and inevitable ; to be borne stoically, since human exertion and foresight were vain. "Help thyself and God will help

* The reader may recollect that a belief in predestination or destiny was encouraged by Napoleon, and had much influence on his troops.

thee," was a precept never in force with the followers of Mahomet, and its reverse has been their fate. The crescent has waned before the cross, and exists in Europe, where it was once so mighty, only by the suffrage, or rather the jealousy of the great Christian powers, probably ere long to furnish another illustration, that " they that take the sword shall perish with the sword."

## RELIGIOUS PRACTICE.

The articles of religious practice are fourfold: Prayer, including ablution, Alms, Fasting, Pilgrimage.

ABLUTION is enjoined as preparative to PRAYER, purity of body being considered emblematical of purity of soul. It is prescribed in the Koran with curious precision. The face, arms, elbows, feet, and a fourth part of the head, to be washed once ; the hands, mouth, and nostrils, three times ; the ears to be moistened with the residue of the water used for the head, and the teeth to be cleaned with a brush. The ablution to commence on the right and terminate on the left; in washing the hands and feet to begin with the fingers and toes ; where water is not to be had, fine sand may be used.

PRAYER is to be performed five times every day, namely, the first in the morning before sunrise ; the second at noon ; the third in the afternoon before sunset ; the fourth in the evening between sunset and dark ; the fifth between twilight and the first watch, being the vesper prayer. A sixth prayer is volunteered by many between the first watch of the night and the dawn of day. These prayers are but repetitions of the same laudatory ejaculation, " God is great ! God is powerful ! God is all powerful !" and are counted by the scrupulous upon a string of beads. They may be performed at the mosque, or in any clean place. During prayer the eyes are turned to the Kebla, or point of the heaven in the direction of Mecca ; which is indicated in every mosque by a niche called Al Mehrab, and externally by the position of the minarets and doors. Even the postures to be observed in prayer are prescribed, and the most solemn act of adoration is by bowing the forehead to the ground. Females in prayer are not to stretch forth their arms, but to fold them on their bosoms. They are not to make as profound inflections as the men. They are to pray in a low and gentle tone of voice. They are not permitted to accompany the men to the mosque, lest the minds of the worshippers should be drawn from their devotions. In addressing themselves to God, the faithful are enjoined to do so with humility; putting aside costly ornaments and sumptuous apparel.

Many of the Mahometan observances with respect to prayer were similar to those previously maintained by the Sabeans; others agreed with the ceremonials prescribed by the Jewish Rabbins. Such were the postures, inflections and prostrations and the turning of the face towards the Kebla, which, however, with the Jews was in the direction of the temple at Jerusalem.

Prayer, with the Moslem, is a daily exercise; but on Friday there is a sermon in the mosque. This day was generally held sacred among oriental nations as the day on which man was created. The Sabean idolaters consecrated it to Astarte, or Venus, the most beautiful of the planets and brightest of the stars. Mahomet adopted it as his Sabbath, partly perhaps from early habitude, but chiefly to vary from the Saturday of the Jews and Sunday of the Christians.

The *second article* of religious practice is CHARITY, or the giving of alms. There are two kinds of alms, namely, those prescribed by law, called Zacat, like tithes in the Christian church, to be made in specified proportions, whether in money, wares, cattle, corn, or fruit; and voluntary gifts termed Sadakat, made at the discretion of the giver. Every Moslem is enjoined, in one way or the other, to dispense a tenth of his revenue in relief of the indigent and distressed.

The *third article* of practice is FASTING, also supposed to have been derived from the Jews. In each year for thirty days, during the month Rhamadan, the true believer is to abstain rigorously from the rising to the setting of the sun, from meat and drink, baths, perfumes, the intercourse of the sexes, and all other gratifications and delights of the senses. This is considered a great triumph of self-denial, mortifying and subduing the several appetites, and purifying both body and soul. Of these three articles of practice the Prince Abdalasis used to say, "Prayer leads us half-way to God, fasting conveys us to his threshold, but alms conducts us into his presence."

PILGRIMAGE is the *fourth grand practical* duty enjoined upon Moslems. Every true believer is bound to make one pilgrimage to Mecca in the course of his life, either personally or by proxy. In the latter case, his name must be mentioned in every prayer offered up by his substitute.

Pilgrimage is incumbent only on free persons of mature age, sound intellect, and who have health and wealth enough to bear the fatigue and expenses of the journey. The pilgrim, before his departure from home, arranges all his affairs, public and domestic, as if preparing for his death.

On the appointed day, which is either Tuesday, Thursday, or Saturday, as being propitious for the purpose, he assembles his wives, children, and all his household, and devoutly commends them and all his concerns to the care of God during his holy enterprise. Then passing one end of his turban beneath his chin to the opposite side of his head, like the attire of a nun, and grasping a stout staff of bitter almonds, he takes leave of his household, and sallies from the apartment, exclaiming, "In the name of God I undertake this holy work, confiding in his protection. I believe in him, and place in his hands my actions and my life."

On leaving the portal he turns his face toward the Kebla, repeats certain passages of the Koran, and adds, "I turn my face to the Holy Caaba, the throne of God, to accomplish the pilgrimage commanded by his law, and which shall draw me near to him."

He finally puts his foot in the stirrup, mounts into the saddle, commends himself again to God, almighty, all wise, all merciful, and sets forth on his pilgrimage. The time of departure is always calculated so as to insure an arrival at Mecca at the beginning of the pilgrim month Dhu'l-hajji.

Three laws are to be observed throughout this pious journey :—

1. To commence no quarrel.

2. To bear meekly all harshness and reviling.

3. To promote peace and good-will among his companions in the caravan.

He is, moreover, to be liberal in his donations and charities throughout his pilgrimage.

When arrived at some place in the vicinity of Mecca, he allows his hair and nails to grow, strips himself to the skin, and assumes the Ihram or pilgrim garb, consisting of two scarfs, without seams or decorations, and of any stuff excepting silk. One of these is folded round the loins, the other thrown over the neck and shoulders, leaving the right arm free. The head is uncovered, but the aged and infirm are permitted to fold something round it in consideration of alms given to the poor. Umbrellas are allowed as a protection against the sun, and indigent pilgrims supply their place by a rag on the end of a staff.

The instep must be bare ; and peculiar sandals are provided for the purpose, or a piece of the upper leather of the shoe is cut out. The pilgrim, when thus attired, is termed Al Mohrem.

The Ihram of females is an ample cloak and veil, enveloping the whole person, so that, in strictness, the wrists, the ankles, and even the eyes should be concealed.

When once assumed, the Ihram must be worn until the pilgrimage is completed, however unsuited it may be to the season or the weather. While wearing it, the pilgrim must abstain from all licentiousness of language ; all sensual intercourse ; all quarrels and acts of violence ; he must not even take the life of an insect that infests him ; though an exception is made in regard to biting dogs, to scorpions, and birds of prey.

On arriving at Mecca, he leaves his baggage in some shop, and, without attention to any worldly concern, repairs straightway to the Caaba, conducted by one of the Metowefs or guides, who are always at hand to offer their services to pilgrims.

Entering the mosque by the Bab el Salam, or Gate of Salutation, he makes four prostrations, and repeats certain prayers as he passes under the arch. Approaching the Caaba, he makes four prostrations, opposite the Black Stone, which he then kisses ; or, if prevented by the throng, he touches it with his right hand, and kisses that. Departing from the Black Stone, and keeping the building on his left hand, he makes the seven circuits, the three first quickly, the latter four with slow and solemn pace. Certain prayers are repeated in a low voice, and the Black Stone kissed, or touched, at the end of every circuit.

The Towaf, or procession round the Caaba, was an ancient ceremony, observed long before the time of Mahomet, and performed by both sexes entirely naked. Mahomet prohibited this exposure, and prescribed the Ihram or pilgrim dress. The female Hajji walk the Towaf generally during the night ; though occasionally they perform it mingled with the men in the daytime.*

The seven circuits being completed, the pilgrim presses his breast against the wall between the Black Stone and the door of tne Caaba, and with outstretched arms, prays for pardon of his sins.

He then repairs to the Makam, or station of Abraham, makes four prostrations, prays for the intermediation of the Patriarch, and thence to the well Zem Zem, and drinks as much of the water as he can swallow.

During all this ceremonial, the uninstructed Hajji has his guide or Metowef close at his heels, muttering prayers for him to repeat. He is now conducted out of the mosque by the gate Bab el Zafa, to a slight ascent about fifty paces distant, called the Hill of Zafa, when, after uttering a prayer with uplifted hands, he commences the holy promenade, called the Saa or Say. This lies through a straight and level street called Al Messa, six hundred paces in length, lined with shops like a bazaar, and terminating at a place Called Merowa. The walk of the Say is in commemoration of the wandering of Hagar over the same ground, in search of water for her child Ishmael. The pilgrim, therefore, walks at times slowly, with an inquisitive air, then runs in a certain place, and again walks gravely, stopping at times and looking anxiously back.

Having repeated the walk up and down this street seven times, the Hajji enters a barber's shop at Merowa ; his head is shaved, his nails pared, the barber muttering prayers and the pilgrim repeating them all the time. The paring and shearing are then buried in consecrated ground, and the most essential duties of the pilgrimage are considered as fulfilled.†

* Burckhardt's *Travels in Arabia*, vol. i. p. 260, Lond. ed. 1829.
† The greater part of the particulars concerning Mecca and Medina, and their respective pilgrimages, are gathered from the writings of that accurate and indefatigable trav-

On the ninth of the month Al Dhu'l-hajji, the pilgrims make a hurried and tumultuous visit to Arafat, where they remain until sunset ; then pass the night in prayer at an Oratory, called Mozdalifa, and before sunrise next morning repair to the valley of Mena, where they throw seven stones at each of three pillars, in imitation of Abraham, and some say also of Adam, who drove away the devil from this spot with stones, when disturbed by him in his devotions.

Such are the main ceremonies which form this great Moslem rite of pilgrimage ; but before concluding this sketch of Islam faith, and closing this legendary memoir of its founder, we cannot forbear to notice one of his innovations, which has entailed perplexity on all his followers, and particular inconvenience on pious pilgrims.

The Arabian year consists of twelve lunar months, containing alternately thirty and twenty-nine days, and making three hundred and fifty-four in the whole, so that eleven days were lost in every solar year.    To make up the deficiency, a thirteenth or wandering month was added to every third year, previous to the era of Mahomet, to the same effect as one day is added in the Christian calendar to every leap-year.   Mahomet, who was uneducated and ignorant of astronomy, retrenched this thirteenth or intercalary month, as contrary to the divine order of revolutions of the moon, and reformed the calendar by a divine revelation during his last pilgrimage.   This is recorded in the ninth sura or chapter of the Koran to the following effect :—

"For the number of months is twelve, as was ordained by Allah, and recorded on the eternal tables * on the day wherein he created the heaven and the earth.

"Transfer not a sacred month unto another month, for verily it is an innovation of the infidels."

eller, Burckhardt ; who, in the disguise of a pilgrim, visited these shrines, and complied with all the forms and ceremonials.  His work throws great light upon the manners and customs of the East, and practice of the Mahometan faith.

The facts related by Burckhardt have been collated with those of other travellers and writers, and many particulars have been interwoven with them from other sources.

* The eternal tables or tablet was of white pearl, extended from east to west and from earth to heaven.  All the decrees of God were recorded on it, and all events past, present, and to come, to all eternity.  It was guarded by angels.

The number of days thus lost amount in 33 years to 363.   It becomes necessary, therefore, to add an intercalary year at the end of each thirty-third year to reduce the Mahometan into the Christian era.

One great inconvenience arising from this revelation of the prophet is, that the Moslem months do not indicate the season ; as they commence earlier by eleven days every year.   This at certain epochs is a sore grievance to the votaries to Mecca, as the great pilgrim month Dhu'l-Hajji, during which they are compelled to wear the Ihram, or half-naked pilgrim garb, runs the round of the seasons, occurring at one time in the depth of winter, at another in the fervid heat of summer.

Thus Mahomet, though according to legendary history he could order the moon from the firmament and make her revolve about the sacred house, could not control her monthly revolutions ; and found that the science of numbers is superior even to the gift of prophecy, and sets miracles at defiance.

END OF VOLUME I.